Pesticide Behaviour in Soils and Water

BCPC Symposium Proceedings No. 78

SYMPOSIUM PROCEEDINGS NO. 78

Pesticide Behaviour in Soils and Water

Chaired by A Walker

Proceedings of a Symposium
organised by the British Crop Protection Council

Held at the Hilton Brighton Metropole Hotel, 13-15 November 2001

BRITISH
CROP
PROTECTION
COUNCIL

© 2001 The British Crop Protection Council
49 Downing Street
Farnham, Surrey GU9 7PH, UK

Tel: +44 (0) 1252 733072
Fax: +44 (0) 1252 727194
Email: md@bcpc.org
Web: www.bcpc.org

British Library Cataloguing in Publication Data
A catalogue record for this book is available from the British Library

British Crop Protection Council
Pesticide Behaviour in Soils and Water
(Proceedings/Monograph Series, ISSN 0306-3941; No 78)

ISBN 1 901396 78 9

Cover design by Major Design & Production Ltd, Nottingham
Printed in Great Britain by Page Bros, Norwich

CONTENTS

DEGRADATION

SESSION 8
RISK MANAGEMENT

SESSION 9
HERBICIDES IN THE ENVIRONMENT: EXPOSURE,
CONSEQUENCES AND RISK ASSESSMENT – PART 1

SESSION 10
HERBICIDES IN THE ENVIRONMENT: EXPOSURE,
CONSEQUENCES AND RISK ASSESSMENT – PART 2

PREFACE

A full understanding of the interacting processes that control the environmental dynamics of pesticides is essential in order to maximise their effectiveness while minimising the risk of environmental contamination. A major environmental concern at present is the potential for pesticides to affect soil or water quality, and the papers in these Symposium Proceedings address several of the issues that are relevant to this concern.

The topic of pesticide behaviour in soils and water has provided the theme for a number of highly successful BCPC Symposia over the past 20 years. Our knowledge and understanding have increased considerably over this period, with the greatest advances made in the general area of quantitative prediction. For this to be successful, we need to understand all of the basic processes that occur in soil (sorption, diffusion, degradation, water flow etc) and the interactions that take place between them. In addition, we need to use our increased understanding of the basic processes to devise appropriate practical management strategies that reduce the potential for environmental contamination.

The papers from the Symposium address all of these important research areas. The initial papers give a broad overview of modelling approaches with discussion of knowledge gaps in our quantitative description of some of the main processes affecting pesticide fate. Subsequent papers deal with aspects of the individual processes (sorption, degradation, mobility), and discuss methods that can be used to measure and describe variability and uncertainty in mathematical modelling. A number of papers then describe approaches to pesticide management that can be used in practice to minimise environmental contamination. The final papers address issues relevant to the regulation of environmental exposure and risk assessment, and the implementation of risk management strategies for pesticides in soil, water and air.

Overall these Proceedings provide an up to date account of our current understanding in several of the important research areas, and they identify where knowledge is still limited and where further research is required.

Allan Walker
Horticulture Research International, Wellesbourne
November 2001

SYMPOSIUM ORGANISING COMMITTEE

Programme Chairman

Professor A Walker · *HRI, Wellesbourne, Warwick. CV35 9EF*

Session Organisers

Dr G D Bending · *HRI, Wellesbourne, Warwick. CV35 9EF*

Dr R H Bromilow · *IACR-Rothamsted, Harpenden, Herts, AL5 2JQ*

Dr C D Brown · *Soil Survey and Land Research, Cranfield University, Silsoe, Bedford, MK45 4DT*

Dr A D Carter · *ADAS Rosemaund, Preston Wynne, Hereford, HR1 3PG*

Dr A C Johnson · *Centre for Ecology and Hydrology (CEH), Maclean Building, Crowmarsh Gifford, Wallingford, Oxon OX10 8BB*

Dr N MacKay · *Cambridge Environmental Assessments, ADAS Boxworth, Boxworth, Cambridgeshire CB3 8NN*

BCPC Programme Policy Committee Chairman

Dr D V Alford · *BCPE, Orchard House, 14 Oakington Road, Dry Drayton, Cambridgeshire CB3 8DD*

Administration Manager

Mr C G Todd · *BCPE, 49 Downing Street, Farnham, Surrey GU9 7PH*

Exhibition and Promotions Manager

Mr G Beaumont · *BCPE, 4 Hay Barn Meadow, Woolpit, Bury St Edmunds, Suffolk IP30 9TU*

Acting Editor-in-Chief and Press Manager

Mrs M L Hart · *BCPE, 2 Old Manor Farm, West End, Long Clawson, Leicestershire LE14 4PE*

Symposium Secretariat

Ms M Moses · *BCPC, 5 Maidstone Buildings Mews, Bankside, London SE1 1GN*

ABBREVIATIONS

Where abbreviations are necessary the following are permitted without definition

acceptable daily intake	ADI		growth stage	GS
acetolactate synthase	ALS		hectare(s)	ha
acetyl CoA carboxylase	ACCase		high performance (or pressure)	
acid dissociation constant	pKa		liquid chromatography	hplc
acid equivalent	a.e.		high volume	HV
active ingredient	a.i.		hour	h
approximately	c.		infrared	i.r.
base pair	bp		inner diameter	id
becquerel	Bq		integrated crop management	ICM
body weight	b.w.		integrated pest management	IPM
boiling point	b.p.		International Organization for Standardization	ISO
British Standards Institution	BSI		in the journal last mentioned	*ibid.*
by the author last mentioned	*idem.*		Joules	J
centimetre(s)	cm		Kelvin	K
Chemical Abstracts Services Registry Number	CAS RN		kilobase pair	kb
coefficient of varience	CV		kilodalton	kD
colony-forming unit(s)	cfu		kilogram(s)	kg
compare	cf.		kilometres per hour	k/h
concentration x time product	ct		least significant difference	LSD
concentration required to kill 50% of test organisms	LC$_{50}$		litre(s)	litre(s)
correlation coefficient	*r*		litres per hectare	litres/ha
counts per minute	cpm		logarithm, common, base 10	log
cultivar	cv.		logarithm, natural	ln
cultivars	cvs.		low volume	LV
dalton	D		mass	*m*
day(s)	d		mass per mass	*m/m*
days after treatment	DAT		mass per volume	*m/V*
degrees Celsius (centigrade)	°C		mass spectroscopy	ms
degrees of freedom	df		maximum	max.
Department of Environment,			maximum residue level	MRL
Food & Rural Affairs	DEFRA		melting point	m.p.
disintegrations per minute	dpm		metre(s)	m
dose required to kill 50% of test organisums	LD$_{50}$		metres per second	m/s
dry matter	d.m.		milligram(s)	mg
Edition	Edn		milligrams per litre	mg/litre
editor	ed.		milligrams per kg	mg/kg
editors	eds		millilitre(s)	ml
emulsifiable concentrate	EC		millimetre(s)	mm
enzyme-linked immuno-sorbant assay	ELISA		minimum	min.
fast-protein liquid chromatography	FPLC		minimum harvest interval	MHI
Food and Drugs Administration	FDA		Ministry of Agriculture Fisheries and Food	
for example	e.g.		(England & Wales)	MAFF
freezing point	f.p.		minute (time unit)	min
gas chromatography-mass spectrometry	gc-ms		moisture content	M.C.
gas-liquid chromatography	glc		molar concentration	M
genetically modified	GM		mole	mol
genetically modified organism	GMO		molecular weight (relative)	*Mr*
gram(s)	g		no observed adverse effect level	NOAEL
gravity	*g*		no observed effect concentration	NOEC

ABBREVIATIONS

Where abbreviations are necessary the following are permitted without definition

no observed effect level	NOEL	technical grade	tech.
no significant difference	NSD	temperature	temp.
nuclear magnetic resonance	nmr	that is	i.e.
number average diameter	n.a.d.	thin-layer chromatography	tlc
number median diameter	n.m.d.	time for 50% loss; half life	DT_{50}
octanol/water partition coefficient	K_{ow}	tonne(s)	t
organic matter	o.m.	ultra low volume	ULV
page	p.	ultraviolet	u.v.
pages	pp.	United Kingdom	UK
parts per billion	ppb	United States	US
parts per million	ppm	United States Department of Agriculture	USDA
parts per trillion	ppt	vapour pressure	v.p.
pascal	Pa	variety (wild plant use)	var.
percentage	%	volume	V
polyacrylamide gel electrophoresis	PAGE	volume median diameter	v.m.d.
polymerase chain reaction	PCR	water dispersible granule	WG
post-emergence	post-em.	weight	wt
power take off	p.t.o.	weight by volume	wt/v
pre-emergence	pre-em.	(mass by volume is more correct)	(m/V)
pre-plant incorporated	ppi	weight by weight	wt/wt
probability (statistical)	P	(mass by mass is more correct)	(m/m)
relative humidity	r.h.	wettable powder	WP
revolutions per minute	rev/min		
second (time unit)	s		
standard error	SE		
standard error difference	SED	less than	<
standard error of means	SEM	more than	>
soluble powder	SP	not less than	≮
species (singular)	sp.	not more than	≯
species (plural)	spp.	Multiplying symbols-	Prefixes
square metre	m^2	mega $(\times 10^6)$	M
subspecies	ssp.	kilo $(\times 10^3)$	k
surface mean diameter	s.m.d.	milli $(\times 10^{-3})$	m
suspension concentrate	SC	micro $(\times 10^{-6})$	μ
systemic acquired resistance	SAR	nano $(\times 10^{-9})$	n
tandem mass spectrometry	MS-MS	pico $(\times 10^{-12})$	p

SESSION 1

INTRODUCTION

Chairman & Prof A Walker
Session Organiser: *HRI, Wellesbourne, UK*

Role of modelling in environmental risk assessment

M H Russell
DuPont Crop Protection, Stine-Haskell Research Center, Newark, DE, USA
Email: mark.h.russell@usa.dupont.com

ABSTRACT

Environmental models are currently used for screening purposes as well as deterministic and probabilistic exposure assessments. Recently, a number of modelling scenarios have been developed in the EU and USA to standardize regulatory assessments of pesticides. Current issues associated with exposure modelling include selection of input parameters, selection of models with appropriate transport mechanisms and use of appropriate modelling endpoints to support regulatory risk assessments.

INTRODUCTION

Environmental fate models are increasingly being used to provide estimates of the concentrations of agricultural chemicals to support environmental and ecological risk assessments. This trend has led to the development of a number of standardized models and modelling scenarios which have been officially endorsed for use in regulatory risk assessments. This paper provides an overview of the various types of models currently being used for regulatory assessments and discusses some of the current issues associated with regulatory modelling.

CURRENT ENVIRONMENTAL MODELS

There are many ways to classify the various types of environmental models. For regulatory purposes, there are three basic types of models, distinguished primarily by the degree of sophistication, level of data required and type of result produced:

1) Screening or regression models – relatively simple models based either on experimental data or the results of more sophisticated models.

2) Deterministic models – moderately to highly complex models with individual algorithms for the various transport and degradative processes in the environment; deterministic models are generally run with a fixed set on input values and provide a single, fixed set of output values.

3) Probabilistic models – moderately to highly complex models which utilize distributions of input values and provide distributions or probabilities of various output values.

Examples of current models

There are currently a wide range of models that have been developed or adapted for regulatory use. Examples of some of the current model are provided in Table 1.

Screening models are generally relatively simple, require minimal input data and provide conservative (i.e. high) estimates of likely environmental concentrations. Environmental concentrations obtained using screening models are useful for initial assessments of the relative importance of various dissipative/degradative pathways, e.g., leaching or fate in aquatic systems. Unfavorable risk assessments based on the result of screening models indicate the need for more refined exposure estimates.

Table 1.　　Examples of current regulatory environmental models

Model	Type (1)	Purpose (2)	Developer
SCI-GROW	s	gw	USEPA
GENEEC	s	sw	USEPA
EU Step 1-2*	s	sw	EU-FOCUS
EU Drift Calculator*	d	sw	EU-FOCUS
TOXSWA	d	sw	ALTERRA
EXAMS	d, p	sw	USEPA
PELMO*	d, p	gw, ro	Fraunhofer Institut
PRZM*	d, p	gw, ro	USEPA, EU-FOCUS
PEARL*	d, p	gw	RIVM, ALTERRA
MACRO*	d, p	gw, dr	SLU

(1) s = screening, d = deterministic, p = probabilistic

(2) sw = surface water, gw = groundwater, ro = runoff, dr = drainage

* FOCUS versions of these models available at ISPRA (2001).

Deterministic models typically have more extensive requirements for input data but can also provide more realistic estimates of environmental concentrations than screening models. Most deterministic models allow the user to provide detailed information on the various transport and degradation mechanisms and provide a time series of output values which can be compared to the duration of various ecotoxicological studies.

A common approach to obtaining probabilistic exposure estimates is to perform a series of deterministic calculations, varying in time (temporal variation) or both time and location (temporal and spatial variation). A probabilistic assessment based on climatic variations can be obtained by running the deterministic model for an extended period of time (typically, 20-30 years) and summarizing the probability of obtaining various exposure concentrations.

A more detailed approach involves varying additional parameters, some of which may be spatially correlated (e.g. chemical properties, soil type, and climatic data). The results of probabilistic modelling provide insights into the range and frequency of temporal and spatial variation in environmental concentrations. Probabilistic results are typically expressed in terms of exceedence probabilities, reflecting the frequency with which specific concentrations are observed throughout the range of scenarios being considered

Development of regulatory modelling scenarios

Deterministic and probabilistic environmental modelling requires the use of large numbers of parameters to appropriately characterize chemical properties and use patterns, characteristics of the soil profiles, climatic variations, and agronomic practices. In order to standardize the modelling approaches used for risk assessment, a number of regulatory modelling scenarios for groundwater and surface water have been developed in the EU and the USA (ISPRA 2001; FOCUS Surface Water 2001; MUSCRAT 2001).

A single modelling scenario typically consists of a selected soil profile, a fixed set of agronomic and cropping factors and a fixed meteorological file. To use the scenario, the user selects an appropriate set of chemical input values and application rates and runs the model for a specific scenario (combination of crop, soil, agronomic practices and climatic conditions). The modelling results can be expressed either deterministically or probabilistically.

Of necessity, modelling scenarios incorporate a large number of assumptions and include consideration of various spatial data layers as well as expert judgment. As a result, environmental concentrations predicted using these scenarios are intended to provide estimates of environmental concentrations in a range of locations that correspond to the assumptions made in the scenario. In some cases, the transport mechanisms in the scenarios studies (e.g. runoff rates and drainage rates) have been calibrated to data from appropriate field to help ensure the establishment of appropriate driving forces.

One of the major challenges with the creation of fixed scenarios is the determination of the likelihood of experimentally observing the calculated result. The mean environmental concentration can be estimated through use of a "typical" scenario and selection of typical (e.g. mean or median) input values. Less likely environmental concentrations (e.g. "worst case") can be created through using a series of worst-case assumptions for creating scenarios and selecting input values, resulting in the creation of an exposure concentration that is thought to be relatively high but with an unknown probability of occurrence. The problem with both of these approaches is that the final calculated results have an unknown probability of occurrence.

Increasingly, probabilistic modelling is being used to help provide more information on the range of environmental concentrations that can result from normal variations in chemical properties and use patterns, soil types and climatic data. The use of multiple modelling scenarios can also provide valuable insights into the variability expected due to location and time. Probabilistic modelling results can help determine specific environmental settings or specific use practices that result in concentrations of concern.

CURRENT ISSUES ASSOCIATED WITH MODELLING

With the widespread adoption of modelling as a tool to provide exposure values for risk assessment, it is appropriate to identify some of the key issues associated with modelling that can influence the simulated results and impact the resulting risk assessment.

Selection of empirical or non-measured input parameters

Almost all models include input parameters which are either empirical or are not readily measurable in laboratory or field studies. These parameters can influence the hydrologic balance in the model (e.g. maximum root depth, maximum plant canopy, pan evaporation correction factor) as well as the chemical balance (e.g. dispersion length, relative rate of degradation with depth).

As a result, it is important that models be parameterized using the best available estimates of these non-measured parameters to ensure appropriate mass fluxes of water and chemical in the modelling scenarios. This problem is commonly addressed through the developed of tables of recommended values and/or the creation of regulatory modelling scenarios in which the empirical and non-measured parameters are fixed.

Selection of chemical input properties

Detailed mechanistic models require a wide range of chemical input data in order to provide acceptably accurate estimates of concentrations in various environmental compartments. The chemical data used for regulatory modelling is obtained entirely from required regulatory laboratory and field environmental fate studies. Most of these studies were not originally designed to provide modelling inputs and may require some judgment and/or reinterpretation prior to being used for modelling. In some cases, it may be necessary to obtain more data than the core regulatory data set to perform environmental fate modelling.

Examples of chemical environmental fate issues that arise in modelling include:

- First-order kinetics are generally required in current models. More complex kinetics may require reinterpretation using standard first-order equations for use in modelling.

- Modelling of foliarly applied chemicals may require measurement of chemical degradation and washoff studies which are not routinely conducted for regulatory submissions.

- More realistic degradation rates in aquatic systems may be obtained from studies in microcosms involving a water column, sediment and aquatic plants in an outdoor setting.

- For some chemicals, it may be necessary to consider sorption kinetics and/or sorption to matrices other than soil (e.g. macrophytes).

- For mobile, slowly degrading chemicals, it may be necessary to measure the variation of degradation rate with soil depth to obtain reasonable estimates of potential concentrations in shallow groundwater.

- To permit simulation of metabolites, the pathway and kinetics for degradation must be defined, including the formation of bound residues.

- To support probabilistic modelling, it may be necessary to perform additional laboratory and/or field studies in order to determine an appropriate distribution of environmental fate values.

Simulation of transport mechanisms

Current models use varying degrees of sophistication to represent the major transport mechanisms responsible from moving applied agricultural chemicals from one compartment to another. Key transport mechanisms associated with surface water and groundwater modelling include spray drift, runoff, drainage and infiltration rates.

Spray drift

Single values of spray drift are commonly obtained from either regression equations or tables of experimental values. These single values include the effects of crop type as well as wind speed and direction. The FOCUS drift calculator is based on drift data published by the BBA (BBA 2000) and adjusts the probability of individual drift events to obtain an overall 90th percentile probability. In addition, it integrates the drift deposition across the width of the receiving water body.

Infiltration, runoff and tile drainage rates

The rate of leaching simulated by groundwater models can vary widely depending upon the assumptions made concerning dispersion coefficients and extent of preferential flow or macropore flow permitted by the model. Similarly, the rate of runoff simulated by a model can vary depending upon the soil type, soil moisture, rainfall intensity and the selection of curve numbers. The rate of tile drainage is a highly site-specific value and is best modeled by calibrating the rate to actual experimental data. For regulatory modelling, it is appropriate to create scenarios in which the infiltration, runoff and/or drainage have been calibrated to representative field studies to ensure appropriate hydrologic responses from the models.

Scale issues

Current regulatory models focus almost exclusively on simulating in-field and/or edge-of-field concentrations. However, there are many natural geographic features which can attenuate offsite movement from agricultural fields. Vegetated filter strips (also called buffer zones) can reduce both runoff and erosion loadings into adjacent surface water while catchment-scale processes integrate individual edge-of-field loadings with runoff and drainage from non-agricultural land. Currently, larger-scale evaluations of pesticide impacts on a catchment scale are based primarily on monitoring studies and efforts are underway to develop appropriate modelling approaches to represent the observed data.

Surface water issues

Most current models represent the hydrology of surface water bodies in a simplistic manner, using a constant volume together with a constant flow rate in and out of the control volume. The newest version of TOXSWA being developed by FOCUS will incorporate consideration of the hydrology of catchments and dynamic water flow rates and depths in calculating concentrations of chemicals entering ditches, ponds and streams (Adriaanse 2001). For more slowly flowing water bodies (ditches and ponds), complete sets of PECsw (predicted environmental concentration in surface water) and PECsed (predicted environmental concentration in sediment) values can be obtained within minutes. For more dynamic settings (e.g. streams), the computational times may require several hours.

Issues in using modelling results in risk assessments

Most current environmental models provide a output series of hourly or daily concentrations in the compartments of interest. This concentration time series can be highly variable with dramatic changes from hour to hour or day to day. In contrast, most ecotoxicological studies are performed either using a constant exposure concentration (e.g. a flow-through aquatic study) or a single dose which declines over time due to degradation or dissipation/dilution (e.g. a static aquatic study).

In order to appropriately compare modelling results to ecotoxicological studies, it is necessary to consider the both the mode-of-action and environmental properties of the chemical as well as the duration of the effects study. For rapidly-acting chemicals which are acutely toxic, it is appropriate to compare the initial predicted concentration with the endpoints from effects studies. For more slowly acting, chronically toxic chemicals, it is more appropriate to use time-weighted-average concentrations from modelling that match the durations used in the effects studies.

When the simulated exposure concentrations are highly transient, it may be appropriate to consider conducting higher-tier effects studies that evaluate the toxicological response of organisms to transient concentrations rather than constant concentrations. In addition, it may be useful to analyze the simulated exposure profile to determine the frequency with which organisms are exposed to concentrations that are know to have a biological effect. Higher-tiered evaluations such as pulsed-dose studies and time-to-event analyses combine elements of exposure modelling with the the conduct of effects studies to provide a more realistic assessment of the toxicological impact of chemicals in the environment.

CONCLUSION

Exposure modelling, supporting field studies and ecotoxicological testing should be performed in a logical sequence of progressive refinement. The degree of sophistication of the modelling should match the ecotoxicological data.

It is reasonable to compare the results of screening and deterministic modelling with standard ecotoxicological endpoints using the concept of a toxicity to exposure ratio (TER). However, when more refined probabilistic modelling assessments are performed, it is appropriate to consider developing probabilistic ecotoxicological endpoints for comparison with these endpoints. Numerous workshops and projects have addressed this probabilistic risk assessment and regulatory guidance is currently being developed both in the EU and the USA (EUPRA 2001; ECOFRAM 2001; PELLSTON 2001).

REFERENCES

Adriaanse P (2001). TOXSWA, Version for FOCUS Surface Water Working Group, Release scheduled for early 2002 on ISPRA website.

Adriaanse P; Russell M H; Yon D (2001). EU drift calculator, Version for FOCUS Surface Water Working Group, Release scheduled for early 2002 on ISPRA website.

Barrett Michael R (1998). The Screening Concentration in Ground Water (SCI-GROW). Documentation provided to Exposure Modelling Work Group in USA.

BBA (2000). Bekanntmachung des Verzeichnisses risikomindernder Anwendungsbedingungen für Nichtzielorganismen. Bundesanzeiger Nr. 100, 9879-9880, Germany.

Burns LA (1997). Exposure Analysis Modelling System (EXAMS II), User's Guide for Version 2.97.5. EPA/600/R-97/047.

ECOFRAM (1999). URL: www.epa.gov/oppefed1/ecorisk/index.htm

EUPRA Workshop (2001). European Workshop on Probabilistic Risk Assessment for the Environmental Impacts of Plant Protection Products. Leeuwenhorst, The Netherlands, 5-8 June 2001.

FOCUS Surface Water (2001). Regulatory scenarios using MACRO, PRZM and TOXSWA, Release scheduled for early 2002 on ISPRA website.

ISPRA (2001). ISPRA website for FOCUS models: arno.ei.jrc.it/focus/

Jarvis N (2001). MACRO, Version for FOCUS Surface Water Working Group, Release scheduled for early 2002 on ISPRA website.

Klein M; Allen R, Russell M H (2001). EU Step 1-2 Calculator, Version for FOCUS Surface Water Working Group, Release scheduled for early 2002 on ISPRA website.

Mangels G; Havens P; Parker R D (1997). Multiple scenario risk assessment tool (MUSCRAT). Version 1.0, beta. Provided to ACPA Exposure Assessment Modelling Working Group and currently under development by USEPA.

Parker R D; Nelson H P, Jones R D (1995). GENEEC: A Screening Model for Pesticide Environmental Exposure Assessment. In *Water Quality Modelling, Proceedings of the International Symposium*, ASAE.

SETAC Pellston Workshop (2001). Application of Uncertainty Analysis to Ecological Risks of Pesticides. Pellston, Michigan, USA, 15-20 September 2001.

Tiktak A; van den Berg F; Boesten J J T I; Leistra M; van der Linden A M A; van Kraalingen D (2000). Manual of PEARL, Version 1.1-sr3. Report 711401008, RIVM, Bilthoven, 142 pp.

Modelling pesticide environmental fate : process understanding and knowledge gaps

N J Jarvis

Department of Soil Sciences, SLU, Box 7014, 750 07 Uppsala, Sweden
Email: nicholas.jarvis@mv.slu.se

ABSTRACT

This paper reviews the state-of-the-art of pesticide environmental fate modelling, emphasizing interactive effects of non-linear and non-equilibrium processes affecting leaching to groundwater, and the incorporation and application of this knowledge in simulation models. The paper also highlights significant gaps in our current understanding of specific environmental compartments where more research is clearly needed.

INTRODUCTION

Since the early 1970's, beginning with the pioneering work of Walker (1974) and Leistra & Dekkers (1976), simulation models have been developed to describe the complex interactions of physical, chemical and biological processes that determine the environmental fate of pesticides. Many of these models are now used in the regulatory process by public authorities, industry and consultants. Models are cost-effective tools, being both cheap and powerful. At best, they can lead to valuable insights and improved understanding, and also allow the user to evaluate the likely impacts of alternative mitigation strategies, while minimizing the need for expensive long-term field experiments. For reasons of cost, field experiments on pesticide environmental fate can only be carried out at a few research sites, and usually only for a limited number of years. Without the theoretical framework and context provided by a model, conclusions that are drawn from the results of such short-term experiments can often be misleading. The results of field experiments are also strongly influenced by the prevailing weather and are only applicable to soils of similar properties. Validated models enable extrapolation of the results of field experiments to strongly contrasting environmental conditions.

It is impossible to discuss process descriptions in models without defining what the model is to be used for. Therefore, this paper largely focuses on the prediction of pesticide leaching to groundwater. However, many of the considerations discussed in this paper will also be relevant to pesticide movement to surface waters via sub-surface flow and drainage. Loss by surface runoff and erosion is also mostly outside the scope of the paper, but some of the discussion relating to generation of macropore flow may also be relevant for surface losses, since macropore flow can, in some respects, be considered as a kind of 'subsurface runoff'. Volatilization is another loss process which is only briefly mentioned, but this is not intended as a general reflection of its importance.

This paper reviews the state of the modelling art, attempting to answer the following questions: which processes are important ? What do we know about these processes ? Why don't we always make use of this process knowledge ? Where do we need to improve our understanding ?

OVERVIEW OF KEY PROCESSES

The fate of a pesticide applied to soil depends on the nature and strength of the sources and sinks, the partitioning between phases in the soil (water, air and solid), and the transport process itself. The ultimate source of the pesticide is the dose multiplied by the fraction of the application reaching the soil, which in turn is affected by crop interception, and loss processes such as volatilization and photolysis. Since leaching responds approximately linearly to dose, even in the presence of preferential flow, these loss processes at the surface may not be so critical for leaching predictions. The major sink term for most pesticides is usually degradation. Small errors in the prediction of degradation, either due to inappropriate process descriptions, or incorrect parameter values, result in disproportionately large errors in the leaching prediction. This is not only because the leaching loss is usually very small compared to degradation, but also because leaching is an exponential function of the half-life, assuming first-order kinetics (Jury et al., 1987). An accurate description of sorption is also necessary, because partitioning determines the availability of pesticide for both leaching and degradation. Model sensitivity analyses, both using the simple 'one-at-a-time' method, and also Monte Carlo approaches, show that leaching is highly sensitive to parameters describing sorption and degradation (Boesten, 1991; Soutter & Musy, 1999). Preferential flow is also a critical process, since from a regulatory point of view, we are usually interested in leaching losses of much less than 1% of the applied amount. In many soils, this is likely to be the result of rapid transport in preferential flow pathways quite unconnected to the much slower movement of the bulk of the compound (Flury et al., 1994).

PROCESS UNDERSTANDING

In recent years, improved understanding of the complex interaction of processes that govern pesticide fate has led to linear/equilibrium model concepts being replaced by non-linear, non-equilibrium approaches. Some examples of this general trend are the use of Freundlich sorption instead of a linear isotherm, kinetic sorption models instead of equilibrium sorption, non-equilibrium preferential flow rather than the physical equilibrium implied by Richards equation, and non-linear degradation models derived by accounting for sorption-degradation interactions or microbial growth processes, rather than simple first-order kinetics. These more advanced process descriptions can predict many phenomena commonly observed in field and laboratory experiments (Richter et al., 1996). For example, 'two-site' (kinetic/equilibrium) sorption models predict increases in the apparent sorption constant with time (Walker et al., 1995). Linear kinetic sorption combined with linear degradation in the liquid phase only (assuming that sorbed pesticide is not available for biodegradation) leads to a biphasic degradation pattern (e.g. McCall et al., 1981). A non-linear equilibrium sorption isotherm combined with first-order degradation in the liquid phase only, leads to a quasi-linear degradation process which may be experimentally indistinguishable from first-order, but where the (apparent) rate constant is strongly dependent on the initial concentration (e.g. Walker, 1976). Models which account for microbial population growth can predict the rapid disappearance of pesticide due to microbial adaptation to repeated applications (e.g. Walker & Welch, 1990). The most important underlying physical reason for the non-equilibrium sorption, degradation and transport processes observed is the heterogeneous nature of the pore space in field soils (Bergström & Stenström, 1998). Much of the soil pore volume (microporosity less than c. 2 μm in size) is physically inaccessible to microorganisms. Pesticide diffusing into such small pores is unavailable for degradation, and this slow diffusion into a sorbing matrix is also largely responsible for the time-dependence observed in sorption, and 'biphasic' departures from first-order degradation kinetics (Scow & Hutson, 1992). Pesticide residing in micropores is also effectively protected against leaching, since diffusion is slow compared to the rapid vertical convective transport occurring in the larger pores. Dual- and even multi-region models have been developed to account for this physical non-equilibrium (Jarvis, 1998), which often results in the accelerated or 'preferential' transport of a small but significant fraction of the pesticide through the unsaturated zone (e.g. Flury, 1996).

This improved process understanding has been incorporated into simulation models designed to predict the environmental fate of pesticides, including some of those used for registration. For example, the PEARL model (http://www.alterra.nl/models/pearl) includes two-site sorption with a Freundlich isotherm, in which the kinetic sites are protected from degradation. The MACRO model (http://www.mv.slu.se/bgf/macrohtm/macro.htm) includes treatment of non-equilibrium water flow in macropores, Freundlich sorption, and also allows the user to specify separate degradation rate coefficients for four different 'pools' in the soil (solid and liquid phases in macropores and micropores). Nevertheless, there are few examples of the application of these more advanced modelling concepts to predict pesticide fate in field soils, even though they clearly can have a large impact on the outcome. Indeed, the failure to account for non-linear, non-equilibrium processes is certainly the cause of significant discrepancies between predictions and measurements in many model applications (Walker, 1976; Thorsen *et al.*, 1998; Beulke *et al.*, 2000). With respect to regulatory modelling, none of these newer modelling concepts have really gained a firm foothold, except for non-linear Freundlich sorption. There are perhaps several reasons for this, but one of the most important is the lack of data and perceived lack of appropriate tools to parameterize these more advanced process descriptions. In principle, the tools for parameter estimation do exist, in the form of inverse modelling techniques (Vink *et al.*, 1994; Dieses *et al.*, 1999; Kätterer *et al.*, 2001). The main problem is that more complex model descriptions require more detailed experiments and more comprehensive data in order to unequivocally distinguish between the many different process descriptions and parameterisations that are possible. Two examples of the potential pitfalls in distinguishing different process descriptions should suffice: Richter *et al.* (1996) demonstrated that biphasic degradation curves can be equally well explained by a deterministic model based on linear kinetic sorption and linear degradation restricted to the liquid phase, and by a model based on first-order degradation kinetics, but assuming spatial variability of the rate coefficient described by a gamma function (Gustafson & Holden, 1990). They pointed out that only additional data on the time-course of bound residues would allow discrimination between the two models. Gaber *et al.* (1995) demonstrated that both physical non-equilibrium and kinetic sorption influenced the leaching of atrazine in undisturbed soil columns, and that without the application of a tracer, it would have been impossible to distinguish between parameters controlling diffusion exchange between pore regions and parameters controlling kinetic sorption. Indeed, it is well known that the 'mobile-immobile' model of physical non-equilibrium is mathematically identical to a one region flow model assuming two-site (equilibrium-kinetic) sorption (Nkeddi-Kizza *et al.*, 1984).

KNOWLEDGE GAPS

Soil surface conditions

Tillage affects the 'roughness' or microrelief of the soil surface, the number, size distribution and continuity of large pores, and thus the extent of macropore flow (e.g. Trojan & Linden, 1992; Brown *et al.*, 1999). Therefore, it may be possible to control preferential flow through soil surface preparation, but little research has been performed on this topic, even though conceptual models of these processes were developed as early as the 1970's (Dixon & Petersen, 1971). Microtopography of the soil surface may also play an important role in sandy soils without macropores. Hydrophobicity of the thin air-dry surface layer will cause small-scale surface runoff and flow concentration in depressions. Ritsema & Dekker (1995) demonstrated a significant lateral re-distribution of bromide tracer into preferential regions of the near-surface soil following just 1 mm of rain soon after application. A related problem is the microtopography deliberately created by ridge till systems, commonly used, for example, in potato cultivation (Boesten, 2000), so that infiltration is concentrated to the furrow regions.

Following tillage, the soil surface is exposed to rainfall for several weeks before crop growth provides effective surface cover. This leads to a consolidation of the cultivated layer and on susceptible soils, destruction of macroporosity and sealing of the surface. These surface crusts have significantly smaller hydraulic conductivities, but they are not continuous. Local surface runoff will occur during rain, leading to concentration of infiltration through non-crusted patches and dessication cracks. Nothing is known about the influence of this kind of preferential flow on pesticide leaching, but some preliminary simulations based on measured seasonal variations in soil surface hydraulic conductivity due to crusting suggest that it may lead to order of magnitude differences in pesticide leaching from the topsoil (Messing, 1993).

During dry weather, the surface few millimetres of soil quickly becomes air-dry. Sorption is known to dramatically increase as the soil gets very dry (Hance & Embling, 1979) and this, in turn, strongly affects pesticide availability for volatilization and perhaps also for leaching by preferential flow. However, it is difficult to measure moisture effects on sorption of concentrated pesticide solutions in thin surface layers (Boesten, 2000). Furthermore, numerical limitations in models, together with a lack of knowledge of near-surface hydraulic properties, mean that the occurrence of very dry conditions in the surface few millimetres of soil is not easy to simulate. For these reasons, Boesten (2000) concluded that accurate modelling of volatilization from the soil surface is impossible with current knowledge and techniques.

Processes occurring at and very close to the soil surface cannot be investigated satisfactorily with current models. One-dimensional models implicitly assume a flat soil surface, and often employ a rather coarse spatial discretisation, with computational layers several centimetres thick close to the soil surface. Two-dimensional models applicable to pesticide fate in the soil unsaturated zone do exist (e.g. HYDRUS-2D, http://www.ussl.ars.usda.gov/models/hydrus2d.htm), but they do not account for preferential flow processes. Application of improved two-dimensional models, including physical non-equilibrium concepts, should lead to a better understanding of the importance of soil surface conditions for pesticide leaching.

Preferential flow pathways through the root zone

It is important to understand better the properties and functioning of preferential flow pathways. In recent years, it has become increasingly clear that the location of the pesticide in relation to the location of the water flow pathways is critical for leaching (Bergström et al., 2001). If a mobile pesticide diffuses into the soil matrix, and is no longer in contact with water flowing in macropores, then preferential flow may reduce leaching compared to chromatographic transport (Larsson & Jarvis, 1999). On the other hand, macropore flow soon after application will dramatically increase leaching of otherwise non-mobile compounds, because the pesticide mostly resides either at the soil surface or adsorbed to aggregate surfaces within the topsoil, and is therefore exposed to interaction with the rapidly flowing water. In one preliminary study, Larsson & Jarvis (2000) showed in scenario simulations using MACRO pre-calibrated to a field experiment on a structured clay soil, that the effects of macropore flow should depend strongly on the overall leachability of the pesticide. However, much more work is clearly needed to understand the complex interactions of preferential flow and the sorption and degradation characteristics of pesticides.

The properties of macropore linings and aggregate surfaces are different to those of the bulk soil, with larger clay and organic carbon contents, better nutrient supply and oxygen status, and larger microbiological activity, which results in a larger sorption and degradation capacity per unit mass of soil (Stehouwer *et al.*, 1993; Mallawatantri *et al.*, 1996). The extent to which this is important for pesticide leaching is not known. Much should depend on the characteristic time scales of the processes : macropore flow is fast and degradation is relatively slow, so enhanced microbial activity in macropores may not be important, although some preliminary studies suggest otherwise (Pivetz *et al.*, 1996). The significance of sorption retardation in macropores is still not clear, but it does not seem too important, probably because flow rates are fast in relation to sorption kinetics, and the adsorptive surface area in macropores is small. Field experiments where leaching in the presence of preferential flow has been monitored for several compounds applied simultaneously (Kladivko *et al.*, 1991; Traub-Eberhard *et al.*, 1994) seem to show an equally fast breakthrough regardless of sorption characteristics, but that concentrations are clearly dependent on sorption. It is still unclear whether this sorption effect occurs within macropores during transport, or whether it is a result of the source strength, that is, the solution pesticide concentration in the surface soil layers where macropore flow is most likely generated.

Subsoil and the deep vadose zone

In contrast to topsoil, very little seems to be known about long-term pesticide degradation and transport in the deeper vadose zone. Even though sensitivity analysis suggests that different assumptions concerning subsoil degradation rates may not greatly influence predictions of total leaching (Boesten, 1991), the long-term persistence of small amounts of pesticide in subsoil may act as a diffuse source of pesticide for groundwater contamination. This may have implications for the time required for self-remediation of polluted aquifers. Few studies have investigated the extent of non-equilibrium preferential flow in the deep vadose zone. In many cases, this may diminish with depth (e.g. Li *et al.*, 1997), since soil structure generally becomes weaker in the absence of faunal activity and physical processes like wetting/drying and freeze/thaw. However, preferential flow can occur to significant depths in some hydrogeological conditions, such as in fractured glacial till or chalk (e.g. Jørgensen *et al.*, 1998; Wellings & Cooper, 1983). Preferential flow in the soil root zone may still be critical even when matrix flow dominates transport at depth. This is because the attenuation of pesticides by sorption and degradation will generally be much weaker in the vadose zone (Pothuluri *et al.*, 1990; Moreau & Mouvet, 1997).

Upscaling to the field

One unresolved problem is the extrapolation of results from small-scale experiments to the field-scale relevant for management caused by the spatial variability of soil properties and pesticide sorption and degradation characteristics (e.g. Walker *et al.*, 2001). Stochastic approaches have been applied to this upscaling problem that demonstrate the potentially large effects of field-scale heterogeneity on leaching (e.g. van der Zee & Boesten, 1991). However, the results of such analyses depend on both the assumptions underlying the process descriptions used in the model and on how the model is parameterised. In particular, a lack of information on parameter distributions, and especially correlations, has severely limited progress. For example, many studies have treated the sorption constant and degradation rate coefficient as independent parameter distributions (Di & Aylmore, 1997), which will almost certainly tend to overestimate variability in leaching, since sorption and degradation are often inversely related (Cantwell *et al.*, 1989). Other studies focus on variability in transport characteristics, but ignore variability in sorption and degradation because of lack of data (e.g. Wu & Workman, 1999). One dilemma is that data may exist to characterize parameter distributions in simple screening models (e.g. Jury *et al.*, 1987), but the process descriptions in these models are in some respects too simple (i.e. steady flow, no dispersion). In contrast, process descriptions in complex models are much more realistic, but knowledge of parameter distributions and their correlations is incomplete.

CONCLUDING REMARKS

Great progress has been made in recent years in improving our understanding of the interplay of non-linear and non-equilibrium processes governing pesticide fate in soils. This improved knowledge is also recognized in the process descriptions now included in many models, even though it is not often fully exploited due to lack of data. The challenge now is to design and carry out the necessary experiments to meet the requirements of more complex models. Poor predictions of pesticide fate in field soils are often blamed on inadequate process descriptions in models (models are always simplifications of reality), but are just as likely to result either from a lack of experimental data leading to errors in model identification and parameterisation, or from errors due to extrapolation from limited data to the field-scale in the face of soil heterogeneity.

REFERENCES

Bergström L; Stenström J (1998). Environmental fate of chemicals in soil. *Ambio*, **27**:16-23.

Bergström L; Jarvis N ; Larsson M ; Djodjic F; Shirmohammadi A (2001). Factors affecting the significance of macropore flow for leaching of agrochemicals. In: *Preferential flow. Water movement and chemical transport in the environment*, pp 25-28, ASAE, MI, U.S.A.

Boesten J J T I (1991). Sensitivity analyses of a mathematical model for pesticide leaching to groundwater. *Pesticide Science*, **31**: 375-388.

Boesten J J T I (2000). From laboratory to field: uses and limitations of pesticide behaviour models for the soil/plant system. *Weed Research*, **40**: 123-138.

Brown C D; Marshall V L; Carter A D; Walker A; Arnold D; Jones R L (1999). Investigation into the effect of tillage on solute movement to drains through a heavy clay soil. I. Lysimeter experiment. *Soil Use and Management*, **15**: 84-93.

Beulke S; Dubus I G; Brown C D; Gottesbüren B (2000). Simulation of pesticide persistence in the field on the basis of laboratory data – A review. *Journal of Environmental Quality*, **29**: 1371-1379.

Cantwell J R; Liebl R A; Slife F W (1989). Biodegradation characteristics of imazaquin and imazethapyr. *Weed Science*, **37**: 815-819.

Di H J; Aylmore L A G (1997). Modeling the probabilities of groundwater contamination by pesticides. *Soil Science Society of America Journal*, **61**: 17-23.

Dieses A E; Schlöder J P; Bock H G; Richter O; Aden K; Gottesbüren B (1999). A parameter estimation tool for nonlinear transport and degradation processes of xenobiotics in soil. In: *Human and environmental exposure to Xenobiotics*, eds. A A M Del Re; C Brown; E Capri; G Errera; S P Evans; M Trevisan, pp. 171-180, Cremona, Italy.

Dixon R M; Petersen A E (1971). Water infiltration control: a channel system concept. *Soil Science Society of America Proceedings*, **35**: 968-973.

Flury M; Flühler H; Jury, W A; Leuenberger J (1994). Susceptibility of soils to preferential flow of water. *Water Resources Research*, **30**: 1945-1954.

Flury M (1996). Experimental evidence of transport of pesticides through field soils – a review. *Journal of Environmental Quality*, **25**, 25-45.

Gaber H M; Inskeep W P; Comford S ; Wraith J (1995). Nonequilibrium transport of atrazine through large intact soil cores. *Soil Science Society of America Journal*, **59**: 60-67.

Gustafson D I; Holden L R (1990). Non-linear pesticide dissipation in soil: a new model based on spatial variability. *Environmental Science & Technology*, **24**: 1032-1038.

Hance R J; Embling S J (1979). Effect of soil water content at the time of application on herbicide content in soil solution extracted in a pressure membrane apparatus. *Weed Research*, **19**: 201-205.

Jarvis N J (1998). Modelling the impact of preferential flow on non-point source pollution. In: *Physical non-equilibrium in soils: modeling and application*, ed. H H Selim; L Ma, pp. 195-221, Ann Arbor Press, Chelsea, MI, U.S.A.

Jørgensen P R; McKay L D; Spliid N H (1998). Evaluation of chloride and pesticide transport in a fractured clayey till using large undisturbed columns and numerical modeling. *Water Resources Research*, **34**: 539-553.

Jury W A; Focht D D; Farmer W J (1987). Evaluation of pesticide ground water pollution potential from standard indices of soil-chemical adsorption and biodegradation. *Journal of Environmental Quality*, **16**: 422-428.

Kätterer T; Schmied B; Abbaspour K C; Schulin R (2001). Single- and dual-porosity modelling of multiple tracer transport through soil columns: effects of initial moisture and mode of application. *European Journal of Soil Science*, **52**: 1-12

Kladivko E J; van Scoyoc E G; Monke E J; Oates K M; Pask W (1991). Pesticide and nutrient movement into subsurface tile drains on a silt loam soil in Indiana. *Journal of Environmental Quality*, **20**: 264-270.

Larsson M H; Jarvis N J (1999). Evaluation of a dual-porosity model to predict field-scale solute transport in a macroporous soil. *Journal of Hydrology*, **215**: 153-171.

Larsson M H; Jarvis N J (2000). Quantifying interactions between compound properties and macropore flow effects on pesticide leaching. *Pest Management Science*, **56**: 133-141.

Leistra M; Dekkers W A (1976). Computed leaching of pesticides from soil under field conditions. *Water, Air and Soil Pollution*, **5**: 491-500.

Li K; Amoozegar A; Robarge W P; Buol S (1997). Water movement and solute transport through saprolite. *Soil Science Society of America Journal*, **61**: 1738-1745.

Mallawatantri A P; McConkey B G; Mulla D (1996). Characterization of pesticide sorption and degradation in macropore linings and soil horizons of Thatuna silt loam. *Journal of Environmental Quality*, **25**: 227-235.

McCall P J; Vrona S A; Kelley S S (1981). Fate of uniformly carbon-14 ring labeled 2,4,5,-Trichlorophenoxyacetic acid and 2,4-Dichlorophenoxyacetic acid. *Journal of Agricultural and Food Chemistry*, **29**: 100-107.

Messing I (1993). Saturated and near-saturated hydraulic conductivity in clay soils. *Reports and Dissertations, 12, Department of Soil Sciences, Swedish University of Agricultural Sciences*, Uppsala, Sweden, 66 pp.

Moreau C; Mouvet C (1997). Sorption and desorption of atrazine, deethylatrazine, and hydroxyatrazine by soil and aquifer solids. *Journal of Environmental Quality*, **26**: 416-424.

Nkeddi-Kizza P; Biggar J W; Selim H M; van Genuchten M T; Wierenga P J; Davidson J M; Nielsen D R (1984). On the equivalence of two conceptual models for describing ion exchange during transport through an aggregated oxisol. *Water Resources Research*, **20**: 1123-1130.

Pivetz B E; Kelsey J W; Steenhuis T S; Alexander M (1996). A procedure to calculate biodegradation during preferential flow through heterogeneous soil columns. *Soil Science Society of America Journal*, **60**: 381-388.

Pothuluri J V; Moorman T B; Obenhuber D C; Wauchope R D (1990). Aerobic and anaerobic degradation of alachlor in samples from a surface-to-groundwater profile. *Journal of Environmental Quality*, **19**: 525-530.

Richter O; Diekkrüger B; Nörtershauser P (1996). *Environmental fate modelling of pesticides.* VCH Verlag: Weinheim, Germany.

Ritsema C J; Dekker L W (1995) Distribution flow: a general process in the top layer of water repellent soils. *Water Resources Research*, **31**: 1187-1200.

Scow K M; Hutson J (1992). Effect of diffusion and sorption on the kinetics of biodegradation: theoretical considerations. *Soil Science Society of America Journal*, **56**: 119-127.

Soutter M; Musy A (1999). Global sensitivity analyses of three pesticide leaching models using a Monte Carlo approach. *Journal of Environmental Quality*, **28**: 1290-1297.

Stehouwer R C; Dick W A; Traina S J (1993). Characteristics of earthworm burrow lining affecting atrazine sorption. *Journal of Environmental Quality*, **22**: 181-185.

Thorsen M; Jørgensen P R; Felding G; Jacobsen O H; Spliid N H; Refsgaard J C (1998). Evaluation of a stepwise procedure for comparative validation of pesticide leaching models. *Journal of Environmental Quality*, **27**: 1183-1193.

Traub-Eberhard U; Kördel W; Klein W (1994). Pesticide movement into subsurface drains on a loamy silt soil. *Chemosphere*, **28**: 273-284.

Trojan M D; Linden D R (1992). Microrelief and rainfall effects on water and solute movement in earthworm burrows. *Soil Science Society of America Journal*, **56**: 727-733.

van der Zee, S E A T M; Boesten J J T I (1991). Effects of soil heterogeneity on pesticide leaching to groundwater. *Water Resources Research*, **27**: 3051-3063.

Vink J P M; Nörtershauser P; Richter O; Diekkrüger B; Groen K P (1994). Modeling the microbial breakdown of pesticides in soil using a parameter estimation technique. *Pesticide Science*, **40**: 285-292.

Walker A (1974). A simulation model for prediction of herbicide persistence. *Journal of Environmental Quality*, **3**: 396-401.

Walker A (1976). Simulation of herbicide persistence in soil. I. Simazine and prometryne. *Pesticide Science*, **7**: 41-49.

Walker A; Welch S J (1990). Enhanced biodegradation of dicarboxymide fungicides in soil. In: *Enhanced biodegradation of pesticides in the environment*, eds. K D Racke; J R Coats, ACS Symposium Series, **426**: 53-67.

Walker A; Welch S J; Turner I J (1995). Studies of time-dependent sorption processes in soils. In: *Pesticide movement to water*, eds. A Walker, R Allen, S W Bailey, A M Blair, C D Brown, P Günther, C R Leake, P H Nicholls, pp 13-18, BCPC Farnham, U.K.

Walker A; Jurado-Exposito M; Bending G D; Smith V J R (2001). Spatial variability in the degradation rate of isoproturon in soil. *Environmental Pollution*, **111**: 407-415.

Wellings S R; Cooper J D (1983). The variability of recharge of the English chalk aquifer. *Agricultural Water Management*, **6**: 243-253.

Wu Q J; Workman S R (1999). Stochastic simulation of pesticide transport in heterogeneous unsaturated fields. *Journal of Environmental Quality*, **28**: 498-512.

Towards a generalised linear model of groundwater pollution by pesticides

F Worrall

Dept. of Geological Sciences, The University of Durham, Science Laboratories, South Road, Durham, DH1 3LE, UK

ABSTRACT

This study has brought together extensive groundwater monitoring datasets from the UK and the US to examine the underlying controls on the causes of groundwater pollution by pesticides. The study examined firstly the role of chemical properties in controlling occurrence in groundwater, secondly, the role of the properties of the site of application, and finally, brought these factors together to test their relative importance and propose combined models based on both site and chemical properties. The study: (1) developed a model of the occurrence of pesticides in groundwater based on molecular topology; (2) developed a method of calculating groundwater vulnerability, independent of compound type, directly from borehole observations; (3) showed that groundwater vulnerability in agricultural catchments was governed by soil and hydrologic factors, but was independent of land-use; and (4) showed that both chemical and site factors have an independent and significant effect on groundwater contamination, but that the interaction of these factors is the important control. These methods are leading to a generalised linear model of groundwater pollution by pesticides that brings with it new opportunities in risk assessment and risk management.

INTRODUCTION

The problem of pesticide pollution of groundwater has meant that a range of techniques has been applied to understanding and predicting this problem. The properties that control the pollution can be broadly classified into two groups: site and chemical factors. A number of methods have been developed using either site or chemical factors.

The site factor includes such properties as land-use, soil, aquifer and climate. The combination of site factors that give rise to pollution have been taken together as groundwater vulnerability tools. Groundwater vulnerability has slightly varying definitions. Palmer *et al.*, (1995) recognised that differing soil and hydrogeological conditions will give rise to differing vulnerabilities and afford different degrees of protection to the underlying aquifer. It is important to note that this concept of vulnerability is independent of the nature of the pollutant. A range of vulnerability tools have been developed, e.g. DRASTIC (Aller *et al.*, 1987). Other research has extended the range of parameters included and the concept has been taken forward to develop regional vulnerability maps (e.g. Palmer *et al.*, 1995).

These systems have a number of flaws. Firstly, the inclusion or exclusion of variables into the vulnerability assessment systems is often arbitrary and based solely on expert opinion as to the weighting between factors (e.g. Aller *et al.*, 1987). Secondly, the indices are typically not based on observations or measurements of groundwater contamination and even when physically-based models are used they are prone to errors in the model assumptions or in choosing input parameters. Thirdly, these schemes have rarely been validated or tested against observational data (Merchant, 1994). When validation is performed evidence can be contradictory, eg. for the DRASTIC system (Maas et al., 1995). More fundamentally there is an underlying assumption that that is it possible that the variation observed in the occurrences of pesticides is due only to variation in soil or climatic conditions without reference to the properties of the contaminant concerned.

Conversely, the chemical properties of contaminants alone have been used to assess the risk of groundwater pollution. Such screening methods have most frequently based their judgements on adsorption, degradation or solubility parameters (e.g. Gustafson, 1989). As for vulnerability assessment systems these methods based solely on chemical properties have tended to develop scores and indices based on expert opinion of the weighting of chemical parameters. Even those methods based on observations of groundwater contamination, rather than a priori combinations of parameters (e.g. Gustafson, 1989), have been shown to be inapplicable outside the region for which they were calculated (Wooff et al., 1999). The classification of compounds into polluting/non-polluting or mobility classes based on such schemes is prone to error when allowance is made for the natural variation in the parameters they use (e.g. K_{oc} and soil half-life). It has, however, been possible to show that despite the large site-to-site variation in such parameters as K_{oc} and degradation half-life it is possible to differentiate those compounds that are found in groundwater from those that are never observed (Worrall et al., 2000) with this separation being statistically significant. Proving that it is possible to differentiate polluting from non-polluting compounds shows that it is viable to base contamination screening methods solely on chemical properties. However, the importance of the role of chemical properties relative to site properties in controlling the transport of contaminants is not known.
This paper takes each of these factors separately, the site and chemical, and then examines their relative importance.

THE CHEMICAL FACTOR

Given the site variability in K_{oc} and half-life it necessary to use other properties to explore the chemicals role in controlling groundwater pollution. Worrall (2001) using logistic regression differentiated compounds found in groundwater from those known to be used in the surveyed regions but not found in the groundwater on the basis of the molecular connectivity parameters. Molecular connectivity parameters are dependent only on the structure of the compound and not variable from site to site. The model was developed for 47 compounds from a groundwater in the midwest US and tested against a study from California of 41 compounds. The result correctly classified 96% of the data, and 91% when validated against the Californian data. The result can be visualised if only the two most important parameters are considered (Figure 1). Considering the most important parameter, 86% of the data was correctly classified by a simple inequality:

$$^{6}\chi_{p}^{v} < 0.5 \quad \text{(i)}$$

Where: $6\chi^{v}{}_{p}$ = the sixth-order path connectivity.

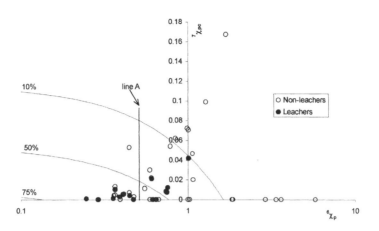

Figure 1. Plot of the sixth-order path connectivity ($6\chi^{v}{}_{p}$) vs. seventh-order path-cluster connectivity ($7\chi^{v}{}_{pc}$) in comparison to the best-fit probability of the compound being a leacher. Line A represents Eqn (i).

On Figure 1 it is possible to discern two trends in the non-leacher compounds, one in increasing $6\chi^{v}{}_{p}$. This trend is represented by linear compounds of a variety of pesticide classes increasing in chain length suggesting that it represents control by molecular size. The second trend is one of both increasing $6\chi^{v}{}_{p}$ and $7\chi^{v}{}_{pc}$ which is represented by cyclic compounds from a range of pesticide classes. This trend highlights that the complexity of branching (represented by $7\chi^{v}{}_{pc}$) is important.

THE SITE FACTOR

How can we estimate the effect of the site of application upon its fate?. If we consider an example from a large groundwater monitoring programme in California. Over a period of several years atrazine was analysed for 1791 times in water from a large number of boreholes throughout the Great Valley of California. Atrazine was found in 165 of them – a proportion of 9%. In one particular borehole, over the same time period, atrazine was tested for 24 times and found 11 times – a proportion of 45%. The difference between these two proportions represents the vulnerability of the borehole compared to the regional average. The method of Worrall (in press) works on this basis and presents a method for firstly showing that the difference between two proportions is statistically significant, secondly to show how to combine information from a range of compounds, and thirdly, to show how to convert the difference between proportions into the probability of finding the next compound that is monitored for. The method developed in Worrall (in press) was for multiple observations of single compounds. The method was extended to work with single observations of multiple compounds and applied to an extensive survey of pesticide occurrence in shallow aquifers of the Midwest US (Worrall & Kolpin, in press – Figure 2). When the data is of sufficient spatial density it is possible to map the vulnerability of groundwater as a probability of finding the next compound to be monitored for.

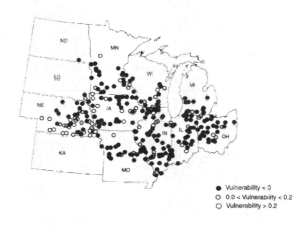

Figure 2. Distribution of vulnerability for a 303 borehole study of the midwest USA

This system has a range of advantages over present vulnerability assessment techniques. The method directly estimates vulnerability from borehole data, it does not rely on expert opinion of combination of variables that are presumed to be important in controlling groundwater pollution. The method predicts a probability of groundwater pollution that is independent of compound type and is not just a relative indice. Because the method is developed within a Bayesian statistical framework it combines information from a range of sources and can easily be updated as new information becomes available. The estimate of vulnerability is calculated independently of the properties of the borehole catchment and as such can be correlated with properties of that catchment to understand what controls leaching.

COMPARING SITE & CHEMICAL FACTORS

Previous sections have explored each factor separately from the other, but as outlined in the introduction groundwater pollution should be dependent on both factors and so it is important to compare their relative roles to discover whether each factor is important when compared to each other; is one factor more important than the other? For example, is the distribution of pesticides in groundwater related more to the variation of properties between sites or by the variation in the properties of compounds being applied in that region? Equally, we need to assess the importance the interaction of these factors, i.e. their dependence upon each other. Taking two extensive groundwater surveys one in the midwest USA and one in Southern England general linear modelling was used as a means of comparing variation between compounds and between boreholes. For each study it was also possible to compare results between consecutive years. The use of a general linear modelling approach means that not only can the significance of a factor be assessed but also its interactions.

Results showed that neither in the US nor UK study was the difference between consecutive years significant (at the 95% level). However, for one of the years in each of the two surveys it was possible to test the difference within a year in comparison to the differences between compounds and sites. In each of the national studies this within-year factor was statistically significant suggesting that seasonality is more important than variations in climate that could occur between years. In both the UK and US studies both the site and compound factors were significant (at the 95% level) on their own and independent of each other (Table 1). However, the percentage of the variance explained by these factors alone was very small, especially in comparison to the percentage of variance explained by the interaction of these two factors.

Table 1. Percentage of the variance of a dataset explained by each of the factors considered in each of the groundwater surveys.

Dataset	USA	UK
Source of Variance	% of variance	% of variance
Site	14	13
Chemical	5	4
Interaction	65	67
Measurement error	16	16

This is the first time that any statistical validity for groundwater vulnerability tools has been tested, i.e. showed that there site properties are significant independent of chemical properties or between and within-year variation, but that this effect is small. Equally, this result confirms that of Worrall et al., (2000) that there is a significant difference between leachers and non-leachers. The greatest proportion of the variance is explained by the interaction between site and chemical factors. The interaction of site and chemical factors can be considered in two ways. First, this is part of processes known to effect all pesticides, e.g. adsorption is considered as a combination of a compound's innate properties and the fraction of organic matter in the soil. Second, that the significance of the interactions shows that a site's vulnerability to contamination is compound specific. These findings could be limited by the range of compounds and conditions included in these surveys, but the two studies in very different settings, and examining compounds with a considerable range of chemical properties, came to very similar results. The measurement error is indicative of the fit of the model to the data. The magnitude of the measurement error in these studies is of the same order of magnitude as the analytical detection limit used so suggesting additional factors need not be included.

CONCLUSIONS

This study has examined pesticide pollution to groundwater as a combination of chemical and site factors. The study has shown that:

i)   leaching compounds can be distinguished from non-leaching compounds on the basis of molecular descriptors;
ii)   the important molecular properties are both molecular size and the molecules complexity of branching;
iii)   groundwater vulnerability can be calculated directly from borehole observations;
iv)   both site and chemical factors have a significant effect on the occurrence of pesticides in groundwater with the former being the most important; and
v)   the most important control on pesticide pollution of groundwater is the interaction of site and chemical factors.

The approach taken by this study and the results shown have important implications for both the risk assessment and risk management of pesticides.

ACKNOWLEDGEMENTS

The author is grateful to D Kolpin (United States Geological Survey), J Troiano and B Johnson (California Dept. of Pesticide Regulation) and T Besien (UK Environment Agency) for supplying the data upon which the work is based.

REFERENCES

Aller L; Bennett T; Lehr J H; Petty R J; Hackett G (1987). *DRASTIC: A standardised system for evaluating groundwater pollution potential using hydrogeologic settings.* U.S. Environment Protection Agency, Ada, Oklahoma, EPA/600/2-87/035.

Gustafson D I (1989). Groundwater ubiquity score: a simple method for assessing pesticide leachability. *Environmental and Toxicological Chemistry* **8:** 339-357.

Maas R P; Kucken D J; Patch S C; Peek B T; Van Engelen D L (1995). Pesticides in eastern North Carolina rural supply wells: land-use factors and persistence. *Journal of Environmental Quality* **24:** 426-431.

Merchant J W (1994). GIS-based groundwater pollution hazard assessment – a critical review of the DRASTIC model. *Photogrammetric Eng. Remote Sensing,* **60**: 1117-1128.

Palmer R C; Holman I P; Robins N S; Lewis M A (1995). *Guide to groundwater vulnerability mapping in England and Wales.* National Rivers Authority, Bristol.

Worrall F; Wooff D; Seheult A H; Coolen F (1998). A simple Bayesian approach to the interpretation of environmental fate and behaviour data for pesticide registration. *Pesticide Science* , **54(2)**: 99-112.

Wooff D A; Seheult A H; Coolen F; Worrall F (1999). A Bayesian reappraisal of environmental fate and behaviour data used in pesticide registration. In *Statistics for the Environment: 4*, Barnett and Turkman (eds.), John Wiley & Sons.

Worrall F; Wooff D; Seheult A H; Coolen F (2000). New approaches to the assessment of environmental fate of pesticides. *Jour. Geol. Soc.*, **157**: 877-884.

Worrall F (2001). A molecular topology approach to predicting pesticide pollution of groundwater. *Environ. Sci. Tech.* **35**: *2282-2287.*

Worrall F Direct assessment of groundwater vulnerability from borehole observations. In *Sustainable Groundwater Development*, Hiscock, Davison and Rivett (eds.), Geol. Soc. of London spec. publ. *(in press).*

SESSION 2

SORPTION AND MOBILITY (SMALL SCALE)

Chairman &   Dr R H Bromilow
Session Organiser: *IACR-Rothamsted, Harpenden, UK*

Effect of long-term sorption kinetics on leaching as calculated with the PEARL model for FOCUS scenarios

J J T I Boesten
Alterra, PO Box 47, 6700 AA Wageningen, The Netherlands
Email: boesten@alterra.wag-ur.nl

A M A van der Linden
RIVM, PO Box 1, 3720 BA Bilthoven, The Netherlands

ABSTRACT

Accurate estimation of pesticide/soil input parameters for leaching models such as PEARL is of paramount importance for meaningful use of these models in registration procedures. Adding non-equilibrium sorption into PEARL can alter the estimated transformation rate to be used as input to the model, and this effect was examined. We found that this transformation rate (as compared to the rate used when only equilibrium sorption is assumed) has to be multiplied by a correction factor whose value will often be close to 1.0 plus the quotient of the non-equilibrium Freundlich sorption coefficient divided by the equilibrium Freundlich sorption coefficient. This correction has a significant effect on calculated leaching in most cases. We recommend the re-evaluation of the available transformation rate studies whenever non-equilibrium sorption is included in leaching assessments with PEARL.

INTRODUCTION

The FOCUS groundwater scenarios have recently been developed for assessment of pesticide leaching in the EU registration process (FOCUS, 2000). These scenarios have been parameterised for four models, one of which is PEARL. Within the FOCUS scenarios, all parameters are fixed except the properties of the pesticide and its interaction with soil. Sorption parameters in PEARL have a large effect on calculated leaching, and so their estimation is of paramount importance. Sorption in PEARL is described with a two-site model: sorption at site 1 is an equilibrium process described by a Freundlich isotherm whereas sorption at site 2 is a non-equilibrium process described by pseudo first-order kinetics. The FOCUS guidance for input parameters recommends that non-equilibrium sorption should be ignored unless substance-specific data are available. Adding non-equilibrium sorption to a version of the PESTLA model that contained the same two-site sorption model as is used in PEARL considerably reduced the predicted leaching (Boesten, 1991). However, calculations with PEARL showed that adding non-equilibrium sorption had almost no effect on calculated leaching and sometimes even increased leaching (B Gottesbüren & J R van de Veen, personal communication, 2000). There is a conceptual difference in the description of the transformation rate between this PESTLA version and PEARL: in PESTLA it is assumed that the rate is proportional to the total system concentration whereas PEARL assumes that the rate is proportional to the concentration in the equilibrium domain only, thus excluding the amount sorbed at the non-equilibrium site. In this study we attempt to elucidate how this conceptual difference in the description of the transformation rate may cause the difference in calculated leaching when non-equilibrium sorption is included.

SHORT DESCRIPTION OF THE PEARL MODEL

We describe here briefly the most relevant parts of the PEARL model (Leistra *et al.*, 2001). The concentration of pesticide in the soil system, c^*, is given by:

$$c^* = \theta c + \rho X_{EQ} + \rho X_{NE} \qquad (1)$$

in which θ is volume fraction of water, ρ is dry bulk density, c is pesticide concentration in liquid phase and X_{EQ} and X_{NE} are contents of pesticide sorbed at the equilibrium and non-equilibrium site, respectively. PEARL includes also pesticide present in the gas phase but we ignore this here because it is not relevant for this study. Sorption at the equilibrium site is described by a Freundlich isotherm:

$$X_{EQ} = K_{EQ} c_R \left(\frac{c}{c_R}\right)^N \qquad (2)$$

in which K_{EQ} is the Freundlich coefficient, N is the Freundlich exponent and c_R is a reference value of c (set at 1 mg L^{-1}). Sorption at the non-equilibrium site is described with pseudo first-order kinetics:

$$\frac{\partial X_{NE}}{\partial t} = k_D \left[F K_{EQ} c_R \left(\frac{c}{c_R}\right)^N - X_{NE} \right] \qquad (3)$$

in which t is time, k_D is the desorption rate coefficient and F is the quotient of the Freundlich non-equilibrium coefficient divided by the Freundlich equilibrium coefficient.

PEARL assumes that the rate of transformation of pesticide, R_T, is proportional to the concentration in the equilibrium part of the system:

$$R_T = k_{T,EQ}(\theta c + \rho X_{EQ}) \qquad (4)$$

in which $k_{T,EQ}$ is the rate coefficient for transformation in the equilibrium part of the system. We define the half-life for transformation in the equilibrium part of the system as $H_{EQ} \equiv \ln2 / k_{T,EQ}$. Eq. 4 implies that pesticide sorbed at the non-equilibrium site is not transformed. Theoretically it would be more consistent to assume no transformation at the equilibrium site either (so only transformation in liquid phase). However, this would imply that half-lives that are usually available from pesticide registration procedures cannot be used directly as input to PEARL which is undesirable. Eq. 4 has the advantage that it is fully consistent with other models if non-equilibrium sorption is ignored. The pesticide flux in the gas phase is described by Fick's law and that in the liquid phase by a convection/dispersion equation.

EFFECT OF NON-EQUILIBRIUM SORPTION PARAMETERS ON ESTIMATED TRANSFORMATION RATES

Procedure

The normal procedure in pesticide registration is to derive half-lives from transformation rate studies in the laboratory assuming first-order kinetics. However, it is questionable whether such half-lives are accurate enough to be used as input to PEARL if sorption at non-equilibrium sites is included. This was tested as follows: (i) it was assumed that the PEARL submodel for transformation and sorption as described by Eqns 2 to 4 is valid, (ii) using this submodel (Eqns 1 to 4), the course of the remaining amount of pesticide in time was calculated with a small FORTRAN programme for hypothetical laboratory transformation studies for a range of half-lives (H_{EQ}) and sorption coefficients, (iii) this course in time was fitted to first-order kinetics for the total remaining amount which implies that the transformation rate is assumed to be proportional to the total system concentration:

$$R_T = k_{T,SY} c *$$ (5)

in which $k_{T,SY}$ is the transformation rate coefficient for the system concentration. We define the half-life for transformation of the system concentration as $H_{SY} \equiv \ln 2 / k_{T,SY}$.

In the calculations, dry bulk density was 1.0 g/ml and the volume fraction of water was 0.2. The initial pesticide concentration was 1.0 mg/L (initially present in the equilibrium part of the system). The Freundlich exponent was 0.9 and pesticide was assumed not to be present in the gas phase. The Freundlich coefficient for the equilibrium site, K_{EQ}, varied from 0 to 4 L/kg (i.e ranging from 0 to about 95% sorption). The half-life H_{EQ} varied between 1 and 1000 days. The default values $F = 0.5$ and $k_D = 0.01$ d^{-1} as recommended in the PEARL manual were used (Tiktak et al., 2000, p. 50). In each run, the calculation period was three times the half-life H_{EQ}. Eqns 3 and 4 were integrated using rectilinear integration with a time step of less than 2% of H_{EQ} to ensure sufficient accuracy.

The course of the amount remaining with time was characterised by 100 points in time equally spaced. These 100 points were fitted to first-order kinetics using linear regression after log-transformation which resulted in a value of H_{SY}. The results are analysed in terms of the quotient defined as $Q \equiv H_{SY} / H_{EQ}$. So the deviation of Q from unity is a measure for the differences in half-lives derived from laboratory studies via fitting to first-order kinetics and the corresponding equivalent half-lives that should be used as input for the PEARL model.

Results

Figure 1 shows that the quotient Q increases with increasing equilibrium sorption coefficient. As could be expected, Q is always 1 at zero sorption because then non-equilibrium sorption has no effect on the system. The figure shows also that Q increases when the half-life increases from 1 to about 100 days. However, when the half-life increases to higher values, Q decreases again. For a half-life of 1000 days and a sorption coefficient of about 4 L/kg, Q is about 1.5. Figure 1 shows that Q approaches 1 when the half-life approaches zero. This may be understood as follows: at very short half-lives, non-equilibrium sorption will have a negligible effect on the decline in the system for times up to three times the half-life H_{EQ} so the effect of non-equilibrium sorption is not detectable in the fitting procedure.

This explanation suggests that the fitting procedure itself has an effect on Q for short half-lives. We checked this via an alternative procedure in which the simulation period was fixed to 100 days instead of to three times the half-life H_{EQ}. This resulted indeed in a completely different relationship between Q and H_{EQ}: now Q approached infinity when H_{EQ} approached 0. This is understandable because a simulation period of 100 days for a half-life H_{EQ} of a few days implies a fast decline for about the first 10 days, followed by a slow decline of the last few percent left in the remaining 90 days. The fitting procedure for H_{SY} is then dominated by the slow decline which results in high Q values.

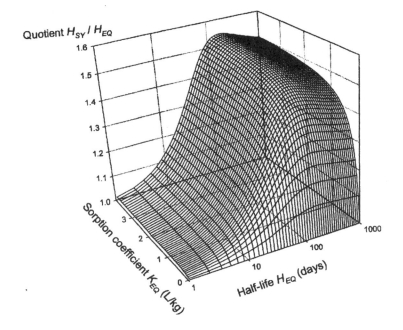

Figure 1. The quotient Q of the half-life for transformation of the system concentration (H_{SY}) divided by the half-life for transformation of the equilibrium part of the system concentration (H_{EQ}) as a function of both the Freundlich equilibrium sorption coefficient (K_{EQ}) and the half-life H_{EQ}.

Now we attempt to analyse quantitatively the behaviour of Q at long half-lives. If the decline resulting from transformation is slow as compared to sorption kinetics, X_{NE} will approach its equilibrium value after some time and remain close to that value. In this analysis we assume that the Freundlich exponent is 1 (so linear sorption isotherm). This will be closely approximated because $N = 0.9$. It is assumed that sorption at the non-equilibrium sorption site can be approximated by assuming equilibrium. Then elimination of c from Eqn 4 using Eqn 1, leads to the following rate equation:

$$R_T = k_{T,EQ} \left[\frac{\theta + \rho \, K_{EQ}}{\theta + \rho \, (1+F) K_{EQ}} \right] c^* \tag{6}$$

So these approximations imply that the transformation rate is both proportional to the equilibrium part of the system concentration and to the system concentration itself. Combination of Eqns 5 and 6 leads to the following expression for Q:

$$Q = \frac{\theta + \rho \, (1+F) \, K_{EQ}}{\theta + \rho \, K_{EQ}} \tag{7}$$

If sorption is high, θ can be ignored in Eqn 7 which then reduces to $Q = 1+F$, so $Q = 1.5$ in our case. This corresponds well with the result found in Figure 1 for long half-lives and strong sorption. We checked for $H_{EQ} = 1000$ d whether Eqn 7 is also a reasonable approximation for the range of K_{EQ} from 0 to 4 and found that the value predicted by Eqn 7 differed always by less than 5% from the calculated values shown in Figure 1. The approximation by Eqn 7 suggests that Q is more or less proportional to $1+F$. We checked this via calculations for $F = 4$ and found indeed a graph with a shape similar to that shown in Figure 1 but with Q approaching 5 for long half-lives and strong sorption as was expected.

SENSITIVITY OF LEACHING CALCULATED FOR FOCUS GROUNDWATER SCENARIOS: THE EFFECT OF ADDING NON-EQUILIBRIUM SORPTION

The previous analysis showed that there is interaction between the selection of the non-equilibrium sorption parameters and the selection of the half-life H_{EQ} within PEARL. We will assess the importance of this interaction via calculations for the Kremsmünster FOCUS scenario (FOCUS, 2000) using FOCUS PEARL v1.1.1. All pesticide parameters except K_{OM}, H_{EQ}, F and k_D were taken to be those for substance D as described by FOCUS (2000, p. 61). The crop was winter wheat and the pesticide was assumed to be applied to soil at a rate of 1.0 kg/ha on 1 May. Leaching was calculated as a function of K_{OM}. We compared calculations in which non-equilibrium sorption is excluded (i.e. $F = k_D = 0$) with calculations in which it is included using the default values for F and k_D recommended by Tiktak et al. (2000), so $F = 0.5$ and $k_D = 0.01$ d^{-1}. The calculations in which non-equilibrium sorption is excluded will be called "the EX calculations" and those including this sorption will be called "the IN calculations".

We consider the following case: the half-life for both EX and IN calculations was based on the same transformation rate study carried out in the laboratory with a soil having 3% organic matter and with other system properties as used for calculating Figure 1. In the normal practice of pesticide registration, four transformation rate studies would be used instead of one but we limit ourselves here to only one study for illustrative purposes. We consider two transformation rates and assume that the results of the transformation rate study can be described well with Eqn 5 using either a half-life H_{SY} of 10 or 100 days. This implies for the EX calculations that the half-life H_{EQ} was fixed at either 10 or 100 days because it is then by definition equal to the half-life H_{SY}. For the IN calculations the half-life H_{EQ} had to depend on the selected K_{OM} value to ensure consistency with the laboratory study: we calculated H_{EQ} via requiring that the selected combination of K_{EQ} and half-life H_{EQ} resulted in a half-life H_{SY} of 10 or 100 days for the transformation rate study. This was done via the same procedure as used for calculating Figure 1. This implies that the half-life H_{EQ} (used as input to PEARL) decreases with increasing K_{OM} for the IN calculations. For instance, for $H_{SY} = 10$ days, the selected half-life H_{EQ} decreased from 10 to 9.08 days if K_{OM} increased from 0 to 30 L/kg; for $H_{SY} = 100$ days, the selected half-life H_{EQ} decreased from 100 to 68 days if K_{OM} increased from 0 to 200 L/kg. The background of this is that the fraction of $c*$ that is present at the non-equilibrium site increases with increasing K_{OM} and that this fraction is not subject to transformation.

The predicted concentrations in leachate (Figure 2) show that the difference between IN and EX calculations increased with increasing K_{OM} as would be expected because by definition there is no difference at zero sorption. The difference between EX and IN calculations is larger at the half-life of 100 days than at the half-life of 10 days. For illustrative purposes we also made calculations in which non-equilibrium sorption was added but without correcting the half-life H_{EQ} (thus violating the requirement that the transformation rate in the laboratory study had to be described well). Figure 2 shows that then almost no difference was found between IN and EX calculations. This shows that including non-equilibrium sorption is only meaningful if the transformation rate is re-evaluated to be consistent with the results of the laboratory studies.

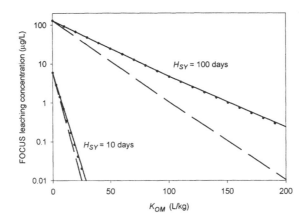

Figure 2.   The concentration of an example pesticide leaching to groundwater as a function of K_{OM} as calculated with PEARL for the Kremsmünster FOCUS scenario and winter wheat after application of 1.0 kg/ha to soil on 1 May. Solid line: equilibrium sorption only; dashed line: non-equilibrium sorption included and half-life H_{EQ} corrected based on laboratory study on transformation rate; dotted line: non-equilibrium sorption included but half-life H_{EQ} not corrected.

CONCLUSIONS AND RECOMMENDATIONS

If non-equilibrium sorption is used in a PEARL calculation, the transformation rate to be used has to be multiplied by a correction factor that ranges between 1.0 and about 1.0 plus the quotient of the non-equilibrium Freundlich sorption coefficient divided by the equilibrium Freundlich sorption coefficient. This correction leads to a substantial decrease of calculated leaching in most of the cases. We recommend the re-evaluation of the available transformation rate studies if non-equilibrium sorption is included in leaching assessments with PEARL. Given the complexity, inclusion of non-equilibrium sorption is only recommended for higher-tier evaluations.

REFERENCES

Boesten J J T I (1991) Sensitivity analysis of a mathematical model for pesticide leaching to groundwater. *Pesticide Science* **31**: 375-388.

FOCUS (2000) FOCUS groundwater scenarios in the EU review of active substances. Report of the FOCUS Groundwater Scenarios Workgroup, EC document Sanco/321/2000 rev. 2, 197 pp. Available at http://arno.ei.jrc.it/focus.

Leistra M; van der Linden A M A; Boesten J J T I; Tiktak A; Van den Berg F (2001). PEARL model for pesticide behaviour and emissions in soil-plant system; Description of the processes in FOCUS PEARL v 1.1.1. Alterra report 13, RIVM report 711401009, 117 pp. Available at www.alterra.nl/models/pearl.

Tiktak A; Van den Berg F; Boesten J J T I; Leistra M; Van der Linden A M A; Van Kraalingen D W G (2000). Manual of FOCUS PEARL version 1.1.1. RIVM report 711401008, Alterra report 28, 144 pp. Available at www.alterra.nl/models/pearl.

The measurement of time-dependent desorption and its influence on modelling movement of a pesticide metabolite through soil to groundwater

C R Leake, C M Burr, I A J Hardy, S L McMillan-Staff, G Reinken, R J Wicks
Aventis CropScience, Ongar Research Station, Ongar, Essex, CM5 0HW, UK
Email: christopher.leake@aventis.com

ABSTRACT

To explain the differences observed between modelling predictions and movement in the field of a pesticide metabolite, the influence of time on soil desorption processes was studied with eight contrasting soil types. In comparison with the standard adsorption/desorption approach, a significant increase in retention with time of the (predicted to be rather mobile) metabolite was observed. Data from four contrasting field sites showed that under European field conditions the compound remained mainly in the surface 10cm layer. Estimation of leaching using computer models has traditionally been conducted using the Freundlich adsorption K_{oc} value and the first-order-kinetics half-life as input values. When modelling potential movement to deeper soil layers, both desorption characteristics and hysteresis effects, together with their dependence with time, have an important role. In modelling the movement of this metabolite in soil, movement was over-predicted when using parameters from the non-aged samples when compared with field data. In contrast, modelling with the time-dependent desorption data, even over relatively short ageing periods of 3 days and 10 days, resulted in a significant improvement in predicted movement. To improve the model predictions of chemical movement in soil, desorption characteristics and their time dependence should be included in the model input and processing.

INTRODUCTION

In the assessment of likely leaching potential of plant protection products and their major metabolites, the accepted approach is to measure the K_{OC} in a range of soil types, normally at least four, over a range of at least five concentrations (OECD Guideline 106, 2000). Although the desorption characteristics may also be determined, it is currently not standard practice to use these data in the estimation of the movement of compounds in soil or in calculations of potential concentrations in groundwater. The phenomenon of hysteresis has been recognised for many years e.g. Bailey & White 1964; Green 1974; Calvet 1980; Koskinen 1990; Zhu & Selim 2000. More recently the effect of time on the sorption processes has also been shown to be important (Walker *et al.,* 1995; Cox & Walker 1999; Oi 1999). The FOCUS Ground-water Scenarios Working Group has identified time-dependent sorption processes as a major factor influencing the uncertainty of model predictions for those compounds that show a significant increased sorption over time (FOCUS, 2000). This investigation was conducted to determine a possible explanation for the discrepancy observed for the metabolite, between the predicted movement in soil by modelling and results from field studies.

MATERIALS AND METHODS

The adsorption of the radiolabelled metabolite was investigated in four contrasting soil types and in a sediment using four concentrations (0.04, 0.2, 1 and 5 mg L^{-1}) (Burr 1999), based on the OECD guideline 106. In preliminary studies, an adsorption equilibrium time of 48 hours and a desorption equilibrium time of 1 hour were obtained, and a soil to solution ratio of 1:3 was established. In addition to the adsorption phase, up to five desorption cycles were performed by removal of the supernatant solution and replacement with fresh 0.01M $CaCl_2$. A quantitative recovery of the radioactivity was obtained, by summation of that in the supernatant solutions, that present in the solvent extracts of the soils and that released by combustion of the remaining soil. The Freundlich adsorption constants K_f and the $1/n$ values for each soil were calculated using the Freundlich equation taking into account the concentration of the metabolite in the residual soil water. The K_f values were then expressed as K_{OC} values according to the organic-carbon content of each soil.

To investigate the effect of time on the desorption process, two further experiments were conducted. In the first (McMillan-Staff 1999), the design of which was based on the OECD guideline (2000), the radiolabelled metabolite was applied to 15 g portions (dry soil equivalent) to each of four contrasting soils at four equivalent concentrations (0.04, 0.2, 1 and 5 mg L^{-1}) for each soil. The metabolite was added in this case directly to the soil so each soil sample received either 375 μg, 75 μg, 15 μg or 3 μg of the metabolite. Some soil samples then had 75 ml of 0.01M $CaCl_2$ added and were shaken at 20°C for 24 hours. This was followed by centrifugation, removal of the supernatant solution and replacement with fresh 0.01M $CaCl_2$ for a total of up to four cycles. The remaining samples were incubated at 45% of the soil moisture content at 20°C in the dark for either 3 days or 10 days. After the incubation period of either 3 days or 10 days, the samples were treated in the same manner as the time zero samples. In the second experiment to investigate the effect of time on the desorption process, a similar design was employed. Four contrasting soils were obtained from field sites in Europe. In preliminary investigations, an adsorption equilibrium time of 48 h and a desorption equilibrium time of 24 h were obtained, with a 1:3 soil to solution ratio (Burr 2000). The four concentrations were 0.04, 0.2, 1 and 5 mg L^{-1} and the samples were analysed immediately and after 3 days and 10 days ageing at 45% of maximum water holding capacity. There was identical handling of the data as in the adsorption experiment

A terrestrial field dissipation study was conducted at four sites in Europe: Bologna, Italy; Chazay, Southern France; Goch, Germany and Manningtree, UK (Wicks 1999). Plots were treated with the parent compound at a nominal rate of 1600 g a.i ha^{-1} to bare soil. Four plots at each site were sampled during the first 12 months after application with five samples per plot at 10 cm incremental depths to 30 cm and then sampling to 60 cm. Samples were composited within each plot at each depth. A limit of quantification of 0.005 mg kg^{-1} (wet weight), which was equivalent to 7.5 g ha^{-1} or about 9 g ha^{-1} on a dry weight basis, was obtained for both the parent compound and the metabolite. Soil samples were frozen, shipped and stored frozen for up to 6 months. Analysis was by Accelerated Solvent Extraction with water:acetone 20:80 followed by LC/MS/MS.

For all model calculations the simulation model PELMO (PEsticide Leaching MOdel) version 3.00 after Service Pack II (Feb 2000) was used, chosen as it is one of the recommended European registration models (Kloskowski and Nolting 1998; FOCUS 2000).

RESULTS AND DISCUSSION

The initial adsorption study with the metabolite (Burr 1999) showed that the K_{oc} value was relatively low and that the $1/n$ value was significantly below 1 (Table 1). The overall recovery of radioactivity was good, ranging from 97.8 to 99.8%.

Table 1. Organic carbon (OC), K_f, $1/n$ and K_{oc} values for the metabolite under standard adsorption conditions

Soil type (USDA)	OC (%)	K_f (L kg^{-1})	$1/n$	K_{oc} (L kg^{-1})
Silt loam	0.5	0.11	0.832	23
Sandy loam	1.2	0.43	0.867	36
Sandy clay loam (sediment)	2.3	0.64	0.957	28
Silt loam II	1.9	0.32	0.811	17
Loam	2.0	0.56	0.821	28
Overall mean values (excluding the sediment)			0.83	26

The adsorption determination for the metabolite in the four contrasting field soils confirmed the low K_{oc} value when measured by the standard OECD test (Table 2).

Table 2. Metabolite adsorption on the four field soils.

Soil type (USDA)	OC (%)	K_f (L kg^{-1})	$1/n$	K_{oc} (L kg^{-1})
Bologna (clay loam)	1.3	0.36	0.889	28
Chazay (loam)	1.5	0.38	0.895	25
Goch (silt loam)	2.5	0.88	0.858	35
Manningtree (sandy loam)	1.1	0.26	0.915	24
Overall mean values			0.89	28

This indicated that the metabolite was a potentially mobile compound under field conditions. Laboratory aerobic metabolism studies (not presented in this paper) indicated a soil half-life at 20°C in excess of 100 days. However the desorption data in the batch/equilibrium study showed significant hysteresis in all the soil types (Figure 1). Data from the field dissipation study in four contrasting soil type/climatic regions in which the precipitation plus irrigation was in excess of the historical average showed the majority of the metabolite residues remained in the surface 0-10 cm layers. During a 12-month period, no movement was detected below 20 cm at three of the sites and no movement below 30 cm at the fourth site (Table 3). These results were not consistent with the predicted movement using the standard batch/equilibrium model input parameters.

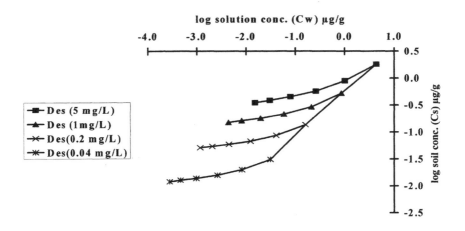

log solution conc. (Cw) µg/g

Legend:
- Des (5 mg/L)
- Des (1 mg/L)
- Des (0.2 mg/L)
- Des (0.04 mg/L)

Figure 1   Desorption hysteresis as a function of treatment concentration in loam soil.

Table 3.   Distribution with depth of metabolite (concentration in g ha^{-1}) in the four field locations.

Location/ Soil	Depth (cm)	3 Day	7 Day	14 Day	1 Mon	2 Mon	4 Mon	6 Mon	9 Mon	12 Mon
Clay loam	0-10	<LQ	38.9	32.6	46.3	60.7	25.9	16.7	<LQ	-
(Bologna,	10-20	-	<LQ	<LQ	<LQ	<LQ	<LQ	<LQ	<LQ	-
Italy)	20-30	-	-	-	<LQ	<LQ	<LQ	-	-	-
	30-60	-	-	-	-	-	-	-	-	-
Loam	0-10	34.9	47.2	98.4	40.4	53.1	<LQ	<LQ	<LQ	-
(Chazay,	10-20	-	<LQ	<LQ	<LQ	19.9	11.8	<LQ	<LQ	-
France)	20-30	-	-	<LQ	<LQ	<LQ	<LQ	<LQ	-	-
	30-60	-	-	-	-	-	-	<LQ	-	-
Silt loam	0-10	<LQ	<LQ	34.3	68.1	71.8	55.0	28.0	20.1	18.5
(Goch,	10-20	-	<LQ	<LQ	<LQ	<LQ	<LQ	12.3	11.9	<LQ
Germany)	20-30	-	-	<LQ	<LQ	<LQ	<LQ	<LQ	<LQ	<LQ
	30-60	-	-	-	-	-	-	-	-	-
Sandy loam	0-10	15.7	54.0	71.7	40.8	89.1	44.5	14.3	18.5	22.4
(Manningtree,	10-20	-	-	<LQ	<LQ	19.8	39.2	16.9	16.2	13.9
UK)	20-30	-	-	-	<LQ	<LQ	<LQ	9.1	12.1	10.7
	30-60	-	-	-	-	-	-	<LQ	<LQ	<LQ

Mon = Month   <LQ = Less than the limit of quantification of 9 g ha^{-1} - = Not determined

The significant increase in the $K_{oc\ des1}$ value over the relatively short periods of 3 days and 10 days (Table 4) indicates the potential effect over a longer period is likely to be even greater. A linear relation can be found between the square root of the time interval for desorption ("ageing period") and the increase in the effective sorption. This linear relationship found for all eight soils is indicative of a possible diffusive-type sorption mechanism (e.g. diffusion of the metabolite into the soil or soil organic matrix).

Table 4.   Metabolite-aged desorption determinations on eight soils at three time intervals.

Soil reference (USDA)	Day 0 $K_{oc\,des1}$	Day 3 $K_{oc\,des1}$	Day 10 $K_{oc\,des1}$
Loam	18 (1)	43 (2.4)	56 (3.1)
Sand	23 (1)	70 (3.0)	105 (4.6)
Clay loam	11 (1)	34 (3.1)	57 (5.2)
Silt loam (sediment)	32 (1)	41 (1.3)	ND
Bologna (clay loam	26 (1)	43 (1.7)	61 (2.3)
Chazay (loam)	25 (1)	26 (1.0)	53 (2.1)
Goch (loam)	31 (1)	50 (1.6)	61 (2.0)
Manningtree (sandy loam)	22 (1)	52 (2.4)	62 (2.8)
Overall mean values	23.5 (1)	44.9 (1.9)	65.0 (2.8)

ND – Not determined. Figures in parentheses are ageing factors, calculated by dividing by the K_{ocdes1} at Day 0.

Modelling the movement in the soil profile was undertaken using the PELMO 3.0 model applying the actual application rates (900 g ha^{-1} every third year) and effective crop interception, (50-80% for potatoes). In addition to the standard input values for the metabolite, the K_{OC} values were changed to reflect the aged K_{ocdes1} values. The average penetration depth after 7 months was estimated to be 14 cm using 3-day desorption data and 11 cm with 10-day desorption data (Figure 2). The inclusion of the desorption data in the model showed that the distribution with depth was more consistent with the field data where the metabolite was mainly confined to the 0-10 cm layer at all four sites, with little movement to the 10-20 cm or 20-30 cm layers. Consequently the movement of the metabolite in soil can only be accurately modelled when the time-dependent desorption is taken into account.

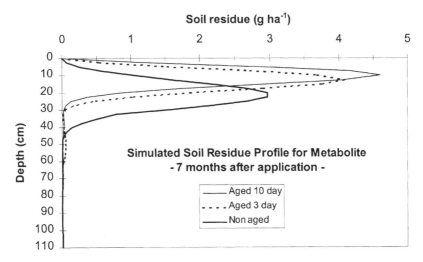

Figure 2. Example of the simulated profile for the metabolite in soil demonstrating the relative effect of ageing.

CONCLUSIONS

In modelling the movement of plant protection products and their metabolites in soil, the desorption characteristics may be of greater importance than the adsorption K_{OC}. Also, even over relatively short periods (up to 10 days), the time dependence of the desorption characteristics is important and though there is currently much less information available, it is likely that the increase will continue for longer time periods. To improve modelling predictions, both the desorption characteristics and their time dependence should be included.

REFERENCES

Bailey G W; White J L (1964). Review of adsorption and desorption of organic pesticides by soil colloids, with implications concerning pesticide bioactivity. *J. Agric. Food Chem* **12**: 324-332.

Burr C M (1999) [^{14}C]-RPA 412636: Adsorption/desorption to and from four soils and a sediment. Aventis CropScience Report 201886.

Burr C M (2000) [^{14}C]-RPA 412636: Adsorption to and aged desorption from four European soils obtained from field dissipation study sites. Aventis CropScience Report 202660.

Calvert R (1980) Adsorption-desorption phenomena In: *Interactions Between Herbicides and the Soil*.ed. R J Hance, Academic Press, London.

Cox L; Walker A (1999) Studies of time dependent sorption of linuron and isoproturon in soils. Chemophere **38**: 2707-2718.

FOCUS (2000) FOCUS groundwater scenarios in the EU plant protection product review process. Final report of the FOCUS Groundwater Scenarios Workgroup, EC Document Reference Sanco/321/2000 rev.2: 1-202.

Green R E (1974). Pesticide-clay-water interactions. In: *Pesticides in Soil and Water*. ed. W D Guenzi, pp 3-66 SSSA, Madison, WI. USA.

Kloskowski R; Nolting H-G (1998) Mitteilungen - Die Abteilung fuer Pflanzenschutz und Anwendungstechnik der Biologischen Bundesanstalt gibt bekannt: Offizialisierung von PELMO 3.00. Nachrichtenblatt des Deutschen Pflanzenschutzdienstes, Vol 50, No 10: 271.

Koskinen W C; Harper S S (1990) The retention process: Mechanisms. In: *Pesticides in the Soil Environment : Processes, Impacts and Modelling*. ed H H Cheng, pp 51-77 SSSA, Madison, WI. USA.

McMillan-Staff S L (1999) [^{14}C]-RPA 412636: Aged desorption. Aventis CropScience Report 202127.

OECD Guideline for the Testing of Chemicals- Adsorption–Desorption Using a Batch Equilibrium Method. Adopted 21st Jan 2000. OECD Paris

Oi M (1999) Time-dependent sorption of imidacloprid in two different soils. *J. Agric. Food Chem.* **47**: 327-332.

Walker A; Welch S J; Turner I J (1995) Studies of time-dependent sorption processes in soils. *Proceedings of the BCPC Symposium – Pesticide Movement to Water 1995* pp. 13-18. ed A Walker, R Allen, S W Bailey, A M Blair, C D Brown, P Gunther, C R Leake and P H Nicholls.

Wicks R J (1999) Field dissipation study in Europe. Aventis CropScience Report 202140.

Zhu H; Selim H M (2000) Hysteretic behaviour of metolachlor adsorption-desorption in soils. *Soil Science* **165**: 632-645

Sorption kinetics of clomazone and pendimethalin in Tasmanian soils – problems for the licit opium poppy industry?

J P Cumming, R B Doyle, P H Brown

School of Agricultural Science, University of Tasmania, GPO Box 252-54, Hobart Tasmania 7001, Australia.

Email: cummingj@utas.edu.au

ABSTRACT

Clomazone and pendimethalin sorption kinetics were examined on the separated fractions of four Tasmanian soils. In all soils the Kd of clomazone and pendimethalin sorption increased in the order; sand<silt<clay<particulate organic matter. The kinetics of sorption increased in the order of slowest to fastest; clay<silt<sand<particulate organic matter. The degree of sorption of both herbicides increased with increasing humification of organic matter associated with soil fractions. Pendimethalin exhibited greater sorption and faster kinetics on all soil fractions compared with clomazone, which may explain accumulation of pendimethalin soil residues.

INTRODUCTION

The Tasmanian cropping industry, and in particular the licit morphine poppy industry, relies upon the use of residual herbicides for seasonal weed control. Clomazone and pendimethalin are two such products gaining wide use, but with this has come carry-over problems. Clomazone (2-[(2-chlorophenyl)methyl]-4,4-dimethyl-3-isoxazolidinone) applied post-emergence to opium poppies (*Papaver somniferum*) has caused damage in a subsequent crop of malting barley (*Hordeum vulgare*). Pendimethalin (*N*-(1-ethylpropyl)-3,4-dimethyl-2,6-dinitrobenzenamine) provides residual weed control in pyrethrum daisies (*Tanacetum cinerariaefolium*) but with potential for subsequent carry-over effects upon opium poppy crops. As a result, accurate herbicide application is required to avoid carry-over effects and maintain crop-rotation choice in the Tasmanian production system. Initial soil sorption measurements indicated that herbicide persistence was linked to adsorption to soil colloids. Furthermore, this initial study indicated that the varied nature of individual soil constituents may have a large bearing upon sorption. The objective of this research was to evaluate the kinetics and degree of sorption to various soil fractions in four important agricultural soils in Tasmania.

METHODS AND MATERIALS

Soils

The kinetics of clomazone and pendimethalin sorption were studied in soil fractions of four soils; clay loam ferrosol with > 5% free iron oxides (ferrosol), acidic silty loam (sodosol), smectitic black cracking clay (vertosol), and a hydrophobic loamy sand with large amounts of particulate organic matter (kurosol). All soils were classified according to the Australian soil classification system (Isbell 1996).

Soils were fractionated into sand (>20µm), silt (2-20µm) and clay (2µm) by sedimentation according to the method of Kunze and Dixon (1986). No chemical agents were used, disruption of aggregates being achieved by mechanical agitation and sonification. Particulate organic matter (POM) was separated using an aqueous solution of sodium polytungstate ($Na_6(H_2W_{12}O_{40}).H_2O$) of density 1.6 Mg m^{-3} (Golchin et al., 1994). Clay-fraction separation of whole clay (<2 µm) and fine clay (<0.02 µm) fractions was achieved by sedimentation and centrifugation (Laird et al., 1991. A sample of the clay fractions extracted from the ferrosol and vertosol was also treated with 30% H_2O_2 for removal of organic matter (Kunze and Dixon 1986). This oxidised ferrosol sample was also treated with sodium dithionite and sodium citrate in a system buffered with sodium bicarbonate (DCB treatment) for removal of free Fe compounds (Kunze and Dixon 1986).

The chemistry of the clay fractions was investigated by X-ray diffraction (XRD), selected fractions also being examined by scanning electron microscopy (SEM). Total carbon was determined by dry combustion in a LECO furnace, and total N by Kjeldahl digestion.

Sorption kinetics of herbicides onto the soils

The kinetics of clomazone and pendimethalin adsorption by the soil fractions were determined using the batch equilibration method. Each soil fraction (1.0 g or 0.5 g for POM, in triplicate) was equilibrated with 0.01M $CaCl_2$ (5 ml) containing clomazone (1 mg L^{-1}) or pendimethalin (0.4 mg L^{-1}). Incubation times were 0.5, 1, 2, 4, 8 and 24 hours, after which samples were centrifuged for 5 min at 10,000 rpm, filtered to 0.45 µm and extracted with dichloromethane.

Chemicals and analysis

Analytical grade (99.1%) clomazone and pendimethalin were obtained from the Australian Standards Laboratory. All quantification was performed using a Varian Saturn GC-MS/MS operated at 28°C. Samples (2 µL) were injected into the column at 40°C using a carrier gas of helium at a flow rate of 2 ml min^{-1}. This column temperature was maintained for 1 minute, increased to 190°C at 30°C min^{-1}, and finally increased at 10°C min^{-1} to 280° C and held there for 6 minutes.

RESULTS

The key chemical components of each soil fraction are presented in Table 1. The organic matter associated with each soil fraction was qualitatively assessed according to palynological classification (Tyson 1995) to determine the most dominant type of organic matter present.

Table 1.   Characteristics of soil fractions and organic matter

Soil fraction	Mass (%)[a]	Total carbon (%)	C:N ratio	Organic matter type[b]	Clay matrix[c]
Kurosol	100	2.1	21	PH/AOM/CH	SM/IL
POM	1.2	27	29	PH/CH	-
Sand	90	1.35	22	AOMc	-
Silt & clay	9	9.29	13	CM	
Sand-OM	-	-	-	-	-
Sodosol	100	2.4	19	AOM/PH/CM	Kaolin
POM	1	28	25	PH	-
Sand	85		23	AOM	-
Silt & clay	12		15	CM/AOM	Kaolin
Silt & clay-OM[d]	-	-	-	-	
Ferrosol	100	5.3	12	CM/PH/OAM	Kaolin
POM	2.1	25	24	PH	-
Sand & silt	12	6.28	21	OAM	-
Clay	82	5.22	10	CM	Kaolin
Clay–OM&Fe[e]	-	-	-	-	-
Vertosol	100	3.4	14	CM/OAM/PH	Smectite
POM	0.8	26	29	PH/CH	-
Sand & silt	46	1.72	34	OAM	-
Clay	33	4.33	10	CM	Smectite
Fine clay	18	1.84	7	CM	SM/IL
Fine clay -OM	-	-	-	-	SM/IL

[a] Percentage of the total soil mass.
[b] Dominant organic matter present in order of content in each fraction; PH- phytoclast material, AOM- amorphic organic matter, CH– charcoal, CM- clay/humic association.
[c] Clay mineralogy as determined by XRD; a single entry represents greater than 90% of a dominant mineral present, SM/IL indicates mixed smectite/illmenite.
[d] Treated with H_2O_2 to remove organic matter.
[e] Treated with H_2O_2 to remove organic matter and DCB to remove free iron compounds.

The POM fractions in all soils contained large amounts of relatively undegraded plant debris or phytoclast (PH) material. In addition, the POM fraction of the vertosol, and to a lesser extent of the kurosol, contained appreciable amounts of charcoal. As has been reported previously (Karapanagioti et al., 2000) the presence of charcoal may explain the comparatively high Kd value (Table 2) and slow sorption kinetics (Figure 1) for clomazone on the vertosol POM fraction. In contrast, the presence of amorphous organic coatings (AOM) in the sand fraction of the kurosol provided an important sorptive site for rapid uptake of clomazone (Figure 1). The silt/clay fraction of the sodosol shown in Figure 1 exhibited an intermediate reaction rate for the uptake of clomazone, which is indicative of a clay/humic association (CM).

Clomazone sorption kinetics increased in the order of slowest to fastest; clay < sand < POM. The relative contribution of each soil fraction to the sorption of clomazone by the whole soil was affected by the type and distribution of organic matter. Soil clay fractions with a lower C:N ratio (Table 1), and hence more humified organic matter, exhibited a greater affinity for clomazone (Table 2). The readily accessible POM, which constituted less than 2% of soil mass in all soils, contributed over 5% to clomazone sorption by each soil (Table 2). Clomazone also exhibited an apparent affinity for pure clay fractions, in particular the smectite clay fraction of the vertosol (Table 2).

Table 2.   Sorption of clomazone and pendimethalin by the soil fractions.

Soil fraction	% soil mass[a]	Clomazone Kd (ml g^{-1})	% contribution to soil Kd[b]	Pendimethalin Kd (ml g^{-1})	% contribution to soil Kd[c]
Kurosol	100	1.8	-	157	-
POM	1.2	7.6	5	1806	14
Sand	90	1.5	85	111	79
Silt & clay	9	3.5	10	202	8
Sand-OM	-	0.1	-	26	-
Sodosol	100	1.7	-	170	-
POM	1	6.6	5	1962	13
Sand	85	1.2	68	115	63
Silt & clay	12	2.7	27	247	24
Silt & clay-OM[d]	-	0.8	-	88	-
Ferrosol	100	3.6	-	194	-
POM	2.1	7.2	5	1693	19
Sand & silt	12	3.7	55	108	28
Clay	82	2.5	46	176	53
Clay–OM&Fe[e]	-	1.2	-	112	-
Vertosol	100	2.4	-	191	-
POM	0.8	13	6	1994	11
Sand & silt	46	1.1	21	80	17
Clay	33	2.6	51	218	48
Fine clay	18	2.1	22	203	24
Fine clay-OM	-	1.8	-	164	-

[a] Percentage of the total soil mass.
[b] Percentage contribution of soil fraction to whole-soil clomazone sorption.
[c] Percentage contribution of soil fraction to whole-soil pendimethalin sorption.
[d] Treated with H_2O_2 to remove organic matter.
[e] Treated with H_2O_2 to remove organic matter and DCB to remove free iron compounds.

The hydrophobic pendimethalin molecule had a very strong affinity for organic surfaces, with very rapid sorption kinetics in each soil fraction (Figure 2), and in particular POM. In all soil fractions, pendimethalin sorption reached equilibrium before 4 hours, if not 2 hours. In addition, POM fractions exhibited large Kd values for pendimethalin, and contributed significantly to whole soil sorption (Table 2). Pendimethalin also showed greater adsorption to clay than sand fractions, which is most likely linked to the degree of humification of OM in the clay fractions. Importantly, clay fractions treated to remove organic matter also exhibited a strong affinity for pendimethalin, with relatively slow sorption kinetics (Table 2 and Figure 2).

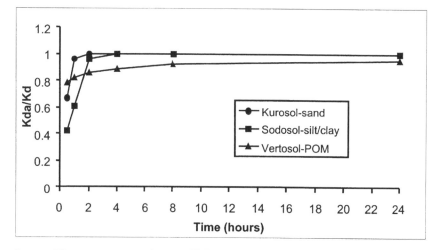

Figure 1.   The apparent sorption coefficient of clomazone normalized by equilibrium sorption coefficient (Kda/Kd) versus time.

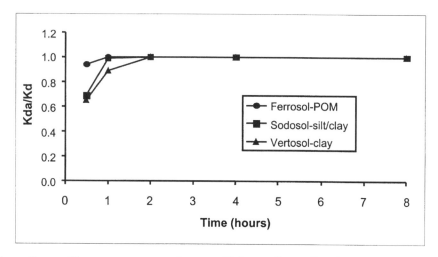

Figure 2.   The apparent sorption coefficient of pendimethalin normalized by equilibrium sorption coefficient (Kda/Kd) versus time.

CONCLUSION

Clomazone and pendimethalin exhibited a strong affinity for clay/humic associations (CM) which may result in accumulation of residues in the clay-rich ferrosol and vertosol. In addition, exposed organic surfaces such as POM provide a site for rapid strong binding of herbicide. It is likely that exposed POM surfaces and AOM coatings in sand fractions represent a labile pool of bound herbicide in each soil. Such of a pool of herbicide would be readily subject to desorption given mechanical disruption and/or increased soil moisture.

ACKNOWLEDGEMENTS

Serve-Ag PTY LTD project partners and HRDC Australia for project funding, Dr G. Rowbottom for his assistance with GC-MS/MS analysis.

REFERENCES

Golchin A; Oades J M; Skjemstad J O; Clarke P (1994). Study of free and occluded organic matter in soils by solid state CP/MAS NMR spectroscopy and scanning electron microscopy. *Australian Journal of Soil Research* **32**,: 285-309.

Isbell I B (1996). The Australian soil classification system. CSIRO Publishing Melbourne.

Jackson M L (1985). In: *Soil chemical analysis - advanced course, 2nd edition*, pp. 100-166. M L Jackson, Madison, WI;

Karapanagioti H K; Kleineidam S; Sabatini D A; Grathwohl P; Ligouis B (2000). Impacts of heterogenous organic matter on phenanthrene sorption: Equilibrium and kinetic studies with aquifer material. *Environmental Science Technology* **34**: 406-414.

Kunze G W; Dixon J B (1986). Agronomy Monograph 9. In: *Methods of soil analysis Part 1, 2nd edition*, ed A L Page; pp. 91-100; ASA and SSSA: Madison, WI.

Laird D A; Yen P Y; Koskinen W C; Steinheimer T R; Dowdy R H (1994). Sorption of atrazine on soil clay components. *Environmental Science Technology* **28**: 1054-1061.

Tyson R V (1995). *Sedimentary Organic Matter: Organic Facies and Palynofacies;* Chapman & Hall, London.

Incorporation of soil-pH dependent behaviour in pesticide leaching assessment

A M A van der Linden and A Tiktak
RIVM, PO Box 1, 3720 BA Bilthoven, The Netherlands
Email: ton.van.der.linden@rivm.nl

M Leistra
Alterra Green World Research, PO Box 47, 6700 AA Wageningen, The Netherlands

ABSTRACT

Until now, pH effects have been assessed in a simplified way in the evaluation of the leaching potential of pesticides in the Netherlands. If a substance shows pH-dependent sorption, a conservative approach is followed in which the sorption constant under worst-case conditions is taken for the assessment. In general this means that a relatively low value for the sorption coefficient is used in the calculations.

Some models used in the evaluation for pesticide registration have built-in routines that describe pH-dependent sorption, so this aspect can be taken explicitly into account. For instance, the PEARL model uses a routine that calculates the overall sorption coefficient from the sorption coefficients of the low-pH and high-pH species, as determined by the pK_a of the pesticide and the pH of the soil.

The rate of pesticide transformation in soil may also be pH-dependent, in which case the selection of the transformation rate coefficient (or half-life) differs from normal selection procedures. As none of the commonly available models has options for taking pH-dependent transformation into account, the leaching potential must be assessed by analysing the full range of possible soil-pH values.

As an example, calculating the leaching of a herbicide for the range of soil-pH values normally encountered in arable fields shows that the selection of the right parameters is very important. Surprisingly, the highest leaching of this substance appeared to be in the middle of the pH range. Certainly, such sensitivity analysis allows optimisation of the further testing of other substances, if needed.

INTRODUCTION

Reference scenarios for the assessment of the leaching potential of plant protection products have recently been developed (FOCUS, 2000), to be used in first-tier assessments. Pesticide sorption and transformation parameters and these scenarios can be used as input to appropriate leaching models and the leaching potential can be calculated. The results of the calculations are then used in the registration evaluation at the EU level. This procedure can probably be applied to approximately 80% of the substances registered in the Netherlands. The pH of the soil was not a selection criterion in the search for representative profiles, so the general procedure cannot be used for substances liable to charge transitions at typical soil pH values; for example substances having a pK$_a$ value (for acid dissociation) in the range 3 to 8. For such substances, a more refined approach, involving expert judgement, is recommended. In the Netherlands to date, generally a conservative approach has been followed, taking into consideration worst-case conditions with respect to leaching including the sorption constants having to be determined in soils with pH between 7 and 8.

For many substances, not only plant protection products, a relatively high correlation has been found between the sorption coefficient and the pH of the soil or sediment (for example, Moreale and van Bladel (1980), Schellenberg et al., (1984), Fontaine et al., (1991)). Schellenberg et al., (1984) found that for chlorophenols the sorption is related to the proportion of the neutral species, although deviations were found for the highly substituted congeners. The deviations were attributed to sorption of phenolate ions in soils of higher pH. Nicholls and Evans (1991) elaborated on the theory and suggested the use of a sorption coefficient derived from both neutral and ionised species, together with the pK$_a$ of the substance and the soil pH.

Information in *The Pesticide Manual* (Tomlin 1997) revealed that pH-dependent sorption behaviour might be relevant for approximately 20% of the pesticides registered in the Netherlands. Furthermore, such behaviour might also be relevant for metabolites of other substances. It was therefore decided to include pH-dependent sorption behaviour as an option in the PEARL model (Leistra et al., 2001; Tiktak et al., 2000). The use of this option in PEARL and the effect of taking pH-dependent sorption into account in the evaluation procedure and on a national scale is demonstrated below.

RELEVANT CONCEPTS IN PEARL

PEARL uses a concept of equilibrium sorption according to the Freundlich equation, with non-equilibrium sorption being optional (Leistra et al., 2001; Tiktak et al., 2001). A second option, pH-dependent sorption, is relevant for this study and is described below in more detail. The combination of non-equilibrium sorption and pH-dependent sorption is possible in the PEARL model, but not used in this study.

The dissociation of monovalent weak acids is described by:

$$HA \Leftrightarrow H^+ + A^-$$ (Eq. 1)

in which HA is the neutral molecule, H$^+$ is the hydrogen ion and A$^-$ is the anion. The degree of dissociation of the weak acid is described by:

$$pH = pK_a + \log\frac{(A^-)}{(HA)}$$ (Eq. 2)

with the brackets indicating the activity of the species and pK$_a$ defined as pK$_a$ = -log$_{10}$(K$_a$) and K$_a$ the acid dissociation constant. In the remainder of the text activities are set equal to molarities.

For each of the substances a sorption coefficient may be defined:

$$K_{om,HA} = \frac{X_{om,HA}}{c_{HA}}, \qquad K_{om,A^-} = \frac{X_{om,A^-}}{c_{A^-}}$$ (Eq. 3a, b)

with for each species, HA and A⁻:

    X_{om} = content sorbed to organic matter (kg/kg)

    c = concentration in solution (kg/m³)

    K_{om} = sorption coefficient on basis of soil organic matter (m³/kg)

The combined coefficient $K_{om,com}$ for sorption as a function of pK_a and pH can be expressed as:

$$K_{om,com} = \frac{K_{om,HA} + K_{om,A^-} \cdot M_{rel} 10^{pH-pK_a-\Delta pH}}{1 + M_{rel} 10^{pH-pK_a-\Delta pH}} \qquad (Eq.\ 4)$$

with:

    Kom,com = coefficient for the sorption of the combination of HA and A⁻ on soil organic matter (m³/kg)

    M_{rel} = relative molar mass of A⁻ as compared to HA

    ΔpH = pH-shift, pH-units (see below)

At low pH-values, mainly HA is present and the sorption is dominated by sorption of the neutral molecule; the exponent in Eq. 4 becomes negative, almost eliminating the second term at the right-hand side while the denominator approaches 1. In contrast, at high pH the denominator becomes large, therewith eliminating the contribution of the neutral molecule. The anions are repelled by the negative charge of the surfaces of organic matter and clay minerals, so sorption is often low. However, the anions may show some residual sorption due to hydrophobic interactions between a more hydrophobic part of the molecule and organic matter. Equation 4 can also be used for weak bases, where the protonated species is more strongly sorbed than the neutral molecule. In Eq. 4 an additional term ΔpH or pH-shift is included to account for discrepancies between experimental conditions in sorption tests and the conditions for which one wants to calculate the leaching of a substance. The pH of the soil is dependent on the way it is measured. Several methods exist, of which the most obvious differences between the methods are the composition and the concentration of the solution used to prepare the slurry, usually H_2O, KCl or $CaCl_2$. It is likely that the concentration of exchangeable cations and the way in which the pH is measured affect the pH-value obtained.

RESULTS

Dinoseb, a herbicide that is no longer on the market (Tomlin, 1997), has a pK_a of 4.62 and therefore is expected to show pH-dependent sorption behaviour. Indeed, re-evaluation of sorption data in the (old) registration dossier revealed a relationship with pH. As different methods were used for measuring the pH of the soil, all pH values were converted to $pH(CaCl_2)$. Values of $pH(H_2O)$ were lowered by 0.6, whereas $pH(KCl)$ values were raised by 0.1. The fitting to the PEARL formula, using the PRISM2 package (Graphpad Software, Inc.), led to K_{om} sorption coefficients of 500 L/kg for the neutral molecule and 23 L/kg for the anion. The average half-life for dinoseb was 50.2 days. Using these sorption and transformation data in the standard Dutch evaluation procedure (net application rate 1 kg/ha), the predicted leaching of dinoseb below 1 m depth is 2.8% (maximum average concentration in the groundwater between 1 and 2 m depth is 5.7 µg/L). This would lead to a negative decision in the registration procedure. Using GeoPEARL (PEARL in combination with a GIS) (Tiktak *et al.*, 2001), we investigated whether this relatively high leaching would be predicted to occur in extensive areas of the Netherlands. The potential leaching of the substance was calculated for over 6000 different input combinations, derived from the soil map and climatic conditions as registered by the 15 main weather stations in the Netherlands. These calculations show that in large areas of the Netherlands leaching above the 0.1 µg/L would indeed be expected (Figure 1, the 300 mg/ha leaching level roughly corresponds with this registration threshold). There are also large areas where leaching would be expected to be low. The main reason for the limited leaching is the lower pH, with corresponding higher sorption coefficient. Application of dinoseb took place to a large part in the vulnerable areas i.e. areas with soil pH around 7, so the denial of the registration seems justified.

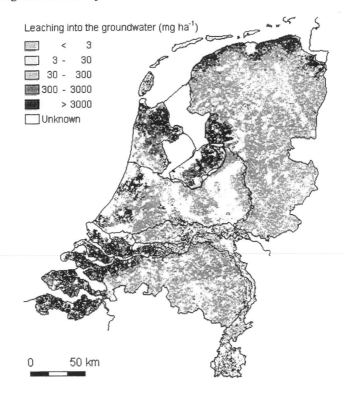

Leaching into the groundwater (mg ha^{-1})

	< 3
	3 - 30
	30 - 300
	300 - 3000
	> 3000
	Unknown

0   50 km

Figure 1. Potential leaching of dinoseb as calculated with GeoPEARL.

Not only sorption might be pH-dependent but transformation also. This was recently shown for a newly developed herbicide, submitted for registration in the Netherlands (name and properties are not given here because of confidentiality), which has two principal metabolites. As for other weak acids, the sorption coefficients declined with increasing pH and the sorption data could be fitted well to the PEARL formula, using the default value of zero for the pH-shift. The transformation rate of this herbicide is also correlated with the pH; the transformation rate increased with pH. As the correlation with pH for the metabolites was rather poor, constant rates were assumed. With both sorption and transformation dependent on the pH, the definition of any potentially vulnerable situations is not obvious. Using corresponding values as input into the PEARL model (while keeping all other input constant), one might cross one or more contour lines in leaching diagrams (Boesten and van der Linden 1991); indicating one or more orders of magnitude difference in leaching. The leaching of this new herbicide and its metabolites was calculated for five scenarios, differing only in pH (Table 1). The pH was assumed to be constant over the whole soil profile. The leaching is indicated as fraction of the leaching in the scenario with pH 6. It turned out that the calculated leaching for the parent was greatest at pH 6 while for the second metabolite the leaching was greatest at pH 5.5. The calculated leaching for the first metabolite showed a slightly increasing trend towards pH5. The differences are probably due to different relationships of sorption with pH.

Table 1. Leaching of a herbicide and its two principal metabolites showing both pH-dependent sorption and pH-dependent transformation as function of the soil pH.

Substance	Relative leaching (pH 6 = 1) at pH($CaCl_2$)				
	5	5.5	6	6.5	7
Parent	0.07	0.97	1.00	0.11	0.00
Metabolite 1	2.59	2.50	1.00	0.55	0.36
Metabolite 2	1.00	1.80	1.00	0.60	0.50

DISCUSSION

The pH($CaCl_2$), with the $CaCl_2$ concentration at 0.005 moles per litre, is usually thought to reflect best the pH of the soil solution under normal field soil conditions. Sorption experiments almost always are performed using such a solution. In transformation experiments, the water content is intended to reflect field conditions, so there also the pH($CaCl_2$) will best describe the incubation conditions. If other pH measurements are available, it seems best to correct to the pH($CaCl_2$) value. The correction can be done in the PEARL model by introducing the appropriate pH-shift value. It is however recommended to correct outside PEARL if data from different methods are available.

The surface of soil minerals and soil particulate organic matter is usually charged. The pH value at the surface is up to 2 pH-units lower than the pH of the soil solution. Some authors, e.g. Nicholls and Evans (1984), developed formulae to account for this difference in pH. By means of the pH-shift parameter in the PEARL model, it is also possible to correct for this surface acidity. In the examples shown, but also in other cases, it was not necessary to correct for this effect and the default value of zero led to reasonably good fits. When the pH-shift parameter was fitted, it was not possible to obtain a value between 0 and 2 in any of the cases. The lack of sorption data below the pK_a of the substances made it impossible to draw conclusions on the necessity of the pH-shift parameter.

Often the relation between the sorption coefficient and the pH is described as a log-linear sorption relation (for example, Schellenberg et al., 1984). Such a relation may describe the measured coefficients reasonably well if the pH of the soils is within a few pH units of the pK_a value of the substances. To determine which approach more accurately represents the sorption changes with pH means using sorption data for pH ranges beyond those normally found in agricultural soils, particularly for pH values below the pK_a of the substance. At higher pH, anions may contribute to the sorption and then the overall sorption is underestimated when using a log-linear approach. It will depend on the transformation rate whether in such cases the leaching is also underestimated.

CONCLUSIONS AND RECOMMENDATIONS

The PEARL model has an option to account for pH-dependent sorption. This option is very useful in simulating the leaching behaviour of substances having a pK_a value in the range 3 to

8. With this option, the evaluation of leaching for these substances can be refined and tailor-made decisions can be taken. The theoretical basis of this option has a potential advantage over an approach using empirical log-linear relationships, which are generally used. To determine whether this approach more accurately represents sorption changes with pH further investigations, especially with data from sorption experiments performed at pH values below the pK_a of the substance, are necessary.

The transformation of substances can also be dependent on the soil pH value. PEARL has no option to account for this and therefore a scenario analysis, in which the pH of the soil changes over the relevant range, is recommended to evaluate the leaching in such cases. At the moment it is unclear whether the effect of the pH on the transformation is attributable to the availability of the substance or whether other processes are involved.

The use of information in soil maps and climatic databases is very useful to get insight in the variability of the leaching of substances. This improved knowledge might be used in the registration evaluation process. If transformation is pH-dependent, such evaluations have to be performed for several relevant scenarios.

REFERENCES

Boesten J J T I; A M A van der Linden (1991). Modeling the influence of sorption and transformation on pesticide leaching and persistence. *Journal of Environmental Quality* **20**: 425 – 435.

FOCUS (2000). FOCUS groundwater scenarios in the EU review of active substances. Report of the FOCUS Groundwater Scenarios Workgroup, EC document Sanco/321/2000 rev. 2, 197 pp. Available at http://arno.ei.jrc.it/focus.

Fontaine D D; Lehmann R G; Miller J R (1991). Soil adsorption of neutral and anionic forms of a sulfonamide herbicide, flumetsulam. *Journal of Environmental Quality* **20**: 759-762.

Leistra M; van der Linden A M A; Boesten J J T I; Tiktak A; Van den Berg F (2001). PEARL model for pesticide behaviour and emissions in soil-plant system; Description of the processes in FOCUS PEARL v 1.1.1. *Alterra report 13, RIVM report 711401009*, 117 pp. Available at www.alterra.nl/models/pearl.

Moreale A; van Bladel R (1980). Behavior of 2,4-D in Belgian soils. *Journal of Environmental Quality* **9**: 627-632.

Nicholls P H; Evans A A (1991). Sorption of ionisable organic compounds by field soils. 1. Acids. *Pesticide Science* **33**: 319-330.

Schellenberg K; Leuenberger Ch; Schwarzenbach R (1984). Sorption of chlorinated phenols by natural sediments and aquifer materials. *Environmental Science Technology* **18**: 652 – 657.

Tiktak A; Van den Berg F; Boesten J J T I; Leistra M; Van der Linden A M A; Van Kraalingen D W G (2000). *Manual of FOCUS PEARL version 1.1.1. RIVM report 711401008, Alterra report 28*, 144 pp. Available at www.alterra.nl/models/pearl.

Tiktak A; Van der Linden A M A; De Nie D S (in prep). Modelling the risk pesticide leaching at a regional scale in the Netherlands. The GeoPEARL model.

Tomlin C D S (Ed.) (1997). *The Pesticide Manual 11th edition*. British Crop Protection Council, Farnham, Surrey, UK.

Characterisation of sorption for the modelling of pesticide fate

S Beulke, C D Brown, I G Dubus
Cranfield Centre for EcoChemistry, Cranfield University, Silsoe, Beds MK45 4DT, UK
E-mail: s.beulke@cranfield.ac.uk

A Walker
HRI, Wellesbourne, Warwick, CV35 9EF, UK

ABSTRACT

This paper discusses the implications of simplifying assumptions concerning sorption on which the modelling of pesticide fate is traditionally based. Sorption is often measured by intense shaking of soil with large volumes of water. Evidence indicates that the values obtained are not fully applicable to field conditions. The assumption of a characteristic, instantaneous sorption equilibrium is also not valid. This is partly due to the slow diffusion of pesticides into soil aggregates. An inverse relationship is found between the rate of equilibration and aggregate size. The calculation of sorption parameters from Koc values and soil organic carbon content is of sufficient accuracy in many cases, but predictions for soils with low organic carbon contents, including many subsoils, are subject to considerable error. Sorption coefficients and Freundlich exponents from different experiments are often averaged and used as input data for modelling. This approach is not mathematically valid and can introduce bias into environmental risk assessments.

INTRODUCTION

Mathematical simulation models are important tools for assessing the risk that pesticides may pose to the environment. Their capacity to provide a realistic assessment depends to a large extent on a correct description of pesticide sorption. Sorption controls the availablity of a pesticide in the soil solution and hence its potential for transport to water resources. Models have been shown to be very sensitive to sorption parameters, particularly the Freundlich exponent (Dubus *et al.*, 2000). Nonetheless, simplistic assumptions are often made in the characterisation of sorption which necessarily introduce uncertainty into the assessment.

SORPTION EXPERIMENTS AND MODEL PARAMETERISATION

Influence of soil:solution ratio

It is generally assumed that sorption in undisturbed soils in the field can be characterised by the results from batch studies which allow intense contact between the pesticide and soil particles and are carried out at a low soil:water ratio. In the field, soil moisture rarely exceeds field capacity which raises the question of the extent to which measurements in soil slurries give an accurate estimate of sorption in natural soils at realistic moisture contents.

Soil:solution ratio has been shown to influence the sorption coefficients obtained although different studies have given contrasting results. Greater dispersion of soil aggregates during shaking of the soil-water suspension may expose additional sorption sites and may result in increasing sorption coefficients with increasing soil:solution ratio (Grover and Hance 1970). Conversely, a decrease in sorption coefficients with increasing soil:solution ratios was found by Celorie *et al.*, (1989). Pesticide molecules can be sorbed to suspended solids or dissolved organic matter (Chiou *et al.*, 1986), whereby the apparent concentration in the liquid phase is increased and the sorption coefficient decreased. This effect is more pronounced at larger water contents because the concentration of suspended particles is greater under these conditions. Boesten (1990) concluded from a literature review and a statistical analysis that sorption coefficients are independent of water contents, but sorption experiments should be conducted at water contents as close as possible to field conditions to increase accuracy.

Several methods to determine sorption coefficients under more realistic moisture conditions are available (e.g. Celorie *et al.*, 1989). Walker and Jurado-Exposito (1998) compared sorption determined by standard methodology with that derived from a centrifugation technique which used small volumes of water relative to the mass of soil. Sorption of the herbicides isoproturon, diuron and metsulfuron-methyl was initially smaller using the centrifugation technique than the standard method. This was probably due to the ready availability of sorption sites in the shaken systems. Thus more pesticide may be available for leaching to depth shortly after application than will be predicted from equilibrium sorption coefficients measured in shaken laboratory systems at high water contents.

Sorption non-equilibrium

In standard laboratory experiments, air-dried and sieved soil (2 mm) is shaken with an aqueous pesticide solution. It is assumed that a characteristic distribution of the pesticide between the solid phase of the soil and the solution is established within two to four hours. In longer-term experiments, however, an initial decrease in solution concentration is often followed by a slow further decrease and sorption equilibrium is not reached until several hours or days have passed (Ma and Selim 1994). Natural soils in the field do not comprise uniform 2-mm sieved particles, but are made up of variable-sized aggregates which, during significant leaching events, will be at moisture contents close to field capacity. Recent data have shown that slow equilibration becomes more pronounced as the aggregate size increases, indicating that diffusion to the internal matrix can be a rate-limiting step (Walker *et al.*, 1999; Figure 1).

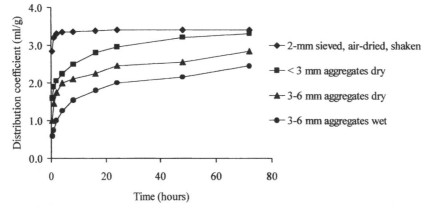

Figure 1. Kinetics of isoproturon sorption by different aggregate classes from a heavy clay soil

Under intense rainfall conditions that promote leaching events, the time for interaction between the pesticide and a soil aggregate is short and equilibrium between sorbed and solution phases will only rarely be achieved. The mechanisms of sorption in flowing systems have not been extensively studied and the true applicability of parameters derived in static systems in the laboratory to flowing systems in the field has not been established.

Influence of soil properties

Sorption is often assumed to be mainly associated with soil organic matter and sorption coefficients are expressed per unit of organic carbon content of the soil (Koc value). The data package for pesticide registration requires estimates of Koc from laboratory studies with a number of soils. Sorption of the pesticide in an untested soil can then be estimated from a knowledge of its organic carbon content and the Koc value. Although this approach can give a good approximation to the average situation, Koc values can vary considerably amongst soils. Koc values for ethofumesate determined in sandy loam soils with organic carbon contents of 1.3 to 7.1% ranged from 203 to 307 ml/g with a coefficient of variation of 14% (Beulke 1998). For metazachlor they varied from 75 to 136 ml/g with a CV of 21% (Figure 2).

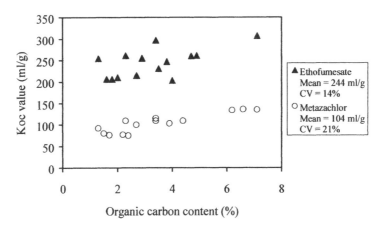

Figure 2. Koc values for ethofumesate and metazachlor in ten soils

The Koc concept assumes that sorption of pesticides to mineral soil constituents can be neglected and that the sorption capacity of organic matter is similar in all soils. These assumptions seem to be valid for hydrophobic, non-polar compounds (Businelli 1993) although Chiou (1989) pointed out that the dominant role of organic matter is restricted to saturated systems. The importance of mineral soil components increases under unsaturated conditions. For polar substances, a strong relationship between sorption and organic matter often cannot be found unless soil organic carbon content varies over a wide range (Calvet 1993).

A further illustration of the limitations in use of the Koc to predict sorption (Figure 3) has been derived from data of Walker and Crawford (1968). There was a highly significant linear correlation between atrazine sorption and soil organic carbon content ($R^2 = 0.97$) with an average Koc of 105 ml/g. However, the data show that use of the Koc concept to predict sorption in soils with low soil organic carbon will be subject to considerable error. Five of the soils used by Walker and Crawford were subsoils, and these had the five lowest organic carbon contents in the dataset shown in Figure 3. Clearly, this raises serious questions over the confidence with which the Koc approach can be used to derive sorption parameters in deeper soil layers. In this example, however, the selection of the average Koc of 105 ml/g would result in an over-estimation of pesticide leaching and thus be a conservative assessment.

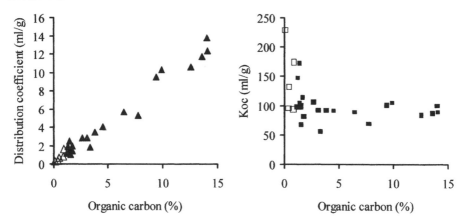

Figure 3. Distribution coefficients and Koc values for atrazine plotted against organic carbon content for five subsoils (Δ, □) and 22 topsoils (σ, ν)

The variability in Koc values of a pesticide can be incorporated into assessments of pesticide leaching by probabilistic modelling. This involves sampling a large number of Koc values from statistical distributions and running a simulation model with each of the sampled values. The likelihood of exceeding a threshold concentration in leachate can be quantified on the basis of the resulting distribution of model output. A log-normal distribution is often appropriate to characterise the variability in Koc values (e.g. Novak *et al.* 1997). Data compiled by Gottesbüren (1991) indicate that the distribution of Koc values may follow variable patterns, although the size of the dataset was limited (Figure 4). Further work is needed to evaluate whether Koc values do follow typical statistical distributions and how many measurements are required for their characterisation.

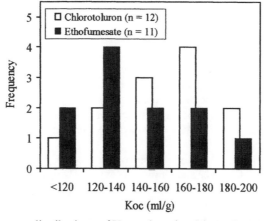

Figure 4. Frequency distributions of Koc values for chlorotoluron and ethofumesate

Averaging non-linear sorption coefficients

The Freundlich isotherm is often used to characterise sorption and another source of error in modelling pesticide fate is associated with the parameterisation of this particular relationship. The Freundlich isotherm has the generalised form:

$$S = K_f \, C^{\frac{1}{n}}$$

with S = sorbed amount (mg/kg), K_f = sorption coefficient (ml/g), C = concentration in solution (mg/l), 1/n = Freundlich exponent. This relationship has two parameters, Kf and 1/n, which must be considered as paired values. For pesticide registration purposes, sorption is determined in experiments with a number of soils. Kf or Koc values from these experiments are averaged and used to predict concentrations of the pesticide in surface water or groundwater. The same procedure is usually followed for the Freundlich exponent. This approach is not valid in a mathematical sense The predicted concentration resulting from the mean sorption coefficient and 1/n value differs from the average of simulations carried out separately for each of the four combinations. This is due to non-linearity in the Freundlich isotherm and in the relationship between sorption and pesticide leaching.

Concentrations in leachate of two hypothetical pesticides were calculated using the FOCUS groundwater scenario for Hamburg (FOCUS 2000) to demonstrate the effect of averaging sorption parameters. It was assumed that sorption was measured in four soils (Table 1). Application was made once a year at 1 kg/ha to winter cereals one day before crop emergence. Simulations were carried for 26 years using the model PELMO FOCUS 1.1.1. Concentrations for the years 6-26 were used for evaluation (FOCUS 2000). Data simulated for these 20 years and each of the four pairs of Koc and 1/n values (80 concentrations) were combined, sorted in ascending order and the overall 80th percentile concentration was derived. This was compared with the 80th percentile concentration for average Koc and 1/n values (Table 1).

Table 1. 80th percentile concentrations in leachate at 1-m depth simulated with PELMO for 4 pairs of Koc and 1/n values and for average parameters (degradation half-life = 30 d)

Pesticide 1			Pesticide 2		
Koc	1/n	80th percentile concentration	Koc	1/n	80th percentile concentration
(ml/g)		(µg/l)	(ml/g)		(µg/l)
50	0.87	6.68	100	0.87	0.117
59	0.70	0.001	118	0.70	<0.001
45	0.95	15.3	90	0.95	1.97
70	0.90	2.69	140	0.90	0.020
Overall		**8.35**	Overall		**0.55**
56 (mean)	0.86 (mean)	**4.05**	112 (mean)	0.86 (mean)	**0.019**

Large differences were found between the overall 80th percentile concentration derived from individual runs with paired Koc and 1/n values and the concentration simulated on the basis of average parameters (Table 1). Discrepancies were larger for the more strongly sorbed pesticide 2 (factor 28) than for pesticide 1 (factor 2.1). Results for the two hypothetical pesticides and the single soil scenario used in this study cannot be generalised and the effect is likely to be smaller when 1/n is closer to 1. However, simulated pesticide leaching is often very sensitive to Koc and 1/n and averaged parameters should be used with care.

CONCLUSIONS

The modelling of pesticide sorption is based on simple concepts which were developed several decades ago. Some simplifications may be insignificant at the macroscopic scale, but others restrict our ability to accurately assess the transport of pesticides to water resources. The implications of the strong variability and uncertainty in sorption parameters are just beginning to be considered. A refinement of sorption concepts and further work on innovative experimental and modelling techniques are needed to address these issues.

REFERENCES

Beulke S (1998). Untersuchung und mathematische Beschreibung des Abbaus von Herbiziden im Boden in Abhängigkeit von Wirkstoffverfügbarkeit, mikrobieller Biomasse und Aktivität. Ph.D. diss. Technical University Braunschweig, Germany.

Boesten J J T I (1990). Influence of solid/liquid ratio on the experimental error of sorption coefficients in pesticide/soil systems. *Pesticide Science* **26**: 31-41.

Businelli M (1993). Significance and limitations of partition coefficients. *Proc. IX Symposium Pesticide Chemistry: Mobility and Degradation of Xenobiotics*, 265-275.

Calvet R (1993). Comments on the characterization of pesticide sorption in soils. *Proc. IX Symposium Pesticide Chemistry: Mobility and Degradation of Xenobiotics*, 277-288.

Celorie J A; Woods S L; Vinson T S; Istok J D (1989). A comparison of sorption equilibrium distribution coefficients using batch and centrifugation methods. *Journal of Environmental Quality* **18**: 307-313.

Chiou C T (1989). Theoretical considerations of the partition uptake of nonionic organic compounds by soil organic matter. *SSSA Special Publication* **22**: 1-29.

Chiou C T; Malcolm R L; Brinton T I; Kile T E (1986). Water solubility enhancement of some organic pollutants and pesticides by dissolved humic and fulvic acids. *Environmental Science and Technology* **20**: 502-508.

Dubus I G; Brown C D; Beulke S (2000). Sensitivity analyses for leaching models used for pesticide registration in Europe. SSLRC research report to MAFF.

FOCUS (2000). FOCUS groundwater scenarios in the EU review of active substances - The report of the work of the Groundwater Scenarios Workgroup of FOCUS (FOrum for the Co-ordination of pesticide fate models and their USe). Sanco/321/2000 rev.2, 202pp.

Gottesbüren B (1991). Konzeption, Entwicklung und Validierung des wissensbasierten Herbizid-Beratungssystems HERBASYS. Ph.D. diss. Hanover University, Germany.

Grover R; Hance R J (1970). Effect of ratio of soil to water on adsorption of linuron and atrazine. *Soil Science* **2**: 136-138.

Ma L; Selim H M (1994). Physical nonequilibrium modelling approaches to solute transport in soils. *Advances in Agronomy* **58**: 95-150.

Novak J M; Moorman T B; Cambardella C A (1997). Atrazine sorption at the field scale in relation to soils and landscape position. *Journal of Environ. Quality* **26**: 1271-1277.

Walker A; Crawford D V (1968). The role of organic matter in adsorption of the triazine herbicides by soils. In: *Isotopes and Radiation in Soil Organic Matter Studies.* International Atomic Energy Agency, Vienna, pp. 91-105.

Walker A; Jurado-Exposito M (1998). Adsorption of isoproturon, diuron and metsulfuron-methyl in two soils at high soil:solution ratios. *Weed Research* **38**: 229-238.

Walker A; Turner I J; Cullington J E; Welch S J (1999). Aspects of the adsorption and degradation of isoproturon in a heavy clay soil. *Soil Use and Management* **15**: 9-13.

SESSION 3

POSTER SESSION A

Session Organisers: Dr R H Bromilow
IACR-Rothamsted, Harpenden, UK;

Dr G D Bending
HRI, Wellesbourne, UK

and

Dr A C Johnson
Centre for Ecology and Hydrology,
Wallingford, UK

The influence of lipophilicity and formulation on the distribution of pesticides in sediment/water systems

R H Bromilow, A A Evans, P H Nicholls
IACR-Rothamsted, Harpenden, Herts, AL5 2JQ, UK
Email: Richard.Bromilow@bbsrc.ac.uk

ABSTRACT

The sorption of pesticide by sediment and the influence of pesticide formulation on this process have been examined in small-scale mesocosms. Eight pesticides, spanning a range of physicochemical properties, were individually applied to the water. Sorption equilibrium was reached at between 15 and 30 days, the proportion of pesticide then in the sediment ranging from 20% for the acidic and so polar triasulfuron to 97% for the lipophilic permethrin; this behaviour was not influenced by formulation. Sorption coefficients measured in batch tests over two hours gave good estimates of the equilibrium distribution. It is concluded that lipophilicity is the chief determinant of pesticide distribution in sediment/water systems, and predictions based on this were acceptable for initial appraisals.

INTRODUCTION

Pesticides reach surface waters either from point sources, such as spills or tractor washings, or from diffuse sources such as contaminated water draining from sprayed fields. If concentrations of a pesticide exceed the threshold value set for the Environmental Quality Standard, then damage will be caused to the ecology of the aquatic system. Additionally much surface water is used for drinking water and as such has to meet the EU standards.

Knowledge of the behaviour of a pesticide in sediment/water is generally a registration requirement for agricultural pesticides, this usually being studied in small-scale systems of volume about 500 ml with the overlying water gently stirred. Being done primarily for registration purposes and so on a compound-by-compound basis, little has been drawn together on the overall principles of such processes. The present study investigated the behaviour of eight pesticides spanning a wide range of physicochemical properties, and examined also the influence of formulation on the redistribution and loss processes.

MATERIALS AND METHODS

Pesticides

The pesticides used were analytical grade and the formulated materials were commercial products (Table 1). [*α-benzyl-*[14]C]Permethrin had a specific activity of 67 MBq mmol[-1] (2.2 GBq mmol[-1] for the sorption tests).

Sediment/water system

Sediment and water were collected from a pristine shallow pool at Great Linford, Bedfordshire, U.K. The moist sediment was sieved to 5 mm and thoroughly mixed; it comprised 64% sand (63-2000 µm), 20% silt (2-63 µm) and 16% clay (<2 µm), with 2.5% organic carbon and pH 7.32 (water).

The test vessels (Figure 1) were designed according to the guidelines for the registration studies of pesticides (BBA Guidelines, 1990; Hill *et al.*, 1994). Wide-necked glass jars (500-ml) contained wet sediment (120 g containing 51.7 g solids) and pond water (400 ml). After allowing the sediment to settle, pesticide (80 µg per jar) was introduced into the overlying water using the diluted formulated product (0.2 ml) or acetonitrile (0.2 ml) for the pure pesticide; this amount represents overspray at 180 g a.i. ha^{-1}. The water was gently stirred by a stainless-steel blade (2.5 cm diameter) rotated at 60 rpm. Eight replicate vessels were set up for each test, two of which had water analysed regularly whilst the other six were destructively sampled to obtain a mass balance, usually over a 90-day period. The vessels were kept in the dark at 10°C.

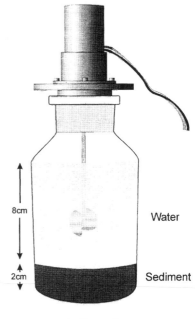

8cm — Water

2cm — Sediment

Figure 1. Sediment/water system

Sorption measurements

Air-dry sediment (0.2 to 0.5 g according to the expected K_d) was shaken for 2 hours with pesticide dissolved in 0.01M aq CaCl$_2$ (10 ml of *ca* 0.2 µg pesticide ml^{-1}; 25 ml of 0.001 µg ml^{-1} for permethrin). After centrifugation, the supernatant solution was analysed.

Chromatographic analysis

The non-radiolabelled compounds in the water phase were determined by direct injection into a high-pressure liquid chromatograph (HPLC) fitted with a 50-µl loop and a C-18 reverse-phase column (20 cm x 4.6 mm ID). The running solvent was methanol/water or acetonitrile/water, with detection by UV. This procedure was insufficiently sensitive for chlorpyrifos, which was extracted from water aliquots (20 ml) with dichloromethane prior to evaporation and redissolving in HPLC running solvent (1.0 ml). To analyse the sediment, the overlying water was removed by suction, methanol (300 ml) was added to the sediment and the vessel orbitally shaken for four hours. Aliquots (25 ml, in duplicate) were evaporated and redissolved in HPLC running solvent as described above, with 20-µl loop injections. [^{14}C]Permethrin was extracted similarly, the residues being subjected to thin-layer chromatography on silica gel with hexane + ethyl acetate (65 + 35, v/v) as elution solvent. Bands containing parent [^{14}C]permethrin, R$_F$ 0.65, were scraped off and subjected to liquid scintillation counting. All analyses were corrected for the appropriate recovery factors.

Table 1.   Pesticide properties, formulations and behaviour in the sediment/water systems

Pesticide[a]	log K_{ow}	Formulated product [b]			Sorption coefficient K_d (l kg^{-1})	Proportion[c] predicted in sediment (%)	DT_{50} (day)
		EC	SC	WG			
Triasulfuron[d] (h)	1.6	-	-	Logran	0.2	19.2	>90
Isoproturon (h)	2.48	-	Isoguard	-	2.3	36.1	>90[e]
Chlorotoluron (h)	2.5	-	Dicurane	-	1.8	32.5	55-85
Phenmedipham (h)	3.6	Stefes Forte 2	Betanal Flo	-	20.7	77.4	2.5-4
Difenoconazole (f)	4.2	Plover	-	-	48	85.8	>90
Chlorpyrifos (i)	4.99	Dursban	-	-	83	92.1	55[f]
Pendimethalin (h)	5.18	Stomp 330	Stomp 400	-	125	95.2	60[g]
Permethrin (i)	6.1	Permasect 25	-	-	343	98.2	15-20

[a] h, herbicide; f, fungicide; i, insecticide.
[b] Emulsifiable concentrate (EC), suspension concentrate (SC) or water-soluble granule (WG).
[c] Proportion predicted from the batch K_d to be in the sediment at equilibrium.
[d] Triasulfuron is acidic, pKa 4.64; the log K_{ow} is given for the undissociated acid.
[e] Value for the pure isoproturon; enhanced degradation started at 60 d for the suspension concentrate.
[f] Extrapolated from 45 d.
[g] Value for the two formulated products; enhanced degradation started at 14 d for the pure pendimethalin.

RESULTS AND DISCUSSION

Batch sorption measurements

The measured sorption coefficients (K_d) onto the sediment in the equilibration tests over 2 h spanned three orders of magnitude (Table 1). For the seven non-ionised pesticides, there was a straight-line relationship between log K_d and log K_{ow} :-

$$\log K_d = 0.62 \log K_{ow} - 1.12 \quad (r^2 = 0.97) \qquad (1)$$

Normalising this to sorption on the sediment organic matter (4.3%) gives:-

$$\log K_{om} = 0.62 \log K_{ow} + 0.25 \qquad (2)$$

This relationship is comparable to that derived by Briggs (1981) from sorption measurements over many non-ionised pesticides and soils, viz:

$$\log K_{om} = 0.53 \log K_{ow} + 0.62 \qquad (3)$$

This gives confidence that Eqn. 2 can be used to predict sorption of a wide range of non-ionised pesticides on sediments with differing contents of organic matter.

Pesticide behaviour in laboratory-scale sediment/water systems

Examples of the changes in distribution pattern with time are given for four compounds spanning the observed range of behaviour (Figure 2). Sorption behaviour was not influenced by the application vehicle. Although most redistribution from the water to the sediment took place within 30 d of application, interpretation was complicated by the substantial degradation over the 90-d period for compounds such as phenmedipham and permethrin.

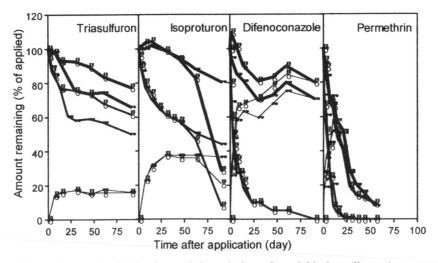

Figure 2.   Redistribution and degradation of pesticide in sediment/water systems □ pure pesticide; ♦ formulated; thin lines, sediment; medium lines, water; thick lines, total (mass balance).

To eliminate the complication of degradation, the distribution patterns of the eight pesticides in the systems over time were expressed as a percentage of the amount recovered. These show that the proportion of pesticide moving into the sediment layer increased with increasing lipophilicity (Figure 3). For the most polar compound, triasulfuron, only 20% was sorbed, equilibrium being reached in about 15 d and then remaining constant. For the most lipophilic compounds, pendimethalin and permethrin, at equilibrium over 95% of the compound was sorbed by the sediment, final equilibrium being reached only after 20-30 d. It appeared that diffusion into the 2-cm deep sediment layer was complete for the weakly sorbed triasulfuron within 15 d, but the larger mass transfer required to reach equilibrium for a strongly sorbed compound required about twice that length of time to achieve by diffusive processes.

The distribution at equilibrium was close to that predicted on the basis of the independent K_d measurements, allowance being made for the water within the sediment layer. Predictions of the equilibrium distribution made by the database/expert system 'Physicochemical Evaluation - The Environment' (PETE) using log K_{ow} alone as the compound-specific input factor (Nicholls 1994) were reasonably accurate as exemplified for isoproturon (Figure 4). About 40% of the isoproturon was found in the sediment at equilibrium, compared to predictions of 37.1 and 41.2% made from K_d and K_{ow} respectively.

Compounds differed considerably in their rates of degradation in the sediment/water systems

(Table 1). Phenmedipham was rapidly hydrolysed. Triasulfuron and difenoconazole were the

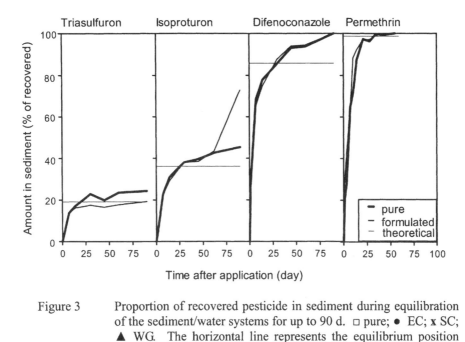

Figure 3   Proportion of recovered pesticide in sediment during equilibration
                of the sediment/water systems for up to 90 d. □ pure; ● EC; x SC;
                ▲ WG. The horizontal line represents the equilibrium position
                predicted from the *Kd* value measured in the batch tests.

most stable with about 25% loss over 90 d. Pure isoproturon also behaved similarly, but the
SC formulation showed enhanced degradation after 60 d. In contrast, pendimethalin, the only
other compound showing enhanced degradation, did so only for the pure compound after 14 d
and not for the EC and SC formulations up to 90 d. It should be noted that the final
concentration of acetonitrile in the vessels was 0.05%, less than the maximum permissible of
0.1% given by the SETAC guidelines.

CONCLUSIONS

The extent of movement of pesticides into sediment following application to the overlying
water was strongly dependent on the pesticide lipophilicity though not influenced by the
formulation vehicle. In these small-scale systems with a layer of sediment 2 cm deep,
equilibrium was reached between 15 and 30 d, the more strongly sorbed compounds taking
the longer time. A good linear free-energy relationship between log K_d and log K_{ow} was found
for the seven non-ionised compounds; this allowed predictions of such behaviour for other
non-ionised pesticides and organic contaminants, as examined with the PETE programme.
The acidic triasulfuron, largely ionised at the sediment pH, was very weakly sorbed.

Degradation rates differed for the compounds, ranging from relatively high for
phenmedipham (DT$_{50}$ 2.5-4 d) to low for triasulfuron and difenoconazole (DT$_{50}$ >>90 d).
Differences between formulated and pure materials occurred only for isoproturon and
pendimethalin; however, enhanced degradation occurred for the SC isoproturon and not the
pure, but for the pure pendimethalin and not for the EC or SC.

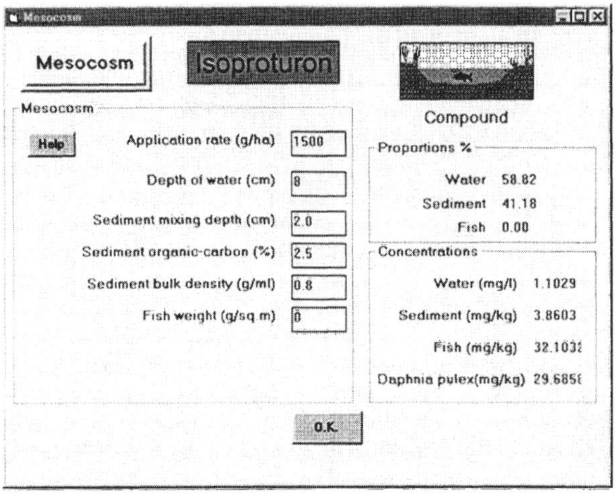

Figure 4.   Prediction from log K_{ow} of the distribution of isoproturon in the sediment/water system using the PETE database/expert system.

The distribution behaviour in this system, which was based on pesticide-registration guidelines, was consistent and not influenced by formulation. This last finding, presumed to be of general applicability, means that pesticide registration authorities can assess this aspect of environmental behaviour based on the properties of the pure substance without the need to consider the formulation type.

ACKNOWLEDGEMENTS

This project was funded by MAFF Pesticides Safety Directorate. We also thank Andrew Stevenson of the Hanson Environmental Studies Centre for the sediment samples.

REFERENCES

BBA Guidelines for the examination of plant protectants in the registration process. Part IV, 5-I. Degradability and fate of plant protectants in the water-sediment system. (1990).

Briggs G G (1981). Theoretical and experimental relationships between soil adsorption, octanol-water partition coefficients, water solubilities, bioconcentration factors, and the parachor. *Journal of Agricultural Food Chemistry* **29**: 1050-1059.

Hill I R; Matthiessen P; Heimbach F (eds) (1994). Guidance document on sediment toxicity tests and bioassays for freshwater and marine environments. Society of Environmental Toxicology and Chemistry (SETAC) Europe, 105 pp.

Nicholls P H (1994). 'Physicochemical Evaluation : The Environment' an expert system for pesticide preregistration assessment. *Proceedings of the BCPC Conference - Pests and Diseases 1994*, 1337-1342.

Formulations of the anionic herbicide imazaquin based on its sorption on crystal violet-montmorillonite complexes

T Polubesova, S Nir, B Rubin
Faculty of Agricultural, Food and Environmental Quality Sciences, The Hebrew University of Jerusalem, Rehovot, 76100, Israel
Email: polubeso@agri.huji.ac.il

M Borisover, Z Gerstl
Institute of Soil, Water and Environmental Sciences, The Volcani Center, ARO. 50250 Bet Dagan, Israel

ABSTRACT

Our aim was to design formulations of the anionic herbicide imazaquin to reduce its leaching and migration. Sorption of imazaquin on crystal violet (CV)-montmorillonite complexes was studied. CV-montmorillonite complexes become positively charged with adsorption of CV above the cation exchange capacity (CEC) of montmorillonite, and thus are able to adsorb organic anions. Organo-clay complexes at a CV loading of 40 and 70% above the CEC were studied. The Langmuir equation provided a good fit to the isotherms of imazaquin sorption on CV-montmorillonite complexes. However, for charged complexes an equation which combines electrostatics with specific binding was preferred. When the concentration of the CV-clay-imazaquin complex in the suspension was 5 g/L, the extent of desorption of imazaquin into water was around 5%. The presence of sulphate, acetate and phosphate in large excess over imazaquin decreased herbicide sorption according to the sequence phosphate > acetate > sulphate. Leaching of imazaquin from CV-montmorillonite formulations in soil was significantly less than that of technical imazaquin. CV-montmorillonite complexes appear to be suitable for preparation of organo-clay-imazaquin formulations that may reduce herbicide leaching in soil significantly.

INTRODUCTION

A severe problem encountered with many herbicides is their transport through the soil and contamination of underlying groundwater. Imazaquin is a pre- and post-emergence herbicide used for control of broadleaf weeds in legume crops. Imazaquin is negatively charged at the basic pHs commonly found in the calcareous soils of Mediterranean countries. Imazaquin exhibits low adsorption and high leaching in soils (Loux & Reese 1992). Our aim was to design formulations of imazaquin to reduce herbicide migration to non-target areas. Crystal violet (CV)-montmorillonite complexes become positively charged with adsorption of CV above the cation exchange capacity (CEC) of montmorillonite (Rytwo *et al.*, 1995) and thus are able to adsorb organic anions. We studied the suitability of CV-montmorillonite complexes for preparation of organo-clay-imazaquin formulations to reduce herbicide leaching.

MATERIALS AND METHODS

Imazaquin, 97% purity, was obtained from AGAN Chem. Manuf. (Ashdod, Israel). Crystal violet as the chloride salt was purchased from Fluka Chemie AG (Buchs, Switzerland). The chemical structures of imazaquin and crystal violet are shown in Fig. 1.The clay mineral used was Wyoming Na-montmorillonite SWy-1 obtained from the Source Clays Repository (Clay Minerals Society, Columbia, MO). The cation exchange capacity of the clay was 0.80 mmol/g. The CV-montmorillonite complexes, containing 40% and 70% of CV above the CEC, were prepared according to Rytwo et al., (1995).

Adsorption experiments were carried out as described in Polubesova et al., 2000. The concentrations of the CV-clay complex suspensions were 5 g/L. Twenty four hours were sufficient to reach equilibration of imazaquin sorption. To study the effect of electrolyte concentration on the adsorption of imazaquin, the following electrolytes were added: Na_2SO_4, CH_3COONa, and Na_3PO_4.

Desorption of imazaquin was determined in water and in electrolyte solutions. We tested the possibility that loosely bound imazaquin will be desorbed in 2 hours (first step), with strongly bound herbicide being released over the next 24 hours (second step). Twenty mL of distilled water were added to the samples with pre-adsorbed herbicide. The concentrations of the CV-clay–imazaquin complex suspensions were 5 g/L. The tubes were kept at $25 \pm 1°C$ under continuous agitation for 2 hours then centrifuged for 20 min at 15000g and imazaquin was measured in the supernatant solution. The samples were then shaken for 24 hours at the same temperature, and desorption was determined again by the same procedure. Desorption by electrolyte solutions was determined after 24 hours of agitation of samples with pre-adsorbed imazaquin by 10- and 100m-eqv/L solutions of Na_2SO_4, CH_3COONa, and Na_3PO_4. For analysis, all supernatant solutions were filtered through Teflon filters (ISI, Israel) of 0.2 μm pore diameter. Imazaquin was analyzed by HPLC (Merck Hitachi 6200) equipped with a diode array detector at a wavelength of 242 nm. The reverse-phase column was LiChrospher[R] 100 RP-18 (5 μm), and the mobile phase was a mixture of 60% methanol and 40% water with 0.65 mM trifluoroacetic acid. The flow rate was 1.0 ml /min.

Binding coefficients of sorption were calculated using the Langmuir equation and a model for ion adsorption, which combines electrostatics with specific binding (Nir et al., 1994).

Leaching experiments were performed in Rehovot sandy soil (pH 7.5, organic matter content 0.2%, sand 95.5%). Plexiglass columns (25 cm in length and 5 cm i.d.), with glass fiber wicks of 25 cm length attached to the bottom, were packed with air-dry soil and 0.01M $CaCl_2$ was applied at the rate of 47 ml/hr using an HPLC pump to establish steady-state conditions. The flow was temporarily interrupted and solutions of technical imazaquin and suspensions of the imazaquin formulated on CV-70%-montmorillonite were applied to the surface of the columns after which application of the 0.01M $CaCl_2$ was resumed. Effluents were collected with an automated fraction collector and analysed by HPLC. The water content of the soil was determined at the end of experiment. Pore volumes were calculated by dividing corresponding cumulative volumes of the collected effluent by the water content of soil.

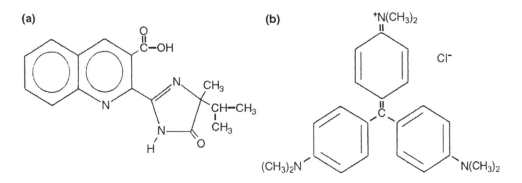

Fig. 1. The chemical structure of imazaquin (a) and crystal violet (b).

RESULTS AND DISCUSSION

The imazaquin sorbed on the positively charged CV-montmorillonite complexes reached 93-95% of the amount added for CV-40% and CV-70% complexes (40% indicates that sorption of CV exceeds the CEC by 40%). Pure montmorillonite sorbed only 2% of the amount added. CV release in sorption experiments was 3.5% and 2.4% for the CV-70% and CV-40% complexes, respectively. The Langmuir equation provided a good fit to the isotherms of imazaquin sorption on CV-montmorillonite complexes with $R^2=1$.

Binding coefficients calculated using the Langmuir equation were 3800 and 4000 M^{-1} for CV-40%- and CV-70%-montmorillonite complexes, respectively. The binding coefficients calculated using the model for ion adsorption were 40 M^{-1} for CV-40%- and 20 M^{-1} for CV-70% - montmorillonite complexes with $R^2=1$. At higher CV loadings, a significant fraction of the CV molecules interacted between themselves and were less available for interactions with imazaquin. Similar results were obtained for the interaction of benzyltrimethylammonium- and benzyltriphenylammonium-montmorillonite complexes with alachlor, metolachlor and norflurazon (Nir *et al.*, 2000) and for the interaction of a rhodamine B–montmorillonite complex with atrazine (Borisover *et al.*, 2001).

The proposed model for imazaquin sorption on CV-clays is a combination of electrostatic adsorption and hydrophobic interaction. Calculations of the binding coefficients using the ion-adsorption model were preferred because they encompass both mechanisms of imazaquin sorption.

Imazaquin sorption onto CV-clay was not affected by small amounts of sulphate and acetate, but was decreased in the presence of the same amounts of phosphate (Table 1). When these anions were added in amounts which exceeded those of imazaquin by 100 and 1000 times, they competed with imazaquin for the surface sites of the CV-clay complex and significantly reduced herbicide sorption according to the sequence phosphate > acetate > sulphate.

Table 1. Effect of sulphate, acetate and phosphate on the adsorption of
imazaquin on CV-70%-montmorillonite

Imazaquin/anion ratio[1]	Imazaquin adsorbed, (μmol/g)	Reduction in adsorption (%)
-	17.68	-
	Sulphate	
1:1	17.55	0.7
1:10	17.20	2.7
1:100	16.37	7.4
1:1000	15.71	11.1
	Acetate	
1:1	17.67	0
1:10	17.63	<0.5
1:100	15.81	10.6
1:1000	14.77	16.5
	Phosphate	
1:1	17.40	7.2
1:10	13.17	29.8
1:100	5.37	71.4

[1] Imazaquin added at 18.76 μmol/g

The degree of desorption of imazaquin from CV-clay complexes in water was small (Table 2). The desorbed amount, in the first and second step combined (loosely and strongly sorbed imazaquin), was only 3.8-5.5 % of that sorbed for both complexes at the concentration of the CV-clay–imazaquin complex suspensions 5 g/L.

Table 2.   Desorption of imazaquin from CV- montmorillonite complexes

Imazaquin added, (μmol/g)	Imazaquin adsorbed (μmol/g)	Imazaquin desorbed (% of adsorbed)	
		Step 1	Step 2
CV-70%-montmorillonite			
4.75	4.53	4.2	5.3
23.75	22.20	4.1	5.5
CV-40%-montmorillonite			
4.75	4.43	3.8	4.7
23.75	21.50	4.2	4.9

Desorbed amounts of imazaquin from the CV-clay complex by sulphate, acetate and phosphate for 10 and 100 meq/L of electrolyte solutions are presented in Table 3. Imazaquin was strongly bound to the surface and was not fully desorbed even by anions added at 100 meq/L, which was 1000-4000 times higher than the concentrations of the sorbed herbicide. Phosphate was the most effective anion in desorbing imazaquin.

Table 3.   Desorption of imazaquin from CV-70%-montmorillonite
            complex in the presence of electrolytes

Electrolyte added	Imazaquin desorbed (% of adsorbed)			
	10 meq/L (Imaz. adsorbed 4.71 µmol/g)	100 meq/L (Imaz. adsorbed 4.54 µmol/g)	10 meq/L (Imaz. adsorbed 23.7 µmol/g)	100 meq/L (Imaz. adsorbed 22.2 µmol/g)
Na_2SO_4	17.5	33.0	23.2	37.9
$NaCH_3COO$	9.6	28.7	11.2	32.6
Na_3PO_4	55.0	63.2	57.9	68.9

Results of leaching experiments are shown in Table 4, in which the amount of water added is presented as equivalent rain. Leaching of imazaquin from CV-montmorillonite formulations was significantly less than that of technical imazaquin for the whole range of pore volumes. Only 25% of imazaquin from the organo-clay formulation was released at 1.56 pore volumes versus 93% of technical imazaquin. Thus the results of leaching and batch experiments are consistent, indicating strong sorption and relatively small (and slow) release of imazaquin from CV-montmorillonite complexes. CV-montmorillonite complexes appear to be suitable for preparation of organo-clay-imazaquin formulations, which may significantly reduce imazaquin leaching.

Table 4.   Leaching of imazaquin through soil columns (25 cm long, 5 cm i.d.)

Pore volume	Equivalent rain (mm)	Fraction of imazaquin leached through column	
		Technical imazaquin	Imaz.-CV-70%-mont. formulation
0.17	12	0	0
0.35	24	0	0
0.52	35	0	0
0.69	47	0	0
0.86	59	0.05	0.02
1.03	70	0.59	0.11
1.21	82	0.89	0.17
1.38	94	0.92	0.22
1.56	106	0.93	0.25

ACKNOWLEDGEMENT

This research was supported by Grant 1317 from Israeli Ministry of Science, Culture and Sport.

REFERENCES

Borisover M; Graber E R; Bercovich F; Gerstl Z (2001). Suitability of dye-clay complex for removal of non-ionic organic compounds from aqueous solutions. *Chemosphere* **44:** 1033-1040.

Loux M M; Reese K D (1992). Effect of soil pH on adsorption and persistence of imazaquin. *Weed Science* **40:** 490-496.

Nir S; Rytwo G; Yermiyahu U; Margulies L (1994). A model for cation adsorption to clays and membranes. *Colloid and Polymer Science* **272:** 619-632.

Nir S; Undabeytia T; Yaron-Marcovich D; El-Nahhal Y; Polubesova T; Serban C; Rytwo G; Lagaly G; Rubin B (2000). Optimization of adsorption of hydrophobic herbicides on montmorillonite preadsorbed by monovalent organic cations: interactions between phenyl rings. *Environmental Science and Technology* **34:**1269–1274.

Polubesova T; Undabeytia T; Nir S; Chertkova L; Van Damme H; Annabi-Bergaya F (2000). Adsorption of sulfometuron and other anions on pillared clay. *Journal of Environmental Quality* **29:**948-954.

Rytwo G; Nir S; Margulies L (1995). Interaction of monovalent organic cations with montmorillonite: adsorption studies and model calculations. *Soil Science Society of America Journal* **59:** 554-564.

Effect of sewage-sludge amendment on simazine and 2,4-D behaviour in soil: laboratory and field studies

L Cox, R Celis, M C Hermosín, J Cornejo

Instituto de Recursos Naturales y Agrobiol., CSIC, PO Box 1052, 41080 Sevilla, Spain
EMail: lcox@irnase.csic.es

ABSTRACT

Laboratory and field studies have been designed to assess the influence of sewage-sludge amendment on the fate of simazine and 2,4-D in soil. A soil from IRNAS experimental farm was treated in the laboratory with a composted sewage sludge at the rate of 10 % (w/w). Herbicide sorption behaviour on amended and unamended soils was studied:- sorption by batch technique, degradation by soil incubation at 20°C and leaching in handpacked soil columns under saturated/unsaturated flow conditions. For the field study, the sewage sludge was applied at a rate of 10 kg m^{-2} to experimental plots, and herbicides were applied at 2.5 kg ha^{-1} to these and to unamended plots. Triplicate soil samples from the plots (0-10, 10-20 and 20-30 cm depth) were collected periodically and extracted for herbicide content. Sorption coefficients measured in the laboratory for both herbicides increased upon amendment, whereas simazine half-life remained unaffected and 2,4-D half-life was decreased. Simazine breakthrough curves in amended soil columns were broader and showed slower breakthrough when compared to unamended soil. No 2,4-D was leached from amended soil or unamended soil columns. The field study revealed higher amounts of simazine and 2,4-D in the upper 10 cm of amended soils than unamended soils. Only very small amounts of simazine were detected below 20 cm, without significant differences between amended and unamended soils. 2,4-D was not detected below 20 cm.

INTRODUCTION

Organic amendments, commonly used to enrich soils of low organic matter content, can modify surfaces of soils and subsurface materials so increasing sorption potential and reducing pesticide contamination of groundwater (Barriuso *et al.*, 1996; Cox *et al.*, 1997, 2000). The subsequent increase in soil organic matter is also known to stimulate soil microbial activity, which could potentially lead to accelerated degradation, reducing both the total amount of chemical available for leaching and the potential for herbicides to injure crops planted in rotation (Felsot and Shelton 1993; Topp *et al.*, 1996; Cox *et al.*, 1997, 2000). Accordingly, the study of the influence of organic amendments on pesticide behaviour in soil is of great interest when making decisions to fertilize soil or to dispose of organic wastes such as sewage sludge.

The aim of this study was to assess the influence of sewage-sludge amendment on sorption, degradation and movement of pesticides in soil. For this purpose, we selected two herbicides widely used in agriculture, simazine and 2,4-D, and performed laboratory and field studies with a soil amended with sewage sludge.

MATERIALS AND METHODS

Herbicides and soil

High-purity (>98 %) simazine (Riedel-de Haën, Germany) and 2,4-D (Sigma, St. Louis, MO) were used for laboratory studies. For the field study, commercial simazine (Gesatop, 90 WG) and 2,4-D (Primma Din, 70 % w/v) products were used.

The soil used in laboratory experiments was taken from 0-10 cm depth, air dried and treated with sewage sludge at a rate of 10 % w/w. Physicochemical properties of the original unamended soil and sewage-sludge amended soil were determined and are given in Table 1.

Table 1. Physicochemical properties of original and sewage-sludge amended soils

Soil/depth (cm)		pH	Organic matter (%)	Sand (%)	Silt (%)	Clay (%)
Original soil						
	0-10	7.6	0.90	64	19	17
	10-20	7.8	0.51	61	22	17
Amended soil						
	0-10	7.4	1.24	63	18	19
	10-20	7.9	0.72	58	23	19

Batch sorption and degradation kinetics

Sorption studies were performed by batch equilibration procedure. Duplicate samples (5 g) of unamended and amended soils were treated with 0.01M aq. $CaCl_2$ herbicide solutions (10 mL) of initial concentration (Ci) of simazine ranging from 0.5 to 10 μM or 2,4-D from 5 to 100 μM. The suspensions were shaken at 20±2°C for 24 h and then centrifuged at 31000g. Equilibrium concentrations (Ce) in the supernatant solutions were determined by HPLC under the following conditions: Nova-Pack column, 150 mm length x 3.9 mm i.d.; column packing, C18; flow rate, 1 mL min^{-1}; eluent system, 70:30 water-acetonitrile for simazine and 55:45 diluted H_3PO_4 (pH = 2.0):methanol for 2,4-D; UV detection was at 230 nm. Detection limits were 0.01 and 0.02 mg L^{-1} for simazine and 2,4-D, respectively. Differences between Ci and Ce were assumed to be the amounts sorbed (Cs). Sorption isotherms were fitted to the Freundlich equation, and sorption coefficients K_f and $1/n_f$ calculated.

Duplicate samples (500 g) of each soil were treated with a 100 mg L^{-1} ethanol solution of simazine or a 100 mg L^{-1} aqueous solution of 2,4-D to give a concentration of 5 mg kg^{-1} and 2.3 mg kg^{-1} of dry soil, respectively. Maximum application rates of simazine and 2,4-D were 5 and 2.3 kg ha^{-1}, respectively. The moisture content was adjusted to 40% of the water-holding capacity and soil samples were thoroughly mixed by passing them through a sieve at least 4 times. Herbicide-treated soil samples were transferred to Kilner jars where they were incubated at 20°C for 50 d (simazine) or 15 d (2,4-D). Moisture contents were maintained constant throughout the experiment by adding distilled water as necessary. Soils were sampled periodically and frozen till analyzed. Herbicide residues were extracted by shaking soil (10 g) with methanol (20 mL, simazine) or 55:45 diluted H_3PO_4 (pH = 2.0):methanol (20 mL, 2,4-D) for 24 h and extracts were analyzed by HPLC. Recoveries were greater than 90% for both herbicides. In order to calculate half-lives from dissipation curves, we assumed that the differences between the amount of simazine or 2,4-D applied and those extracted were due to degradation in the soil.

Leaching experiments

Herbicide leaching in soils was studied using methacrylate columns, 20 cm long and 16.66 cm^2 section, handpacked with unamended and amended soils from 0-10 cm depth. After saturation of the soil columns with 0.01M $CaCl_2$, simazine and 2,4-D corresponding to application rates of 5 kg ha^{-1} and 2.3 kg ha^{-1} respectively were applied to the top of the soil columns. The columns were leached with 0.01M $CaCl_2$ (50 mL) daily and leachates collected, volumes measured and herbicide concentrations determined by HPLC.

Field study

Field experiments were performed on a 4 x 16 m experimental plot located at IRNAS experimental farm (SW Spain). The plot was divided into four subplots (4 x 4 m): two for simazine treatment and two for 2,4-D (each with and without sewage-sludge application). The sewage sludge was applied in February 2000 at a rate of 10 kg m^{-2} and application was followed by chisel to 5 to 10 cm depth. One day after the sewage-sludge amendment, the herbicides were applied at a rate of 2.5 kg ha^{-1}. Triplicate soil samples from 0-10, 10-20 and 20-30 cm depth were collected periodically from the plots over 75 d with a total water input (rain plus irrigation) of 172 mm. Soil samples were air-dried and extracted for simazine or 2,4-D as described earlier.

RESULTS AND DISCUSSION

Batch sorption and degradation kinetics

Sorption coefficients (K_f) increased for both herbicides upon amendment (Table 2), although for 2,4-D the differences were not significant. The increase in sorption capacity of the amended soils is attributed to the increase in organic matter content, since both herbicides have been shown to be sorbed to this soil component (Celis et al., 1999; Cox et al., 2000). The coefficients $1/n_f$, which indicate sorption intensity, were much lower for 2,4-D than for simazine. Low $1/n_f$ coefficients indicate that there is a limit in sorption capacity as solution concentration increases (Giles et al., 1960).

There were no significant differences in simazine half-life upon amendment, though amendment reduced the half-life of 2,4-D to less than half (Table 2). The increase in organic carbon content upon amendment has been shown to promote biodegradation (Felsot and Shelton 1993; Topp et al., 1996; Cox et al., 1997), which is the main process affecting the fate of 2,4-D in soils (Veeh et al., 1996). Conversely, 2,4-D dissipation rates have been reported to be lowest on the soil on which sorption was greatest (Johnson et al., 1995).

Leaching experiment

Simazine breakthrough in the soil columns took place later in amended soil than in unamended soil (Figure 1). Also, the simazine BTC in amended soil was broader, with a much lower maximum concentration detected in leachates than in those from the unamended soil. Total recovered simazine in this soil was greater than 60% compared to 30% in the amended soil, which difference in behaviour can be attributed to the increase in sorption upon amendment.

Table 2. Sorption coefficients (K_f, $1/n_f$) and half-lives ($t_{1/2}$) for simazine and 2,4-D in original unamended and sewage-sludge amended soil

Herbicide/	Sorption			Degradation	
Soil	Kf	$1/n_f$	R^2	$t_{1/2}$ (day)	R^2
Simazine					
Unamended	0.63 (0.60-0.67)[†]	0.89(±0.05)	0.99	26.0 (23.1-33.5)	0.98
Amended	1.03 (0.99-1.08)	0.87(±0.04)	1.00	31.2 (27.1-35.6)	0.92
2,4-D					
Unamended	1.04 (0.84-1.30)	0.51(±0.14)	0.96	3.24 (2.88-3.78)	0.97
Amended	1.40 (1.14-2.70)	0.55(±0.14)	0.89	1.10 (1.08-1.11)	1.00

[†] Numbers in parentheses are standard error about the mean

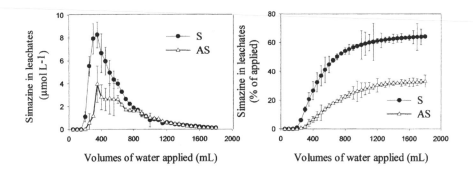

Figure 1. Simazine breakthrough curves in unamended (S) and amended (AS) soils

Sorption gives rise to retardation in movement and later breakthrough (Beck *et al.*, 1993), which also favours degradation due to longer residence of pesticide molecules in the soil columns. 2,4-D was not leached from soil columns, which can be attributed to the rapid degradation of 2,4-D observed in both soils.

Field Study

Larger amounts of simazine in the top 10 cm were recovered from the amended soil than unamended soil (Table 3). This can be attributed to the increase in sorption, as revealed in sorption studies. It should also be noticed that simazine was moved further in the unamended soil, as indicated by the higher amounts detected below 10 cm than in the amended soil, which also agreed with the earlier breakthrough in the soil column studies. However, only very small amounts of simazine were detected below 20 cm, there being no significant differences here between the two soils.

As with simazine, larger amounts of 2,4-D were detected in the first 10 cm of sewage-sludge amended soil and smaller amounts below 10 cm when compared with the unamended soil (Table 4). No 2,4-D was detected below 20 cm. This small movement of 2,4-D in soil, despite its anionic character, is due to its rapid degradation in soil, as shown in the laboratory studies.

Table 3. Simazine concentrations in the field trial of non-amended (S) and sewage-sludge amended (AS) soils

Soil depth (cm)	Simazine concentration ($mg\ g^{-1}$ dry soil)					
	Time after herbicide application (day)					
	1	5	13	20	29	75
S						
0-10	1.56(±0.12)[†]	1.53(±1.01)	1.41(±0.39)	1.61(±1.12)	1.07(±0.09)	0.32(±0.21)
10-20	0.23(±0.04)	0.20(±0.11)	0.46(±0.15)	0.46(±0.15)	0.51(±0.33)	0.12(±0.11)
20-30	0	0	0	0.05(±0.03)	0.14(±0.12)	0.07(±0.01)
AS						
0-10	2.34(±0.28)	2.13(±0.67)	2.05(±0.45)	2.12(±0.66)	1.45(±0.18)	0.74(±0.20
10-20	0.01(±0.01)	0.02(±0.01)	0.12(±0.02)	0.14(±0.01)	0.43(±0.10)	0.12(±0.02)
20-30	0	0	0	0.08(±0.09)	0.25(±0.05)	0.06(±0.05)

[†] Numbers in parentheses are standard error about the mean

Table 4. 2,4-D concentrations in the field trial of non-amended (S) and sewage-sludge amended (AS) soils

Soil depth (cm)	2,4-D concentration ($mg\ g^{-1}$ dry soil)					
	Time after herbicide application (day)					
	1	5	13	20	29	75
S						
0-10	0.92(±0.02)[†]	0.57(±0.08)	0.69(±0.06)	0.45(±0.11)	0	0
10-20	0.03(±0.01)	0.03(±0.01)	0.10(±0.05)	0.30(±0.11)	0	0
20-30	0	0	0	0	0	0
AS						
0-10	1.31(±0.18)	0.68(±0.10)	1.03(±0.51)	0.57(±0.13)	0	0
10-20	0	0	0	0.15(±0.10)	0	0
20-30	0	0	0	0	0	0

[†] Numbers in parentheses are standard error about the mean

CONCLUSIONS

The addition of sewage sludge to soil gave rise to an increased sorption of the herbicides in the laboratory studies, which caused more retention of pesticide in the top 10 cm of the soil profile in a field study with the amended soil. This increase in sorption will reduce pesticide movement in soil and, consequently, the risk of groundwater contamination if heavy rain takes place shortly after herbicide application.

ACKNOWLEDGEMENTS

This work has been partially supported by the CICYT project AMB96-0445-CO2-02 and by the Research Group RNM-124 of Junta de Andalucía.

REFERENCES

Barriuso E; Houot S; Serra-Wittling C (1996). Influence of compost addition to soil on the behaviour of herbicides. *Pesticide Science* **49,** 65-75.

Beck A J; Johnston A E J; Jones K C (1993). Movement of nonionic organic chemicals in agricultural soils. *Critical Reviews in Environmental Science and Technology* **23**, 219-248

Celis R.; Hermosín M C; Cox L; Cornejo J (1999). Sorption of 2,4-dichlorophenoxyacetic acid by model particles simulating naturally occurring soil colloids. *Environmental Science and Technology* **33**, 1200-1206.

Cox L; Celis R; Hermosín MC; Becker A; Cornejo J (1997). Porosity and herbicide leaching in soils amended with olive-mill waste water. *Agriculture Ecosystems and Environment* **65**, 151-161.

Cox L; Celis R; Hermosín, M C; Cornejo J; Zsolnay A; Keller K (2000). Effect of organic amendments on herbicide sorption as related to the nature of the dissolved organic matter. *Environmental Science and Technology* **34**, 4600-4605.

Felsot A S; Shelton D R (1993) Enhanced biodegradation of soil pesticides: Interactions between physicochemical processes and microbial ecology. In: *Sorption and Degradation of Pesticides and Organic Chemicals in Soils* pp. 227-251. SSSA Special Publication 32, Madison, WI.

Giles C H; McEwan S N; Nakhwa S N; Smith D (1960). Studies in adsorption. Part XI. A system of classification of solution adsorption isotherms and its use in diagnosis of adsorption mechanisms and in measurement of specific surface area in solids. *Journal of the Chemical Society*, 3973-3993.

Johnson W G; Lavy T L; Gbur E E (1995). Persistence of triclopyr and 2,4-D in flooded and nonflooded soils. *Journal of Environmental Quality* **24**, 493-497.

Nelson D W; Sommers L E (1982). Total carbon, organic carbon and organic matter. pp. 539-579. In: A.L. Page *Methods of Soil Analysis. Part 2*, ed. A.L. Page, American Society of Agronomy, Madison, WI.

Topp E; Tessier L; Gregorich E G (1996). Dairy manure incorporation stimulates rapid atrazine mineralization in an agricultural soil. *Canadian Journal of Soil Science* **76**, 403-409.

Veeh R H; Inskeep W P; Camper A K (1986) Soil depth and temperature effects on microbial degradation of 2,4-D. *Journal of Environmental Quality* **25**, 5-12.

Porosity and surface fractal dimension of soils as affecting sorption, degradation and mobility of polar herbicides

R Celis, L Cox, M C Hermosín, J Cornejo
Instituto de Recursos Naturales y Agrobiol., CSIC, PO Box 1052, 41080 Sevilla, Spain
EMail: rcelis@irnase.csic.es

ABSTRACT

Sorption, degradation and soil porosity are major factors influencing pesticide mobility in soil. In this paper, we attempt to show a link between soil porosity, as described by the soil-surface fractal dimension (D_s), and herbicide behaviour in soil. We have studied the sorption, persistence and leaching of two polar herbicides (clopyralid and thiazafluron) in one sandy and two silty clay soils and related these to the porosity characteristics of the soils. Very little sorption in batch tests or degradation of clopyralid was observed in the three soils but there was considerable sorption and degradation of thiazafluron. Despite its negligible sorption, clopyralid displayed broader breakthrough curves in the two silty clay soils than in the sandy soil, which was attributed to the presence of small-sized pores and in turn with slightly higher D_s values of the silty clay soils. For thiazafluron, the higher D_s values associated with the silty clay soils compared to the sandy soil resulted in greater degradation during leaching compared to the batch experiment. This was attributed to retention or entrapment of the herbicide in stagnant, small-sized pores, which may have increased the residence time of the herbicide in the soil column, so retarding leaching and enhancing degradation.

INTRODUCTION

Sorption, degradation and movement through the soil profile determine the fate of pesticides in soil and aquatic environments. Sorption and degradation are generally inversely related to pesticide mobility (Beck *et al.*, 1993); soil physical properties such as texture, aggregate size and pore-size distribution also affect the transport of these solutes in soil (Cox *et al.*, 1999).

Even though the importance of soil structure to many soil processes, such as solute leaching, is well recognised, the progress from qualitative appreciation to quantitative understanding of structure-process interactions remains very slow (Crawford *et al.*, 1997). The recent recognition of soil as a fragmented porous medium, appropriate for fractal representation, has resulted in an increasing interest in the development of models relating soil fractal parameters, such as the soil-surface fractal dimension, to structure-dependent soil properties such as solute movement. In this work, we have compared the leaching patterns of the polar herbicides clopyralid (3,6-dichloropicolinic acid) and thiazafluron (1,3-dimethyl-1-(5-trifluoromethyl-1,3,4-thiadiazol-2-yl)urea) in one sandy and two silty clay soils, and related these to herbicide sorption, persistence and the porosity characteristics of the soils. Mercury intrusion porosimetry and nitrogen adsorption techniques were used to characterise soil porosity in the macro- and micropore range, respectively. Porosity data were interpreted in terms of fractal geometry, and soil-surface fractal dimensions (D_s) were used as a descriptor of soil structure.

MATERIALS AND METHODS

Herbicides and soils

Analytical standards (chemical purity > 99%) of clopyralid and thiazafluron were supplied by the manufacturers.

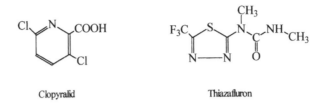

Clopyralid   Thiazafluron

The three soils were agricultural soils from Southern Spain: one sandy soil and two silty clay soils. Soil samples were air-dried, sieved to pass a 2-mm mesh and stored at 4°C. Their classification and physicochemical properties were determined by standard methods and the clay mineralogy by X-ray diffraction on orientated specimens (Table 1).

Table 1. Physicochemical properties of the soils

Soil	pH	Organic matter (%)	Fe (%)	Sand (%)	Silt (%)	Clay (%)
Soil 1 (*Typic Rhodoxeralf*)	7.9	0.99	0.98	71	9	20
Soil 2 (*Xerofluvent*)	7.7	2.24	0.82	12	44	44
Soil 3 (*Entic Pelloxererts*)	7.6	2.54	0.50	12	36	52

Porosity measurements

The distribution of pore radii of soil samples from 40 to 4×10^{-3} μm was determined using a Carlo Erba 2000 mercury depression and intrusion porosimeter. A sample of each soil (0.25 g) was heated at 90°C for 24 h, then outgassed at room temperature for 30 min prior to obtaining the mercury intrusion curve. Surface fractal dimensions corresponding to the mercury porosimetry (macropore) range were calculated according to the Pfeifer and Avnir (1983) equation:

$$\frac{-dV_p}{dr} \propto r^{\,2-Ds(Hg)}$$

where V_p is the volume of pore radii r and $D_s(Hg)$ is the surface fractal dimension corresponding to the mercury porosimetry range, which can be calculated from the slope of the logarithmic plot of dV_p/dr against r.

Nitrogen adsorption isotherms of soil samples were obtained using a Carlo Erba Sorptomatic 1900. Samples were outgassed at 90°C and equilibrated under vacuum for 24 h before measuring the nitrogen adsorption curve. Pore-size distributions were obtained in the range 10^{-3} to 3×10^{-2} μm using the Dollimore and Heal (1964) method assuming cylindrical pores in the calculations. Surface fractal dimensions of the soils corresponding to the nitrogen adsorption (micropore) range were calculated from nitrogen adsorption data using the Avnir and Jaroniec (1989) relationship:

$$V_{ads} \propto [\log(p_o/p)]^{D_s(N_2)-3}$$

where V_{ads} is the volume of nitrogen adsorbed at the relative pressure p/p_o and $D_s(N_2)$ is the fractal dimension of the surface accessible to nitrogen. $D_s(N_2)$ can be obtained from the slope of the plot of log (V_{ads}) against log [log (p_o/p)] in the low adsorption potential region (Avnir and Jaroniec, 1989).

Batch sorption and degradation kinetics

Duplicate slurries of soil/herbicide solution (500 g : 500 mL) were prepared in amber-glass bottles (1 L) with an initial herbicide concentration (C_{ini}) of 10 μM for thiazafluron and 2 μM for clopyralid. A blank bottle (without soil) was used as a control to account for possible abiotic degradation and volatilisation. The soil slurries were sampled at 0.25, 0.5, 1, 2, 4, 7, 10 and 14 days. The sample aliquot (approximately 20 mL suspension) was centrifuged and the herbicide concentration of the aqueous supernatant solution (C_t) determined by HPLC. The amount of herbicide removed from the aqueous solution (C_s) was calculated from the difference between the herbicide concentration in the blank bottles (C_{ini}) and C_t. For thiazafluron, the soil pellets were extracted with methanol (2:1 methanol:soil), whereas for clopyralid the soil was extracted with a 3:1 mixture of 1M NaCl : 0.1M NaOH (4:1 extractant:soil). The water content of the soil, with C_t herbicide concentration, was used to correct data from the soil extraction. The difference between the herbicide removed from the solution (C_s) and that extracted from the soil (C_r) was assumed to be degraded and/or irreversibly bound ($C_d = C_s - C_r$) (Allen and Walker, 1987).

Leaching experiments

Herbicide leaching in soils was studied using methacrylate columns, 20 cm long and 16.66 cm^2 section. After saturation of the soil columns with 0.01M CaCl$_2$, the amount of thiazafluron and clopyralid corresponding to the maximum application rate in soils (12 kg ha^{-1} and 100 g ha^{-1}, respectively) was applied. The columns were leached with 0.01M CaCl$_2$ (25 mL daily during the first 10 days of the experiment, then 50 mL daily until the end of the experiment). Leachates were collected daily, volumes measured and herbicide concentrations determined by HPLC.

RESULTS AND DISCUSSION

Porosity measurements

The values of pore volumes (V_p) for the macro- and micropore range, measured by mercury intrusion porosimetry and nitrogen adsorption respectively, and the D_s values for the three soils are given in Table 2. Although there was no clear correlation between $V_p(Hg)$ and the clay or organic matter content of the soils, the increase in $D_s(Hg)$ values from soil 1 to soil 3, reflecting increasing surface tortuosity as a result of predominance of small-size pores (Celis et al., 1996), was clearly related ($r^2 > 0.87$) to the clay and organic matter content of the soils (soil 1 < soil 2 < soil 3, Table 1). Filling of coarse pores by clay and organic matter has been shown to result in high soil D_s values as a result of a predominance of fine-sized pores which increase soil tortuosity (Bartoli et al., 1991).

Nitrogen adsorption isotherms were used to calculate the volumes of pore radii < 0.025 μm, $V_p(N_2)$ and the surface fractal dimensions, $D_s(N_2)$, corresponding to the micropore range (Avnir and Jaroniec 1989). These values, summarised in Table 2 for the three soils, show an increase in both $V_p(N_2)$ and $D_s(N_2)$ from soil 1 to soil 3, suggesting increasing numbers of micropores in the order soil 1 < soil 2 < soil 3. The similar pattern of D_s values obtained by mercury intrusion porosimetry and nitrogen adsorption techniques seems to indicate that these two pore-size measurements are related, the increase in surface fractal dimension being associated primarily with the clay and organic matter contents.

Table 2. Mercury intrusion and nitrogen adsorption pore volumes (V_p) and derived surface fractal dimensions (D_s) for the three soils.

Soil	V_p (Hg) 40 μm > r > 0.025 μm (mm^3 g^{-1})	V_p (N$_2$) r < 0.025 μm (mm^3 g^{-1})	V_p (total) r < 40 μm (mm^3 g^{-1})	$D_s(Hg)$	$D_s(N_2)$
Soil 1	122	24	146	2.76 ± 0.05[†]	2.71 ± 0.01
Soil 2	164	34	198	2.93 ± 0.04	2.79 ± 0.01
Soil 3	59	45	104	3.11 ± 0.06	2.81 ± 0.01

[†] standard error about the mean

Batch sorption and degradation kinetics

Sorption coefficients, K_d (= C_s/C_t), on the different soils were calculated from the amount of herbicide sorbed at 24 h in the batch kinetic experiment. K_d values are shown in Table 3, along with the percentage of herbicide degraded after 14 d of incubation (%D_{14d}) and the half-life values ($T_{1/2}$) obtained by extrapolation of the C_d vs t curves.

Table 3. Distribution coefficients, K_d (L kg^{-1}), degradation percentage, %D_{14d}, and half-life, $T_{1/2}$ (days) of herbicides in soils calculated from the batch kinetic experiments.

Soil	Clopyralid			Thiazafluron		
	K_d	%D_{14d}	$T_{1/2}$	K_d	%D_{14d}	$T_{1/2}$
Soil 1	0.01 ± 0.01[†]	0	-	0.7 ± 0.1	45 ± 3	15
Soil 2	0.05 ± 0.03	0	-	1.8 ± 0.1	20 ± 1	45
Soil 3	0.05 ± 0.03	0	-	2.0 ± 0.1	22 ± 1	40

[†] standard error about the mean

There was very little sorption and degradation of clopyralid in the three soils and considerable sorption and degradation of thiazafluron. The pK$_a$ of clopyralid (pK$_a$= 2.3) indicates that at the pH of the soils the compound would be very largely in its anionic form and therefore would be repelled by negatively charged soil colloids. For thiazafluron (log K$_{ow}$= 1.8), soils 2 and 3 (with higher clay and organic matter contents and higher D_s values) displayed the highest sorption and the lowest degradation rates, indicating that sorption protected the herbicide from degradation (Table 3).

Leaching experiment

The position of the maximum concentration peak (close to one pore volume), the symmetry of the breakthrough curves, and the total amounts of herbicide recovered (> 90%) for clopyralid in all three soils indicate little retention and degradation in the soil columns (Fig. 1), in agreement with the batch slurry results. However, despite its negligible sorption and degradation in all three soils, clopyralid displayed slightly broader breakthrough curves in the two silty clay soils than in the sandy soil (as can be clearly seen in the expanded clopyralid figure). This can be attributed to retardation of the herbicide molecules by diffusion and hydrodynamic dispersion into the small pores of soils 2 and 3 and indicated that high D_s values, as an indicator of abundance of small size pores or great tortuosity in the pore system, can be related to flattening and widening of the breakthrough curves for low-sorbing and persistent chemicals such as clopyralid. A similar feature was found by Ping *et al.*, (1975) for the acidic, non-sorbing herbicide picloram in a silty soil.

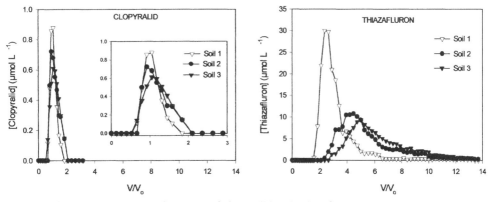

Figure 1. Breakthrough curves of clopyralid and thiazafluron in the three soils.

The pore volumes required to reach the maximum concentrations in the breakthrough curves for thiazafluron directly correlated with the K$_d$ values given in Table 3 (r^2 = 0.998), indicating that the position of the maximum concentration peak was mainly determined by the extent of sorption (Beck *et al.*, 1993). Total amounts of thiazafluron recovered after the leaching experiment (soil 1 = 90% soil 2 = 74%, soil 3 = 72%) showed greater degradation in the silty clay soils 2 and 3 than that in soil 1. This was in contrast to the batch slurry results, where the greatest degradation occurred in the less sorptive sandy soil 1. Again, the abundance of small-sized pores in soils 2 and 3, reflected by their high D_s values, may have reduced the hydrodynamic dispersion and diffusion processes of the herbicide molecules to and from stagnant micropores, enhancing the residence time of the herbicide in those pores and in turn the likelihood for degradation. In the batch experiment, the lower soil/solution ratio, as compared to the soil column, and the effective shaking facilitated diffusion and favoured degradation in soil 1 because of the lower sorption.

CONCLUSIONS

This interpretation of herbicide leaching on the basis of soil fractal structure supported the usefulness of the fractal approach to describe soil structure by a single numerical value (i.e., D_s) and to address the relation between soil structure and solute movement. Greater herbicide retention and degradation in soil columns was strongly related to the presence of small-size pores and in turn with high D_s values in soil. These findings may, therefore, help progress from qualitative appreciation to quantitative understanding of structure-process interaction, which is one of the most important and beneficial features of soil fractal theory.

ACKNOWLEDGEMENTS

This work has been partially supported by the CICYT project AMB96-0445-CO2-02 and by the Research Group RNM-124 of Junta de Andalucía. We thank Novartis (thiazafluron) and Dow Chemical (clopyralid) for supplying the pure compounds.

REFERENCES

Allen R; Walker A (1987). The influence of soil properties on the rates of degradation of metamitron, metazachlor and metribuzin. *Pesticide Science* **18**, 95-111.

Avnir D; Jaroniec M (1989). An isotherm equation for adsorption on fractal surfaces of heterogeneous porous materials. *Langmuir* **5**, 1431-1433.

Bartoli F; Philippy R; Doirisse M; Niquet S; Dubuit M (1991). Structure and self-similarity in silty and sandy soils: the fractal approach. *Journal of Soil Science* **42**, 167-185.

Beck A J; Johnston A E J; Jones K C (1993). Movement of nonionic organic chemicals in agricultural soils. *Critical Reviews in Environmental Science and Technology* **23**, 219-248.

Celis R; Cornejo J; Hermosín M C (1996). Surface fractal dimensions of synthetic clay-hydrous iron oxide associations from nitrogen adsorption isotherms and mercury porosimetry. *Clay Minerals* **31**, 355-363.

Cox L; Calderón M J; Hermosín M C; Cornejo J (1999). Leaching of clopyralid and metamitron under conventional and reduced tillage systems. *Journal of Environmental Quality* **28**, 605-610.

Crawford J W; Verrall S; Young I M (1997). The origin and loss of fractal scaling in simulated soil aggregates. *European Journal of Soil Science* **48**, 643-650.

Dollimore D; Heal G R (1964). An improved method for the calculation of pore size distribution from adsorption data. *Journal of Applied Chemistry* **14**, 109-114.

Pfeifer P; Avnir D (1983). Chemistry of noninteger dimensions between two and three. *Journal of Chemical Physics* **79**, 3558-3565.

Ping C L; Cheng H H; McNeal B L (1975). Variation in picloram leaching patterns for several soils. *Soil Science Society of America Journal* **39**, 470-474.

Herbicide partitioning to hard surfaces

C T Ramwell

Cranfield Centre for EcoChemistry, Cranfield University, Shardlow Hall, Shardlow, Derby, DE72 2GN, UK

Email: c.ramwell@cranfield.ac.uk

ABSTRACT

The herbicide atrazine, despite having a low K_{oc}, partitioned to asphalt and concrete, but not to granite ballast. Partitioning accounted for 36 and 16% loss of formulated product when applied to asphalt and concrete respectively. Partitioning was enhanced for formulated atrazine compared to technical grade.

INTRODUCTION

The current UK approach to regulating herbicides applied to hard surfaces is highly precautionary and assumes that 100% of the applied compound is removed within 25 mm of rainfall. An improved Tier 1 risk-assessment model has been developed (Hollis *et al.*, 2000) but its use remains limited due to a lack of knowledge on processes affecting the loss of herbicides following application.

The K_{oc} (organic carbon/water partition coefficient) of a pesticide is fundamental to predicting its behaviour in soils. The natures of soils and hard surfaces (*e.g.* concrete) are intrinsically different and the K_{oc} value does not necessarily reflect the behaviour of the compound on hard surfaces. Furthermore, in the field, pesticides are in contact with a 3-dimensional 'volume' of soil whereas on a hard surface they are in contact with a 2-dimensional 'area' of material. Consequently, existing methods for determining the adsorption/desorption of pesticides to soil may not be suitable for representing processes occurring on hard surfaces, but quantification of a partition coefficient (K_p) for herbicides and hard surfaces could assist in understanding their fate and behaviour.

The aim of this study was to develop a method for determining herbicide partitioning to hard surfaces and to explore relationships between physico-chemical properties and sorption. Furthermore, the development of laboratory-scale methodology to investigate pesticide behaviour on hard surfaces will enable more accurate comparisons between compounds, and could provide a basis for further, process-based research in this area.

Compounds (*e.g.* triazines, ureas) were chosen to span a range of hydrophobicity; this should enable more accurate prediction of the behaviour of a wide range of amenity pesticides. Surfaces used in the experiment – concrete, hot-rolled asphalt and granite ballast – represent materials commonly treated with herbicides in the UK. The study is ongoing and only atrazine results are presented here.

METHODS AND MATERIALS

The principle of determining a partition coefficient between a herbicide and a hard-surface material followed OECD guidelines for quantifying adsorption, in that the wearing surface of the material was exposed to a test compound whose concentration was measured over time.

The hard-surface materials comprised commercially available concrete paving slabs cut to 0.1 m x 0.15 m blocks. Asphalt slabs were made to the same size using 30/14 hot-rolled wearing-course asphalt. Granite ballast was measured by weight (0.5 kg) rather than area as this is the unit commonly associated with this material. All surfaces were new and were washed with water prior to use.

Pyrex glass dishes were used to hold the test solution. The volume of solution used (250 ml) was determined such that, when in position, approximately 3 mm depth of the slab was exposed to the solution ensuring that the wearing course was the main adsorption site. Slabs were raised at each corner on a small, glass bead. Both technical grade atrazine and formulation (MSS Atrazine 50 FL, a suspension concentrate containing 500 g a.i. l^{-1}) were investigated. The required concentration of the solution was calculated by dividing the mass of active that would be applied to a 0.015 m^2 area at label application rate by the nominal volume of 250 ml. The solution was made up in a ten-litre aspirator and divided between the dishes to minimise variation between replicates. Distilled water was the solvent for both the technical grade and formulated atrazine.

The experiment was conducted in the dark at room temperature (18°C) and the solution was stirred throughout. Each test was conducted in triplicate. Dishes containing the test solution but no slab served as a control. An asphalt slab placed in distilled water served as a control to ensure no interference during analysis. Ballast was placed in stainless steel containers and all the surfaces of the ballast were exposed to the solution. A control of the solution containing no ballast was run in parallel. These containers were agitated using a shaker. Samples (1.0 ml) were taken prior to the slabs being placed in the solution (t = 0), and after 2, 6, 24 and 144 hours. Samples were stored in glass vials at 4°C prior to analysis.

After 144 hours (T_{144}), the slabs were removed from solution and air dried for 24 hours. After a 10 second rinse in distilled water (250 ml), the slabs were transferred into clean water (250 ml) and desorption studied by taking samples (1.0 ml) after 1, 24 and 144 hours. Samples were analysed by HPLC fitted with a Genesis C18 reverse phase TMS end-capped ODS column (150 x 4.6 mm) with 4 μ packing and using a mobile phase of 65% methanol to 35% water.

Total losses of atrazine to the hard-surface materials were calculated by subtracting the mass of atrazine desorbed following exposure to clean water over 144 h from the mass present after 144 h of sorption in the first phase. Partitioning to the hard surface was determined in relation to the control and was calculated by dividing the mean total loss of atrazine to the hard surface by the mean concentration of the control at 144 h. Mass rather than concentration was used in the data analysis to account for the successive one millilitre decrease in water volume due to sampling. Students t-test was used for data analysis. The partition coefficient was calculated as a ratio of the mean mass of atrazine partitioned to the hard-surface area (mg m^{-2}) after 144 hours to the mean atrazine concentration of the solution after 144 hours.

RESULTS

There was no interference in analysis by leachates from asphalt. On the whole, variability at each time point for the different treatments was good (standard deviation < 0.1); for the few exceptions, the maximum standard deviation was 0.32. All samples contained less than 23 mg L^{-1} of atrazine hence the solubility limit (33 mg L^{-1}) was not exceeded.

Atrazine partitioning to the hard surfaces was calculated as a percentage of the control. Within six hours of the concrete and asphalt slabs being exposed to the formulated atrazine, 7% of the active ingredient had been removed regardless of material type (Figure 1).

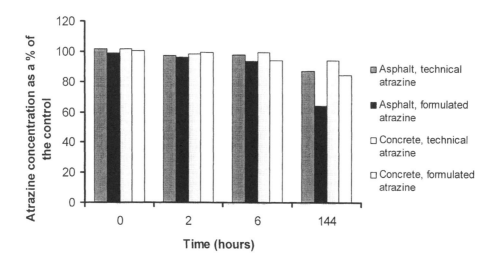

Figure 1. The percentage of atrazine remaining in solution when exposed to asphalt and concrete surfaces.

This compares to a loss of 2-3% of the technical grade during the same time period. After 144 hours, atrazine partitioning to asphalt was significantly ($P < 0.01$) greater than to concrete, and atrazine losses were enhanced when present as formulation rather than technical grade.

There was no partitioning of atrazine to granite ballast either as the formulated product or technical grade (Figure 2).

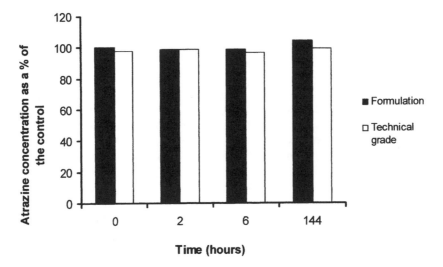

Figure 2. The percentage of atrazine remaining in solution when exposed to ballast.

Partition coefficients (measured at T_{144}) for technical grade atrazine were less than for the formulated product (Table 1). The K_ps also reflect the greater partitioning to asphalt than to concrete.

Table 1. K_p values for atrazine : asphalt and concrete at T_{144}.

Surface Type	K_p (L m^{-2})	
	Technical grade	Formulation
Asphalt	2.44	9.17
Concrete	1.09	3.09

DISCUSSION

Greater partitioning of atrazine to asphalt rather than to concrete may be explained by both the physical and chemical characteristics of asphalt. An asphalt surface is more pitted than a concrete surface and hence the larger surface area will create more potential sorption sites. Furthermore, solution may be physically retained in the fissures by capillary forces. The presence of organic carbon in asphalt would also enhance its sorption capacity.

Minimal retention of atrazine by concrete surfaces was also observed by Shepherd & Heather (1999). However, concentrations of atrazine in runoff water for their study were such that there was an 'unexplained' loss from the system of 80% of the active (MSS Atrazine 50 FL) applied to asphalt and 65% when applied to concrete. The current study indicates that less than half this loss may be explained by partitioning to the surface. Nevertheless, Parsons *et al.*, (1998) accounted for *ca.* 85% of the applied atrazine to a concrete surface in runoff; thus only *ca.* 15% was unaccounted for which is comparable to the quantity partitioned in the current study.

Shepherd and Heather (1999) also demonstrated an increase in atrazine loss from ballast with increasing rainfall and the rate of loss did not decrease significantly after 25 mm of rainfall. This finding indicates that the removal of atrazine was not limited by its availability which is in accordance with the current study where no significant partitioning occurred. Other studies examining herbicide losses from railway formations have demonstrated the ability of herbicides to be leached (Heather & Shepherd 1999; Torstensson 1994) but these results contrast to a study by Ramwell (unpublished data) where herbicides were not detected above 0.1 µg L^{-1} in surface or groundwaters following herbicide application to a railway. It is probable that lower rainfall and greater distances between the treated area and sampling sites in the latter study militated against detection of the herbicides. If herbicides do not partition to granite ballast or if such partitioning is very limited, then knowledge of the composition of the ballast formation would be required to enable the more accurate prediction of herbicide leaching in this medium.

This study indicates that the formulation may enhance partitioning of atrazine to asphalt and concrete, possibly due to the presence of 'stickers'. (Although the working concentrations of the technical grade and formulated atrazine differed, a study by Shepherd (2000) suggested that atrazine partitioning was not affected by concentration). Other research has demonstrated differences between the active ingredient and formulated atrazine when studying degradation and it was proposed that the ratio of surfactant to active may influence the rate of reactions (Texier *et al.*, 1999). The influence of formulation on the ability of a compound to adhere to a hard surface may therefore be specific to the active substance, and research involving further compounds would be required to substantiate the findings of this study.

CONCLUSIONS

Atrazine, despite having a low $K_{oc,}$ partitioned to asphalt and concrete, but not to ballast. Preferential partitioning to asphalt may be both a physical and chemical process. The surfactants used in the formulated product appeared to enhance the ability of atrazine to partition to both asphalt and concrete, but this effect was not observed for ballast.

The study provides a relatively simple method for quantifying partitioning in a controlled environment, such that comparisons between compounds can be made with confidence. Further quantification of partitioning of herbicides with a range of K_{oc} values is to be conducted and this will enable investigation into the possibility that K_{oc} may be used as a predictor of herbicide sorption to hard surfaces. Comparison of results generated in the laboratory to field studies will indicate the importance of partitioning in describing herbicide removal from hard surfaces.

ACKNOWLEDGEMENTS

This work formed part of a study funded by MAFF (PL-0537).

REFERENCES

Hollis J M; Syed B; Shepherd A J; Ramwell C T; Heather A I J (2000). Development and evaluation of a regulatory first tier model for predicting surface water exposure resulting from herbicides applied to land not intended to bear vegetation. *Soil Survey & Land Research Centre report to MAFF*, 40 pp.

Parsons R G; Brockelsby C D; Newby S E (1998). Adherence of herbicides to hard surfaces. *Book of Abstracts - 9th International Congress, Pesticide Chemistry: The food-environment challenge*, pp.6C-012.

Shepherd A J; Heather A I J (1999). Factors affecting the loss of six herbicides from hard surfaces. *Proceedings of the XI Symposium Pesticide Chemistry – Human and Environmental Exposure to Xenobiotics 1999*, pp. 777-784.

Shepherd A J (2000). Herbicide losses from engineered surfaces: Management practices and impacts, Cranfield University, unpublished PhD thesis.

Texier I; Giannotti C; Malato S; Richter C; Delaire J (1999). Solar photodegradation of pesticides in water by sodium decatungstate. *Catalysis Today*, **54**: 297-307.

Torstensson L (1994). Mobility and transformation of diuron in railway embankments. *Proceedings of the 5th International Workshop Environmental Behaviour of Pesticides and Regulatory Aspects*, pp. 366 – 371.

Estimation of pesticide parameters from static and dynamic experiments by two independent modelling groups

B Gottesbüren, K Platz, J R van de Veen
BASF Agricultural Centre Limburgerhof, 67117 Limburgerhof, Germany
Email: bernhard.gottesbueren@basf-ag.de

I G Dubus, S Beulke
Cranfield Centre for EcoChemistry, Cranfield University, Silsoe, Beds, MK45 4DT, UK

ABSTRACT

The behaviour of a pesticide was tested in laboratory, micro-lysimeter, field lysimeter and field dissipation studies. Field lysimeter data were used by two independent modelling groups for estimating Koc and DT50 values. DT50 values derived from dynamic systems (micro-lysimeter, lysimeter) were shorter than those in static laboratory studies. Optimised Koc values differed somewhat between modelling groups and methods, due to differences in the approach to calibration. Total residues in independent field studies were better simulated with parameters derived from dynamic than static systems.

INTRODUCTION

Degradation and sorption parameters to predict the environmental behaviour of pesticides are traditionally determined in static laboratory studies. These parameters may not always be applicable to field conditions (Beulke *et al.*, 2000). The behaviour of a compound (denoted Y) was tested under static and dynamic conditions and at different scales in laboratory incubation, batch equilibrium, micro-lysimeter, lysimeter and field dissipation studies. A subset of these studies was used by two independent modelling groups for automatic and manual parameter estimation. The suitability of these parameters to predict the behaviour of compound Y under different environmental conditions was evaluated.

EXPERIMENTAL STUDIES

DT50 values in soil (the time for 50% dissipation of the pesticide), K_{OC} values (sorption coefficients normalised to soil organic carbon content) and n_f values (Freundlich exponents) were derived from static laboratory degradation and sorption studies with the test substance for a number of soils (Table 1).

Table 1.   Properties of test compound Y in laboratory experiments

	DT50 (days)[1]	Koc (l/kg)	nf
No. of studies	6	21	19
Minimum	22	17.0	0.76
Maximum	59	109.0	1.00
Average	40	39.3	0.92
Median	37	32.5	0.94

[1] at 20°C and 40% maximum water-holding capacity

DT50 values ranged from 22 to 59 days with an average of 40 days. Average values for K_{OC} and nf were 39.3 dm³/kg and 0.92, respectively. For three soils (sandy loams A and B, loam C), data were available for more than one type of experiment. Batch sorption and micro-lysimeter studies were performed with all three soils and sandy loam A was also used in the field lysimeter study. Batch sorption data (K_{OC}/nf) for sandy loam A, sandy loam B and loam C were 30 l/kg / 0.91, 28 l/kg / 0.94 and 23 l/kg / 0.93, respectively.

Three replicate micro-lysimeter studies were performed under controlled conditions with undisturbed topsoil (0-28 cm) to get an insight into the leaching and degradation behaviour of compound Y under conditions closer to the field. The micro-lysimeters were irrigated at an average infiltration rate of 3.4 mm/day during a 100-day study period. Degradation and sorption parameters of compound Y in sandy loam A (Table 2) were derived from breakthrough curves with CXTFIT-2.1 (Toride et al., 1995) assuming linear sorption (nf = 1). Where amounts leached were too small to obtain reasonable fits (sandy loam B, loam C), DT50 values were calculated from the mass balance.

Table 2. Sorption and degradation of compound Y in undisturbed soil columns

Soil	Amount of Compound Y (% of applied)			K_{OC} from BTC (l/kg)	DT50 at 20°C (days)
	Soil	Leachate	Dissipated		
sandy loam A (rep. 1)	1.3	47.3	51.4	20	14 [a]
sandy loam A (rep. 2)	-	-	-	22	16 [a]
sandy loam A (rep. 3)	-	-	-	21	7 [a]
sandy loam A (mean)	-	-	-	22.1	12.2
sandy loam B	6.9	0.6	92.5	>> 50	20 [b]
loam C	1.3	0.8	97.9	>> 50	< 7 [b]

[a] DT50 and K_{OC} estimated simultaneously from the BTC (=breakthrough curve) with CXTFIT-2.1.
[b] DT50 estimated from the applied and residual mass of compound Y in the soil column and the mass in leachate assuming first-order decay.

Dissipation of compound Y in field studies was investigated under a range of environmental conditions (5 studies in Europe, average air temperatures 14.0-19.1°C; 3 studies in the US, 11.5-16.6°C; 3 studies in Canada, 3.4-7.7°C). In Europe, sampling started in spring after a single application and continued until residues fell below the limit of quantification (usually <100 days). Multiple applications were made in the US and Canada. Samples were taken up to >360 d after the last treatment in September. Field dissipation rates were corrected to degradation rates at the reference temperature for a standardised evaluation and comparison with laboratory values at 20°C using the relationship

$$k_{act} = k_{ref. at 20°C} \ Q_{10}^{\frac{T - 20}{10}}$$

with k_{act} = measured degradation rate in the field (1/day), $k_{ref. at 20°C}$ = standardised degradation rate at 20°C (1/day), Q_{10} = factor of change in degradation for a change in temperature by 10°C (fixed at 2.2) and T = measured daily temperature (°C).

Daily degradation rates were calculated with the ModelMaker program using measured daily temperatures. The degradation rate at the reference temperature was optimised for best fit to the experimental data. First-order DT50 values obtained with and without temperature correction are listed in Table 3.

Table 3.   Field DT50 values of compound Y (measured and corrected to 20°C)

Site	Application time/ sampling period	Average temperature (°C)	DT50 (days)	DT50 at 20°C (days)
EU1	spring / <100 d	17.7	14.2	11.7
EU2	spring / <100 d	19.1	7.3	6.3
EU3	spring / <100 d	14.0	37.5	27.6
EU4	spring / <100 d	16.6	4.9	5.8
EU5	spring / <200 d	16.7	22.2	13.2
US6	autumn / >360 d	13.5	19.6	13.1
US7	autumn / >360 d	11.5	12.8	10.1
US8	autumn / >360 d	16.6	7.1	8.7
CAN9	autumn / >360 d	7.7	25.6	15.0
CAN10	autumn / >360 d	8.8	15.4	11.7
CAN11	autumn / >360 d	3.4	54.4	17.5
Minimum – Maximum			4.9 – 54.4	5.8 – 27.6
Arithmetic mean (Median)			20.1 (15.4)	12.8 (11.7)

The field first-order DT50 values were more scattered (5-54 d) and the distribution was more skewed than the DT50 values standardised to 20°C (6-28 d).

A lysimeter study was performed over 3 years according to the German lysimeter guideline (soil = sandy loam A). Application to two replicate lysimeters (B and C) was made in the first year only, whereas a third lysimeter (A) received applications in year 1 and 2. Annual average concentrations in the leachate from individual lysimeters were below 0.1 µg/l (< 0.001 to 0.04 µg/l).

PARAMETER ESTIMATION FROM FIELD LYSIMETER STUDIES

The sensitive parameters K_{OC} and DT50 were estimated from the breakthrough curves of compound Y in leachate from field lysimeters either by (i) automatic calibration of PESTRAS (Freijer *et al.*, 1996) by inverse modelling using a Simplex procedure which aimed at minimising the sum of squared residuals (modelling group A) or (ii) automatic calibration of PEARL (Tiktak *et al.*, 2000) by inverse modelling using a Marquardt-Levenberg procedure (group B) or (iii) manual calibration of PEARL using expert judgement and visual fit to estimate suitable parameters (group B).

The hydrology of the lysimeters was first calibrated by adjusting evapotranspiration within reasonable limits. This was achieved by modifying leaf-area indices of the crops (group A) or by changing crop-specific evapotranspiration factors, leaf-area indices and factors for bare-soil evaporation (group B). Thereafter, Koc and DT50 values were calibrated to improve the fit to concentrations of compound Y in the lysimeter leachates (Figures 1a and 1b). Optimised parameters obtained by the two groups are given in Table 4. The automatic calibration by group B yielded different optimised Koc and DT50 values depending on parameters not included in the calibration and, in contrast to group A, depending also on the starting values.

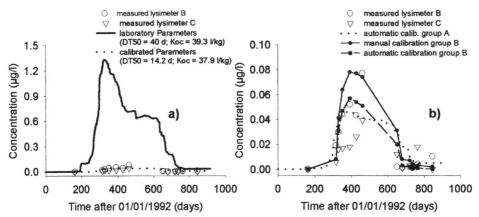

Figure 1 Measured and simulated concentrations of compound Y in lysimeters B and C using initial and calibrated parameters (a) and parameter combinations calibrated by the two modelling groups (b)

Table 4. Optimised parameters obtained from the lysimeter study

Lysimeter	DT50 (days)				K_{OC} (l/kg)			
	A	B	C	Mean	A	B	C	Mean
Group A automatic	14.4	14.8	13.4	14.2	40.2	35.7	37.8	37.9
Group B automatic		9.8				12.4		
Group B manual		14.0				19.5		

A substantial improvement of the simulated breakthrough curve compared to measurements could be obtained by all optimisations. The differences between the optimised are small compared to the range of parameters obtained in static laboratory systems.

COMPARISON OF PESTICIDE PARAMETERS FROM DIFFERENT STUDIES

Degradation parameters obtained in the dynamic systems (micro-lysimeter, field study and field lysimeter study) were similar (Table 5), irrespective of the parameter estimation technique and the modelling group.

Table 5. Pesticide parameters for compound Y obtained from different experiments

	Static system	Dynamic systems				
	Laboratory	Micro-lysimeter (*sandy loam A*)	Field dissipation (average)	Group A (autom.)	Group B (autom.)	Group B (manual)
DT50 (d)	40	12.2	12.8	14.2	9.8	14.0
K_{OC} [l/kg]	39.3	22.1	-	37.9	12.4	19.5

The difference between the optimised values is small compared to the range of parameters obtained in static laboratory systems. The Koc value for the micro-lysimeter study was not directly comparable with those for the remaining studies because it was based on linear sorption (nf = 1). Freundlich exponents for the remaining studies were in the range of 0.90-0.94. The Koc value derived by automatic model calibration by group A (37.9 l/kg) agreed well with that from the laboratory study (39.3 l/kg) whereas the values for automatic and manual calibration by group B were smaller (12.4 and 19.5 l/kg, respectively). Automatic calibration by the two groups resulted in different calibrated parameters (Table 5), but simulated patterns of concentrations were similar (Figure 1). Discrepancies between results from the two groups and between manual and automatic calibration may be caused by several factors, including differences in the calibration of hydrology, the models used to simulate pesticide leaching (PESTRAS vs. PEARL), parameters not included in the calibration, the procedure used to calculate concentrations at the time of sampling and optimisation criteria.

EXTRAPOLATION

The parameters estimated from the lysimeter study should be considered as independent results and should be verified. Koc and DT50 values derived using different approaches were used to simulate the behaviour of compound Y following the last application to three Canadian field sites where environmental conditions differed markedly from those in the lysimeter studies. A comparison was made between (i) the total simulated and measured residues in the field (Figure 2) and (ii) the distribution of residues within the soil profile (Figure 3). The application rate was adjusted in the models in order to match the maximum residue in soil which was observed 1-3 days after application.

The persistence of compound Y in Canadian field studies was over-estimated when laboratory DT50 values were used (Figure 2). The use of DT50 values calibrated against data obtained under outdoor lysimeter conditions resulted in a close fit. Although the DT50 values were almost identical, PEARL predicted faster dissipation than PESTRAS for CAN10 ; this was due to differences in other parameters influencing degradation and in simulated movement of pesticide to depth. Simulated dissipation over winter at CAN11 using PEARL was slower and matched the data better than PESTRAS, because PEARL assumes smaller degradation rates than PESTRAS below 5°C and zero degradation below 0°C. Concentrations of the pesticide within the soil profile (Figure 3) were better simulated when calibrated parameters from dynamic systems were used for modelling compared with laboratory data from static systems.

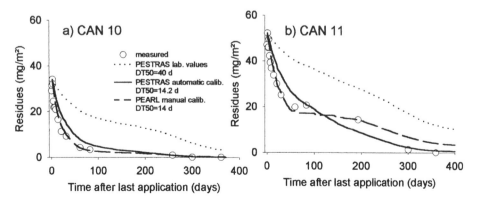

Figure 2. Measured and simulated residues of compound Y in the Canadian field studies

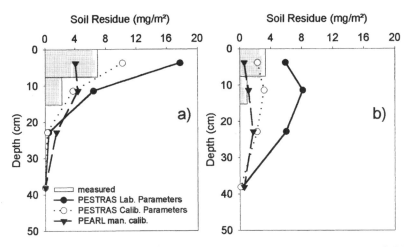

Figure 3. Measured and simulated distribution of residues in the CAN10 field study
(a) after 31 days (b) after 61 days

CONCLUSIONS

Degradation parameters derived from experiments under dynamic conditions appear to give better estimates of pesticide behaviour in the field than those from traditional laboratory studies. A significant improvement of the predictive capacity of pesticide fate models can be achieved. Non-uniqueness of parameter sets obtained by calibration should be noted but discussed in the context of the variability of laboratory parameters. The calibrated parameters have to be verified with independent experimental results before they are used for extrapolation to different environmental conditions. The sequence calibration -> verification -> extrapolation should be followed. Possible implications for regulatory experiments and the modelling of pesticide fate should be investigated further.

ACKNOWLEDGEMENTS

Work by modelling group B was funded within the Pesticides Research Programme of the UK Department of the Environment, Food and Rural Affairs.

REFERENCES

Beulke S; Dubus I G; Brown C D; Gottesbüren B (2000). Simulation of pesticide persistence in the field on the basis of laboratory data – a review. *Journal of Environmental Quality*, **29**: 1371-1379.

Freijer J I; Tiktak A; Hassanizadeh S M; van der Linden A M A (1996). PESTRAS v.3.1: A one-dimensional model for the assessment of the fate of pesticides in soil. RIVM, Report no. 715501007, Bilthoven, The Netherlands.

Tiktak A; van den Berg F; Boesten J J T I; van Kraalingen D; Leistra M; van der Linden A M A (2000). Manual of FOCUS PEARL version 1.1.1. RIVM report no. 711401008, Bilthoven, The Netherlands.

Toride N; Leij F J; van Genuchten M Th (1995). The CXTFIT code for estimating transport parameters from laboratory of field tracer experiments. Version 2.0.

Evaluation of lysimeter experiments in the Netherlands: case studies

A A Cornelese, A M A van der Linden and A J Verschoor
RIVM, PO Box 1, 3720 BA Bilthoven, The Netherlands
Email: adi.cornelese@rivm.nl

ABSTRACT

The tiered approach in the admission of plant protection products in Europe opens the opportunity to perform higher tier experiments like lysimeter studies, if in the first tier there appears to be a risk of leaching. The interpretation of such studies requires a great deal of expert judgement, which makes a more transparent standardisation method desirable. Simulation models can be used to translate the results of lysimeter studies to other leaching scenarios. However simulated results of lysimeter experiments usually deviate from measured concentrations. This paper gives a suggestion on how to cope with these deviations in the evaluation procedure. A lysimeter study should be computer-simulated as well as possible. The resulting ratio between calculated and simulated leaching, called the simulation error, might be used as a correction for the estimated leaching for other scenarios. Simulation errors however may vary substantially. This variability is used to derive upper confidence limits for the leaching in evaluation scenarios.

INTRODUCTION

The leaching potential of a plant protection product is usually assessed following a tiered approach. Lysimeter experiments enter the assessment when in the first tier it is concluded that there is some risk of leaching. Evaluation of higher tier experiments and their use in taking decisions requires a great deal of expert judgement. To avoid too great an influence of expert judgement in decision making, a transparent standardisation method is required.

A computer simulation model can be used to translate the results of lysimeter studies by comparing measured and computed leaching. A proposal for a standardisation method was done by van de Veen & Boesten (1996), who used the model PESTLA to describe lysimeter studies. Because of the rather large variability in lysimeter experiments, interpretation still required experts. Therefore the search for more transparent interpretation methods continued. In the Netherlands a group of experts from various research institutes developed a guidance for the interpretation of lysimeter experiments (Verschoor *et al.*, 2001). This guidance describes how to convert expert judgement to quantitative rules for evaluation. The lysimeter study should be computer-simulated as well as possible and the result is compared with measured leaching. The resulting ratio between calculated and measured leaching is the so-called simulation error.

Eq. 1

$$SE = \frac{C_{lys}}{M_{lys}}$$

SE = *simulation error*
C_{lys} = *cumulative leaching simulated*
M_{lys} = *cumulative leaching measured*

The simulation error is based on the accumulated leaching, which seems to be a robust parameter in simulation and is also easily obtained from measurements. With the calculated simulation error it will be possible to extrapolate the results of lysimeter studies to any scenario, for example a vulnerable scenario in the area of intended use. In a deterministic approach the refined estimated concentration can be calculated by:

Eq. 2
$$C_{re} = \frac{C_{target}}{SE}$$

C_{re} = refined estimated concentration (μg/l)
C_{target} = max. concentration in the upper groundwater in a target use scenario (μg/l)

However, reported simulation errors are sometimes rather large (Dressel, 2000). This would mean that a large correction should be made to obtain the refined estimated concentration, which is undesirable. In this paper we show that simulation errors might decrease if full advantage is taken of model options to describe the lysimeter scenario adequately. Furthermore, a proposal for development of the standardisation procedure to fit a probabilistic approach is provided.

METHOD

Existing data for a number of lysimeter experiments from a study by BASF (Dressel, 2000) were reinterpreted with the help of the PEARL model (Tiktak et al., 2000; Leistra et al., 2001). For this purpose original model input (for the leaching model PESTRAS) was adjusted to fit the PEARL input requirements. Several scenario options within the model PEARL were used to refine the predicted leaching of a compound. In the simulation model, PEARL, the user is able to account for pH-dependent sorption and non-equilibrium sorption. Incorporation of these variables in the simulation might reduce the calculated simulation error.

From the ratio between simulated and measured mass fluxes, simulation errors were calculated according to equation 1. The distribution of the simulation errors is used to derive a statistical method to introduce a correction variable for use in registration procedures. In principle only those lysimeters were used with at least one of the input parameters sorption and degradation determined for the specific lysimeter soil. If more than ten DT_{50} and K_{om} values were available from laboratory studies median values were sometimes used.

RESULTS AND DISCUSSION

The cumulative mass flux for all lysimeters was calculated over a period of at least three full years whereas measurements proceeded over a much shorter period of time. The simulations, however indicate that the time span of the measurements was sufficient to measure the cumulative leaching. An example of one of the simulations is shown in Figure 1.

Table 1 summarises the results of the simulations done for 7 lysimeter studies, performed with one compound, and states the calculated simulation errors.

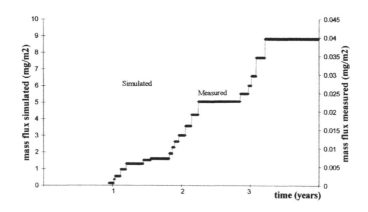

Figure 1. Example of measured and simulated mass fluxes in one lysimeter.

Table 1: Mass fluxes (mg/m^2) of substance at lower boundary and calculated simulation errors for all simulations.

Study	Mass flux measured	Cumulative mass flux at lower boundary for simulation options			Simulation error for simulation options		
		standard	non equi-librium	pH dependent	standard	non equi-librium	PH dependent
1	0.0042	0.36	0.19	0.011	84.75	45.45	2.69
2	0.0156	0.57	0.30	0.098	37.03	19.23	6.27
3	0.0433	0.89	0.46	0.134	20.41	10.64	3.09
4	0.0297	1.84	0.90	0.239	62.50	30.30	8.03
5	0.0463	2.52	1.18	0.284	55.56	25.64	6.13
6	0.038	1.58	0.12	1.84	41.58	3.24	48.4
7	0.0143	0.24	0.016	0.431	16.67	1.09	30.2

Standard calculation

Simulation of the lysimeter scenario with the PEARL model with default options for sorption parameters resulted in calculated simulation errors of 17 to 85. This indicates an overestimation by the model of the total mass of substance leached with these factors. The description of the leaching behaviour by the model seems to be not very accurate.

Effect of non-equilibrium sorption

The PEARL model has an option to account for non-equilibrium sorption (Tiktak et al., 2000; Leistra et al., 2001). Adding non-equilibrium sorption may reduce leaching and therefore reduce overestimation by the model, or in other words decrease the simulation error. For the simulations here the recommended default values for the parameters describing the non-equilibrium sorption process were used.

Using the non-equilibrium sorption option in PEARL requires that also the transformation rate of the compound is adjusted (Boesten, this issue), the transformation rate has to be multiplied with a correction factor. A factor of 1.2 was selected to correct the half-live in the simulations.

From the results (Table 1) we see a decrease in simulation error, compared to the standard simulation. This means a decrease in overestimation of leaching by the model. For the lysimeters 6 and 7 the simulation error is almost 1 which means that measured and simulated results are nearly equal. It should be mentioned that for these two lysimeters no data on sorption and transformation for the lysimeter soil are available. Simulations were thus performed with median value from a large number of laboratory experiments. Therefore the low simulation error calculated might be a coincidence.

Effect of pH dependent sorption.

For substances with a low acid dissociation constant (pK$_a$ value) pH dependent sorption may influence leaching. The substance used on the seven lysimeters discussed has a pK$_a$ of 3.3 and therefore simulating pH-dependent sorption would be appropriate. From the available data, sorption constants of 1000 L/kg for the neutral molecule and 10 L/kg for the anion were derived and used as input to the model in these seven lysimeters. In table 1 the results of simulations using pH dependent sorption are reported. In these calculations only equilibrium sorption is considered.

From the results we see that the simulation error decreases for the lysimeters 1 to 5 compared to initial calculations. For the lysimeters 6 and 7 the simulation error increases compared to calculations for non-equilibrium sorption. Again it should be mentioned that DT$_{50}$ and K$_{om}$ values for these lysimeters were not determined for the lysimeter soil and median values were taken. Overall we can say that simulation errors can decrease if we are able to describe the lysimeter more accurately in a simulation model. The availability of information on a lysimeter study is therefore very important.

Assessment factor

From the results we see that for one compound in different scenarios the simulation error can vary by an order of magnitude. Considering this large variation in simulation errors for one compound a decision based on one simulation error only is quite uncertain. In pesticide registration we don't like to underestimate leaching. Therefore a probabilistic approach, in which an assessment factor based on the variability of the simulation error and the number of experiments, seems to be justified.

The calculation of the refined estimate concentration might be done according to equation 3.
Eq. 3

$$C_{re} = \frac{C_{target}}{F}$$

with

$$F = \overline{SE} - t_{prob} * \sigma / \sqrt{n}$$

$\overline{SE}$	= mean simulation error
n	= number of simulation errors
σ	= standard deviation of population of simulation errors
t_{prob}	= χ^2 probability factor

and the mean and standard deviation obtained from a log-normal fit of distribution of the simulation errors.

Now a confidence level, for example 80%, 90% or 95%, has to be chosen to obtain the assessment factor and the refined concentration estimate.

The results of the seven lysimeters discussed here (compound A) and four more experiments (compounds B and C) (Dressel, 2000) were fitted to a log-normal distribution. Simulation errors of compound B were 17.45, 1.92, 13.3 and for compound C 2.22.

Table 2. Statistical parameters of the simulation error according to a log-normal distribution.

	Standard PEARL	Standard PEARL	Non-eq	pH-dep	PESTRAS
Compounds	A (7), B (3), C (1)	A	A	A	A
Mean	38.55	44.55	24.9	14.51	59.94
Stdev	68.07	26.9	48.16	19.4	83.53
Logstd	1.19	0.56	1.25	1.01	1.04
N	11	7	7	7	7

Here we see that the addition of 4 extra simulation errors to the data set results in a decrease in simulation error.

Example

Suppose that the simulation error of a lysimeter experiment is 38.55. If we want to have 80% confidence that we do not underestimate the leaching, the leaching in the target scenario is not divided by 38.55 (according to eq. 2) as was indicated by the single lysimeter experiment, but by 3.81 (according to eq. 3). Suppose that the concentration calculated for the target scenario was 0.3 µg/l. The refined estimate concentration is then 0.3/3.81 = 0.08 µg/l.

In table 3 the influence of additional experiments and the choice of the confidence level on the assessment factor is summarised. If the number of studies increases the assessment factor will increase and the refined concentration will decrease.The calculated concentration in the example can be read as "there is 80% confidence that the concentration leached is lower than 0.08 µg/l".

Table 3. Value of the assessment factor in dependence of the number of lysimeter experiments and the desired confidence level. (avg. simulation error: 38.55, log standard deviation: 1.19).

Prob.	75%	80%	90%	95%
χ^2 value	0.645	0.845	1.282	1.645
n				
1	6.06	3.81	1.15	0.43
2	10.42	7.50	3.22	1.59
3	13.25	10.13	5.07	2.86
4	15.29	12.11	6.66	4.05
5	16.86	13.69	8.01	5.14

It must be emphasised that these calculations are based on 11 separate lysimeter runs only. Consequently the standard deviation is quite large, resulting in relatively large safety margins.

The safety margin, $t_{prob} * \sigma / \sqrt{n}$, can be decreased by:

1. extension of the database containing simulation errors (which decreases σ),
2. providing more lysimeter experiments for the substance of concern (n)
3. choosing a lower confidence level (χ^2).

CONCLUSIONS AND RECOMMENDATIONS

Interpretation of higher tier experiments reveals that models, which are used today in pesticide registration evaluation, are not capable of reproducing exactly the observed leaching levels. When taking advantage of more advanced options of these models, it is possible to reduce deviations. This was demonstrated for a number of studies, using the PEARL model. For the risk assessment reasonable certainty is required that the substance is safe with respect to leaching. Therefore a method is developed to derive assessment factors based on observed simulation errors and basic probabilistic theory; the value of the assessment factor being dependent on the desired confidence level and the number of higher tier experiments for the specific compound. Based on the uncertainty in the simulation error, the assessment factor is usually lower than the simulation error.

The method proposed here was illustrated using 11 lysimeter studies, with only three different substances. We recommend that a larger database is established, covering more compounds. This would supply more insight in the applicability of this method.

ACKNOWLEDGEMENT

We would like to gratefully thank the BASF Aktiengesellschaft, Agricultural Centre Limburgerhof, for supplying us with digital data on lysimeter studies as used in a report by J Dressel. And for giving us permission to use the data to develop the method proposed here.

REFERENCES

Boesten J J T I; Van der Linden A M A (this issue). Effect of long-term sorption kinetics on leaching as calculated with the PEARL model for FOCUS scenarios, this issue, 6 pp.

Dressel J (2000). Comparison of experimental lysimeter results with calculated predicted environmental concentrations (PEC$_{gw}$) of several pesticides for lysimeter specific scenarios and the Dutch standard scenario, confidential data by BASF Aktiengesellschaft.

FOCUS (2000) FOCUS groundwater scenarios in the EU review of active substances. Report of the FOCUS Groundwater Scenarios Workgroup, EC document Sanco/321/2000 rev.2, 197 pp. Available at http://arno.ei.jrc.it/focus.

Leistra M; Van der Linden A M A; Boesten J J T I; Tiktak A; Van den Berg F (2001). PEARL model for pesticide behaviour and emissions in soil-plant systems; Description of the processes in FOCUS PEARL v 1.1.1. Alterra-report 13, 115 pp. Available at www.alterra.nl/models/pearl.

Tiktak A; Van den Berg F; Boesten J J T I; Leistra M; Van der Linden A M A; Van Kraalingen D W G (2000). Manual of FOCUS PEARL version 1.1.1. RIVM report 711401008, Alterra report 28, 144 pp. Available at www.alterra.nl/models/pearl.

Van de Veen J R; Boesten J J T I (1996). Evaluation of field and lysimeter studies on the leaching of pesticides from soil using the PESTLA model. Report 117, DLO Winand Staring Centre, Wageningen, The Netherlands, 93 pp.

Verschoor A J; Boesten J J T I; Brouwer W W M; Leistra M; Van der Linden A M A; Linders J B H J; Pol J W (2001). Evaluation of leaching in lysimeter and field studies. Part I. Parent substances. RIVM report 601506007, 41 pp.

Mobility of herbicides used for weed control in maize in lysimeter experiments

L Guzzella, F Pozzoni, S Rullo
Water Research Institute - CNR, 20047 Brugherio (Milan), Italy
Email: guzzella@irsa.rm.cnr.it

G Giuliano
Water Research Institute - CNR, 00198 Rome, Italy

ABSTRACT

The transport of chemicals from agricultural fields to groundwater bodies is mainly due to water infiltration through soil. Evaluation of the leaching phenomenon of chemicals is often difficult because of the spatial heterogeneity in the natural soil profile. This heterogeneity is frequently due to the preferential flow phenomenon, a term which describes several physical non-equilibrium flow processes. This phenomenon is critical for herbicide leaching and groundwater contamination since significant amounts of herbicide may by-pass the biologically and chemically active topsoil.

Quantitative evaluation studies on the extent of preferential movement are scarce in the literature. In this investigation, transport of herbicides terbuthylazine, alachlor, metolachlor, linuron and monolinuron were studied in an experimental site equipped with lysimeters. The field site is located at Treviglio (BG) in a cereal crop tillage area, particularly vulnerable to groundwater contamination. Three different rainfall situations were simulated: in the first campaign a constant water seal was applied to reach the interstitial water saturation in the more superficial soil horizons; in the second one an intermittent rainfall simulation condition (30 mM/day of rain) was applied; in the third one natural precipitation was followed.

The temporal trend of herbicide concentrations in the leachates collected from the installed lysimeters allowed the description of the breakthrough curves at different depths (30-60-80-100-180 cm). The herbicide degradation was followed analyzing their main metabolites in leachates and in the groundwater samples. Results showed significant differences both between the three sampling campaigns and with each simulation. A constant water seal ensured infiltration rates and herbicide concentrations reached the maximum contamination levels because much of the soil adsorption capacity was by-passed. In all the campaigns, the results showed two main processes of herbicide transport: in the first pattern the herbicide flow was mainly due to water infiltration through macropores; in the second one, the transport was driven through the soil by matrix flow. Metolachlor and monolinuron were considered as the most mobile herbicides.

INTRODUCTION

The transport of chemicals from agricultural fields to the groundwater bodies is mainly due to water infiltration through soil. The evaluation of the leaching phenomenon of chemicals often causes difficulty because of the spatial heterogeneity in the natural soil profile. This heterogeneity is frequently due to a preferential flow phenomenon, a term which describes several physical non-equilibrium flow processes (Kamra, 1996).

In fine textured soils, large and discontinuous macropores consisting of shrinkage cracks, earthworm channels or root holes operate as preferential flow pathways and can cause rapid movement of chemicals through the unsaturated zone. Preferential flow is not confined solely to heavy clay soils, although they represent the worst case. The phenomenon is critical for herbicide leaching and groundwater contamination since significant amounts of herbicide may bypass the biologically and chemically active topsoil (Ghodrati & Jury, 1992; Harris *et al.,* 1994).

Quantitative evaluation studies on the extent of preferential movement are rare in the literature. In this investigation, transport of chloride and the herbicides terbuthylazine, alachlor, metolachlor, linuron and monolinuron were studied in an experimental site equipped with lysimeters. The experimental field is located at Treviglio (BG) in a maize crop tillage area, particularly vulnerable to groundwater contamination.

METHODS AND MATERIALS

The studied area is located in the Eastern Lombardy plane between Oglio and Adda rivers, at 120 m a.s.l. on an 80 m thickness Würm fluvial-glacial deposit consisting of gravel, sand and conglomerates. The experimental site pertains to the fundamental level of the Po plane. The field is located at the South-East of Treviglio (BG). The watertable is surficial and flows between 5-9 meters of depth in NE-SW direction. Soil is Typic Hapludalf (USDA Soil Taxonomy) and its texture is loamy from topsoil to 120 cm of depth, silty clay loamy from 120 to 150 cm and sandy loamy from 150 to 480 cm with 50% of gravel. The soil is carbonated, the organic carbon content decreases from the topsoil value of 2.7% to 0.02% in the deepest layer (more than 200 cm of depth). The maximum clay content is 26-27% and was measured in the 70-106 cm soil layer. The area is classified as highly vulnerable to groundwater pollution, having a good water drainage.

Suction cup (0.5 L) lysimeters in Teflon (called T) and in ceramic (called C) material (Timco, USA) were installed in the plot (20 m² area) to collect water samples from soil pores at 30, 60, 80, 100 and 180 cm of depth (Figure 1). Manometer type tensiometers were installed at the same depth of lysimeter cups, to monitor water saturation conditions of the different soil horizons.

The commercial Aresin (Hoechst Schering AgrEvo, Germany), Siolcid SC (SIAPA, Italy), Lasso Microtech (Monsanto, Italia) and Primagram TZ products (Ciba Geigy, Switzerland) containing monolinuron (41.5 %), linuron (37.6%), terbuthylazine (15%), alachlor (48%) and metolachlor (30%) respectively were used in the three experiments for the herbicide application during 1997-1999 years with one exception: in the second one only Lasso Microtech and Primagram TZ were applied.

The herbicide solution was applied by using a water reservoir with tube irrigation system, with the aim of obtaining a good uniformity in herbicide distribution on the experimental plot. Three experimental campaigns were undertaken in different hydraulic conditions, in order to assess the influence of soil humidity and permeability on herbicides transport pathways. In the first campaign a constant water seal was applied to reach the interstitial water saturation in the more superficial soil horizons, the added water amount varied from 600 L/day to 1,200 L/day; in the second one an intermittent rainfall simulation condition (30 mm/day of rain for 21 days) was applied and in the third one no artificial water was supplied, except for the 600 L solution used for herbicides application, the natural precipitation events were recorded by the installed rain gauge.

The herbicides analyses were conducted by concentrating water samples on 200 mg Lichrolut EN column (Merck, Germany) and analysing the extracts with HPLC Diode-Array 1050 (Hewlett Packard, USA) equipped with an automatic sampler and Lichrospher 5100 C18 column (25 cm x 4.6 mm) (Guzzella *et al.*, 1998 and 2000).

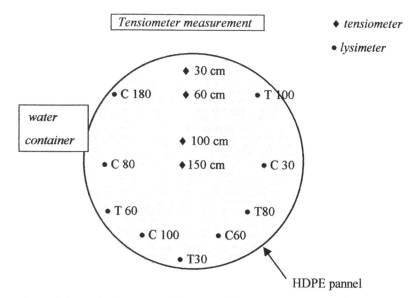

Figure 1.   Schematic diagram of the experimental plot showing relative locations of instruments.

RESULTS AND DISCUSSION

Results showed significant differences both between the three sampling campaigns and with the different simulations (Figures 2, 3 and 4). The constant water seal and the natural precipitation experiments enhanced infiltration rates and herbicide concentrations reached the maximum values (Figures 2 and 4). The results showed two main process of herbicide transport: the herbicide flow was mainly due to water infiltration through macropores and therefore the herbicide concentrations were very high as in the C30 and T80 lysimeters in the first experiment and in the T30, C80 and T80 lysimeters in the third experiment; the transport was driven through the soil by matrix flow and the herbicide concentrations were lower in the C60 and C80 lysimeters in the second experiment and the T30, C60 and T100 lysimeters in the third experiment .

In both the experiments the herbicides were partially retained by soil as showed by the attenuated and delayed response of leachate concentrations. The phenomenon is particularly evident for terbuthylazine and linuron which were characterized by the highest value of K_{oc} and the lowest solubility with respect to monolinuron, metolachlor and alachlor.

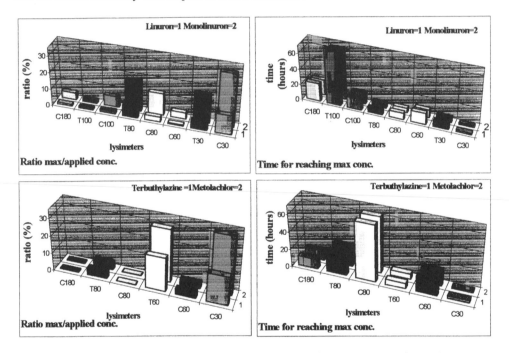

Figure.2. Time necessary for reaching the maximum concentration and
ratio of maximum value to applied concentrations of herbicides
in the first campaign.

In the second experiment (Figure 3) the herbicide maximum concentrations were generally lower that those measured in the other two studies, the time necessary for reaching the maximum concentrations were greater and therefore preferential water flow was less relevant.

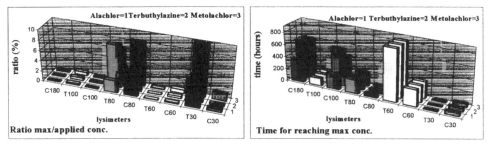

Figure 3. Time necessary for reaching the maximum concentration and ratio of maximum value to applied concentrations of herbicides in the second campaign.

The greatest herbicide concentrations were detected in the more surficial lysimeter (T30) and at 80 cm of depth where a consistent clay soil horizon was present. Considering the herbicides applied in the second experiment, metolachlor showed the highest leaching capacity in all the installed lysimeters. In fact, the highest metolachlor concentrations were measured in the leachates due to its chemo-dynamic properties that it indicate high water solubility. On the contrary, the pattern of alachlor did not follow its chemo-dynamic properties: alachlor mobility profile showed a great similarity to the terbuthylazine one. An explanation of this phenomenon may be found in the preparation of the commercial product; the alachlor in microencapsuled formulate will reduce the leaching from soil.

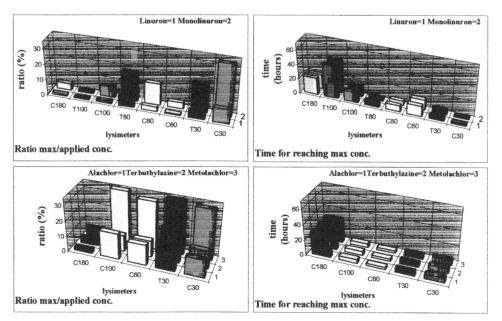

Figure 4. Time necessary for reaching the maximum concentration and ratio of maximum value to applied concentrations of herbicides in the third campaign.

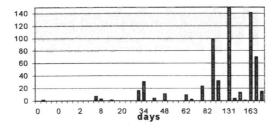

Figure 5.   Natural rainfall (mm/day) in the third experiment

The natural precipitation trend of the third experiment is showed in Figure 5. The first consistent rainfalls were recorded after 24 days of dry time period and therefore the herbicide transport was initially driven only through the water applied during herbicide soil treatment. The herbicide application modalities (the 600 L solution used for the plot treatment) too seemed therefore to influence the herbicide leaching from top soil horizon.

CONCLUSIONS

The constant hydraulic water head applied in the first experiment and the natural precipitation simulation of the third experiment promoted rapid downward transport and leaching. Amongst the herbicides tested, metolachlor and monolinuron showed the greatest mobility from agricultural topsoil to groundwater.

ACKNOWLEDGEMENTS

The study was conducted with the financial support of the Strategic Project *Environment and Territory* (1995-98) promoted by the National Research Council CNR of Italy and of the Research Program of the Environmental Ministry on *The presence of pesticide transformation products in groundwater* (1998-2001). The authors thank Adolfo De Paolis and Luciano Previtali for their technical help in the set up and sampling organisation of the Treviglio field.

REFERENCES

Ghodrati M; Jury W A (1992). A field study of the effects of soil structure and irrigation method on preferential flow of pesticides in unsaturated soil. *J.Contam. Hydrol.*, **11**:101-125.

Harris G L; Nocholls P H; Bailey S W; Howse K R; Mason, D J (1994). Factors influencing the loss of pesticides in drainage from cracking clay soil. *Journal of Hydrology*, **159:** 235-253.

Guzzella L; Pozzoni F; Giuliano G (1998) Mobility, leaching and degradation investigation for terbuthylazine and metolachlor in the unsaturated zone by lysimeter experiments.

M Herbert; K Kovar: Groundwater Quality: Remediation and Protection, *Proceedings of the TGA 1998 Conference, Tubingen, Germania,* settembre 1998, 1-3.

Guzzella L; Pozzoni F; Giuliano G (2000). Field study on mobility and persistence of linuron and molinuron in agricultural soil. *International Journal of Environmental Analytical Chemistry,* **78:** 87-106.

Kamra S K; Lennartz B; Meyer-Windel B; Widmoser P (1996). Moment analysis to characterize leaching behaviour of pesticides. In: *The Environmental Fate of Xenobiotics:* 187-194. Pavia: La Goliardica Pavese.

A pilot study of the movement of permethrin into freshwater sediments

I J Allan, W A House
Centre for Ecology and Hydrology, Winfrith Technology Centre, Winfrith Newburgh, Dorchester, Dorset, DT2 8ZD, UK
Email: IJAL@ceh.ac.uk

N Warren, A Parker
PRIS, University of Reading, Whiteknights, P.O.Box 217, Reading, RG6 6AB, UK

J E Carter
School of Environmental and Applied Sciences, University of Derby, Kedleston Road, Derby, DE22 1GB, UK

ABSTRACT

Experimental fluvarium channels were used to investigate the degradation and sorption to bed sediments of highly toxic *cis* and *trans* permethrin in freshwater environments. The results indicate similar net half-lives in synthetic solutions and river water of 67 d and 60 d for the *cis* and *trans* isomers respectively. The presence of a natural sediment (both with and without burrowing *oligochaete* worms) enhanced the removal of permethrin from the overlying water with penetration to 20 mm depth in 43 days. Initial mathematical modelling results are consistent with a diffusion-adsorption model.

INTRODUCTION

Freshwater sediments have been shown to act as sinks for many types of micro-organic contaminant including PCBs, organochlorine and pyrethroid insecticides. Studies have detected the presence of the pyrethroid, permethrin, in water and surface sediments in some contaminated rivers (e.g. Long *et al.*, 1998). However, there is a lack of information about the kinetics of degradation in fresh waters and the degree of penetration of permethrin into natural sediments (House *et al.*, 2000). The present work examines the losses of permethrin from aqueous solution in experimental fluvarium channels in the presence and absence of river sediment.

ANALYTICAL PROCEDURES

Cis permethrin (99.8% purity) was supplied by The Laboratory of the Government Chemist (Teddington, Middlesex, UK), and the *trans* isomer (99.8%) from the Laboratory of Dr Ehrenstorfer (D-86199 Augsburg, Germany). Decachlorobyphenyl (DCBP, 99.8% purity) was used as internal standard. Waters and sediments were analysed using the methods described by Long *et al.*, (1998).

FLUVARIUM CHANNEL EXPERIMENTS

Fluvarium channels were used as described by Zhmud *et al.*, (1997).

Channels without sediment

Experiments were performed in the absence of sediment under a range of conditions as shown in Table 1. At the beginning of each experiment the channels were filled with 24 litres of either 10 mmol/litre $KHCO_3$ to simulate the ionic strength of river water or water that had been in contact with sediment (taken from the end of the experiment with the channel containing sediment as described below). Each channel was then spiked with a solution containing both isomers of permethrin in acetone and either exposed to natural light or covered and kept dark. Samples of water were collected at different times and analysed for permethrin. The volume of water in channels was maintained constant. The solution pH, dissolved oxygen concentration and temperature were recorded at intervals through the experiment.

Table 1. Summary of the experiments with the channels containing only water. Mean pH and temperature are given for both channels. RW: River Water.

Exp. No.	Spiking level (μg)		Characteristics				No samples
	cis	*trans*	Mean pH	Mean temp (°C)	Channel 1	Channel 2	
1	480	480	8.9	13.0	light	light	6
2	480	480	8.6	11.6	light	light	8
3	480	1200	8.8	11.6	light	dark	25
4	480	480	9.0	14.2	light / RW	dark / RW	17

Channel containing water and sediment

Surface bed-sediment (< 5 cm depth) was collected from the River Calder in Yorkshire (NGR SE409258) in May 2000 and sieved (2 mm) onsite. One of the channels was filled to 50 mm depth with the sediment and 20 litres of 10 mmol/litre $KHCO_3$. The channel was spiked with 400 μg of *cis* and *trans* permethrin and left for 6 weeks. Experiments with other solutes have shown a mixing time for the channels of *ca* 10 min. Water samples were taken at intervals for permethrin analysis and the solution pH, dissolved oxygen concentration and temperature recorded throughout the experiment. Within a week, a layer of diatom biofilm developed at the interface that subsequently diversified to a filamentous community. After four weeks, the channel was divided widthways into two equal sections: Section A which naturally contained few native *oligochaete* worms (as judged by their activity at the surface) with Section B supplemented by the equivalent of 1000 worms/m². The worms were also collected in May 2000, from surface bed sediments from the River Aire in Yorkshire (NGR: SE534255) and were identified as *Limnodrilus* spp. and *Potamothrix* spp. with some *Tubifex* spp. (probably *Tubifex tubifex*). After 6 weeks, the water was removed and sediment horizontally sectioned every millimetre down to 5 mm, then single sections between 5-10 mm, 10-30 mm and finally every 10-mm down to the bottom using a slicing tool. Sediment sections were sub-sampled for permethrin analysis, porosity determination, and centrifuged to collect porewaters for dissolved silicon analysis. The latter results provide information on bioturbation effects on porewater movement (Zhmud *et al.*, 1997). A sample of biofilm was also collected at the end of the experiment and analysed for permethrin.

RESULTS AND DISCUSSION

Recoveries for both SPE and SFE were similar to those given by Long *et al.*, (2000).

Adsorption-degradation reactions

The mean temperature and pH for both channels are given in Table 1. The dissolved oxygen concentrations were not measured in Experiments 1 and 2 but were between 95 and 100 % saturation in Experiments 3 and 4. In all of the four experiments in the absence of sediment (as listed in Table 1), the variation in total mass of permethrin present in solution over time followed a similar trend. Experiment 3 was typical (Figure 1).

The data from each experiment were divided into a set where sorption was the main process occurring, and a second one where degradation was the main pathway for loss of permethrin from the overlying water. The separation into two sets of data was done from the intercept of the two linear portions of the first-order rate plots. First-and second-order reaction kinetics were applied to these data to obtain net sorption and degradation rates for both isomers, i.e. isomer interconversion was not taken into account. This analysis indicated that the rapid loss (at < 1 d) was caused by adsorption on the walls of the channels, whereas the much slower rate after one day was caused by degradation. Permethrin is highly hydrophobic (pK_{ow}=6.1 at 20 °C) and adsorbs to glass and PTFE (Sharom *et al.*, 1981; House & Ou, 1992).

Rate constants of sorption and degradation (k_{ads} and k_{deg} respectively) were deduced from first-order kinetic plots. The results are summarised in Tables 2 and 3 and show an intercept close to zero and good correlations, i.e. r^2> 0.6. The correlation coefficients for the first-order plots were consistently higher than the second-order plots. The first-order degradation rate constant for the *cis* isomer is in good agreement with the value of 8.75 x 10^{-6} min^{-1} determined in sandy- loam soils by Jordan *et al.*,(1982) but the value for the *trans* isomer is much smaller in comparison i.e. 34.0 x 10^{-6} min^{-1}.

Table 2. First-order rate constants and standard deviations for the degradation and sorption for *cis* and *trans* permethrin determined from changes in overlying water concentration.

	Permethrin	Type of reaction	k_{ads}/ 10^{-3}min^{-1}
Water	*cis*	sorption	1.57 ± 0.21
Water	*trans*	sorption	1.71 ± 0.22
Sediment	*cis*	sorption	2.72
Sediment	*trans*	sorption	3.01
			k_{deg}/ 10^{-6}min^{-1}
Water	*cis*	degradation	8.04 ± 5.85
Water	*trans*	degradation	8.78 ± 2.44
Sediment	*cis*	degradation	10.44
Sediment	*trans*	degradation	7.43

A statistical t-test (95 % confidence limit) applied to the set of data presented in Table 3 did not show any significant differences between the results from the experiments, *viz*: light/dark, *cis* / *trans* isomers and river water/synthetic solution, with the exception of Experiment 3. This showed higher k_{deg} for the *trans* isomer compared with the *cis*. The t-test also showed no differences in the rate constants over the temperature range measured (Table 1).

Table 3. Degradation rates and half-lives in the different experimental conditions.

Compound	Exp. No.	Conditions	Range $k_{deg}/10^{-6}$ min^{-1}	Half-life/days
cis permethrin	3	Light	6.33	76.0
	3	Dark	5.15	93.5
	4	Light, river water	16.7	28.8
	4	Dark, river water	7.07	68.1
trans permethrin	3	Light	10.08	47.8
	3	Dark	9.78	49.2
	4	Light, river water	10.14	47.5
	4	Dark, river water	5.12	94.0

Uptake of permethrin by the bed-sediment

The mean temperature, pH and dissolved oxygen saturation of the overlying solution was 19.8 °C, 8.8 and 90 % respectively. In the presence of sediment the concentration of permethrin in the solution overlying the sediment decreased rapidly during the first day as shown in Figure 1 with final concentrations after 43 d of 0.03 and 0.01 µg/litre for the *cis* and *trans* isomers respectively. Generally the *trans* isomer was found at a slightly lower concentration than the *cis* isomer throughout the experiment. As expected, the sorption rates in the experiment containing sediment are higher than with water only (Table 2). However, the degradation rates are in the range of values obtained with the channels containing only water (Table 2). After 43 days, permethrin was observed to have penetrated to a maximum depth of 20 mm with a concentration of the *trans* isomer generally higher than the *cis* (Table 4). The profile of total permethrin in Section A was steeper than in Section B which contained an enhanced density of tubificids (Figure 2). The concentrations in the deeper sediment, i.e. > 5 mm, were consistently slightly higher in Section B compared with Section A. The concentration in the biofilm was found to be approximately 470 ng/g (dry weight) for both isomers. Overall the results show that the sediment was a sink for permethrin with 97 % of the total permethrin in the sediment bed.

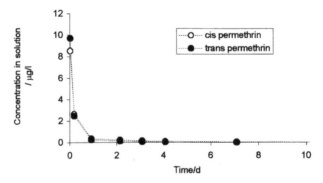

Figure 1. Changes in the solution concentration of the permethrin isomers overlying the bed-sediment in the channel in Experiment 3.

Table 4. Profiles of the isomers and porosity in horizontally sliced sediments. All concentrations expressed as µg/kg (dry weight of sediment). ND: Not Detected.

Depth (mm)	Section A		Section B		Porosity
	cis	trans	cis	trans	
0.5	407	630	108	476	0.74
1.5	272	306	125	350	0.73
2.5	110	164	110	239	0.62
3.5	92	109	80	167	0.86
4.5	65	43	66	103	0.68
7.5	ND	70	57	64	0.54
20	ND	ND	25	ND	0.59
35	ND	ND	ND	ND	0.65
45	ND	ND	ND	ND	0.49

However, the mass balance at the end of the experiment was relatively poor with only 40 % of the initially spike (i.e. 800 µg of total permethrin) accounted for in the overlying solution and sediment. This difference may be a result of several factors including the adsorption of permethrin to the channel sides, degradation in the water and sediment and losses to the biofilm not quantified in the experiment. In particular the concentration found at the first sampling time at t= 15 min was much lower than the expected value of 20 µg/litre for each isomer. This decrease was not caused by adsorption to the channel as a prediction using the rate constant in Table 2 gave a decrease of *ca* 1 µg/litre in 15 min and was too fast for degradation reactions (see above). Hence the reason for this decrease is as yet unknown and further experiments to investigate this are underway.

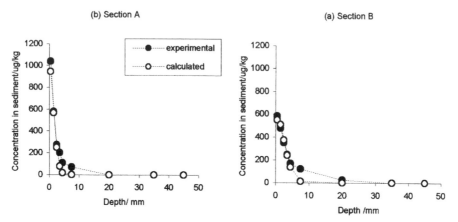

Figure 2. Comparison of the sediment profiles for total permethrin generated by MATHCAD for the effective diffusion coefficient, D=0.85 x 10^{-10} m²/s for Section A and D=2.2 x 10^{-10} m²/s for Section B. The sediment partition coefficient K_d was taken as 652 litres/kg for both isomers.

The movement of total permethrin into the sediment was analysed for the two channel sections: (a) Section A, with no enhancement of worms and (b) Section B, with enhancement of worms. A MATHCAD model was used to optimise agreement in a conservative system between the measured and calculated concentrations in the overlying water and concentrations found in the sediment profile by adjusting an effective diffusion coefficient for a chosen value of the sediment distribution coefficient, K_d (Daniels *et al.*, 1998).

The results from the MATHCAD model are shown in Figure 2 for the two sediment sections, A and B. The sediment partition coefficient was fixed at 652 litre/kg, the average value measured for the isomers in adsorption batch experiments at 10°C after 5 days shaking. The best predictions for the concentrations in the overlying solution were 17.2 and 3.6 µg/litre for Section A and 16.8 and 2.4 µg/litre for Section B at t=15 min and at the end of the experiment respectively. The higher initial concentration (*cf* experimental value of 18.2 µg/litre for the total isomer concentration) and lower final concentration in the solution are consistent with losses through adsorption and degradation not included in this model. The optimised values of the effective diffusion coefficient (Figure 2) are of the expected magnitude and close to the range of 0.5 to 1.6 x 10^{-10} m^2/s found for simazine and lindane in sediment core experiments (Daniels *et al.*, 1998). The higher value found for Section B might reflect bioturbation effects although the dissolved silicon profiles in the porewaters from the two sections were in close agreement.

ACKNOWLEDGEMENT

We thank Dr Patrick Armitage for help with the experiments involving bioturbation. I, Allan thanks NERC for the award of a Ph.D. studentship.

REFERENCES

Daniels W M; House W A; Zhmud B V; Rae J E; Parker A (1998). Diffusive movement of simazine and lindane in river-bed sediments. *Pesticide Science* **54:** 212-222.

House W A; Ou Z (1992). Determination of pesticides on suspended solids and sediment:investigations on the handling and separation. *Chemosphere* **24:** 819-832.

House W A; Long J L A; Rae J E; Parker A; Orr D R (2000). Occurrence and mobility of the insecticide permethrin in rivers in North-East England. *Pest Management Science* **56:** 597-606.

Jordan E G; Kaufman D D; Kayser A J (1982). The effect of soil temperature on the degradation of cis, tran –permethrin in soil. *Journal Environmental Health* **B17:** 1-17.

Long J L A; House W A; Parker A; Rae J E (1998). Micro-organic compounds associated with sediments in the Humber rivers. *Science of the Total Environment* **210/211:** 229-255.

Long J L A; House WA; Parker A; Rae J E (2000). The collection and analysis of river sediments for the investigation of their role in the translocation of micro-organic contaminants. In: *Pesticide/soil interactions*, eds J Cornejo and P Jamet, pp 397-407. INRA: Paris.

Sharom M S; Solomon K R (1981). Adsorption and desorption of permethrin and other pesticides on glass and plastic materials used in bioassay procedures. *Canadian Journal Fisheries and Aquatic Sciences* **38:** 199-204.

Zhmud B V; House W A; Denison F H (1997). Release kinetics and concentration profile of dissolved silicon in compacted sediments. *Journal Chemical Society Faraday Transactions I* **93:** 3473-3478.

Assessment of the environmental properties and effects of pesticide degradation products

A B A Boxall, C J Sinclair

Cranfield Centre for EcoChemistry, Shardlow Hall, Shardlow, Derby, DE72 2GN, UK
Email: a.boxall@cranfield.ac.uk

ABSTRACT

When released into the environment, pesticides may be degraded by plants, micro-organisms and chemical processes. Under EU Directive 91/414/EEC the environmental impact of relevant transformation products needs to be assessed. Currently the only approach for assessing the potential risk of a transformation product is to perform a series of experimental investigations. This is a drain on resources. This study is therefore being performed to 1) explore relationships between parent and metabolite toxicity that can be used to identify potentially relevant metabolites in the future; and 2) assess the use of quantitative structure-activity relationships for predicting metabolite toxicity. A large dataset has been compiled containing information on the ecotoxicity of a range of pesticide metabolites and their parent compounds. The dataset has been used to explore relationships between parent and metabolite ecotoxicity and to test quantitative structure-activity relationship (QSAR) techniques. Results obtained to date indicate that, in general, metabolites are of similar or lower toxicity than the parent compounds. A small proportion of metabolites were more toxic. These differences in toxicity could be explained by an enhancement in the uptake of the metabolite compared to the parent (due to changes in hydrophobicity or dissociation constant) or the presence of pesticidal activity in a metabolite. For a large proportion of substances, predictions of ecotoxicity using a QSAR for daphnids were similar to experimentally-derived data. There were however a large number of substances where toxicity predictions were unreliable.

INTRODUCTION

When released into the environment, plant protection products may be degraded by micro-organisms and/or chemical processes. Under EU Directive 91/414/EEC, the environmental impact of selected pesticide transformation products needs to be assessed. Draft guidelines on the assessment of metabolites have been recently developed (CTB, 1999).

Currently, the only approach for assessing the fate and effects of degradation products is to perform experimental studies (e.g. LC50 fish studies). This is a drain on resources in terms of both cost and time. A more pragmatic approach would be extremely useful, particularly one that could be used in a lower tier of the risk assessment process. This could aid in the identification of relevant metabolites, the results acting as a trigger for relevant experimental work.

One possible alternative is to use information on the properties, biodegradability, ecotoxicity and mode of action of the parent compound along with modelling approaches to predict the environmental fate and effects of degradation products. By using these approaches it may be possible to assess the environmental fate and effects of a metabolite based primarily on its structure. However, before such approaches can be incorporated into the risk assessment process, their suitability for metabolite assessment needs to be demonstrated.

This study is therefore being performed to assess the suitability of these approaches and to develop a framework that integrates predictive approaches and experimental testing to assess the environmental risk of metabolites. This paper presents initial results from the project and includes an assessment of:

1) the relative toxicity of metabolites compared to parent compounds;

2) the suitability of structure-activity relationships for predicting the ecotoxicity of metabolites to non-target organisms.

MATERIALS AND METHODS

An extensive search of the scientific literature, environmental databases and PSD disclosure documents was performed to obtain data on the ecotoxicity of pesticides and their metabolites. The resulting data were input into an Accord for Excel spreadsheet. For those substances where multiple assay values were available, the median value was calculated and these values were used in the analyses described below.

Data on the toxicity of parent compounds and associated metabolites were compared to determine the proportion of metabolites that were more or less toxic than parent compounds. To account for the inherent variability in ecotoxicity test results, a metabolite that was more than an order of magnitude more or less toxic than the parent compound was considered to have either enhanced or reduced toxicity.

The acute toxicity of the metabolites to *Daphnia magna* was predicted using Topkat Version 6.0 (Accelrys, 2001). Topkat is an *in silico* method for predicting the fate, toxicity and ecotoxicity of organic chemicals. The relationships used by the programme are based on high quality data. All predictions obtained using Topkat that satisifed the validation criteria of the programme (i.e. those that were classed by the programme as reliable and within the optimum prediction space) were compared with experimental data to assess the suitability of the programme for predicting metabolite ecotoxicity.

RESULTS

Data were obtained on the ecotoxicity of thirty-five active compounds and forty-seven associated environmental degradation products. The data covered a range of organisms and endpoints including aquatic and terrestrial test species. The compounds covered a wide range of pesticide classes (Table 1).

Table 1. Pesticidal and target class identification of active compounds used in the data analysis. Numbers of parent compounds represented are shown in parentheses

Insecticides	Fungicides	Herbicides
Carbamate (2)	N-trihalomethyl thio (1)	Sulfonylurea (3)
Pyrethroid (2)	Strobilurin analogue (1)	Aryloxyalkanoic acid (2)
Organophosphate (4)	Azole (1)	Quinolinecarboxylic acid (1)
Benzoylurea (1)		Benzonitrile (1)
Oxime carbamate (2)		Chloroacetanilide (1)
Cyclodiene organochloroine (1)		Urea (1)
		1,3,5-triazine (2)
		Aryloxyohenoxypropionate (1)
		Alkanamide (1)
		Anilide (1)
		Bis-carbamate (1)

(* pesticidal classes from Tomlin, 2000) Compounds without class (4)

Comparison of metabolite toxicity with parent toxicity for fish, daphnids and algae (Figure 1, 2 and 3 respectively) indicated that the majority of the metabolites have a toxicity equal to or less than the parent compound.

For fish, only one out of 30 of the metabolites tested was more toxic than the parent, whereas for daphnids, 3 out of 30 metabolites were more toxic than their parent. For algae, all of the metabolites had similar or lower toxicity values than their parent.

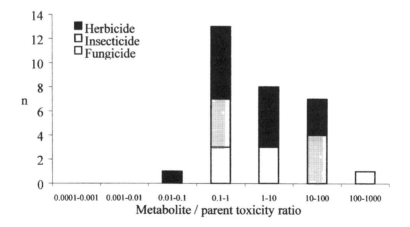

Figure 1. Comparison of metabolite toxicity to parent toxicity to fish (OECD recommended species), 96h LC50.

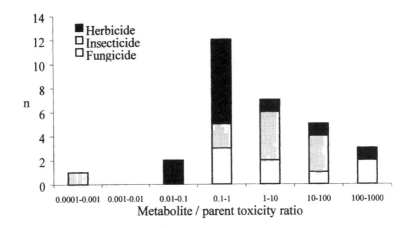

Figure 2. Comparison of metabolite toxicity to parent toxicity to Daphnia (*D. magna* and *D. pulex*), 48h LC50 (mortality) / EC_{50} (intoxiciation).

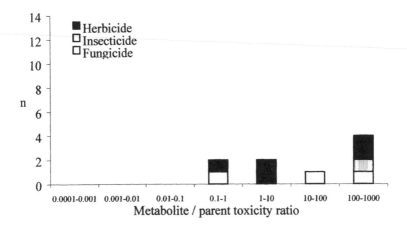

Figure 3. Comparison of metabolite toxicity to parent toxicity to green algae, 72h EC50.

Predictions for a large proportion of the metabolites studied (i.e. 56%) were either outside the Optimum Prediction Space or classified by the Topkat programme as unreliable. These were therefore not considered in the comparison of predicted and experimental data.

Predictions that satisfied all validation criteria were compared to experimentally-derived data (Figure 4). For a large proportion of the substances (61%), predictions were similar to experimental values (i.e. within an order of magnitude). There were however, a number of substances where the predictions differed from experimental values by more than an order of magnitude.

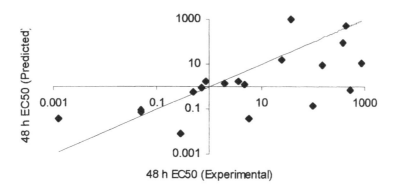

Figure 4. Relationship between experimental and predicted 48 h EC50 values for *Daphnia magna*. The line x=y is shown.

DISCUSSION

When released to the environment pesticides can be subjected to degradation by microorganisms and/or chemicals processes resulting in the formation of metabolites. It is generally thought that these degradation products have less pesticidal activity and lower toxicity than their active parent compounds. The results of this study support this assumption with the majority (94%) of metabolites examined having either similar or lower toxicity than their parent compound.

However, for four metabolites, the toxicity of the metabolite was greater than the toxicity of the parent compound. For two of the metabolites, 3,5,6-trichloro-2-pyridinol (a degradation product of triclopyr) and formaldehyde (a degradation product of glyphosate), the metabolites were more hydrophobic than the parent compounds (based on data from Hansch *et al.*, 1995 and Tomlin, 1997). For these compounds, it is possible therefore that the change in hydrophobicity results in an increased bioconcentration potential and hence increased toxicity.

2,4-dichlorophenol, was more toxic to daphnids than its parent 2,4-D. 2,4-dichlorophenol has a substantially higher pKa value than 2,4-D (i.e. 7.89 compared to 2.73) (Serjeant & Dempsey, 1979; Tomlin, 2000). Therefore under environmental pH conditions, the parent is likely to be more dissociated than the metabolite. The dissociated parent would therefore have a lower bioconcentration factor than the metabolite, explaining the increase in toxicity.

For the organophosphorus compound acephate, the degradation product methamidophos was more toxic than the parent compound. This metabolite is a commercial active ingredient so would be expected to have a specific mode of action.

The suitability of the Topkat programme for predicting the toxicity of metabolites was assessed. Predictions for a large proportion of metabolites obtained were similar to experimentally-derived data. However, there were a number of instances where Topkat either under-predicted or over-predicted metabolite toxicity. The initial work is therefore promising but further work is required before QSARs can be usefully applied in the assessment of metabolite toxicity.

In summary, the work to date has identified a number of possible rules that can be used in the identification of relevant metabolites. Initial assessments of the use of QSARs indicate that the models are suitable for predicting the ecotoxicity of selected compounds. Future work will involve the further expansion and analysis of the database.

ACKNOWLEDGEMENTS

The authors gratefully acknowledge the support of the Pesticides Safety Directorate (DEFRA). Opinions expressed within this paper are those of the authors and do not necessarily reflect the opinion of the sponsoring organisations.

REFERENCES

Accelrys (2001) TOPKAT 6.0: Assessing the toxicity of organic chemicals using QSTR models. Accelrys, Oxford, UK.

CTB (1999) Draft guidance document on relevant metabolites. Document SANCO/221/2000-Rev.2 of October 1999.

Hansch C; Leo A; Hoekma D (1995) Exploring QSAR hydrophobic electronic and steric constants. *ACS Professional Reference Book.* American Chemical Society: Washington DC.

Serjeant E P; Dempsey B (1979). Ionisation constants of organic acids in aqueous solution. Pergamon: Oxford.

Tomlin C D S (1997). *The Pesticide Manual,* Eleventh Edition. British Crop Protection Council: Farnham.

Tomlin C D S (2000). *The e-Pesticide Manual Version 1.1.* British Crop Protection Council: Farnham.

Estimation of standardized transformation rates of a pesticide and its four soil metabolites from field dissipation studies for use in environmental fate modelling

J Dressel

BASF Aktiengesellschaft, Agrarzentrum Limburgerhof, 67114 Limburgerhof, Germany
Email: joachim.dressel@basf-ag.de

C Beigel
BASF Corporation, P.O. Box 400 Princeton, NJ 08543-400, USA

ABSTRACT

In this study, first-order transformation rates of a pesticide and its four main soil metabolites were estimated from results of seven field dissipation studies using the ModelMaker 4.0 software. A standardization procedure was incorporated in the models to calculate degradation rates at reference conditions defined in FOCUS, i.e. soil temperature of 20°C and soil moisture at pF2. The corrections were imple-mented using the same equations as in the FOCUS groundwater models, i.e. the Arrhenius and Walker equations for temperature and moisture, respectively, and the actual daily temperature and soil moisture values measured in the field studies. The resulting transformation rates were evaluated statistically. Estimates of the average field dissipation behavior of the parent compound and its metabolites were provided. The average standardized half-life of the parent was used to successfully predict disappearence in three independent field trials. The main advantages of the standardization method are 1/ it accounts for seasonal climatic variability, and therefore provides an accurate description of the field data, and 2/ the standardized parameters are applicable in a broad range of climate conditions.

INTRODUCTION

Pesticide degradation parameters derived from field studies may be used in the FOCUS tier 1 risk assessment of leaching to groundwater (FOCUS, 2000). The automatic correction of the transformation rates to actual soil temperature and moisture conditions then needs to be dis-abled in the simulation models "unless the modeller attempts to standardise the results ac-counting for differences between field and reference soil temperature/moisture". Without those corrections, the estimated transformation rates can only be used for modeling scenarios with climatic conditions similar to those of the field experiments.

Moreover, the description of field dissipation data with lumped transformation rates is often difficult due to the seasonal variability of the climatic conditions over the study duration. A refined approach standardising the field transformation rates to the FOCUS reference soil moisture and temperature conditions is presented here, that can be used for parent and me-tabolites of a pesticide substance.

METHODS AND MATERIALS

Description of the field dissipation studies

The field dissipation of a pesticide a.i., referred to as parent has been studied on ten bare-soil trial sites, covering a wide spectrum of soil characteristics (texture, organic carbon content, pH), and climatic conditions (temperature, precipitation) representative of arable agriculture in Europe and the USA (Table 1).

At seven sites, soil concentrations of the parent and its four metabolites were available, while at the three other sites only three metabolites were analyzed.

Table 1. Characteristics of the field dissipation trials. Trials 1 to 7 were used for parameter estimation, trials 8 to 10 were used for validation.

Trial	Texture of topsoil, C_{org} [%]/ pH	Trial duration [d]	Number of data points	Soil/air temp. source	Average air temp.	Precipitation measurement, sum	Soil moisture determination (depth used)
1	Loam 2.3 / 7.9 (H_2O)	635	17	nearby	5.7	on site 1146	TDR*, on site (0-0.3 m)
2	Sandy loam, 0.5 / 7.8 (H_2O)	537	18	nearby	17.9	on site 2915	TDR*, on-site (0-0.3 m)
3	Loam, 2.1 / 6.3 (H_2O)	529	18	on site	13.3	on site 2041	TDR*, on site (0-0.3 m)
4	Sandy loam, 0.7 / 5.1 (H_2O)	540	16	nearby	22.0	on site 3067	Calculated (0-0.3 m)
5	Sandy loam, 0.6 / 7.7 ($CaCl_2$)	356	7	nearby	19.0	nearby 896	not measured
6	Sand, 0.5 / 7.7 ($CaCl_2$)	362	7	nearby	17.5	nearby 648	not measured
7	Loamy sand, 1.8 / 5.6 ($CaCl_2$)	368	7	nearby	9.5	nearby 644	not measured
8	Sandy loam, 1.1 / 6.2 ($CaCl_2$)	352	7	nearby	9.5	nearby 672	not measured
9	Loam, 1.2 / 5.0 ($CaCl_2$)	354	8	nearby	9.6	nearby 903	not measured
10	Sandy loam, 0.6 / 5.6 ($CaCl_2$)	357	7	nearby	10.1	nearby 632	not measured

TDR = Time Domain Reflectometry

Model for calculation of standardized dissipation parameters

Based on the proposed route of dissipation of the pesticide in soil, a mathematical compartment model was developed using the parameter estimation and simulation software Model-Maker V.4.0 (Cherwell ScientificPublishing Ltd., Oxford, UK) to describe the field data (Fig. 1). The model was adapted from this general model for the trials where a metabolite was not detected. The model consists of a system of differential equations with specific parameters. Transformation processes (flows) between the compartments were described using first-order reactions. The standardization of transformation parameters to the reference soil temperature (20°C) and moisture (pF2) is shown in the model.

For each standardized degradation rate constant k, a variable k_{act} (t, k, T, θ) was created, representing the actual daily transformation rate, function of time t, the daily temperature T and the daily soil moisture θ listed in the look-up table T1, and calculated using the correction equations of Arrhenius and Walker with the default parameters from FOCUS (2000).

Optimization method and statistics

The transformation rates were optimized using the Marquardt algorithm (ordinary least-squares). The overall coefficient of determination r^2, the standard deviations and type-1 error rates of the estimated parameters, as well as the correlation matrix were determined for each data set. In addition, all distibutions of residuals were evaluated.

The standard deviation $\sigma_{k\ Parent}$ of the lumped degradation rate of the parent molecule, which is the sum of the degradation rates from parent to the metabolite and sink compartments, was calculated from the variances σ^2 of the individual rate constants calculated in ModelMaker:

$$\sigma_{k_{Parent}} = \sqrt{\sum \sigma^2_{k_{individual}}}$$

The type-1 error rates α for the estimated parameters were calculated using a two-sided t-distribution on the ratio $t=\hat{a}_i/\sigma_i$ of the estimated parameter $\hat{a}_i$ and its standard deviation σ_i, with df degrees of freedom: $\alpha = \mathrm{Prob}\,(T \geq |t|; df)$.

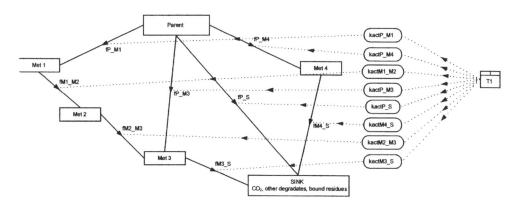

Figure 1.   ModelMaker 4.0 compartment model showing the soil dissipation pathway (solid arrows are mass fluxes) and the implementation of the influence of temperature and soil moisture on dissipation (dotted arrows), via a lookup table T1 containing the daily values.

Calculation of average formation fractions and half-lives

For each individual field trial the molar formation fractions for the metabolites were calculated from the formation rates using the following equation: The mean formation fraction for each metabolite had to be normalized so they sum up to 1 (mass conservation).

$$ff_{met\_i} = \frac{k_{parent \rightarrow met\_i}}{\sum\limits_{j=1,3,4,Sink} k_{parent \rightarrow met\_j}}$$

with ff_{met_i} = molar formation fraction
i = 1, 3, 4, Sink

Calculation of average half-lives

From the standardized transformation rates k_{Parent} and k_{M1_M2}, k_{M2_M3}, K_{M3_Sink}, and k_{M4_Sink} obtained from the parameter optimization procedure, the half-live values $t_{1/2}$ for each molecule at each trial site were calculated using the equation: $t_{1/2}=\ln 2/k$. Only the half-lives with a type-1 error rate of less than 5 % were considered significant and averaged arithmetically.

RESULTS

Description of soil dissipation by first-order kinetics

Examples of the results of the optimizations performed with the compartment model (with standardization) are listed in Table 2 for site 4. The optimized kinetic parameters obtained for parent and metabolites are given with their standard deviation, type-1-error rate, the significance decision, and the half-life corresponding to the reported rate, and with the overall coefficients of determination r^2 of the optimization.

The dissipation of parent, equivalent to the sum of the transformation to the metabolites 1, 3, and 4, and to the sink, was well described in all sites, as shown in Figure 2 for site 4. Here, for all substances except Met 2 the model described the data very well, which was also reflected by the statistical evaluation: The dissipation rates of all substances but Met 2 could be shown to be significant in site 4.

Overall, the measured data for all sites were well described by the first-order compartment models with corrections for temperature and soil moisture ($r^2 = 0.94$ to 0.99). This was confirmed by the significance levels of the lumped rate constants of the dissipation of the parent compound of about 95% for site 1, and above 99.9% for all other locations, indicating that the parameters contribute significantly to the fits, and therefore can be estimated by this procedure. The standard deviations of the lumped parameters are low, indicating that the estimates are reliable. In addition, the residuals were evenly distributed.

cance ranging from about 92% for one site, to above 95% for two other sites, to more than 99.9% for the three remaining sites. Overall, the residuals were evenly distributed. The description of the disappearance of metabolites 1, 2, and 3 was more difficult and gave variable results.

Still, the type-1-error rates of the individual parameters showed a level of significance about or above 95% for three, two, and five of the seven sites. The distribution of the residuals was therefore not equally good for all sites.

Calculation of field degradation half-lives

The half-life values of the field degradation of the parent and metabolites standardized to reference conditions, calculated from the estimated rate constants are listed in

Table 3. The standardized half-life for the parent compound varied from less than 3 d at one site to about 33 d at two sites. The average half-life in the seven field dissipation trials was 14.1 d.

Using this half-life for prediction, the field dissipation of the parent in the three independent trials was described accurately. The standardized half-lives varied from 57 to 90 d for Met 1, 10 to 126 d for Met 2, 19 to 116 d for Met 3, and 3 to 13 d for Met 4. The average field half-lives of Met 1, Met 2, Met 3 and Met 4 are 70, 68, 70 and 10 d, respectively.

Calculation of the formation of the metabolites

The fractions of the metabolites formed from the degradation of the parent compound are listed in

Table 4. Met 2 is formed from Met 1 and therefore not listed. The formation fractions of the metabolites 1, 3, and 4 range from 5 to 37 %, 7 to 34 %, and 9 to 59 % and reflect natural variability of the degradation process.

The transformation fractions to the sink compartment range from 2 to 86 % and indicate a natural variability in the formation of bound residues, other de gradates or CO_2. The normalized arithmetic means of the formation fractions of Met 1, Met 3, and Met 4 were 17.1, 16.5, and 32.9 %, whereas the average transformation to the sink compartment amounted to 33.5 %.

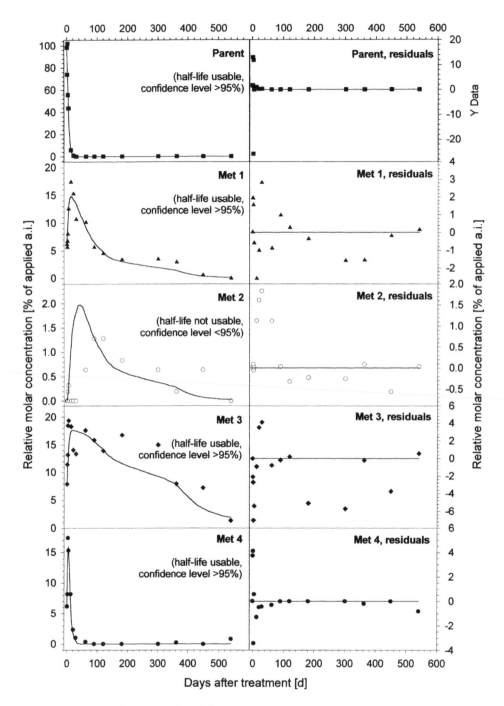

Figure 2.   Left: Measured and fitted residues of parent and the four metabolites at site 4. Right: Corresponding distribution of residuals.

Table 2: Site 4: optimization results (79 degrees of freedom, r^2=0.9556).

Parameter	Estimated rate [d^{-1}]	Standard deviation [d^{-1}]	Type-1 error rate	Significance (95% confidence level)	Corresponding half-life [d]
k_{P_M1}	0.0289	0.0025	1.16E-18	+	
k_{P_M3}	0.0299	0.0006	1.88E-61	+	
k_{P_M4}	0.0985	0.0025	1.05E-53	+	
k_{P_Sink}	0.1093	0.0003	3.46E-129	+	
k_{Parent}	**0.2666**	**0.0036**	**9.2E-75**	**+**	**2.6**
k_{M1_M2}	0.0121	0.0028	4.47E-05	+	57.3
k_{M2_M3}	0.0723	0.0532	0.1780	-	9.6
k_{M3_Sink}	0.0093	0.0004	4.46E-37	+	74.5
k_{M04_Sink}	0.2761	0.0133	9.91E-34	+	2.5

Table 3. Half life values of Parent and Metabolites in 7 field trials corresponding to the lumped, standardized degradation rates k (Table 2, Figure 2).

Site	1	2	3	4	5	6	7	Arithmetic mean
Parent	32.5	32.7	5.4	2.6	11.0	5.9	8.4	**14.1**
Met 1	n.s.	62.4	90.0	57.3	n.s.	n.s.	n.s.	**69.9**
Met 2	n.s.	126.0	9.5	n.s.	n.s.	n.a.	n.a.	**67.7**
Met 3	n.s.	115.5	47.2	74.5	66.0	n.s.	18.6	**64.4**
Met 4	4.1	5.6	23.1	2.5	n.s.	n.a.	13.0	**9.7**

n.s.: non-significant, confidence level of the estimated degradation rate < 95%
n.a.: non-applicable, no significant levels of the compound detected in the field trial

Table 4. Molar formation fractions of the metabolites directly formed by the degradation of BAS 635 H.

From parent	1 [%]	2 [%]	3 [%]	4 [%]	5 [%]	6 [%]	7 [%]	Mean [%]	Normalized mean [%]
Met 1	10.8	10.3	23.5	31.1	5.1	7.2	37.4	17.9	17.1
Met 3	11.2	17.8	25.6	7.1	19.2	6.6	33.7	17.3	16.5
Met 4	36.9	54.0	21.0	59.4	9.4		26.5	34.5	32.9
Sink	41.0	17.8	29.8	2.4	66.4	86.2	2.4	35.1	33.5
Sum	100.0	100.0	100.0	100.0	100.0	100.0	100.0	104.9	100.0

CONCLUSION

Average standardized halflives and formation fractions were estimated from field studies for a parent and its metabolites after exclusion of non-acceptable datasets by statistical criteria. The resulting standardized parameters were used successfully to predict the transformation of the parent in three independent trial sites. The standardization is doubly advantageous as it allows a more accurate description of the field data over the seasons, and the standardized rates are valid for the prediction of environmental concentrations under a variety of climatic conditions.

REFERENCES

FOCUS (2000). *FOCUS groundwater scenarios in the EU review of active substances,* report of the FOCUS groundwater scenarios workgroup, EC Doc. Ref. SANCO/321/2000 rev.2.

Degradation of isoxaflutole and metabolites in surface and subsoils under field conditions

R L Jones, I A J Hardy, R E Lee, K M Hurst
Aventis CropScience, 2 T W Alexander Drive, Research Triangle Park, NC 27709-2014, USA
Email: russell.jones@aventis.com

ABSTRACT

Field studies conducted with isoxaflutole in 1999 and 2000 included soil sampling at five locations in the United States. Parent isoxaflutole degraded rapidly with a half-life less than 4 days. The biologically active metabolite RPA 202248 degraded with a half-life of 1 to 3 weeks. Degradation rates for the biologically inactive metabolite RPA 203328 were not determined but appeared to be somewhat faster than for RPA 202248. Degradation rates measured in these studies were similar to those observed in previous field dissipation studies conducted in the U.S. and Europe. At two of the sites, heavy rainfall following application resulted in small amounts of the two metabolites moving via preferential flow into subsoils. Since no further movement of surface residues into subsoils occurred, degradation rates in surface and subsoils could be compared. At both locations degradation of the two metabolites in the subsoils continued at a rate comparable to the degradation of the metabolites remaining in the surface soil.

INTRODUCTION

Isoxaflutole is the active ingredient in Balance herbicide, which is applied prior to emergence to control weeds in maize. Degradation of isoxaflutole and its two principal soil metabolites (RPA 202248, a diketonitrile metabolite and RPA 203328, a benzoic acid metabolite) is primarily by soil organisms (Figure 1 presents chemical structures) although parent can also degrade by hydrolysis. Isoxaflutole rapidly degrades to RPA 202248, which in turn degrades to RPA 203328, which finally degrades to carbon dioxide. RPA 202248 is biologically active while RPA 203328 in biologically inactive. All three compounds are relatively mobile in soil (Koc values of 122, 92, and 69 mL/g for parent, RPA 202248, and RPA 203328, respectively), are essentially non-volatile, and do not degrade by photolysis in soil.

Figure 1. Chemical structures of isoxaflutole and its two principal metabolites.

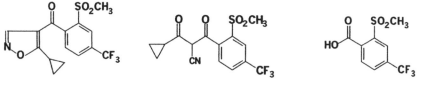

| Isoxaflutole | RPA 202248 | RPA 203328 |

Field studies in the United States in 1999 and 2000 included soil sampling following carefully controlled applications at five test sites. This paper reports the dissipation rates measured in these studies. Since losses by other mechanisms such as runoff, leaching, drainage, photolysis, and volatilization were minor compared to degradation, the dissipation rates measured in these studies are close to the actual degradation rates in soil.

MATERIALS AND METHODS

Applications of isoxaflutole at a rate of 157 g/ha were made to two 1.8 ha test plots in Nebraska and Iowa in spring 1999. In spring 2000 isoxaflutole was applied at a rate of 102 g/ha to a 1.8 ha test plot in La Porte County, Indiana and at a rate of 157 g/ha to two larger plots of 30 and 11 ha in Allen and Owen Counties in Indiana. Table 1 provides a brief description of the properties of the surface soil at each of the five locations. The application rate was confirmed by analysis of 16 filter paper samples collected immediately after application. At each site soil cores were also collected immediately after application and 0.25, 0.5, 1, 2, 4, and 6 months after application. At each sampling interval, 16 soil cores were collected (four from each of four subplots) in 0.15 m depth increments. The depth of the core varied from 0.15 m for the samples collected immediately after application to a depth of up to 1.2 m depending on the position of residues in the soil profile. Cores taken immediately after application were collected by pushing a 75 mm diameter tube into the soil. The remaining samples were collected by a 83 mm bucket auger with appropriate procedures to avoid contamination during the raising and lowering of the auger. All samples were thoroughly mixed in the field and subsampled to provide the necessary volume for analysis. At the Nebraska, Iowa, and La Porte, Indiana sites, samples collected 2 months and later were composited to provide one sample per depth per subplot. At the other two Indiana locations, samples were similarly composited except for those collected immediately after application.

Table 1. Surface soil properties in the five U.S. studies conducted in 1999 and 2000.

Location	Properties of the Surface Soil (0-0.3 m)		
	Soil Texture	Organic Matter (%)	pH
Merrick County, Nebraska	loam	2.0	5.8
Sioux County, Iowa	loam	5.7	6.7
La Porte County, Indiana	sandy loam	3.5	5.8
Allen County, Indiana	silty clay	3.0	7.4
Owen County, Indiana	silt loam	1.6	6.2

Residues of isoxaflutole and its two principal metabolites were extracted from soil samples by shaking in an acetonitrile: 0.8 % formic acid solution for fifteen minutes. The mixture was centrifuged, and the supernatant diluted to the desired concentration for analysis by LC/MS/MS using a C-8 column and ^{13}C internal standards. The limit of quantification was

0.4 ng/g for parent isoxaflutole and RPA 202248 and 2 ng/g for RPA 203328. The limit of detection was 0.11 ng/g for parent isoxaflutole, 0.04 ng/g for RPA 202248, and 0.29 ng/g for RPA 203328.

The amount of parent and the two metabolites remaining in the soil as a function of depth was calculated from the soil concentrations, bulk density, and the depth increment. Model Manager Version 1.1, (Cherwell Scientific) was used to determine the dissipation rates of parent and RPA 202248.

RESULTS AND DISCUSSION

The degradation rates from Model Manager expressed as half-lives from the five test sites are shown in Table 2. Parent degraded quite rapidly at all locations with a half-life of 2-4 days and the biologically active metabolite RPA 202248 degraded with a half-life of about 1-3 weeks. The shorter half- life at the Allen County, Indiana location was due mainly to a low value obtained at one sampling interval so the actual degradation rate at this location was probably not significantly different from the other four locations. Figure 2 shows the disappearance of parent isoxaflutole and the rise and decline of RPA 202248 for the La Porte County, Indiana site. The pattern was similar at the other four sites.

Table 2. Degradation rates of isoxaflutole and RPA 202248 observed in the five U.S. studies conducted in 1999 and 2000 (from Model Manager).

Location	Half-Life (days) for Specified Compound	
	Isoxaflutole	RPA 202248
Merrick County, Nebraska	2.6	14
Sioux County, Iowa	2.3	19
La Porte County, Indiana	3.7	20
Allen County, Indiana	NC	14*
Owen County, Indiana	NC	7*

NC Not calculated due to high amounts of RPA 202248 in initial samples.
*Calculated from total parent isoxaflutole plus RPA 202248 residues

The degradation rates observed in the 1999 and 2000 studies are similar to the degradation rates observed in the field dissipation studies previously conducted in the United States and Europe (Table 3). The slow degradation rate at the California site was probably the result of the extremely dry soil conditions for several months prior to the start of the study. The half-lives for RPA 202248 in Table 3 are not directly comparable with the half-lives in Table 2. The half-lives for RPA 202248 in Table 3 were calculated with a simple regression using only the data RPA 202248 after the peak concentration was reached, ignoring the degradation in the first few days of the study as well as the formation of RPA 202248 after the peak concentration was reached. Thus, the half-lives of RPA 202248 in Table 3 represent an upper bound on the actual half-life values. For example, the half-lives of RPA 202248 for the Goch and Manningtree locations calculated using Model Manager (which includes degradation of RPA 202248 occurring at the start of the study as well as the effect of formation of RPA 202248 throughout the study) were 17 and 10 days, respectively.

Figure 2. Residues of isoxaflutole and RPA 202248 as a function of time in days at the La Porte County, Indiana site. The fitted lines are those for the half-life values reported in Table 2 (this figure was generated by Model Manager).

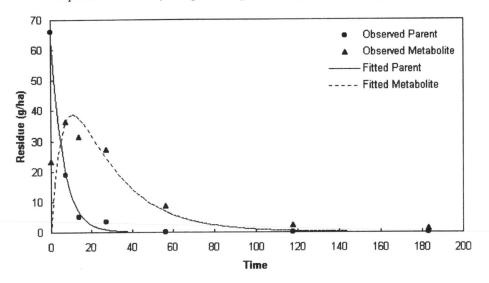

Table 3. Degradation rates observed in previous field dissipation studies conducted with isoxaflutole in the United States and Europe.

Location	Half-Life (days) for Specified Compound	
	Isoxaflutole	RPA 202248
U.S Field Dissipation Studies		
San Juan Baustista, California	1.4	125
York, Nebraska	1.5	8
Clayton, North Carolina	3.0	16
Euphrata, Washington	2.2	13
European Field Dissipation Studies		
Mereville, France	0.7	16
Goch, Germany	1.7	24
Bologna, Italy	0.5	22
Manningtree, United Kingdom	0.9	17

The degradation rates of the non-biologically active metabolite RPA 203328 at each of the test sites were not determined because of the relatively small amount formed and its continuous formation and degradation. Residues of RPA 203328 peaked at 10-22 percent of applied in the 0.5 to 1 month samples and appeared to degrade at a faster rate than RPA 202248, although its continuous formation meant that concentrations of this metabolite were present when RPA 202248 was also present.

At two of the sites, Merrick County, Nebraska, and Sioux County, Iowa, heavy rainfall during the month following application resulted in standing water in the corn fields and a small amount of the two metabolites moving into subsoils via preferential flow. Since little movement of residues in the soil profile occurred after one month following application, this provided an opportunity to compare degradation rates observed in subsoils and surface soils. Given the limitations imposed by the variability of the data, this examination indicates that the degradation rates in surface soils and subsoils were approximately the same. This is illustrated by Figures 3 and 4, which show the dissipation of residues at the surface and below 30 cm at the Nebraska and Iowa test sites. At the Nebraska site, the dissipation of both RPA 202248 and RPA 203328 below 0.3 m was as fast as in the surface soils. At the Iowa site, the degradation rates in surface and subsoils were similar through about four months. The variability in the six month data was probably associated with the low amount of residues present at this time interval (only about 0.1 to 1 percent of applied). With such small amounts of material remaining the increased variability would be expected due to local heterogeneity in degradation rates as well as lack of precision in analytical results since concentrations are below the limit of quantification. Based on the rainfall occurring between four and six months, the increase in RPA 202248 levels during this time period was not due to movement from surface soils to subsoils.

Figure 3. Effect of depth on degradation of RPA 202248 (DKN) and RPA 203328 (BA) at the Nebraska test site. The lines represent the amount of residues remaining from 1-6 months after application at the soil surface and below 0.3 m.

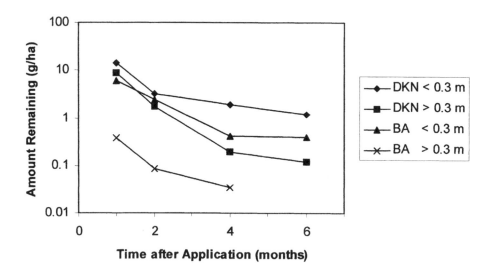

Figure 4. Effect of depth on degradation of RPA 202248 (DKN) and RPA 203328 (BA) at the Iowa test site. The lines represent the amount of residues remaining from 1-6 months after application at the surface and below 0.3 m.

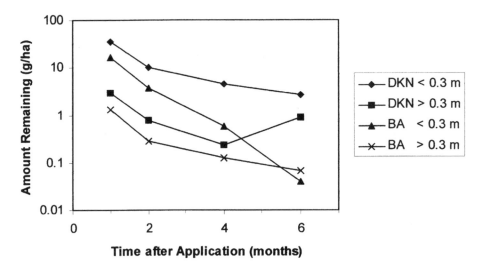

CONCLUSIONS

Field studies conducted at five U.S. locations with isoxaflutole in 1999 and 2000 showed that parent isoxaflutole degraded rapidly with a half-life of under 4 days and the biologically active metabolite RPA 202248 degraded with a half-life of 1 to 3 weeks. These degradation rates were similar to those observed in previous field dissipation studies conducted in the U.S. and Europe. At two of the sites, where heavy rainfall following application resulted in small amounts of the two metabolites moving via preferential flow into subsoils, degradation continued at a rate comparable to the degradation of the metabolites remaining in the surface soils.

Evidence for the enhanced degradation of metalaxyl in UK carrot soils

S R Kenny, J G White, A Walker
Horticulture Research International, Wellesbourne, Warwick, CV35 9EF, UK
Email: Sian.Kenny@hri.ac.uk

ABSTRACT

Laboratory studies were carried out to determine the rates of degradation of metalaxyl in soils from nine fields in which metalaxyl had been used extensively as a soil treatment for the control of cavity spot disease in carrots. In all these fields, the fungicide had failed to control the disease in recent years. A further carrot field was sampled to which metalaxyl had never been applied. Soil samples were taken from 10 stations within each field and each sample was processed individually. Sub-samples of the 10 were also bulked to produce a composite sample for each field. The time taken for 50 % of the fungicide to be degraded (DT_{50}) was calculated using GENSTAT 5, fitting Gompertz or linear regressions to the data. Comparisons were made between the regressions fitted for the composite samples and the average of those fitted for the 10 stations. In fields where the fungicide failed, the DT_{50} values varied from 4 to 14 days. The composite samples produced DT_{50} values that were comparable (4 to 15 days). In the field where no metalaxyl had been applied the average DT_{50} for the 10 stations was 46 days compared with 43 days from the composite sample. A second study was carried out with soil samples from two fields adjacent to one another. One field had no previous history of metalaxyl application whilst the other had a history of application and failure in the control of cavity spot. The DT_{50} values for metalaxyl degradation in soils from these fields were 39.3 and 13.2 days, respectively.

INTRODUCTION

Cavity spot disease of carrots in the UK is largely due to the metalaxyl-sensitive fungus *Pythium violae*. It produces sunken lesions on the carrot root, and is particularly damaging in years of high rainfall. Control of the disease has relied on the use of metalaxyl and, more recently, metalaxyl-M, applied between drilling and first true leaf stage. In recent years deterioration in the performance of metalaxyl has been observed in some fields, both by growers on their own field sites and by scientists during cavity spot field experiments (McPherson, pers. comm.). Populations of the pathogen have been continuously monitored for metalaxyl resistance, using the method of White *et al.*,(1988), but no resistance to metalaxyl has been found.

Various studies have established that metalaxyl is subject to degradation by soil microorganisms (Bailey & Coffey 1985; Droby & Coffey 1991). Recent studies in Western Australia have shown that reduced persistence of metalaxyl in fields used for carrot production is associated with previous metalaxyl use (Davison & McKay 1999). This study aims to examine the persistence of metalaxyl in fields used for carrot production in the UK, and to compare persistence in two adjacent fields with different metalaxyl treatment histories.

MATERIALS AND METHODS

Site selection and sampling methods

Nine fields were identified by UK carrot growers, as having received metalaxyl applications over several years, and recent crop failure due to cavity spot despite metalaxyl use. One field was also identified at HRI Wellesbourne as having no previous history of metalaxyl use.

For each field, approximately 1 kg of top soil was collected from each of 10 stations within the field, along a 250 – 300 m transect. The trowels used for sampling were washed and disinfected between stations and fields to prevent cross contamination between samples. A composite sample was produced for each field by bulking together an equal quantity of soil from each of the 10 station samples, and mixing well. All samples were stored at 5°C prior to the laboratory incubations.

Control soils were difficult to obtain, and despite collecting soil samples from untreated areas like headlands, comparison of these soils with the field samples often revealed considerable differences in characteristics such as pH, making the soils unsuitable as controls.

To address this, a second study was carried out with soil from a further two fields located adjacent to one another. One field had received a number of metalaxyl applications together with a recent metalaxyl-treated carrot crop with cavity spot; the other field had no metalaxyl pre-treatment history. Soil samples were collected from 5 stations within the treated field. These samples were processed separately and bulked to produce a composite sample. Soil was also collected from 5 stations in the untreated field and processed as one bulked sample which was divided to produce 2 replicate subsamples.

Sample preparation and residue analysis

When handling soil, new or autoclaved equipment was used for each sample, and the bench was sprayed with industrial methylated spirit between samples. All soils were sieved to 3mm, and the maximum water holding capacity (MWHC) of the soil from each field was assessed using soil from the composite samples. In addition the moisture content of individual samples was determined and, where necessary, they were air-dried to reduce the water content to below 40 % of the MWHC.

Analytical (99.6 %, Novartis) and technical (97.4 %, Novartis) grade metalaxyl were used throughout the study. A solution of technical metalaxyl (0.5 g/l in water) was pipetted onto the soil sample to give a concentration of 10 mg/kg dry soil and the samples were thoroughly mixed and then transferred to 500 ml pots. For fields 1-4 there were two replicate pots per soil sample. For fields 5-10 this was reduced to one pot per sample. Sterilised distilled water (SDW) was pipetted around the edge of the pots to increase the moisture level to 40 % of the MWHC. The lids were replaced loosely and pots were incubated at 15°C. Sub-samples of soil (15 g) were taken on d 0 and at regular intervals thereafter. On each sampling occasion any water lost from pots was replaced with SDW.

Metalaxyl was extracted from each 15 g sub-sample by shaking with 20 ml methanol for 50 min on a wrist-action shaker. The soil samples were allowed to settle for at least 10 min. Samples of clear supernatant were removed and analysed by hplc using a LiChrospher-RP18 (5μm) column and acetonitrile: water: orthophosphoric acid (70: 30: 0.25 by volume) eluant at a flow rate of 1 ml min^{-1}; detection was by UV absorbance at 210 nm. The retention time of metalaxyl was 3.5 min. The response on hplc was calibrated against a 5 mg/l analytical grade metalaxyl standard.

RESULTS AND DISCUSSION

Examples of the soil residue data are shown in Figures 1, 2 and 3 for fields 1, 5, and 10 respectively. They illustrate the results from the individual soils and those from the composite samples for each field. The times taken for 50 % loss of the metalaxyl (DT_{50}) were determined by fitting either a Gompertz curve or a linear regression as appropriate, using GENSTAT 5. This was carried out for each of the composite samples and by grouping data for each of the 10 stations within the field. The estimated DT_{50} values are listed in Table 1.

Table 1.   Comparison of the DT_{50} (d) derived from fitting of the Gompertz equations or linear regressions to data from the composite sample and 10-station samples.

	DT_{50} (d) of fitted curves / linear regressions	
Field identification number	10 stations processed individually	Composite sample
1	14.4	14.9
2	8.1	8.8
3	8.2	9.0
4	9.2	8.9
5	9.7	8.3
6	3.7	3.6
7	4.0	3.5
8	6.8	5.5
9	7.5	7.1
10	45.7	42.7

Considerable variation in the rate of degradation of metalaxyl was seen between soils from the different fields. The highest DT_{50} value (45.7 d) was recorded in soil from the field (number 10) with no history of metalaxyl treatment, with metalaxyl persisting in all samples for 72 d or more. Despite the variable degradation rate within this field (Figure 3), the DT_{50} of metalaxyl in the composite sample was similar to that based on the regression for the data from the 10 stations.

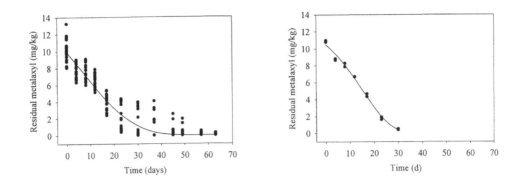

Figure 1.   Comparison of metalaxyl degradation between the 10-station (left) and composite (right) soil samples from field 1.

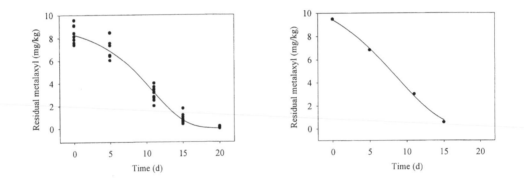

Figure 2.   Comparison of metalaxyl degradation between the 10-station (left) and composite (right) soil samples from field 5.

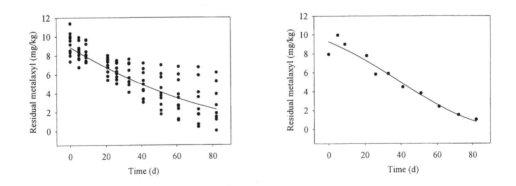

Figure 3.   Comparison of metalaxyl degradation between the 10-station (left) and composite (right) soil samples from field 10.

In soil from nine fields with metalaxyl treatment histories, eight (fields 2-9) had half-lives of less than 10 d (e.g. Figure 2). This parallels the work of Davison & McKay (1999) in Western Australia where half-lives in soil from 3 fields, each with a metalaxyl treatment history and a failed crop, was 10 d or less. In soil from their field with no previous metalaxyl use and successful control of cavity spot, the half-life was 82 d.

Field 1 exhibited the greatest variability in degradation rates between soil samples from the different stations, with metalaxyl persisting in soil samples from 3 stations for over 60 d but at other stations disappearing within 30 d (Figure 1). In soil from all nine fields where performance of the chemical had been poor and disease levels were at or near crop write-off, the DT_{50} was between 4 and 14 d. By bulking together soil samples from individual stations within a field to produce a composite sample, a good indication of metalaxyl performance was still achieved (DT_{50} values of 4 to 15 d). This would appear to be a good approach for soil sampling to predict the behaviour of the fungicide in a particular field.

In the second study with soil from two adjacent fields with similar properties, the degradation rate of metalaxyl was considerably faster in soil from the treated field compared to the untreated field (Figure 4), with DT_{50} values of the bulked composite samples of 13.2 and 39.3 d respectively. Since these fields were located next to each other, were of the same pH, and other properties, yet differed in their metalaxyl treatment histories, this would suggest enhanced microbial degradation of the fungicide was occuring at this site.

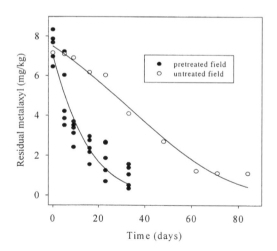

Figure 4.   Comparison of metalaxyl degradation between soil samples from fields with and without pretreatment histories.

Studies have shown that the timing of metalaxyl application is an important factor in the control of cavity spot disease of carrots, and there appears to be a crucial time early in the life of a crop when protection from the pathogen is essential. Gladders & McPherson (1986) found the best control was achieved with metalaxyl (+ mancozeb) applications made between sowing and four weeks post-crop emergence. Clearly, if the fungicide persists for less time in the soil, crop protection will be reduced.

Metalaxyl, and the recently introduced metalaxyl-M, are the only reliable fungicides for the control of cavity spot and are still effective in the vast majority of carrot production areas. Reports of failure of the fungicide on a small number of fields is a cause for concern and these experiments show that enhanced biodegradation could be factor at some of these sites.

ACKNOWLEDGEMENTS

This research was funded by the Horticultural Development Council (HDC). Thanks to UK carrot growers who provided sites and information on cavity spot incidence and metalaxyl histories, Julie Jones for statistical assistance, and Novartis for supplying metalaxyl and advice.

REFERENCES

Bailey A M; Coffey M D (1985). Biodegradation of metalaxyl in avocado soils. *Phytopathology* **75**: 135-137.

Davison E M; McKay A G (1999). Reduced persistence of metalaxyl in soil associated with its failure to control cavity spot of carrots. *Plant Pathology* **48**: 830-835.

Droby S; Coffey M D (1991). Biodegradation and the nature of metabolism of metalaxyl in soil. *Annals of Applied Biology* **118**: 543-553.

Gladders P; McPherson G M (1986). Control of cavity spot in carrots with fungicides. *Aspects of Applied Biology* **12**: 223-233.

White J G; Stanghellini M E; Ayoubi L M (1988). Variation in the sensitivity to metalaxyl of *Pythium* spp. isolated from carrot and other sources. *Annals of Applied Biology* **113**: 269-277.

Degradation of linuron in soils as influenced by different organic amendments and surfactants

M S Rodríguez-Cruz, M J Sánchez-Martín, M Sánchez-Camazano

Instituto de Recursos Naturales y Agrobiología, CSIC, Apdo. 257, 37071 Salamanca, Spain
Email: masorocruz@hotmail.com

ABSTRACT

A study has been made of the influence of contrasting organic amendments and two surfactants on the rate and pathway of linuron degradation in soil. Degradation of the herbicide and the presence of its metabolites were assessed in unamended and amended soil under non-sterilized and sterilized conditions. The results pointed to an inhibition of degradation by liquid humic amendment and peat, an enhanced microbiological degradation by city refuse compost and an inhibition of microbiological degradation by the surfactants, which at the same time favoured chemical degradation of the herbicide. These results demonstrate that the organic amendments and surfactants modify the rate and pathway of linuron degradation in soil. These modifications could be valuable when using simultaneously organic amendments and pesticides in agricultural practices and when using surfactants in technologies for the prevention of pollution and the recovery of soil polluted by hydrophobic organic compounds.

INTRODUCTION

The use of organic amendments and organic residues in agricultural practices has increased considerably in recent years. On the other hand the development of physico-chemical techniques based on the use of surfactants for the prevention of pollution and the recovery of soils polluted by hydrophobic organic compounds is also on the increase. In view of the importance of soil organic matter for the adsorption and mobility of hydrophobic organic compounds in soils, much research has been carried out on the effects that the addition of such organic materials to the soil may have on these processes. However, although such additions may modify the chemical and biological conditions of the soil, little attention has been paid to the effect of amendments and surfactants on the rate and pathway of pesticide degradation.

Linuron is a herbicide belonging to the phenylurea group that is widely used in different types of cultivation. Its degradation in the soil may occur through biochemical, chemical and photochemical mechanisms, giving the following transformation products: N-(3,4-dichlorophenyl-N'-methyl-urea) (M1), N-(3,4-dichlorophenyl-N'-methoxy-urea) (M2), N-(3,4-dichlorophenyl-urea) (M3), and 3,4-dichloro-aniline (M4) (Maier & Härtel 1981). As a result of these processes, its persistence in the soil varies considerably and depends on the characteristics of the soil and the environmental conditions under which it is applied (Walker 1976; Walker & Welch 1991). Studies on the adsorption and mobility of linuron in soils have shown that soil organic matter content is the main parameter involved in these processes (Sánchez-Camazano *et al.*, 2000). Additionally, studies of the effects of agricultural organic amendments and surfactants (Iglesias-Jiménez et al., 1997) on the adsorption of linuron by soils have been carried out. However, to date the effects of the addition of agricultural organic amendments, city refuse compost, and surfactants to the soil on the persistence and degradation of linuron have not been addressed.

In this work, we studied the effect of three organic amendments and two surfactants on the rate and pathway of linuron degradation in soil. The degradation of the herbicide and the presence of its metabolites were assessed in unamended and amended soil under non-sterilized and sterilized conditions.

MATERIALS AND METHODS

The surface horizon (0-15 cm) of a sandy loam soil (<2 mm fraction) with the following characteristics: pH 7.5; organic matter 0.67%; clay 18.1%; silt 15.5% and sand 64.0% was used.

The organic amendments employed were the following: a city refuse compost (CRC) from the urban solid waste treatment plant at Valdemingomez (Madrid, Spain), two commercial organic amendments used in agricultural practices, Grün Garant peat (P) (Deutsche Torfgesellschoft GmbH, Saterland Scharrel, Germany), Humimag liquid humic amendment (LHA) (Braker Laboratories, S. L. Valencia, Spain), and two surfactants, sodium dodecyl sulfate (SDS), an anionic surfactant, and tetradecyltrimethylammonium bromide (TDTMA), a cationic surfactant. Both surfactants were supplied by Aldrich Chemical Co. (Milwaukee, USA). The total organic carbon contents of the amendments were as follows: 28.1% for CRC; 34.7% for P; 22.1% for LHA; 49.9% for SDS; and 60.6% for TDTMA.

Linuron (>99% technical purity) was supplied by Riedel de Häen (Hannover, Germany) and the M1, M2, M3, and M4 (>98% technical purity) metabolites of linuron were supplied by AgrEvo (Valencia, Spain). Linuron is a solid hydrophobic pesticide with a water solubility of 81 mg/litre at 25 °C and a Kow of 1010 (Tomlin 1995).

Fifty grams of unamended soil (as control) and fifty grams of soil amended with the different organic amendments at doses equivalent at 15 t/ha (as total carbon) were placed in covered aluminium cups. The degradation of linuron was studied in non-sterilized and sterilized amendment-soil mixes to elucidate the mechanisms of degradation. Non-sterilized mixes were prepared by directly mixing the organic amendment with the soil, and sterilized mixes were obtained by autoclaving the mixes twice at 120°C for 30 min each time. The sterilized samples were handled aseptically prior to and during the incubation. Before incubation, the water content was adjusted with distilled water to 80% of the field capacity and this moisture content was maintained weekly with distilled water.

Methanol (3 ml) containing 1mg/ml of linuron was then added to the cups and the treated cups were incubated under temperature conditions of 28 ±2°C. At time intervals between 0 and 210 days, three replicates of 5 g were taken and shaken for 24 h with 10 ml of methanol for residue analysis. The standard relative deviations of the results obtained for the replicates were always less than 5%.

The concentrations of linuron and its metabolites in the methanol solution were determined by hplc by the method described previously by Sánchez-Martín *et al.,* (1996) for linuron determination. The apparatus used was a Waters chromatograph (Waters Assoc., Milford, USA) equipped with a model 600E multisolvent delivery system attached to a model 717 autosampler, a model 996 photodiode array detector, and a Millennium 2010 chromatography manager data acquisition and processing system. The detection limits of linuron and its metabolites were 0.010µg/ml. The extraction efficiency measured previously with soil samples spiked with different amounts of linuron was >92%.

RESULTS AND DISCUSSION

Figure 1 shows the degradation kinetics of linuron in the soil unamended and amended with the different organic materials under non-sterilised and sterilised conditions as estimated from the amounts of non-degraded linuron measured in methanol extracts from the samples during the incubation. Fitted to first-order kinetics, the data obtained allow calculation of the rate constant (K) of linuron degradation and the half-life (DT50) of the herbicide. Table 1 shows the K and DT50 values for the linuron degradation in unamended soil and soil amended with the different organic materials.

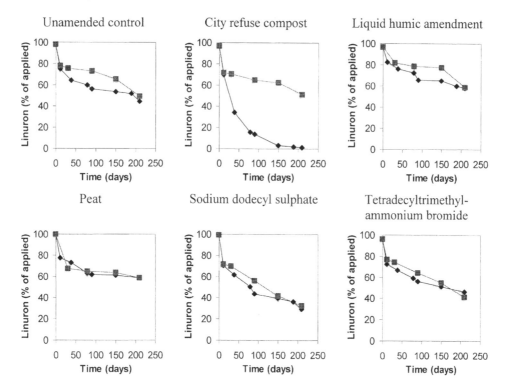

Figure 1.   Degradation kinetics of linuron in unamended and amended soil samples under nonsterilized (—◆—) and sterilized (—■—) conditions.

In the non-sterilized conditions, the DT50 of linuron in the unamended soil was 248 d^{-1} and increased in the soils amended with LHA (344 d^{-1}) and with P (333 d^{-1}). It decreased considerably in the soil amended with SDS (147 d^{-1}) and decreased dramatically in the soil amended with CRC (34 d^{-1}). In the samples of sterilized soils, unamended and amended with CRC, LHA and P, the half-life of linuron increased with respect to that of the non-sterilized soil samples. However, in the soil amended with surfactants, the DT50 of linuron either did not vary (SDS) or decreased slightly (TDTMA).

Table 1.   Rate constants (K) and half-life (DT50) for linuron degradation in unamended and amended soil samples.

Samples	Non-sterilized		Sterilized	
	$K (d^{-1})$	DT50 (d)	$K (d^{-1})$	DT50 (d)
Soil (S)	$27.9 \cdot 10^{-4}$	248	$25.0 \cdot 10^{-4}$	277
S-CRC	$203 \cdot 10^{-4}$	34	$22.0 \cdot 10^{-4}$	314
S-LHA	$20.1 \cdot 10^{-4}$	344	$19.2 \cdot 10^{-4}$	360
S-P	$20.8 \cdot 10^{-4}$	333	$19.4 \cdot 10^{-4}$	357
S-SDS	$46.9 \cdot 10^{-4}$	147	$46.6 \cdot 10^{-4}$	147
S-TDTMA	$29.5 \cdot 10^{-4}$	234	$34.0 \cdot 10^{-4}$	204

Table 2 shows the type and concentrations of the metabolites originated by the degradation of linuron in the non-sterilized and sterilized samples at the different incubation times. In the unamended, non-sterilized soil, the metabolites (M1, M2, M3 and M4), described as products of the microbial degradation of the herbicide (Maier & Härtel 1981), were found. Following sterilization of the soil, only the M4 metabolite was detected. Since microbiological activity will disappear after sterilization, and since M4 can also be originated by chemical hydrolysis of linuron (Maier & Härtel 1981), this metabolite could be attributed to a chemical degradation of the herbicide. These observations, together with the increase in the DT50 value after sterilization, point to the existence of both degradation mechanisms, chemical and microbiological, in the natural soil.

In the non-sterilized soil amended with CRC the M2, M3 and M4 metabolites were detected. After sterilization none of the metabolites was detected. Moreover, the DT50 of linuron in the sterilized soil was 9-fold higher than that of the non-sterilized soil. These findings show that the process of biological degradation of the herbicide is favoured strongly in the presence of CRC due to the strong microbial activity of this organic matter as compared with that of the natural soil and also to the differences in the nature of the microbial population (Perucci 1990).

No degradation products were detected in the samples of soil amended with LHA and P, either under sterilized or non-sterilized conditions. These samples had the highest values for the DT50 of linuron. These organic amendments probably adsorbed the molecules of linuron strongly, inhibiting the biological degradation of the herbicide by soil microorganisms. The inhibition of the degradation of different herbicides adsorbed by the organic components of the soil has been reported by several authors (Alexander 1994). However, despite the absence of metabolites a slight increase in the DT50 value can be seen in the sterilized samples, demonstrating a small loss of the herbicide by microbial mineralisation in the non-sterilized samples.

Table 2.   Linuron metabolites (µg/g) in samples of unamended and amended soil.

Samples	Incubation time (d)	Non-sterilized				Sterilized			
		M 1	M 2	M 3	M 4	M 1	M 2	M 3	M 4
Soil (S)	0	nd	nd	nd	nd	nd	nd	nd	nd
	12	0.03	nd	md	0.06	nd	nd	nd	nd
	39	0.03	nd	nd	0.05	nd	nd	nd	0.03
	79	nd	nd	nd	0.04	-	-	-	-
	90	nd	nd	nd	0.03	nd	nd	nd	0.02
	150	0.02	nd	nd	0.02	nd	nd	nd	0.03
	188	nd	0.44	nd	0.04	-	-	-	-
	210	nd	0.96	0.04	0.08	nd	nd	nd	0.03
S-CRC	0	nd	nd	nd	nd	nd	nd	nd	nd
	12	nd	9.60	nd	nd	nd	nd	nd	nd
	39	nd	9.80	nd	0.19	nd	nd	nd	nd
	79	nd	8.70	0.09	0.03	-	-	-	-
	90	nd	8.38	0.68	nd	nd	nd	nd	nd
	150	nd	0.90	1.36	nd	nd	nd	nd	nd
	188	nd	0.78	1.86	nd	-	-	-	-
	210	nd	0.96	3.00	nd	nd	nd	nd	nd
S-SDS	0	nd	nd	nd	nd	nd	nd	nd	nd
	12	nd	nd	nd	0.34	nd	nd	nd	0.09
	39	nd	nd	nd	0.80	nd	nd	nd	0.19
	79	nd	nd	nd	2.66	-	-	-	-
	90	nd	nd	nd	2.96	nd	nd	nd	0.30
	150	nd	nd	nd	2.60	nd	nd	nd	0.28
	188	nd	nd	nd	1.60	-	-	-	-
	210	nd	nd	nd	3.68	nd	nd	nd	0.38
S-TDTMA	0	nd	nd	nd	nd	nd	nd	nd	nd
	12	nd	nd	nd	0.19	nd	nd	nd	0.03
	39	nd	nd	nd	1.06	nd	nd	nd	0.05
	79	nd	nd	nd	2.72	-	-	-	-
	90	nd	nd	nd	2.24	nd	nd	nd	0.02
	150	nd	nd	nd	2.44	nd	nd	nd	0.72
	210	nd	nd	nd	3.28	nd	nd	nd	1.22

nd = not detected
- = not determinated

In the samples amended with both surfactants in non-sterilized and sterilized conditions, M4 was detected as the only transformation product and the DT50 of linuron was always lower than in the unamended soil. The DT50 of linuron remained unmodified in the soil amended with SDS, and decreased slightly in that amended with TDTMA, after sample sterilization. The effect of surfactants on the degradation of pollutant organic compounds has not been fully elucidated. Thus, whereas some authors have reported the ability of surfactants to inhibit soil microorganisms capable of metabolising organic compounds, others have indicated the capacity of surfactants to increase the desorption of the compounds and hence increase its availability for biological degradation by soil microorganisms (Aronstein et al., 1991).

However, the similar DT50 values of linuron in the non-sterilized and sterilized samples would indicate that chemical rather than microbiological degradation is the major degradation process in the soil. Nevertheless the presence in the extracts of the metabolite 3,4-dichloroaniline, which is characteristics of the chemical hydrolysis of linuron, also indicates that the presence of the surfactants studied here favoured the chemical degradation of linuron.

The results obtained in this work, which demonstrate the potential of organic amendments and surfactants for affecting rates of linuron degradation in soil, could be valuable when using simultaneously organic amendments and pesticides in agricultural practices and when using surfactants in technologies for the prevention of pollution and the recovery of soil polluted by hydrophobic organic compounds.

ACKNOWLEDGEMENTS

This work was financially supported by the Spanish "Comisión Interministerial de Ciencia y Tecnología" as a part of project AMB97-0334. The authors wish to thank L F Lorenzo; J M Ordax and M García-Delgado for technical assistance and AgrEvo S.A. (Valencia, Spain) for kindly supplying the linuron metabolites.

REFERENCES

Alexander M (1994). Sorption. In: *Biodegradation and Bioremediation*, ed M Alexander, pp. 114-130. Academic Press Limited: London.

Aronstein B N; Calvillo Y M; Alexander M (1991). Effect of surfactants at low concentrations on the desorption and biodegradation of sorbed aromatic compounds in soil. *Environmental Science and Technology* **25**: 1728-1731.

Iglesias-Jiménez E; Poveda E; Sánchez-Martín M J; Sánchez-Camazano M (1997). Effect of the nature of exogenous organic matter on pesticide sorption by the soil. *Archives of Environmental Contamination and Toxicology* **33**: 117-124.

Maier-Bode H; Härtel K (1981). Linuron and Monolinuron. *Residue Reviews* **77**: 1-364.

Perucci P (1990). Effect of the addition of municipal solid-waste compost on microbial biomass and enzyme activities in soil. *Biology and Fertility of Soils* **10**: 221-226.

Sánchez-Camazano M; Sánchez-Martín M J; Delgado-Pascual R (2000). Adsorption and mobility of linuron in soils as influenced by soil properties, organic amendments, and surfactants. *Journal of Agricultural and Food Chemistry* **48**: 3018-3026.

Sánchez-Martín M J; Delgado-Pascual R; Iglesias-Jiménez E; Sánchez-Camazano M (1996). Determination of linuron in aqueous soil extracts by high-performance liquid chromatography. *Journal of Chromatography* **754**: 295-299.

Tomlim C (1995). *The Pesticide Manual*. British Crop Protection Council: Cambridge, UK.

Walker A; Welch S J (1991). Enhanced degradation of some soil-applied herbicides. *Weed Research* **31**: 49-57.

Walker A (1976). Simulation of herbicide persistence in soils-II. Simazine and linuron in long term experiments. *Pesticide Science* **7**: 50-58.

Degradation of pesticides in combination and their effect on soil microbial activity

B K Singh, A Walker
Soil and Environmental Sciences, HRI, Wellesbourne, Warwick, CV35 9EF, UK
Email: brajesh.singh@hri.ac.uk

D J Wright
Biology Department, Imperial College, Silwood Park, Ascot. Berks, SL5 7PY, UK

ABSTRACT

The effects of combinations of pesticides (chlorpyrifos, chlorothalonil, fenamiphos) on their degradation rates and on some soil microbial characteristics were studied. There were few interactions between chlorpyrifos and fenamiphos, but the presence of chlorothalonil always resulted in reduced degradation rates of the other compounds. Chlorothalonil also caused a significant reduction in soil microbial biomass and enzyme activities (phosphatase and dehydrogenase).

INTRODUCTION

Most studies of the environmental fate of pesticides are done with single applications of one compound. However, in practice, different pesticides are used to protect the crop from weeds, pathogens and insect pests, and repeated application of individual pesticides is a common occurrence. This is particularly the case in tropical regions with most horticultural crops and with major cash crops like cotton and sugarcane. It is important therefore that studies are made of possible interactions between pesticides when they are applied in combination to soils. The objectives of the experiments reported here were:

1. To investigate the effects of repeated application of pesticides to soil on their degradation rates.
2. To study the possibility of interactions between pesticides in terms of degradation rates when applied in combination.
3. To measure the effects of the chemicals, alone and in combination, on key simple soil microbial properties.

MATERIALS AND METHODS

Pesticides, soils and residue analysis

The compounds chosen for study were chlorpyrifos, chlorothalonil and fenamiphos which are a widely used insecticide, fungicide and nematicide respectively. Commercial formulations of chlorpyrifos and chlorothalonil and analytical grade fenamiphos were used throughout these studies. The soils (sandy loam) were collected from the experimental farm at Silwood Park,

Ascot, UK. Top-soil samples were collected from the 0-10 cm layer at three separate locations approximately 10 m apart to provide three true replicates. They were partially air dried overnight and sieved to pass a 3-mm mesh, and their moisture contents and water holding capacity were determined. One sub-sample (1 kg) of each of the replicate soils was treated with the pesticides chlorpyrifos, chlorothalonil (both suspended in water), or fenamiphos (solution in methanol) to give a concentration of 10 mg a.i./kg dry soil. Other subsamples of each replicate soil were treated with the pesticides at a rate of 10 mg/kg in the combinations:

chlorpyrifos + fenamiphos

chlorpyrifos + chlorothalonil

fenamiphos + chlorothalonil

chlorpyrifos + fenamiphos + chlorothalonil.

All samples treated with the fenamiphos solution in 3 ml methanol were left for 3 to 4 h for the solvent to evaporate. Distilled water was added to all soils to adjust the final moisture contents to 40% of water holding capacity. One set of three replicate samples without pesticide treatment and one set receiving 3 ml of methanol were kept as controls. Soils were mixed by hand initially and then passed through a 3 mm mesh sieve after which samples were incubated at 20°C. The treated soils were sampled periodically for 98 d and analyzed for concentration of pesticides and their metabolites. Once 50% of a specific pesticide had disappeared or 30 d after first treatment (whichever came later), the soil was retreated with another dose of the appropriate chemical or combination of chemicals at 10 mg/kg. A second re-treatment was done 30 days after the first re-treatment irrespective of residue concentration in the soil. Pesticides and their metabolites were extracted from soil with acetonitrile:water (90:10) by shaking for 1 h on a wrist action shaker. The concentration of pesticides and their metabolites were measured by HPLC using Kontron series 300 equipment. The column used was Lichrosorb- RP 18 (250mm x 4mm; Merck) with an isocratic mobile phase at a flow rate of 1ml/min.

Microbial studies

Dehydrogenase phosphatase and total microbial biomass were measured after 30, 60, 90 days from the first pesticide application in all treatments. Soil dehydrogenase and phosphatase activities were measured using the method of Tabatabai (1982). The method of Mele & Carter (1996) was used to determine total microbial biomass.

RESULTS

Pesticide persistence

Degradation of the pesticides in the various treatments approximated to first-order reaction kinetics. Table 1 shows correlation data, together with first-order rate constants and half-lives derived from the dissipation data for each treatment. The half-lives of chlorpyrifos alone and in combination with fenamiphos were about 63 and 64 days respectively in the first treatment, and these were extended to 118 and 193 days respectively when chlorothalonil was included. The degradation rate of chlorpyrifos alone and in combination with fenamiphos was not affected in the second treatment, but the suppression of the degradation rate in the presence of chlorthalonil in the second treatment was much more pronounced with half-lives, 165 and 224 day respectively (Table 1). In the case of fenamiphos there was a slowing of the rate of degradation in all treatments with repeated application, which was particularly pronounced with the third treatment. In all treatments, fenamiphos was first transformed into fenamiphos sulfoxide and then to fenamiphos sulfone. These transformations into the oxidation products were slowed considerably when the soil was treated with chlorothalonil or with chlorpyrifos plus chlorothalonil (data not shown).

In terms of total toxic residues (TTR) the suppressive effect of chlorothalonil was similar whether by itself or in combination with chlorpyrifos. The transformation rate of fenamiphos was not affected by the presence of chlorpyrifos alone. The calculated half-lives for chlorothalonil (Table 1) show that the degradation rates of the second and third applications were slower than that of the first in most of the treatments. There appeared to be a suppression of chlorothalonil degradation when applied in combination with chlorpyrifos, but this was less marked in the triple combination of chlorothalonil plus chlorpyrifos plus fenamiphos.

Table 1.   Correlation coefficients (R^2), first order rate constants (k, day^{-1}) and half-lives (HL, days) for pesticide degradation

Pesticide treatment	First treatment			Second treatment			Third treatment		
	R^2	k	HL	R^2	k	HL	R^2	k	HL
Chlorpyrifos									
CHP	0.979	0.011	63	0.984	0.012	60			
CHP + FEN	0.976	0.011	64	0.986	0.010	68			
CHP + CHTH	0.963	0.006	118	0.971	0.004	165			
CHP + FEN + CHTH	0.889	0.004	193	0.864	0.003	224			
Fenamiphos (parent compound)									
FEN	0.965	0.083	8.4	0.962	0.083	8.4	0.964	0.029	24
FEN + CHP	0.983	0.071	10	0.965	0.083	8.4	0.977	0.028	25
FEN + CHTH	0.984	0.059	12	0.999	0.042	17	0.929	0.018	40
FEN + CHP + CHTH	0.979	0.055	13	0.990	0.036	19	0.966	0.020	36
Chlorothalonil									
CHTH	0.923	0.056	12	0.997	0.035	20	0.949	0.033	21
CHTH + CHP	0.844	0.052	13	0.930	0.028	25	0.605	0.012	60
CHTH + FEN	0.853	0.052	13	0.982	0.050	14	0.943	0.027	26
CHTH + CHP + FEN	0.945	0.057	13	0.961	0.040	17	0.940	0.028	25

CHP=Chlorpyrifos; FEN=Fenamiphos; CHTH=Chlorothalonil

Microbial Studies

Results from the measurement of soil dehydrogenase, phosphatase and total microbial biomass activity at 30, 60 and 90 days after the first treatment are shown in Figure 1. A marked reduction in dehydrogenase activity was observed in all treatments involving chlorothalonil. Suppression of dehydrogenase activity was up to 50% in soil treated with chlorothalonil alone or with chlorothalonil plus chlorpyrifos. Fenamiphos alone or in combination with chlorpyrifos had no adverse effect on dehydrogenase activity, however chlorpyrifos alone had a small suppressive effect. Soil phosphatase activity was suppressed by the application of chlorothalonil alone or in combination with chlorpyrifos.

Application of fenamiphos gave a significant increase in soil phosphatase activity whether alone or in combination with chlorpyrifos. Small reductions in phosphatase activity were observed in the chlorpyrifos treatment especially after 90 days. All treatments involving chlorothalonil (alone or in combination with other pesticides) had significant effects on microbial biomass after 60 and 90 days. Fenamiphos alone or in combination with chlorpyrifos had no effect on microbial biomass. There was a small reduction in biomass in soil treated with chlorpyrifos after the second application.

DISCUSSION

The results of the present study with the individual pesticides were broadly consistent with those reported previously. However, the present results extend those observed previously by inclusion of the pesticide combinations. The half-life of chlorpyrifos when applied alone was 64 days which is very similar to that reported by Racke *et al.,* (1990). The rate of chlorpyrifos dissipation was not affected by the presence of fenamiphos. However degradation of chlorpyrifos was suppressed in the presence of chlorothalonil, and this reduction in the rate of chlorpyrifos degradation was substantial even with the first application.

Chlorothalonil has been reported previously to suppress its own degradation when applied repeatedly (Motonaga *et al.*, 1998). When all three pesticides were applied together, the rate of chlorpyrifos degradation was suppressed further, indicating that there were synergistic interactions between the pesticides. An additive effect cannot explain the results since fenamiphos had no effect on chlorpyrifos degradation when applied in the absence of chlorothalonil (Table 1).

Fenamiphos degradation rate was the same when applied individually or in combination with chlorpyrifos. Repeated application of fenamiphos to this soil did not result in induction of fenamiphos accelerated degradation contrasting with the previous findings of Smelt *et al., (*1996). However, the rate of transformation was reduced when treated with chlorothalonil or the chlorothalonil plus chlorpyrifos combination. Dissipation rates of total toxic residues (TTR) were also considerably reduced when the nematicide was incubated in soil in combination with chlorothalonil or with chlorothalonil plus chlorpyrifos. These effects were solely the result of the presence of chlorothalonil since chlorpyrifos had no effect on fenamiphos degradation.

(a) Dehydrogenase Activity (LSD=17; P=0.05)

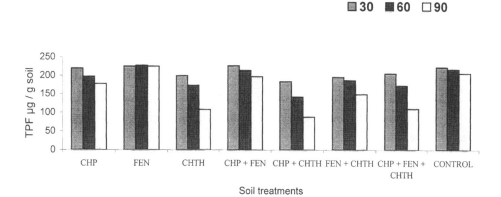

(b) Phosphatase Activity (LSD=8.1; P=0.05)

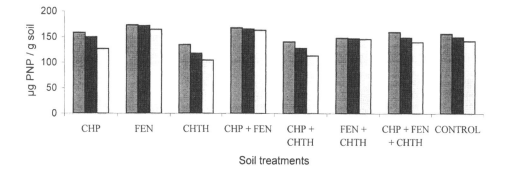

(c) Total microbial biomass (LSD=29; P=0.05)

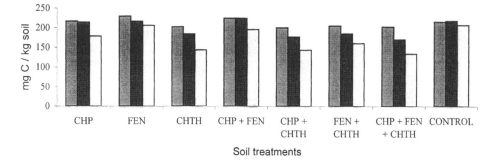

Figure 1. The effect of pesticide combinations on (a) dehydrogenase activity
(b) phosphatase activity and (c) total microbial biomass after 30, 60 and 90 days.
CHP = chlorpyrifos; FEN = fenamiphos; CHTH = chlorothalonil

The degradation of chlorothalonil when applied alone was suppressed by repeated application, which is in agreement with earlier findings of Motonaga *et al.,* (1998). None of the pesticide combinations had any effect on chlorothalonil degradation in the first treatment. However a slight reduction in dissipation rate was observed following the second application in combination with chlorpyrifos.

In the present study all of the measured microbial characteristics were adversely effected by chlorothalonil treatment when applied individually or in combination with the other pesticides. Chlorpyrifos and fenamiphos had little significant effect on the microbial properties investigated. These findings are in agreement with the previous study by Motonaga *et al.,* (1998) which demonstrated that soil respiration was suppressed following the application of chlorothalonil.

The present results provide an additional dimension to the study of environmental fate and ecotoxicology of pesticides and suggest that significant interactions can occur when combinations of different pesticides are applied repeatedly to soils. In our experiments, the combinations of pesticides examined were limited, and the studies were done in a single soil type. Further studies are needed with other pesticide combinations and in other soils.

ACKNOWLEDGEMENTS

B K Singh thanks the Commonwealth Scholarship Commission for financial assistance.

REFERENCES

Mele P M; Carter M R (1996). Estimation of microbial biomass by ninhydrin-reactive nitrogen using liquid chloroform. *Canadian Journal of Soil Science* **76:** 37-40.

Motonaga K; Takagi K; Matumoto S (1998). Suppression of chlorothalonil degradation in soil after repeated application. *Environmental Toxicology and Chemistry* **17:** 1469-1472.

Racke K D; Laskowski D A; Schultz M R (1990). Resistance of chlorpyrifos to enhanced biodegradation in soil. *Journal of Agriculture and Food Chemistry* **38:** 1430-1436.

Smelt J H; Van Der Peppel-Groen A E; Van Der Pas L J T; Dijksterhuis A (1996). Development and duration of accelerated degradation of nematicides in different soils. *Soil Biology and Biochemistry* **28:** 1757-1765.

Tabatabai M A (1982). Soil enzymes, In: *Methods of Soil Analysis, Part 2. Chemical and Microbial Properties,* eds A L Miller & R H Keeney, pp. 903-948. Soil Science Society of America.

Influence of fungal inoculant type and water potential on degradation of mixtures of simazine, dieldrin and trifluralin in soil-based media

S Fragoeiro, A Elyassi, N Magan

Applied Mycology Group, IBST, Cranfield University, Silsoe, Bedford MK45 4DT, UK
Email: n.magan@cranfield.ac.uk

ABSTRACT

A wide range of basidiomycetes has been screened on soil-based media at two water potentials for the ability to degrade mixtures of simazine, dieldrin and trifluralin. The best treatments were found to be *Trametes versicolor*, *Trametes socotrana*, *Polystictus versicolor* and *Pleurotus ostreatus*. These were generally better than *Phanerochaete chrysosporium* in media containing 5-10 ppm of the pesticides. In soil microcosms with two different water potentials mixtures of *P. versicolor* and *T. socotrana* or *P. versicolor* alone were able to degrade >75% of a 5 ppm mixture when inoculated on straw in field capacity soil over a 75 day incubation period. Under water stress conditions the degradation rates were reduced. These studies suggest that it is important to include varying environmental conditions in bioremediation experiments to identify and optimise fungal inoculants for effective breakdown of recalcitrant chemicals in soil.

INTRODUCTION

While a significant amount of research has been carried out on bioremediation of individual pesticides, less research has focussed on mixtures of pesticides. In the present study we have concentrated on a mixture of three pesticides, simazine (a triazine herbicide), dieldrin (organochlorine insecticide) and trifluralin (a dinitroaniline) herbicide, all on the UK "Red List".

Although the soil system is a dynamic one in which fluctuations of environmental factors, especially of temperature and water potential, occurs continuously, few studies have included an examination of these in relation to the degradation of xenobiotics in soil (Kostowska & Rola, 1984; Carter, 1991). Other important factors are soil pH and nutrient status. Indeed, organic matter amendments and aeration have been used previously to enhance the degradation of simazine (Ahonen & Heinonen-Tanki, 1994). Ritter & Scarborough (1995) suggested that optimum conditions for the biological activity at a bioremediation site included pH values of 6.5-8.5, temperature of between 27-35°C, and an organic carbon:nitrogen:phosphorus ratio of 300:15:1. However, the critical factor of water potential was not considered.

The objectives of the present study were: (a) to screen a range of white rot fungi for tolerance and growth on a range of individual and mixtures of simazine, dieldrin and trifluralin under two different water potential regimes and (b) to evaluate fungal species for remediation in soil microcosms held at different steady state water potentials.

MATERIALS AND METHODS

In vitro studies

Fungal species used in this study were *Pleurotus ostreatus*, *Polystictus versicolor*, *Trametes versicolor* and *Phanerochaete crysosporium*.

Initial screening was carried out on soil extract agar (Lang *et al.*, 1997) which was modified to –0.7 and –2.8 MPa water potentials. The soil extract agar was modified with mixtures of pesticides in the range 0 to 10 ppm by addition to the molten agar, thoroughly mixed and poured into 9-cm Petri plates. These were overlayed with sterile cellophane and centrally inoculated with a 4-mm agar plug from the margin of a growing colony of each fungal species. Care was taken to avoid puncturing the cellophane layer to avoid any direct contact between fungal colony and pesticide containing soil extract agar. The temporal growth was used to obtain the growth rates from the linear regression lines of the linear phases. Experiments were carried out with three replicates per fungal treatment and pesticide condition at 15°C. Pesticides obtained from Merck (dieldrin); Dow Agrosciences (trifluralin) and Riedel-de Haen (simazine) were dissolved in methanol.

Soil studies

A soil moisture adsorption curve was made by thermocouple psychrometry. The sandy loam soil (PT008) was supplied by Levington Agriculture. It contained 15% clay, 19% silt, 66% sand, 1% organic matter, with a pH of 6.2. The pesticides (5 and 10 ppm) were added to soil dissolved in acetone (dieldrin and trifluralin) and in tetrahydrofuran (THF, simazine). After thorough mixing, the appropriate amount of water was added to obtain field capacity, -0.065 and –0.28 MPa water potentials and allowed to equilibrate for 24 hrs at 4°C with regular mixing. Moist sterile straw segments (<1 cm lengths) colonised by *P.versicolor* or *T.socotrana* for up to 12-14 days were used as an inoculum. 1 g of straw was added to 10 g soil. For a mixed fungal inoculum 0.5 g of each fungal inoculant was used. Soil microcosms were incubated at 15 and 20°C at the three different water potentials and triplicate samples destructively sampled after 28, 42 and 70 days.

Soil samples (10 g) were extracted in 15 ml acetone, sonicated for 10 mins, shaken at 400 rpm for 10 minutes. This was left in the dark at room temperature for 10 mins to allow the soil to settle. The solvent was filtered through a 0.2μm syringe filter prior to analysis by HPLC. A gradient HPLC methods was used using a Envirosep-PP column with a gradient of 75:25% water:acetonitrile for 15 mins, then changed to 50:50 and back to 75:25 in preparation at 30 mins for the next sample. The flow rate was 1 ml min[-1]. This enabled simazine to be eluted at 4 mins, dieldrin at 17 mins and trifluralin at 20 mins. The acetonitrile phase contained 2% (V/V) THF to help sharpen the peaks. This method gave recoveries of 86.2, 84.8 and 70% for simazine, dieldrin and trifluralin respectively in the same run.

RESULTS

In vitro studies on soil extract agar

Figure 1 shows that all the species grew best at –0.7 MPa water potential on soil extract agar. Overall, *P.versicolor* and *P.ostreatus* and *T.versicolor* were all able to tolerate and grow in the the presence of a mixture of up to 10 ppm of the three pesticides. However, at –2.8 MPa water potential the growth rates were significantly reduced. These fungal treatments were generally much better than *P.chrysosporium* which is often used as a bioremedial fungal inoculant.

In situ studies in soil microcosms

The effect of temperature of incubation (20 and 30°C) on rate of breakdown of the pesticides is shown in Table 1. Overall, breakdown was more rapid at 30 than 20°C by both *P.versicolor* and *P.versicolor +T.socotrana*. However, generally, co-inoculation of the two fungi resulted in a slower degradation rate than *P.versioclor* alone. In the absence of fungal inoculants, natural degradation was also more rapid at 30 than 20°C.

Table 1. The effect of *P.versicolor* or a mixture of *P.versicolor* + *T.socotrana* on degradation of 5 and 10 ppm of the three pesticides after 70 days at 20 and 30°C in field capacity soil.

	Temp (°C)	Conc	Control	*P. versicolor* (Pv)	Pv+*T. socotrana*	LSD (P<0.5)
			Final concentration in soil (ppm)			
Simazine	20	5	2.8	2.0	1.9	0.160
		10	7.8	5.5	5.3	0.272
	30	5	1.0	1.0	1.1	0.169
		10	3.1	1.9	2.1	0.266
Dieldrin	20	5	4.1	2.8	3.1	0.283
		10	8.8	6.4	7.0	0.250
	30	5	4.0	2.5	3.0	0.261
		10	8.4	6.1	6.2	0.266
Trifluralin	20	5	3.2	0 (28 days)	0	0.142
		10	7.2	0 (28 days)	0	0.227
	30	5	1.4	0 (28 days)	0	0.173
		10	3.6	0 (28 days)	0	0.209

Figure 2 shows the impact of changing water potential on degradation of the mixture of pesticides at 20°C over a 70-day incubation period by *P.versicolor*. The relative efficacy of *P.versicolor* was variable with the most significant degradation occurring for trifluralin in field capacity soil. There were also marked differences between the capacity for degradation at different water potentials. With a mixture of pesticides, the degradation of simazine and dieldrin was less than that for trifluralin and also less than that obtained when pesticides were present individually.

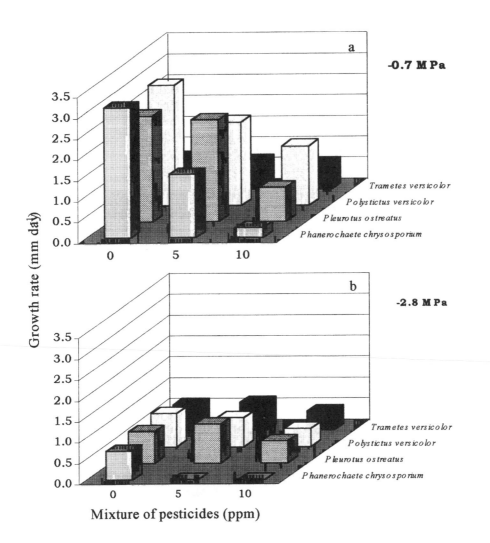

Figure 1. Growth rate (mm day⁻¹) for *Pleurotus ostreatus*, *Polystitcus versicolor*, *Trametes versicolor* and *Phanerochaete crysosporium*, exposed to a mixture of simazine, trifluralin and dieldrin at 0, 5 and 10 ppm at two water potentials (-0.7 and –2.8 MPa).

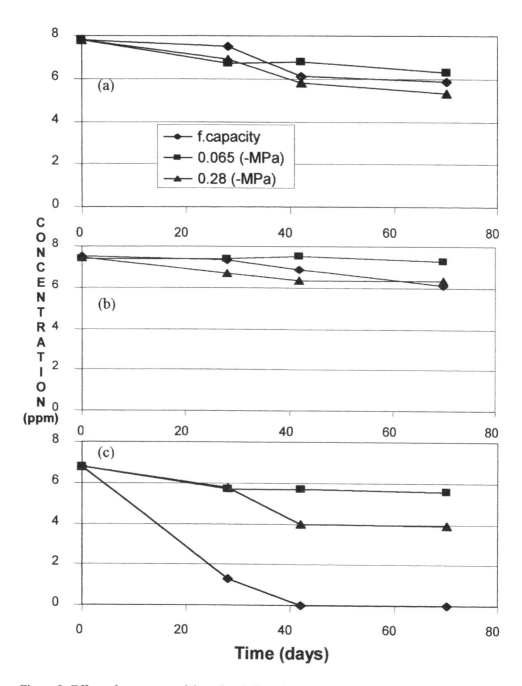

Figure 2. Effect of water potential on the ability of *Polystictus versicolor* to simultaneously breakdown (a) simazine, (b) dieldrin, and (c) trifluralin added at an initial concentration of 10 ppm. The LSDs (P<0.05) were 0.19, 0.18 and 0.12 respectively.

DISCUSSION

This study has shown that some basidiomycete fungi are able to produce the necessary extracellular enzymes which enable growth on up to 10 ppm of a mixture of the three pesticides under study under a wide range of water potential regimes. Fungal species examined were better that *P.chrysopsorium*, strains of which are most often used for aerobic bioremediation of pesticides in soil (Cameron *et al.*, 2000). The impact of water potential and temperature are significant and it is important that these factors are taken into account when examining potential microbial inoculants.

Studies in soil microcosms suggest that the use of mixed fungal inoculants may not be as effective as individual species because of possible antagonism between species. Where mixtures of microorganisms are not antagonistic, then perhaps additive or synergistic effects may be potentially possible. For example, while bacteria are very sensitive to slight changes in soil water potential, fungal inoculants are much more tolerant. Thus, it may be possible to combine such inoculants for more effective bioremediation of pesticides in soil.

The use of carriers for inoculants is important as cheap and available substrates are needed for effective distribution in soil. We have found a 1:10 ratio effective. However, it may be possible to use carriers such as alginate pellets or other immobilisation systems for incorporation into soil. It is important that environmentally realistic screens are used to identify candidate microbial species for degradation of individual and mixtures of pesticides. This is important if inoculants are to be effectively used practically to enhance degradation of the wide range of xenobiotics in contaminated soils. Studies are now in progress in our laboratories to optimise such systems for optimising the bioremedial effectiveness of such inoculants.

REFERENCES

Ahonen U; Heinonen-Tansky H (1994). Degradation and leaching of simazine in Arctic sandy soils. *Acta Agriculture Scandanavica* **44**: 55-60.

Cameron M; Timfeevski S; Aust S (2000). Enzymologyof *Phanerochaete chrysosporium* with respect to the degradation of recalcitrant compounds and xenobiotics. *Applied Microbiology & Biotechnology* **54**: 751-758.

Carter A D (1991). Methods of monitoring soil water regimes and the interpretation of data relevant to pesticide fate and behaviour. In: *Pesticides in Soils and water: Current Perspectives BCPC Monograph No. 47*, ed. A Walker, pp. 143-147. University of Warwick, Coventry: The Lavenham Press Ltd.

Kostowska B; Rola J (1984). Decomposition of simazine in different soils under field and laboratory conditions. In: *Soils and Crop Protection Chemicals, BCPC Monograph No. 27*, pp. 101-108. The Lavenham Press Ltd.

Lang E; Kleeberg I; Zadrazil F (1997). Competition of *Pleurotus* sp. and *Dichomitus squalens* with soil microrganisms during lignocellulose decomposition. *Bioresource Technology* **60**: 95-99.

Ritter W F; Scarborough R W (1995). A review of bioremediation of contaminated soil and ground water. *Journal of Environmental Science & Health* **A30**: 333-357.

The microbial degradation of nM-/μM concentrations of linuron estimated by a *Lemna minor* bioassay

K Hulsen, M Höfte

Department of Crop Protection, Laboratory of Phytopathology, Ghent University, Belgium
Email: khulsen@hotmail.com

ABSTRACT

In this work we studied the degradation of linuron by a microbial consortium (isolated from a linuron-treated orchard) and the strain *Variovorax paradoxus*, which is probably the main actor in this consortium. We used a plant-microbial bioassay, in which the aquatic macrophyte *Lemna minor* L. (duckweed) was used to monitor the biodegradation of linuron when this herbicide was applied to liquid cultures in nano- and micromolar concentrations. The toxicity of linuron to *L. minor* was assessed by several growth-related parameters such as total frond number, total frond area and doubling time. Log-logistic based dose-response analysis revealed significant growth inhibition of *L. minor* after 7 days of exposure to linuron concentrations ≥ 80 nM. The relationship between herbicide dose and plant response was described most accurately by using an equation that is modified for growth stimulation at lower doses. The microbial consortium and the *V. paradoxus* strain significantly protected *Lemna* plants from the toxic effects of concentrations up to 1.28 μM linuron. These results suggest that both inocula were capable of degrading nanomolar concentrations of linuron but there was indication that the consortium performed better than the pure isolate. In addition to the growth-related parameters, chlorophyll *a* fluorescence imaging was used to estimate the outcome of the plant-microbe-toxicant interaction by measuring the specific plant metabolic processes affected by linuron.

INTRODUCTION

Lemna species (duckweed) are often used as a bioindicator to assess phytotoxicity of environmental contaminants (Marwood et al., 2001) or herbicides, including phenylurea herbicides such as diuron (Teisseire et al., 1999). Similarly, Siciliano *et al.,* (1997) reported on the use of prairie grass species as bioindicators to evaluate the outcome of the biodegradation of 2-chlorobenzoic acid by a bacterial inoculum.

In this work we show that duckweed can also be used to study biodegradation of herbicides. This investigation forms part of a larger study about the biodegradation of phenylurea herbicides by a bacterial consortium, which was isolated from a pear orchard with a long history of linuron treatment. When investigating the effect of a biological treatment (bacterial inoculation) in a bioassay, it is important to evaluate and choose between different methods and parameters to estimate the bioindicator response. The following questions were addressed: what is the relationship between the herbicide dose and the response of this aquatic macrophyte? Which parameters are the most effective at expressing this relationship? Is it possible to prevent linuron damage to this sensitive plant by inoculating the plant nutrient solution with a linuron-degrading bacterial consortium or a linuron-degrading bacterium?

To our knowledge, this is the first study to use a *Lemna minor* bioassay to estimate biodegradation efficiency of nM-/$_\mu$M concentrations of linuron.

MATERIALS AND METHODS

Plant material: *Lemna minor* (duckweed) was collected from an artificial pond of the botanical garden of the Faculty of Sciences, Ghent University. A stock culture was maintained on mineral medium in a controlled environment as described by Teisseire & Vernet (2000). The pH of the medium was adjusted to 6.5 and the plants were grown under static conditions in a plant growth chamber at $25 \pm 2°C$. Light was provided with an intensity of approx. 40 $_\mu$mol PAR m^{-2} s^{-1}. For the growth experiments, 30 fronds free from any visible chlorosis were taken from the stock cultures and exposed to the according treatment. For each treatment we used 6 repetitions with 5 fronds/ repetition as initial frond number. The experiments were repeated four times independently from each other.

Enrichment culture. A mixed culture of linuron-degrading bacteria was obtained by the enrichment culture technique from a pear orchard at the Royal Research station of Gorsem (Sint-Truiden, Belgium) as described by El Fantroussi *et al.,* (1999). The bacterial consortium and *Variovorax paradoxus,* which is probably the main actor in the consortium responsible for the degradation of linuron (W. Dejonghe, personal communication), were maintained on a minimal medium supplemented with 25 mg/L linuron as sole carbon and nitrogen source. The inoculum was prepared after subculturing 10% (v/v) of the initial culture to new flasks, which were incubated for four days at 140 rpm and 28° C. After four days 40 ml of this culture was centrifuged at 5000 rpm for 20 minutes. The supernatant was discarded and the cell pellet was resuspended again with 54 ml of sterile water. From this suspension 1 ml was added to 9 ml of the Lemna nutrient medium (10 ml /repetition).

Chemicals: analytical grade linuron (3-[3,4-dichlorophenyl]-1-methoxy-1-methylurea) with a purity of 99% was purchased from ChemService (West Chester, U.K.). Linuron was added to the medium as a solution in methanol (25 mg/L) to give a final concentration range between 0.0025 and 0.32 mg/L (10 –1280 nM).

Phytotoxicity of linuron to *L. minor*: the dose-response of the common duckweed was evaluated by various parameters. The corresponding dataset for each parameter was submitted to a log-logistic analysis in order to generate a specific dose-response-curve for each parameter. The log-logistic model as described by Streibig & Kudsk (1993) and Seefeldt *et al.,* (1995) was used to analyze our data. The commonly used sigmoidal model was modified according to Brain & Cousens (1989) to fit our data at the lowest concentrations.

Growth rate was assessed by total number of fronds, doubling time and total frond area. The data represent the mean and standard deviation of measurements performed on six repetitions per treatment. Total frond area was measured by a Windows based MICRO IMAGE (Olympus) software package and the acquired data were submitted to statistical analysis.

Chlorophyll a fluorescence took place in a Chl *a* fluorescence imaging system that was described by Lootens & Vandecasteele (2000). Only far-red fluorescence (730-740 nm) was measured and provided us with images of ground-fluorescence (F_0) upon radiation with a weak irradiance source (1.6 µmol m^{-2} s^{-1}).

Statistical analysis Each concentration was tested in sixfold and four independent experiments were carried out. All data represent mean values for that particular parameter and were calculated/ compared by one way ANOV A or a non-parametric test. Statistical analysis was performed by means of the SPSS 9.0 statistical software package.

RESULTS

Dose-response of *L. minor* to linuron

To asses the toxicity of linuron to *Lemna minor* we used the log-logistic model (Streibig & Kudsk, 1993) which was modified as proposed by Brain and Cousens (1989) to describe the dose-response relationship since our data plot suggested stimulation of growth for the lowest doses (0.0025 and 0.005 mg/L, 10 and 20 nM respectively).

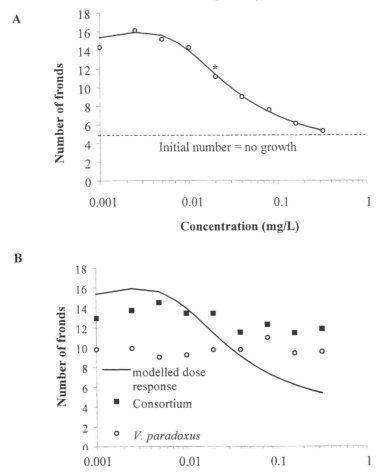

Figure 1. A) Dose-response of *L. minor* (duckweed) to different concentrations of linuron. Asterisk represents the lowest observable effect level, which was found to be 0.02 mg/L. B) Effect of the bacterial consortium and *V paradoxus* on *L. minor* growth.

In total, *L. minor* was exposed to 9 different linuron doses, which were carefully selected to cover the whole range of responses from no visible effect to complete death/ growth inhibition. When various growth parameters were compared according to the model of Brain & Cousens (1989), the total number of fronds parameter gave the most satisfactory fit. Using this parameter it was shown that 0.02 mg/L was the lowest concentration of linuron that caused a significant inhibition of growth after 7 days of exposure to the herbicide (Figure 1A). The circles in this figure represent the experimental data while the curve describes the dose-response calculated according to the model of Brain & Cousens (1989).

In the presence of both bacterial inocula we observed an altered reponse of the *Lemna* plants (Figure 1B). The consortium was capable of protecting *Lemna* plants from the phytotoxic effects of linuron for the whole range of concentrations applied. In contrast, we observed a significant negative effect of the *V. paradoxus* strain when applied together with the lower concentrations of the herbicide. Inoculation with *V. paradoxus* was only beneficial at concentrations ≥ 0.04 mg/L (Figure 2).

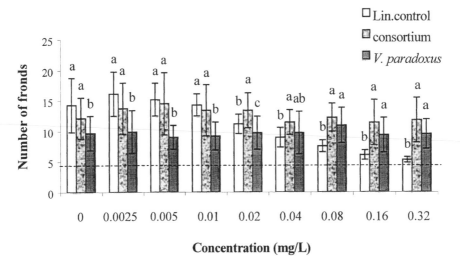

Concentration (mg/L)

Figure 2. The effect of inoculation with a bacterial consortium or a *Variovorax paradoxus* strain on the number of fronds in a *Lemna* bioassay. Different letters above each column represent significant differences at the 5% level.

Chlorophyll a fluorescence imaging

Chl *a* fluorescence was used to determine if the poor level of protection by *V. paradoxus* could be attributed to a difference in metabolism in comparison to the consortium. For this purpose we followed the initial level of fluorescence F_0 of the *L. minor* plants during the first days of the experiment. Since linuron is known to block electron transport and quantum conversion it can be expected that a loss of photosynthetic function (and an increase in F_0) will occur with increasing exposure time. After 1 h exposure of the plants to 0.32 mg/L (= 1.28 µM) linuron we detected an increased F_0 signal when compared to the untreated control. After 48 h, even the effect of 0.005 mg/L became obvious (Figure 3 picture 1-3).

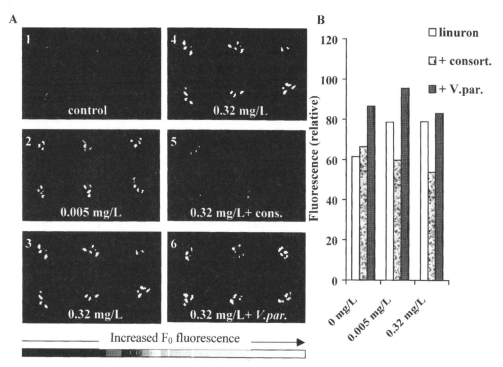

Figure 3. A) Chlorophyll fluorescence images of F_0 taken after 48 h of exposure to the herbicide. B) The graph gives a comparison between the F_0 signal for the different biological treatments measured at 48 h after exposure.

The increasing brightness in the left hand images (1-3) reflects the increased F_0 fluorescence intensity, which is indicative for the herbicide uptake. In an attempt to understand the response of the plants to the different treatments, it became evident that the *V. paradoxus* strain had a negative effect on plant growth. This was in contrast with the observed protective effect when inoculated with the consortium as suggested by a lower F_0 signal (picture 5). Within 48 h exposure of the *Lemna* plants to linuron and/ or the bacteria an increased F_0 was typical for the control plants (without linuron) which were inoculated with *V. paradoxus*. This trend was also observed when the bacterium was inoculated in combinatium with 0.005 and 0.32 mg/L of linuron. In contrast, a significant positive effect on the total number of fronds was observed after 7 days for concentrations > 0.04 mg/L. It appears that the plants were able to recover from the stress caused by residual concentrations of linuron they were exposed to during the first days, which could explain the growth recession when compared to the treatments inoculated with the consortium. A recovery from sublethal doses of a herbicide has previously been shown with *Vicia faba* (Vidal *et al.*, 1995) and in our experiments this suggests a slower or partial degradation of these concentrations in comparison to the bacterial consortium. The origin of the negative effect of *V. paradoxus* on plant growth for concentrations below the L.O.E.L. remains unanswered.

The *Lemna* bioassay inoculated with the bacterial consortium did not show any increase in the ground fluorescence level when the bioassay was spiked with 0.005 mg/L or 0.32 mg/L linuron. This also demonstrates that the degradative capacities of the consortium are more pronounced in comparison to the *V. paradoxus* strain, even when substrate concentrations are very low.

ACKNOWLEDGEMENTS

We would like to thank P Lootens and P. Vandecasteele for providing the chl fluorescence images. The help of L Maeghe with the dose-reponse analysis method is also gratefully acknowledged.

REFERENCES

Brain P; Cousens R (1989). An equation to describe dose responses where there is stimulation of growth at low doses. *Weed Research* **29:** 93-96.

El Fantroussi, S; Verschuere L; Verstraete W; Top E M (1999). Effect of phenylurea herbicides on soil microbial communities estimated by analysis of 16 S rRNA gene fingerprints and community-level physiological profiles. *Applied & Environmental Microbiology* **65:** 982-988.

Lootens P; Vandecasteele P (2000). A cheap chlorophyll a fluorescence imaging system. *Photosynthetica* **38:** 53-56.

Marwood C A; Solomon K R; Greenberg B M (2001). Chlorophyll fluorescence as a bioindicator of effects on growth in aquatic macrophytes from mixtures of polycyclic aromatic hydrocarbons. *Environmental Toxicology & Chemistry* **20:** 890-891.

Siciliano, S D; Germida, J J; Headly J V (1997). Evaluation of prairie grass species as bioindicators of halogenated aromatics in soil. *Environmental Toxicology & Chemistry* **16:** 521-527.

Seefeldt S S; Jensen J E; Fuerst E P (1995). Log-logistic analysis of herbicide dose-response relationships. *Weed Technology* **9:** 218-227.

Streibig J C; Kudsk P, eds (1993). *Herbicide Bioassays.* pp 270. CRC Press: Boca Raton.

Teisseire H; Couderchet M; Vernet G (1999). Phytotoxicity of diuron alone and in combination with copper or folpet on duckweed (*Lemna minor*). *Environmental pollution* **106:** 39-45.

Teisseire H; Vernet G (2000). Is the diuron effect due to a herbicide strengthening of antioxidative defenses of *Lemna minor*? *Pest Biochemistry & Physiology* **66:** 153-160.

Vidal D; Martinez-Guijarro D; Simon E (1995). Chlorophyll fluorescence and photosynthetic O_2 evolution in *Vicia faba* plants treated with methabenzthiazuron. *Photosynthetica* **31:** 9-20.

SESSION 4

SORPTION AND MOBILITY
(LARGE SCALE)

Chairman &   Dr A C Johnson
Session Organiser: *Centre for Ecology and Hydrology,*
                     Wallingford, UK

Field-scale variability of herbicide transport

B Lennartz
Institute of Plant Nutrient and Soil Science, University Rostock, 18051 Rostock, Germany
Email: bernd.lennartz@agrarfak.uni-rostock.de

E Simic, G Destouni
Royal Institute of Technology, Department of Environmental and Civil Engineering, Stockholm, Sweden

ABSTRACT

Ninety-nine undisturbed soil columns were collected in order to characterise a 1.8 ha field site with respect to herbicide leaching. All samples were subjected to leaching experiments under steady state water unsaturated flow conditions. The individual breakthrough curves of the applied bromide and the two herbicides isoproturon and terbuthylazine were averaged to obtain large or field-scale signals which were analysed with a stochastic advective modelling approach. Two different manifestations of preferential transport could be distinguished. The analyses revealed that herbicide transport in one part of the field (0.66 ha) was dominated by preferential flow which increased the total leached mass by 350% and 810% of isoproturon and terbuthylazine respectively.

INTRODUCTION

The behaviour of pesticides, such as herbicides, in the terrestrial environment is predominantly mediated by the vertical transport characteristics of the organic compounds in soils. To what extent chemicals are leached below a certain soil depth depends on the water flux regime on the one hand and on the adsorption process on the other. Both processes are known to vary considerably in the horizontal plane within field units (Lennartz, 1999). The variation of the water flux, especially in field studies, is often captured by analysing the transport behaviour of non-reactive tracers that are known to travel like water through the soil profile. Following the application of a solute pulse, the assessment of solute transport parameters is made from an analysis of the breakthrough curve (BTC). The application of reactive compounds such as herbicides along with the conservative tracer gives additional insight into the transport system.

The vadoze soil zone has been identified as a transport region that is dominated by multiple non-equilibrium effects. These have been conceptualised with respect to transport with the system of soil water regions of different mobility. In the mobile / immobile soil water approach advective solute transport is limited to the mobile region, while transfer into the immobile fraction is diffusion controlled. Another possible manifestation of transport non-equilibrium is that advection takes place in both, the region of fast and the more slowly flowing water. Solute exchange between regions is neglected. The nature of the dominating flow regime can be identified by model analyses of experimental data.

The objective of this study was twofold. A multiple column leaching test with 99 undisturbed soil samples was conducted to obtain a field-scale view of the herbicide leaching situation by averaging the individual BTCs. A succeeding model analyses on the computed large- or field-scale BTCs with a stochastic advective-reactive travel time approach was performed aiming at identifying governing non-equilibrium conditions and their effects on herbicide losses.

METHODS AND MATERIALS

The experimental site Altenholz had a size of 1.8 ha and is located in the vicinity of the city of Kiel in northern Germany (54.4° N, 10° E). The 99 samples were taken at a regular grid with a 15-m spacing. First, sampling started by removing the 5-cm top layer of the soil. Secondly, the stainless steel cylinders (10 cm in length and 5.4 cm in diameter) were slowly inserted vertically into the prepared sampling location. Thirdly, the intact cores were carefully removed from the soil and were sealed with plastic lids for safe transport to the laboratory. Fourthly, crumbed soil surrounding the cores was collected at each sampling location in order to determine additional soil parameters. Soil cores that were not directly used in the leaching experiments were stored at 4° C.

All 99 soil monoliths were subjected to classical displacement tests under unsaturated steady-state flow conditions. The set-up facilitated the simultaneous treatment of 24 samples (Lennartz et al., 1997). Water desaturation of samples was achieved by applying a pressure of -3 kPa at the lower end of the samples which corresponded to natural conditions during the winter period in humid regions. A chemically inert Nylon membrane with an average pore space of 10 μm functioned as a ceramic plate. Herbicide and tracer-free water was supplied at the top of the sample via a sprinkler consisting of a plastic cover preventing evaporation and 4 hypodermic needles. The sprinkler were rotated manually once per day. The chemical composition of the water was adjusted according to naturally occurring rain water. Samples were irrigated at 19-min intervals for 1 s; that resulted in an average water flux density of $q=0.58$ cm d^{-1}. The established flow regime was chosen in order to represent natural conditions, no bypass flow was expected at the adjusted moderate flux density.

Application solutions were prepared from the formulated commercial products Arelon (Hoechst AG) and Gardoprim 500 (Ciba-Geigy GmbH) containing 2.42 mol l^{-1} isoproturon (IPU) and 2.13 mol l^{-1} terbuthylazine, respectively, as a suspension. The chemicals were dissolved in a bromide solution (12.5 mmol l^{-1}) at rates between 2 μmol l^{-1} and 2.05 μmol l^{-1}. The application solution was freshly prepared for every batch of soil samples and subsequently analysed. Observed minor fluctuations in herbicide concentrations probably resulted from using formulated standard agrochemicals for the preparation of the application solution. Two doses of 0.5 ml each were applied at 19-min intervals with a Hamilton high precision syringe to the surface of the soil samples; this corresponded to an average rate for both herbicides of 1.6 kg ha^{-1}.

Model analyses

The advantage of the stochastic advective-reactive modelling approach is that possible biogeochemical mass transfer and transformation processes that may affect a reactive compound during its transport through the vadoze soil zone can be decoupled from pure advection and the different manifestations of preferential flow and transport. One possible manifestation of non-equilibrium transport conditions is that advection occurs only in the mobile soil water region, whereas the remaining soil water fraction is considered to be stagnant. In this classical mobile / immobile soil water concept diffusional mass transfer between regions is an additional important mechanism for solute transport which is quantified in terms of a mass transfer coefficient α [T^{-1}]. The total soil water content θ is the sum of the mobile θ_m and the immobile θ_{im} water fraction: $\theta = \theta_m + \theta_{im}$.

Another non-equilibrium flow and transport scenario is that the soil water is divided into two fractions and that advection takes place in both regions. The non-equilibrium is caused by significant soil water velocity differences between the two water phases. The soil water content is distributed as θ_1 (water content in slow flow paths) and θ_2 (water content in preferential flow paths), so that the total water content is $\theta = \theta_1 + \theta_2$. The flow domains are represented as the weighted sum of two log-normal probability density functions (pdf) which is defined by the mean travel times μ_i and the variances of $\ln \mu_i$ σ^2_i, with index i = 1 referring to the slow flow paths and index i = 2 referring to the preferential flow paths (Destouni et al., 1994).

RESULTS AND DISCUSSION

Two general, but different, types of breakthrough situations could be distinguished with the lysimeters (Figure 1). As expected, in over 90 % of all lysimeters, a chromatographic separation of the applied chemicals in the order bromide, isoproturon and terbuthylazine was observed. However, despite the small adjusted water flux rate and water desaturation, all compounds occurred simultaneously in 7 cases, indicating a pronounced preferential transport situation. The simultaneous occurrence of all 3 chemicals was accompanied by an early arrival at the outlet of the columns, providing further evidence for preferential flow. Assuming pure advective-dispersive transport, concentration maxima of non-reactive tracers should occur in the effluent after the exchange of one pore volume. The range of breakthrough times observed in this study reflects the presence of immobile or slowly moving soil water fractions. This phenomenon of immobile water phases reduces the effective flow cross-sectional area, and has been documented previously for unsaturated flow conditions in undisturbed soil columns (e.g. Jardine et al., 1993). Our experimental results confirm that solute transport under unsaturated flow conditions is always faster than expected from the measured flux density and volumetric water content and therefore is not equilibrated.

The bromide mass recovery ranged from 57% to 125% with a mean of 85% and a CV of 15%. Incomplete mass balances of non-reactive solutes as observed in this case are probably related to the fractionating of soil water in mobile and stagnant water phases. During early stages of the leaching tests solute molecules, following a steep concentration gradient, are transported easily into immobile water regions. At later stages when the centre of solute mass has left the column, the concentration gradient from the stagnant fraction towards the convective moving water phase is less pronounced and solute diffusion out of the immobile region is also less effective. This may lead to a solute release from the columns at concentrations below the detection limit (0.5 mg l^{-1} for bromide), so that a fraction of the applied solute mass is washed from the column after sampling has been terminated. An additional reason for incomplete mass balances that has to be taken into account is a possible mechanical change in soil structure during the experimental run because of processes such as internal erosion effects. These mechanical changes may decrease the accessibility of immobile water regions via diffusion during the experimental run. As a consequence, solute transport into the stagnant zone at the beginning of the experiment may occur unhindered while the transport into the opposite direction at later stages of the test is limited.

Twenty columns had an acceptable mass balance of 100 % ±10 %. The sampling locations of theses samples were located in the south-western part of the field site (Area 2, 1.14 ha). Moreover, these 20 columns, as well as most other columns in Area 2, yielded BTCs with less pronounced preferential flow characteristics than the columns in the remaining north-eastern part (Area 1, 0.66 ha) of the field site. All samples in Area 1 yielded poor bromide mass balance and several of them exhibited bimodal BTCs.

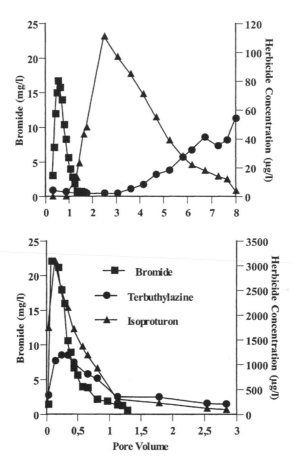

Figure 1.   Examples of individual breakthrough behaviour. Top: Classical separation of non-reactive and reactive compounds. Note: Bromide maximum concentration is reached before the exchange of one pore volume. Bottom: Simultaneous occurrence of all three applied solutes in the effluent indicating pronounced preferential flow.

The data set was separated into four sub-sets: Mass balance columns (MBC), Area 1 columns, Area 2 columns, and the entire data set (Area 1 + Area 2). The individual BTCs of the data sets were summarised by averaging in order to obtain a large or field-scale signal which was subjected to model analyses (Simic *et al.*, 2001).

Examples of the field-scale breakthrough behaviour of bromide and isoproturon are depicted in Figure 2. Whereas the few columns that exhibited an extreme preferential transport regime had obviously only minor effects on the breakthrough behaviour of the conservative compound, they caused a bimodal field-BTC for isoproturon. As the area under the BTCs represents the solute loss it is evident that extreme preferential transport conditions have a great effect on the exported solute mass especially for sorbing compounds.

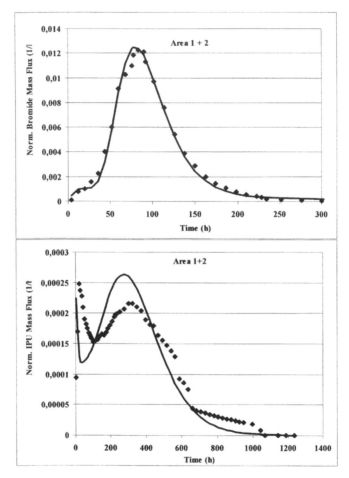

Figure 2.   Large- or field-scale bromide (top) and isoprtoturon (bottom) BTCs as resulting from the averaged 99 individual BTCs representing the entire experimental field site. The solid line indicates the optimised curve assuming two advective flow domains.

The two field-BTCs that were derived from the MBC and from the Area 2 columns could be described best with the mobile/immobile approach while the remaining two large-scale signals required a bimodal function to obtain satisfying optimisation results. The preferential flow columns of Area 1 had a strong influence on the entire data set causing bimodal BTCs of the reactive compounds (Figure 2). The model analyses showed that two different manifestations of non-equilibrium transport modified the breakthrough behaviour of solutes at one field site. However, the different flow scenarios were spatially separated.

In addition to the analyses with the mobile / immobile and the two advective flow domain approaches large-scale BTCs were computed assuming equilibrium transport conditions in order to estimate non-equilibrium effects on the exported herbicidal mass fraction. Results of model analyses are summarised in Table 1.

Table 1.   Modelling results; leached herbicide mass fraction as percentage of (measured) recovered mass with and without consideration of transport non-equilibrium.

	Area 1	Area 2	MBC*	Area 1+2
	Isoproturon			
Tot. leached herbicide mass fract. with transport non-equilibrium (% of observed)	99	94	96	97
without transport non-equilibrium (% of observed)	22	46	54	40
	Terbuthylazine			
Tot. leached herbicide mass fract. with transport non-equilibrium (% of observed)	106	103	100	105
without transport non-equilibrium (% of observed)	11	44	48	31

* Mass balance columns

The rapid transport at Area 1 increased the total leached mass of isoproturon and terbuthylazine by 350% and 810% respectively. At the remaining area of the experimental plot (1.14 ha) immobile water regions caused an increase of the leached mass fraction of 100% and 130% of the respective reactive compounds.

REFERENCES

Destouni G; Sassner M; Jensen K H (1994). Chloride migration in heterogeneous soil, 2. Stochastic modeling. *Water Resources Research* **30**:747-758.

Jardine P M; Jacobs G K; Wilson G V (1993). Unsaturated tranport processes in undisturbed heterogeneous porous media: I. Inorganic contaminants. *Soil Science Society of America Journal* **57**: 945-953.

Lennartz B (1999). Variation of herbicide transport parameters within a single field and its relation to water flux and soil properties. *Geoderma* **91**(3/4): 327-345.

Simic E; Destouni G; Lennartz B (2001). Field-scale herbicide transport through preferential flow paths. *Environmental Science Technology* submitted.

Edge field leaching study of metalaxyl-M and its main metabolite

E Capri, F Ferrari, Z Miao, M Trevisan
Istituto di Chimica Agraria ed Ambientale, Università Cattolica del Sacro Cuore,
Via Emilia Parmense, 84 – 29100 Piacenza, Italy.
Email: chimiv@pc.unicatt.it

ABSTRACT

The study aimed to assess the leaching of the fungicide metalaxyl-M and its main metabolite N-(2,6-dimethylphenyl)-N-(2'-methoxy-acetyl)-alanine) under Italian field conditions. The experiment was carried out in an irrigated 1824 m^2 field, cultivated with pepper. The leaching of the compounds were evaluated following a strict field protocol including several chemical and physical measurements in field and laboratory. The parent compound dissipated quickly in the soil (DT_{50}=20days) being transformed to the main de-methyl metabolite that is more water soluble. Residues were detected frequently in the soil pore water: the maximum concentration of Metalaxyl-M and its metabolite in soil water were 13.9 µg/litre and 8.6 µg/litre respectively, 31 days after the first treatment, then disappearing slowly in 120 days. However, these residues were not detected in the groundwater 8 m deep during the study of 360 days. Taking into account the spatial field variability of the soil properties, as well the applied dose, the PELMO model has been applied to complement the monitored data and the risk assessment analysis.

INTRODUCTION

Metalaxyl is a well known systemic fungicide used to control diseases caused by *Peronosporales* in several crops. Recently new formulations with higher biological efficacy have been developed based on the stereoisomer (R) commercially known as Metalaxyl-M (Figure 1). In soil and water the Metalaxyl-M is transformed quickly to its metabolite via oxidation of the methyl group which is more soluble in water (265 g/litre against 26 g/litre of Metalaxyl-M) but also less persistent in soil. Zadra *et al.*, (2001) have measured a faster soil dissipation of the stereoisomer (R) compared to the racemic mixture.

However, looking at the chemical properties of the a.i. a common question may arise: is the metabolite a potential leacher ?

Figure 1. Metalaxyl-M (DL-N-(2,6-dimethylphenyl)-N-(2'-methoxy-acetyl)-
alanine-methylester) (left) and its metabolite (DL-N-(2,6-
dimethylphenyl)-N-(2'-methoxy-acetyl)-alanine) (right).

The pesticide European directive 91/414/EEC has focused attention on this environmental process affecting water quality. For groundwater quality the measurement of the pesticide leaching in field conditions is the main issue. The method described by the SETAC and EPPO provides an experimental design that does not cover the spatial & temporal diversity of the environmental processes influencing the pesticide fate.

In this paper we report the methodology adopted to measure the leaching of the above a.i. and its metabolite at the field scale and also assess their hazard to the groundwater in Italy.

METHODS AND MATERIALS

Field study

The study protocol applied followed that of Capri *et al.*, (2000), modified for outdoor conditions. Briefly, the field is representative of the typical use of the compound studied and of the normal agricultural practice; it is an irrigated 1824 m^2 plot cultivated with pepper sited in Piacenza (44.92 N; 9.73 E). Unsaturated zone and soil properties were measured and sampling was carried out through the collection of continuous cores down to the shallow groundwater (8 m depth). The soil is deep about 1 m and above an old and deep gravel bed river which is very permeable. Soil is loamy (Vertisol xeric FAO taxonomy) with an uniform vertical mass distribution in texture (about 45 % silt and 33 % clay) and pH (about 8); organic matter decrease from 1.2 % to 0.2 % from the top soil to 120 cm depth.

Pesticide was applied along the crop lines on the 7th June and the 26th June in post emergence of the pepper crop as commercial formulation Ridomil 480EC Gold at 0.134 g/m^2 and 0.109 g/m^2 in the first and second application respectively. The crop was irrigated via drip irrigation every week starting from the plant transplanting (total irrigation 230 mm). Pesticide application and crop interception was measured using paper traps. Unsaturated zone as well the pesticide mobility was investigated by means of soil samples collected in the top soil (0-30 cm divided in 3 layers 10 cm each) and soil-water suction cup installed below the root zone at 60 cm depth: sampling followed a schedule over a time frame of 180 days after the pesticide application. Additional sampling was also done after the main irrigation and precipitation. The groundwater quality in the saturated zone was monitored by means of sampling carried out after the main precipitations and monthly for 1 year after the pesticide application (Figure 2).

Extraction and pesticide analysis

Soil and water samples were extracted with methanol and aqueous buffer solution of pH 10. Metalaxil-M was partitioned from this solution into dichloromethane. The organic phase was brought to dryness and the residues were cleaned up by alumina column chromatography. The aqueous phase was acidified with hydrochloric acid and the metabolite was partitioned into dichloromethane. The organic phase was evaporated, the residues were methylated with diazometane and then were cleaned up by alumina column chromatography. Quantification of both Metalaxil-M and metabolite residues was achieved by GC-MS using selected ion monitoring. The limit of detection was 0.01 mg/kg for both a.i. in soil, 0.10 µg/l for Metalaxil-M and 0.20 µg/litre for the metabolite in water.

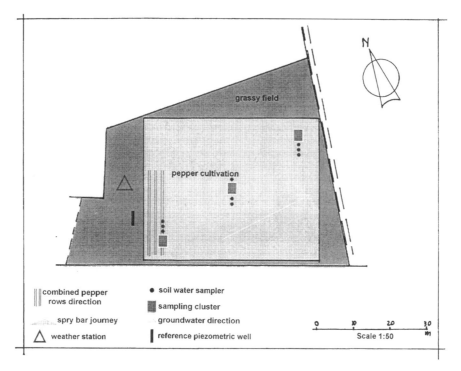

Figure 2.   The experimental field.

Data analysis

Measurement of the pesticide leaching in the field studies can show high spatial variability due to the variability of the soil properties such as organic matter, texture and microbial biomass as well variability of the pesticide application (Vischetti *et al.,* 1997). Geostatistics was the technique used to characterize the spatial variability (Gamma Design Software, 1992) for some of the main properties.

To assess the leaching of the pesticides to the groundwater two different strategies were used: a stochastic approach and the FOCUS methodology (FOCUS, 2000). The former was realised by means of Monte Carlo approach with a sample size equal to 64 obtained considering 80% of occurrence probability, 20 % of unoccurrence probability, 90 % confidential interval (Zewei, 2001) and changing randomly the value of some model input (Table 1); furthermore FOCUS approach with 20-years simulation in the "scenario Piacenza" was applied. Both strategies were not used for validating the models but to obtain data that were not measured in the field such as the outflow concentration below one meter of soil depth and the soil water fluxes.

RESULTS

Pesticide persistence in the soil-water system

A high percentage of the pesticide applied was intercepted by the crop (about 50%) and the load to the soil surface was varying along the field: the semi variance was not significant for the different models (spherical, exponential, linear, linear to sill, gaussian).

Metalaxyl-M was transformed to the metabolite which was detectable in the top soil from the first sampling after the application. Maximum soil concentration of both Metalaxyl-M and metabolite was measured three days after the second application (0.45 mg/kg and 0.033 mg/kg respectively). The DT50 in soil, assuming a first order kinetic, is about 2 weeks for both compounds. However, residue of the pesticide persisted in the soil for some weeks, but after 272 days no residues where detectable in the soil (Figure 3).

Table 1.   Parameter assumption in the Monte Carlo approach. Between the brackets the value for the metabolite.

Input	Distribution Type	Minimum Value	Maximum value	Mean	Standard deviation
Applied dose (g/m²)	Normal			0.361	0.189
Koc (ml/g)	Uniform	109.8 (61.0)	1122.0 (695.1)		
Organic Carbon (%)	Lognormal			0.491	0.048
Dissipation time (days)	Uniform	19.5 (10.4)	86.9 (36.4)		
Sand top soil (%)	Normal			17.92	2.23
Silt top soil (%)	Normal			47.11	1.29
Bulk density (kg/l)	Normal			1.44	0.005

Metalaxyl-M and its metabolite were detected mainly in the top soil (Figure 3) but were measured in the soil-water at 60 cm depth (Figure 4): in the first 130 days after the application pesticide residue were measured in soil pore water with maximum concentration of 14 µg/litre and 8 µg/litre for the Metalaxyl-M and the metabolite respectively. Movement may be due to the high water input used in the field as irrigation.

Both compounds were not detected in the groundwater for one year after the application although an estimated water recharge > 200 mm had occurred due to irrigation.

Table 2.   Descriptive statistic of the model outputs obtained after three years of simulation.

	Metalaxyl-M		Metabolite	
	g/ha	µg/litre	g/ha	µg/litre
Mean	0.0019	0.0005	0.0092	0.0026
Std dev	0.0133	0.0038	0.0369	0.0103
90° perc.tile	0.0010	0	0.0096	0.0030

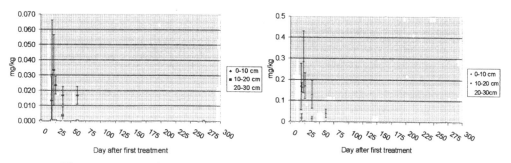

Figure 3.   Metalaxyl-M (right) and metabolite dissipation in soil at different
depth (left).

Actual and potential leaching assessment

Both pesticide and metabolite may not leach to the bottom of the unsaturated zone in the field
test site although they are slightly persistent and mobile in the root soil zone. However, the
detection of residue at 60 cm depth, in only a few samples, from this field test suggest
groundwater contamination is unlikely to be significant

Results of the probabilistic assessment, that included all the possible combinations of
conditions that we can find, indicate that water concentration below 1 meter will be always
below the limit required by 91/414/EEC (<0.1 µg/litre) after two consecutive years of
application (Table 2). This was also confirmed when the Piacenza scenario of the FOCUS
was applied (Boesten *et al.*, 2000) per 20 years

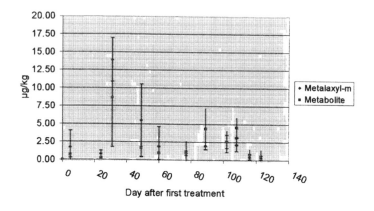

Figure 4.   Metalaxyl-M and metabolite dissipation in soil-water.

The leaching of both a.i. and metabolite after the normal agricultural uses is mitigated throughout a combination of different factors but the low application dose and the plant interception play an important role.

The results reported confirm that deterministic and probabilistic model application which is integrated with the measurement carried in the field can assess the pesticide hazard to contaminate the groundwater. Furthermore, as the model application included the spatial variability of the input measured in the field or estimated, the output obtained will include the uncertainity associated itself with the predictions.

REFERENCES

FOCUS (2000). Focus groundwater scenarios in the EU plant protection product review process. Report of the FOCUS Groundwater Scenarios Workgroup, pp. 197, EC Document Reference SANCO/321/2000.

Capri E; Glass C R; Trevisan M; Del Re A A M (2000). Measurement of the pesticide fate in greenhouses: air, soil and water. In: *Pesticide/Soil interactions: some current research methods*. INRA Editions, Paris, 311-322.

Gamma Design Software (1992). GS+ Geostatistic for the environmental sciences. P O Box 201 Michigan 49080 USA.

Marucchini C; Zadra C (2001) Stereoselective degradation of metalaxyl and metalaxyl-M in soil and sunflower plants. *Chirality (in press)*..

Vischetti C; Businelli M; Marini M; Capri E; Trevisan M; Del Re A A M; Donnarumma L; Conte E; Imbroglini G (1997). Characterization of spatial variability structure in three separate field trials on pesticide dissipation. *Pesticide Science* **50**: 175-182.

Zadra C (2000) *Persistenza e stereoselettività di fitofarmaci a struttura asimmetrica*. Tesi di dottorato, Biblioteca Nazionale, Firenze.

Zewei M, Padovani L ; Capri E ; Del Re A A M ; Trevisan M (2001). Stochastic approach to evaluate pesticide fate in paddy area using the RICEWQ model. First European Modelling Workshop, Silsoe, 18-19 June 2001.

Infiltration of acetochlor metabolites in two contrasted soils

N Baran, C Mouvet, T Dagnac, R Jeannot
BRGM, 3, avenue C Guillemin, BP6009, 45060 Orléans Cedex, France

ABSTRACT

We studied the fate of two acetochlor metabolites, ethanesulfonic acid (ESA) and oxanilic acid (OA), in two contrasting soil types (luvisol and calcosol) under the same climatic conditions. The detection of the metabolites in the soils only 21 days after application, indicated a rapid onset of acetochlor degradation. Greater concentrations of ESA persisted in the calcosol compared to OA, regardless of time lapse or depth, as against an ESA/OA ratio that varied with both time and depth in the luvisol. Sampling the soils 55 days after application, revealed both metabolites at 93 cm depth in the luvisol, and ESA at 51 cm depth in the calcosol (maximum sampling depths).

INTRODUCTION

Acetochlor was registered in France in 2000 and now forms part of substitution programmes. Few data are available on the fate of the chloroacetanilides in general, very few for acetochlor, and even fewer for the acetochlor metabolites. Some laboratory studies have been carried out, but field studies are rare despite the fact that this is the only way to determine all the processes that are or could be involved in the fate of agrochemicals in the environment. Balinova (1997) has shown that acetochlor, like the other chloroacetanilides (metolachlor and alachlor), must be considered as a potential groundwater contaminant. Added to this, Kalhoff *et al.*, (1998) and Kolpin *et al.*, (1998) have detected that acetochlor and its major degradates in groundwater in the USA.

In order to assess the risk of groundwater contamination from acetochlor, a first step is to study the fate of the herbicide in the soil. Thus the purpose of the present study was to determine the fate of two acetochlor metabolites in two agricultural soils under the same climatic conditions.

MATERIALS AND METHODS

The study site is a small hydrogeological basin of some 3 km² whose outlet is a spring tapped for drinking water. It lies within the Paris Basin (70 km west of Paris). The two highly contrasted soils that were selected for the study are a deep silty soil (luvisol-FAO classification) and a shallower, more pebbly, more calcareous soil (calcosol-FAO classification) that is also slightly more clayey in the surface layers (around 20% vs. 15%).

The experimental fieldwork was carried out on two 100 x 70 m maize plots, one in each soil type. A commercial liquid pesticide (Trophee, Zeneca Sopra) was applied to the plots in pre-emergence by spraying directly onto the soil on 19 April 2000. This was the first time that acetochlor had been applied to these plots. A solution of KBr had been applied a few hours before the pesticide treatment. The average applications were (a) 1530 g/ha (+/-387 g) acetochlor and 19,967 g/ha (+/- 7638 g) bromide for the calcosol plot, and (b) 2021 g/ha (+/- 504 g) acetochlor and 32,589 g/ha (+/- 13,730 g) bromide for the luvisol plot.

A national meteorological network raingauge 3.5 km from the site records the daily precipitation. Due to the proximity (850 m) of the two experimental plots, the precipitation is considered as identical for both. The first rain (10 mm) fell on 20 April, *i.e.* one day after treatment.

Soil samples were collected both before the herbicide application and 7, 21 (calcosol) / 27 (luvisol), 55, 168 and 248 days after the application. The two plots were each divided into 4 equal area subplots from which 4 samples were taken during each campaign, thus giving a total of 16 samples per plot per campaign. A 10-cm-diameter percussion corer was used for the sampling, with the maximum sampled depth being 1.0 m in the luvisol, and less in the calcosol where the limestone substratum was at a shallower depth. After removal of the outer part, the cores were cut into segments corresponding to depth intervals of 0-5, 5-10, 10-20, 20-30 cm, etc. Each sample was dried at 40 °C for 3 days then ground to 2 mm.

Bromide was extracted from the soil in a solution of $CaCl_2$ $10^{-4}M$ with 40 minutes agitation, followed by centrifugation and filtering. The extracts were then analysed in an ion chromatograph (Dionex 4500i model) equipped with an As14 column. The two main acetochlor metabolites (Feng, 1991), *i.e.* ESA acetochlor and OA acetochlor, were determined through extraction with a water/acetonitrile mixture and analysed by HPLC/MS. The limits of detection are 0.5 µg/kg and 2.0 µg/kg for the ESA and OA compounds, respectively (Dagnac *et al.*, 2001).

DISCUSSION

Bromide concentrations measured for the soils before application are of the same order (below 0.28 mg/kg) of magnitude as those reported by Flury & Papritz (1993) for different soil types in several countries. The bromide analyses carried out on the 16 cores taken during each sampling campaign on the two plots show a high variability as regards both the measured concentrations at each depth and the overall profiles. On the basis of the bromide profiles (figs. 1 and 2) and mass balances (table 1) obtained for each campaign, two cores corresponding to extreme situations (marked preferential flow for one – PF – , and preponderant matrix transport – MT – for the other) were selected for analysis of acetochlor metabolites.

Both ESA and OA were detected in the two soils 21 (calcosol)/27 (luvisol) and 55 days after treatment (Figs. 1 and 2). At the end of 21 (calcosol)/27 (luvisol) days, the sum of the metabolites present along the profile were, depending on the core, between 8.9% (figure 1: luvisol PF) and 31.2% (figure 1: calcosol MT) of the average applied dose of acetochlor; the onset of acetochlor degradation was thus rapid. These observations are in agreement with the less than 10-day DT50 for acetochlor (Feng, 1991; Mueller *et al.*, 1999) observed in previous incubation experiments and in situ tests.

At 55 days after application, the metabolite percentages in the profiles of the two cores from the same soil are close, whereas at 21/27 days after application the difference between the two cores was much higher, in particular for the calcosol.

Table 1. Percentage of bromide (Br), acetochlor ESA and acetochlor OA in each soil column relative to the average applied doses.

Core	Days after treatment	Cumulative precipitation (mm)	Br % appl. dose	ESA % appl. dose	OA % appl. dose	ESA+OA % appl. dose
Calcosol MT	21	95	127	20.2	11.0	31.2
Calcosol PF	21	95	55	6.1	3.4	9.5
Calcosol MT	55	184	111	6.1	0.2	6.3
Calcosol PF	55	184	36	5.3	0.7	6.0
Luvisol MT	27	115	136	7.5	14.5	22.0
Luvisol PF	27	115	29	3.1	5.8	8.9
Luvisol MT	55	184	69	7.6	5.1	12.7
Luvisol PF	55	184	60	7.4	7.4	14.8

Between 21/27 and 55 days after treatment, the diminution of the metabolite percentages (with respect to the parent molecule) is more obvious in the calcosol than in the luvisol. The fourth campaign (168 days after treatment) showed that the metabolite percentages continue to diminish in both soil types (results not presented). This decrease could be due to different factors. For example, the ESA and OA metabolites could themselves degrade into other subproducts not looked for in the study. They could also become fixed to the solid matrix due to the formation of non-extractable residues. Finally, the degradates could be leached to deeper horizons that were not sampled (*i.e.* to a soil horizon deeper than 1 m and to consolidated limestone); that such leaching is probably not insignificant is indicated by the fact that ESA was detected in the deep horizons of the calcosol after 21/27 days, and that both ESA and OA were found at deeper levels of the luvisol after 55 days than after 21/27 days. As the metabolites were detected in the deepest horizons sampled, it is quite likely that they occur at even deeper levels. The bromide data provide some clues with this respect.

The bromide quantities present in the profile decreased indeed significantly with time (Table 2). Therefore, considering that i) uptake of bromide by maize is limited and ii) bromide does not decay or become fixed to the soil, the bromide losses can only be explained by lateral flow or leaching. The first hypothesis can be excluded due to the absence of a less permeable pedological horizon to give rise to lateral flow. The bromide loss therefore reflects leaching below the sampled horizons, particularly so in the luvisol.

Table 2. Cumulated bromide present in the soil profile expressed as percentage of the applied dose (average of 16 soil cores by period and soil type).

Days after treatment	Cumulative precipitation (mm)	Calcosol (%)	Luvisol (%)
7	46	117	69
21/27	95/115	138	85
55	184	121	56
168	398	14	13

The hypothesis that the acetochlor acid metabolites are leached to depths greater than those sampled here, is also supported by the results of measurements made on 88 wells in the United States (Kalhoff *et al.*,1998; Kolpin *et al.*,1998), which showed that acetochlor degraded to mobile metabolites that were then transported to groundwater before complete mineralization of the parent compounds. We can thus consider that the ESA and OA metabolites are prone to leaching.

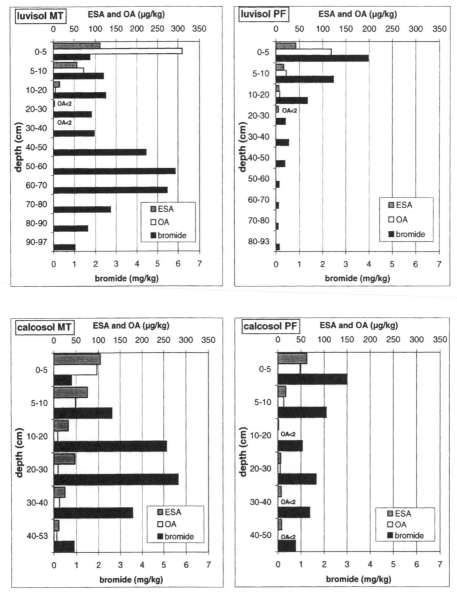

Figure 1. Depth profile of acetochlor ESA and OA, 21 (calcosol) or 27 (luvisol) days after application.
Luvisol MT / Calcosol MT: luvisol/calcosol core with Br profile suggesting matrix transport
Luvisol PF / Calcosol PF: luvisol/calcosol core with Br profile suggesting preferential flow
Detection limit for OA = 2 µg/kg; detection limit for ESA = 0.5 µg/kg

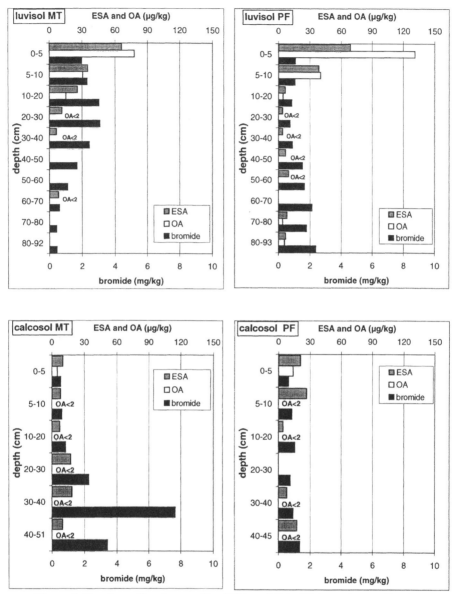

Figure 2. Depth profile of acetochlor ESA and OA, 55 days after application.
Luvisol MT / Calcosol MT: luvisol/calcosol core with Br profile suggesting matrix transport
Luvisol PF / Calcosol PF: luvisol/calcosol core with Br profile suggesting preferential flow
Detection limit for OA = 2 µg/kg; detection limit for ESA = 0.5 µg/kg

Another interesting observation concerns the differences between the soil types in relative contributions of the two acetochlor degradates. In the calcosol, the ESA concentrations are greater than the OA concentrations in all the horizons; the OA metabolite, 55 days following application, was no longer detected at the surface. In the luvisol, on both the second and third campaigns, the OA concentrations were equivalent to or much higher than the ESA concentrations in the uppermost 10 centimetres, whilst in the deeper horizons it is the ESA concentrations that are highest and OA may sometimes no longer be detected. Moreover, the OA concentration 55 days after application is proportionally less than the ESA concentration, as compared to the situation 21/27 days after application. The disappearance of OA with time could indicate that this compound is less stable, is more mobile, or a greater proportion has become non-extractable residues.

Although the bromide data show a greater leaching in the luvisol than in the calcosol (table 2), more ESA and OA remain in the luvisol than in the calcosol (table 1). This strongly suggests that the formation and/or persistence of ESA and OA is different in the two soils. The differences in moisture content and temperature – two parameters that are dominant in the degradation of agrochemicals – resulting from the different soil textures and structures most likely play a key role here.

Based on the data available, a risk of groundwater contamination by ESA and/or OA is strongly suggested, even though no definite conclusion can be drawn on the comparative risk between by ESA and OA on one hand, and between calcosol and luvisol on the other hand.

ACKNOWLEDGEMENTS

The authors would like to thank Monsanto for supplying the analytical standards for OA and ESA degradates, and also the INRA staff who drew up the pedological map of the hydrogeological basin. The work conducted here is supported partly through the PEGASE project, contract EVK1-CT1999-00028, financed by the EU through its 5th PCRDT.

REFERENCES

Balinova AM (1997). Acetochlor: a comparative study on parameters governing the potential for water pollution. *Journal of Environmental Science and Health* **32** :645-658.

Dagnac T; Jeannot R; Mouvet C, Baran N (2001). Determination of chloroacetanilide metabolites in waters and soils by LC/ESI-MS. Poster presented at 2nd MGPR international Symposium of pesticides in food and the environment, Valencia (Spain), 9-12 may 2001

Feng PCC (1991). Soil transformation of acetochlor via glutathione conjugation. *Pesticide Biochemistry and Physiology* **40**: 136-142.

Flury M; Papritz A (1993). Bromide in the natural environment: occurrence and toxicity. *Journal of Environmental Quality* **22**: 747-758.

Kalkhoff S J; Kolpin D W; Thurman E M; Ferrer I; Barcelo D (1998). Degradation of chloroacetanilide herbicides: the prevalence of sulfonic and oxanilic acid metabolites in Iowa groundwaters and surface waters. *Environmental Science & Technology* **32**: 1738-1740.

Kolpin D W; Thurman E M; Linhart SM (1998). The environmental occurrence of herbicides: the importance of degradates in ground water. *Archives of Environmental Contamination and Toxicology* **35**: 385-390.

Mueller T C; Shaw D R; Witt W W (1999). Relative dissipation of acetochlor, alachlor, metolachlor and SAN 582 from three surface soils. *Weed Technology* **13**: 341-346.

Sorption properties of isoproturon and diflufenican on ditch bed sediments and organic matter rich materials from ditches, grassed strip and forest soils.

C Margoum, V Gouy
Cemagref, Unité de Recherche QEPP, 3 bis quai Chauveau, 69336 Lyon Cedex 09, France
Email: christelle.margoum@cemagref.fr

I Madrigal, P Benoit
INRA, Unité Environnement et Grandes Cultures, 78850 Thiverval-Grignon, France

J Smith, A C Johnson, R J Williams
Centre for Ecology and Hydrology, Crowmarsh Gifford, Wallingford, Oxon, OX10 8BB, UK

ABSTRACT

In order to limit non-point source pollution from agricultural pesticides, research programs have been developed to study the different transport and dissipation mechanisms of pesticides from fields to rivers. Sorption is considered as one of the major processes responsible for the decrease of pesticide concentration in run-off. Sorption is thought to be especially important in buffer zones installed to reduce pesticides losses by runoff from agricultural areas. This can occur in grassed areas, such as grassed buffer strips, or forested land, and also in linear ditches collecting surface and drainage waters. Buffer zones contain many elements which could influence pesticide sorption. For example, in ditches a great variety of solid materials may act as sorbents: grasses, tree leaves, woody materials in different states of decomposition, organo-mineral particles or sediments originating from soil erosion. Laboratory experiments were carried out to investigate some of the intrinsic properties of different types of sediment/organic litter. Adsorption and desorption kinetics were studied with the herbicides isoproturon, and diflufenican. Batch experiments were used to determine sorption isotherms and Kd values. The comparison of the different results shows that beside the sorbent organic matter content, which was the main contributory factor for herbicide sorption, organic matter decomposition and origin had to be taken into account to explain the differences observed between ditch, grassed soil and forest litter materials.

INTRODUCTION

Agricultural non-point pollution originates from land areas which intermittently contribute to the transfer of pollutants to water by runoff, drainage, and leaching. Many methods and levels of actions can be developed to reduce the transfer. First, new or improved agricultural practices can be set up, such as choosing the best application period, controlling toxic substance impacts, and combining with non-chemical practices (Baker *et al.*, 1995). However, pesticide losses from fields cannot be totally eliminated. Pesticides leaving a plot may pass through landscape components before reaching rivers; including other fields, ditches, brooks, and vegetative or wooded buffer zones. Since 1992, two French Research Institutes Cemagref and INRA, in collaboration with the Institut Technique des Cereales et des Fourrages (ITCF), have studied the role played by grassed buffer strips in reducing the contamination of runoff water (Patty *et al.*, 1997; Benoit *et al*, 1999). Concerning farm ditches, different experiments have been carried out by Cemagref, on natural sites in Western France (Garon-Boucher *et al.*, in press) and by the Centre for Ecology and Hydrology (CEH) in the Oxfordshire (Williams *et al.*, 1999). Reduction of maximum concentrations and fluxes have been noticed for each site and buffer zone. Pesticide dissipation seems strongly linked to the nature of substratum and also to the physico-chemical properties of the molecules. Furthermore, the diversity of vegetative materials greatly varies spatially and over the season. Therefore, it is important to characterise the relationship between the nature of sorbents found in such buffer zones and pesticide sorption characteristics, namely kinetics, capacities and reversibility.

Research has been carried out on these aspects in rural ditches, grassed strip and forested land in France and the UK. Different natural organic and organo-mineral materials have been sampled in ditches, surface layers of grassed and forest soils. Sorption and desorption properties of these materials were characterised in laboratory classical batch experiments for two ^{14}C labelled herbicides, isoproturon, (3-(4-isopropylphenyl)-1,1-dimethylurea) and diflufenican (2',4'-difluoro-2-(α, α, α-trifluoro-m-tolyloxy)nicotinanilide).

MATERIALS AND METHODS

Chemicals

Isoproturon was uniformly ^{14}C-labelled on the phenyl ring with a specific activity of 2.66×10^9 Bq mmol^{-1} and a radiopurity greater than 95%. It was purchased from Amersham. ^{14}C diflufenican labelled on C2 position of the nicotinamide ring was purchased from Aventis. Specific activity was 7.19×10^8 Bq mmol^{-1} and a radiopurity of 99%.

Table 1.   Properties of the studied herbicides

Characteristics	Isoproturon (IPU)	Diflufenican (DFF)
Solubility in water (mg/litre)	65 (22°C)	0.05 (25°C)
Koc (ml/g)	120	1990
Kow	2.5	4.9

Natural sorbents

Ditch bed sediments were collected in two different natural sites in France and the UK. The French one was sampled in Roujan (southern France). The soils of this catchment are developed from marine, lacustrine or fluvial sediments. The other site in the UK is the Oxford University Farm at Wytham, Oxfordshire. The predominant soil type is heavy clay from the Dentworth series. Both sediments were dried at 40°C, sieved using a 2-mm sieve and analysed for carbon (C) and nitrogen (N) contents (Table 2) before sorption studies.

Dead leaves that can be found in natural ditches in France are commonly oak and chestnut tree leaves. For this study, leaves were collected in autumn and dried at about 30 °C. Other organic materials were collected from an 8 years old grassed strip and a forest floor in an oak forest. Both sites were located at the experimental farm of the ITCF "La Jailliere" (western part of France). The soil is an hydromorphic silt loam on schists of the Massif Armoricain. For the forest floor, the litter was sampled between 0-2 cm after removing from the surface the coarsest debris mainly made of oak leaves in early decomposition. For the grassed strip, the surface layer 0-2 cm, an organic mat with a high density of collar and roots with fine soil aggregates attached to the roots, was separately sampled from the underneath horizons (Benoit *et al.*, 1999). The grassed strip was planted with perennial rye-grass (Lolium perenne) in 1992 (Patty *et al*, 1997). Above ground plant debris as stems and dead leaves at the surface of the mat were collected by cutting before sampling the 0-2 cm layer. From the two litters, light organic fractions (LOF) of the 0-2 cm layer were separated by dry and wet sieving. In both cases, the debris > 2 mm were considered similar to the fractions previously collected at the surface, respectively grass and leaves fraction. The sieved fraction (< 2 mm) was dispersed in water and passed successively through 200 µm and 50 µm sieves. From both size fractions 2mm-200µm and 200-50 µm, and LOF were separated by flotation in water and by successive washing in order to eliminate as far as possible coarse mineral particles. All the organic sorbents were air dried and stored before use in sorption experiments. They were analysed for total C and N content using a CHN autoanalyser. LOF fractions represented early decomposed materials as shown by the decrease in C/N ratio and the decrease in C content with the decrease in particle size (Table 2)

Table 2   Characteristics of the sediments and the organic materials

Samples	Organic C (g/kg)	Total N (g/kg)	C/N
Sediments			
Roujan (F)	10	-	-
Wytham (UK)	36	-	-
Dead leaves	492	12	41
Grassed Strip			
Grass fraction > 2mm	320	16	20
Litter LOF 2 mm – 200 µm	323	13	25
Litter LOF 50-200 µm	243	15	16
Forest Litter			
Leaves > 2 mm	449	14	32
Litter LOF 2 mm – 200 µm	348	15	23
Litter LOF 50-200 µm	340	17	20

Sorption experiments

Ditch sediments

The experiment was carried out for 5 sorption times (5, 20 minutes, 1, 5 and 24 hours) with 3 replicates. In each tube 10 g dry sediments were added to 10 ml 0.22 µm filtered ditch water and the appropriate volume of radiolabelled herbicide solution to reach a final concentration of 5 µg/litre. The mixtures were left on orbital shaker (about 200 shakes/minutes) at room temperature for the appropriate sorption time. After centrifugation, 1 ml of the 0.45 µm filtered supernatant was transferred into scintillation flask for radioactivity measurement by liquid scintillation counting. The herbicide concentrations in supernatant solution (C, in µg/ml) were calculated from the supernatant radioactivity measurements. The amount of sorbed herbicide, x, per mass of sorbent, m (in µg/g sorbent) was calculated from the difference of herbicide concentration before and after sorption. Sorption coefficients K_d were calculated from sorption data at 24 hours to estimate maximum sorption capacities of sediments. K_{oc} coefficients were derived from the K_d values (see equations 1 and 2):

$$Kd = \frac{x/m}{C} \quad (1) \qquad\qquad Koc = \frac{Kd}{OC} \times 100 \quad (2)$$

with OC: organic carbon content of the solid phase (%)

Desorption was then continued with the sorption tubes for 24 hours. The water left in the tube was removed and replaced by fresh water. The tubes were shaken for 30 minutes. Scintillation of the filtered supernatant was measured allowing the calculation of desorbed amounts. Desorbed amounts were expressed as % of initially sorbed amount.

Litter and organic materials

Solutions of ^{14}C-isoproturon and ^{14}C-diflufenican were prepared in calcium chloride (0.01M). Three milliliters of these solutions were added to 100 mg of organic fractions in glass centrifuge tubes with Teflon caps. Triplicate samples of each OM were used with one single concentration: 200 µg/litre for isoproturon and 30 µg/litre for diflufenican. Sorbed amounts were evaluated after 24 h shaking at 23 ± 1°C by the same procedure as described above. Contact times of 24 hours were considered sufficient to estimate sorption coefficients K_d and K_{oc} in order to compare the different organic materials. Desorption was evaluated after 24 h sorption. The supernatant was replaced by the same volume of 0.01M CaCl$_2$ solution and the suspensions were shaken at 23 ± 1°C. Desorption time was 30 minutes for dead leaves and 24 h for grass and forest organic materials. Then the suspensions were centrifuged and desorption was determined as previously described.

RESULTS AND DISCUSSION

Sorption kinetics. Contact time had a great effect on isoproturon sorption particularly on leaves (Figure 1) showing a continuous increase in sorption versus time. This agreed with other studies on isoproturon sorption in soils (Gaillardon & Durr, 1995; Walker & Jurado-Exposito, 1998).

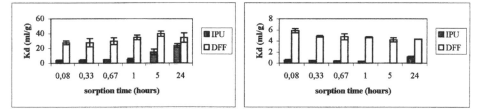

Figure 1. Sorption kinetics on leaves   Figure 2. Sorption kinetics on Roujan sediments

On the contrary diflufenican sorption reached an equilibrium after 5 minutes (Figuress 1 and 2). Considering that short contact times of 5 or 10 minutes are relevant to the natural processes occurring in ditches, these results confirmed field studies showing a greater dissipation in ditches for diflufenican (Williams *et al.*, 1999; Garon-Boucher *in press*).

Sorption capacities

Sediments - Koc values measured for isoproturon on both sediments could be compared with those found in the literature. Common values for soil are 80-230 ml/g. Sorption capacity of diflufenican on sediments was very low, compared to the literature for soils (Table 3).

Litter and organic materials - Comparing K_d and K_{oc} obtained at 24 hours contact time showed that isoproturon sorption on the dead leaves from the ditches was comparable to sorption on leaves from the forest floor (Table 3). For diflufenican, however strong differences were observed between sorption capacities on dead leaves and other organic materials. For isoproturon and diflufenican, sorption on grass was significantly lower than sorption on leaves from the forest floor. Despite higher C content, the grass and leaves fractions had generally lower sorption capacities than the LOF fractions (Table 3). K_d and K_{oc} increased as the size of the LOF decreased, i.e. as decomposition proceeded. This indicated that changes in OM composition during first decomposition stages increased the sorption capacities of both the grass and leaf residues.

Table 3   Sorption coefficients (K_d and K_{oc}) and desorbed amounts in one single desorption (% of initially sorbed amount) for isoproturon and diflufenican on sediments and organic materials.

	Isoproturon			Diflufenican		
	K_d (l/kg)	K_{oc} (l/kg)	% desorbed	K_d (l/kg)	K_{oc} (l/kg)	% desorbed
Sediments						
Roujan (F)	1 ± 0.1†	110 ± 15	5 ± 3	4 ± 0.1	440 ± 10	14 ± 1
Wytham (UK)	2 ± 0.2	63 ± 5	33 ± 3	29 ± 4	805 ± 110	16 ± 2
Dead leaves	23 ± 3	48 ± 6	23 ± 16	34 ± 6	70 ± 13	7 ± 2
Grassed strip						
Grass fraction	10 ± 1	32 ± 3	42 ± 1	322 ± 22	1007 ± 70	5 ± 3
>2mm	32 ± 1	100 ± 2	40 ± 2	733 ± 62	2269 ± 191	2 ± 1
LOF 2 mm-200	30 ± 1	122 ± 3	32 ± 2	663 ±122	2730 ± 501	3 ± 1
µm						
LOF 50-200 µm	24 ± 1	54 ± 3	37 ± 2	666 ± 68	1482 ± 151	5 ± 3
Forest litter	40 ± 1	117± 1	33 ± 1	438 ± 66	1258 ± 190	2 ± 1
Leaves > 2 mm	39± 7	114 ± 21	30 ± 6	714 ± 82	2100 ± 240	4 ± 1
LOF 2mm-200 µm						
LOF 50-200 µm						

† means and standard errors of three replicates

Sorption reversibility - Desorption

The reversibility of sorption was assessed by the proportion of desorbed herbicides after one single desorption period of 30 min (sediment or dead leaves) and 24h (litter OM.).
For the sediments from Roujan, desorption of diflufenican (14%) seemed to be greater than isoproturon (5%). On Wytham sediments and on the organic rich materials, the contrary was observed (Table 3). The behaviour for Roujan may be explained by the sediment nature and the low C content, that meant different interactions between the sorbents and the herbicides. After 30 minutes, 23% of initially sorbed isoproturon was desorbed from dead leaves, but only 7% of initially sorbed diflufenican (Table 3). After 24 hours, 37% of isoproturon was desorbed from forest floor leaves, but only 5% of diflufenican. This indicated that the kinetics of desorption was probably slower for diflufenican than for isoproturon. The comparison of grass and forest litters showed that isoproturon desorption was easier from grass materials (42% from the grass fraction). Again for the more decomposed fractions 50-200 µm LOF, differences between grass and forest litters were smaller. For diflufenican, only 2 to 5 % could be desorbed after 24 h. This confirmed that decomposed organic matter

such as plant residues can play a significant role in non reversible sorption of herbicides (Reddy *et al.*, 1997; Benoit *et al.*, 1999).

CONCLUSION

The present results suggest that origin and degree of decomposition of OM are important factors affecting the sorption of non-ionic herbicides with strong (diflufenican) or medium (isoproturon) hydrophobic characteristics. Non-specific interactions such as partitioning into organic matter are thought to be a major mechanism to explain sorption of such molecules on plant residues (Lickfeldt & Branham, 1995). Increased sorption with decomposition could be explained by as rapid changes in plant residues chemistry with preservation of aliphatic (cutins) or aromatic (lignins) structures or increased specific surface areas. Some extra laboratory experiments are now planed to characterise the organic materials in relation to the observed pesticide adsorption.

The comparative study between herbicide sorption/desorption on sediments and organic materials demonstrated that the presence of organic sorbent in buffer zones or farm ditches could significantly reduce pesticide occurrence in surface water. These laboratory experiments confirmed preliminary results at fields (Garon-Boucher *et al.*, in press; Patty *et al.*, 1997).

REFERENCES

Baker J L; Mickelson S K; Hatfield J L; Fawcett R S; Hoffman D W; Franti T G; Peter C J; Tierney D P (1995). Reducing herbicide runoff: role of best management practices. *Proceedings of the BCPC Conference – Weeds 1995* pp 479-487.

Benoit P; Barriuso E; Vidon P; Réal B (1999). Isoproturon sorption and degradation in a soil from grassed buffer strip. *Journal of Environmental Quality* **28**: 121-129.

Gaillardon P; Durr JC (1995). Influence of soil moisture on short-term adsorption of diuron and isoproturon by soil. *Pesticide Science* **45**: 297-303.

Garon-Boucher C; Gouy V; Laillet B; Dramais G (2001). Retention des produits phytosanitaires dans les fosses de connexion parcelle-cours d'eau. *Revue des Sciences de L'eau, numero special* in press.

Lickfeldt D W ; Branham B E (1995). Sorption of nonionic organic compounds by Kentucky blue grass leaves and thatch. *Journal of Environmental Quality* **24**: 980-985.

Mersie W; Seybold C A; Mc Namee C; Huang J; (1999). Effectiveness of switch grass filter strips in removing dissolved atrazine and metolachlor from runoff. *Journal of Environmental Quality* **28**: 816-821.

Patty L; Réal B; Gril J J; (1997). The use of grassed buffer strips to remove pesticides, nitrate and soluble phosphorus compounds from runoff water. *Pesticide Science*. **49**: 243-251

Reddy K N; Locke M A; Gaston L A (1997). Tillage and cover crop effects on cyanazine adsorption and desorption kinetics. *Soil Science* **162**: 501-509.

Walker A; Jurado-Exposito M (1998). Adsorption of isoproturon, diuron and metsulfuron-methyl in two soils at high soil:solution ratios. *Weed Research*, **38**, 229-238.

Williams R J; White C; Dreymann S; Gouy V; Garon-Boucher C; Souiller C (1999). Fate and behaviour of pesticides in farm ditches. *Proceedings of the BCPC Conference – Weeds 1999*, pp. 675-680.

Pesticide penetration and groundwater recharge on a chalk hillslope in southern England

A H Haria, A C Johnson, M G Hodnett
Centre for Ecology and Hydrology, Maclean Building, Crowmarsh Gifford, Wallingford, Oxfordshire OX10 8BB, UK
Email: atu@ceh.ac.uk

ABSTRACT

Pesticide penetration and groundwater recharge monitoring on a chalk hillslope in southern England identified very different mechanisms of contaminant transport related to the water table depth. On the interfluve, where the groundwater was 18-20 m below the surface, matrix flow only through the deep chalk unsaturated zone was observed. In contrast, the dry valley bottom with a shallow (4-6 m deep) water table experienced rapid preferential water/contaminant transport, as well as matrix flow, to the groundwater.

Unsaturated soil/chalk hydrology demonstrated the importance of the shallow groundwater capillary rise in keeping the unsaturated profile well supplied with water resulting in a reduced storage capacity for rainfall pulses; little water is required to wet the shallow profile before rapid preferential flow events occur. Storage sites on chalk surfaces and at "contact points" remain empty where the groundwater is deeper and rainfall pulses are attenuated as these sites absorb the downward water fluxes. Consequently preferential events here are rare.

The maximum potential mass load of pesticide that might be transported to the groundwater in the preferential events in 1996-7 was determined from bromide tracer studies. Calculations under the worst case scenario showed no more than 0.13 % of the applied pesticide would be transported to the water table rapidly at the shallow groundwater site. A more realistic estimate was between 0.04 % and 0.07 % of the applied pesticide. The work indicates contamination of groundwater by pesticides applied following normal agricultural practice over unconfined chalk can occur, however the major pollution sites are likely to be restricted to the dry valley areas at least in the short term.

INTRODUCTION

With the chalk aquifers of SE England contributing 55% of all groundwater use in the UK, the water quality of this resource is an important issue. Large tracts of the typically thin soils overlying these unconfined aquifers are under arable land use with agrochemical pollution an increasing concern. Chalk is a dual porosity system where water can move through both the matrix and through fractures (Price *et al.*, 1993). Water fluxes through the matrix are relatively slow (~ 1 myr^{-1}) whilst movement through the fissures can be orders of magnitude greater. Consequently, contaminant transported by water through the fissures will arrive quickly to the groundwater with very little opportunity for attenuation and degradation soon after application; whilst the slow transport through the chalk matrix means there is a considerable amount of time likely to be available for attenuation and potential degradation before it reaches the groundwater.

Previous work in southern England on unsaturated Upper chalk over a deep water table (>30 m) determined that preferential fissure flow in the chalk would only occur when the hydraulic conductivity of the matrix has been exceeded (Cooper *et al.*, 1990). This was found to occur rarely, only once in a 5 year study on the Upper Chalk in Hampshire, UK. Importantly, the threshold matric potential above which fissure flow began was identified as -5 kPa suction (Wellings, 1984).

However, some of the cultivation over the chalk is likely to be in the characteristic dry valley bottoms where the groundwater is relatively close to the surface. Under these conditions preferential fissure flow may be more significant, and these areas may represent zones of high risk for agrochemical contamination of the groundwater. A detailed physico-chemical study was established at a chalk site in Hampshire, southern England, to compare recharge processes over shallow and deep ground waters and to determine the implications for contaminant transport. This paper presents some of the results from the 1996-1997 field season.

METHODS AND MATERIALS

The study site was situated on a sloping arable field on the Upper chalk in Hampshire, about 24 km north of Winchester, and comprised of 2 instrumented stations. Station WON 7 was located on the interfluve where the groundwater was 18-20 metres below ground level (mbgl), whilst station WON 4 was located on the dry valley floor where the water table was 4-6 mbgl (Figure 1). Site WON 4 was 382 m down slope of WON 7.

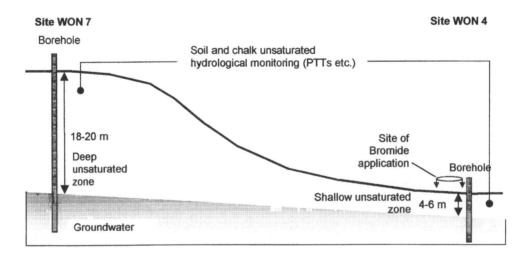

Figure 1.   Schematic diagram of the experimental site showing relative locations of instruments.

The soils are Andover series and, along with the site, are described in more detail by Johnson *et al.,* (2000). Boreholes, installed at both sites using a dry percussion drilling method, were used to take weekly groundwater samples. Additionally, automated daily water samples were collected at WON 4 after pesticide application to assess pesticide concentrations arriving at the groundwater immediately following rainfall.

The pesticides Isoproturon (2.5 kgha^{-1} total in 1994) and Chlorotoluron (2 kgha^{-1} on 30th October 1996) were applied at both sites. Unsaturated chalk water potentials at both sites were measured using pressure transducer tensiometers (PTTs), logging hourly, at 0.5, 1.0, 1.5, 2.0, 2.5 and 3.0 m depths. On 22nd February 1995, 48 L of 50,000 mgL^{-1} KBr tracer solution was applied just upslope of the borehole at WON 4. Profiles of chalk cores were extracted on 28th September 1996 and again on 22nd September 1997 and analysed for Br. By the use of pesticide concentrations measured in the boreholes immediately following rainfall, MORECS data, and by studying the Br peak displacement, a worst case estimate of preferential pollutant transport could be made for the period between core extractions at WON 4.

RESULTS AND DISCUSSION

Weekly baseline borehole sampling showed that where the groundwater was deepest (WON 7), little or no herbicide detections were made. However, where the groundwater was only 4-6 mbgl (WON 4), a regular baseline pesticide signal of around 0.1 μgL^{-1} was distinguished. This suggests that no significant pesticide concentrations are reaching the groundwater at WON 7 whilst there is a regular input of pesticide reaching the groundwater at WON 4. Over the winter recharge period the automatic sampling at WON 4 revealed periodic high spikes of 0.4-0.8 μgL^{-1} of pesticide following rainfall. The high spike concentrations observed in the groundwater immediately following rainfall were strong evidence of rapid preferential contaminant transport taking place through the fissure pathways at this part of the field.

Different recharge processes between the deep groundwater site (WON 7) and the shallow groundwater site (WON 4) are clearly identified by the PTT data for a storm in February 1997. Figure 2 shows time series data of hydraulic potential response to rainfall, for 0.5 m to 3.0 m depths, for WON 7 and WON 4. Matric potentials may be calculated by subtracting the gravitational potential from the hydraulic potential. There are two main points of interest in Figure 2. First is the response in peak flux to peak rainfall down the profile, identified when the hydraulic potential is closest to zero (these are marked on Fig.2 by the short vertical lines crossing the lines of hydraulic potential). At WON 4 peak flux at 3.0 m is approximately 1 day after peak rainfall, whilst at WON 7 peak response at 3.0 m takes 7 days. The second noteworthy point is the difference in matric potential during peak flux at 3.0 m, for the February 1997 storm, at both sites. The matric potential at WON 7 did not exceed -17 kPa whilst at WON 4 it reached -3 kPa. According to previous research, preferential flow will only begin in the chalk when the matrix conductivity has been exceeded, and this only occurs in the Upper chalk at matric potentials greater than -5 kPa (Wellings, 1984). Thus, these conditions were met at the shallow groundwater site (WON 4) but not at the deep groundwater site (WON 7) during this rainstorm.

Why these differences should exist, at the two locations with different depths to the water table, can be explained by the capillary fringe above the water table effectively reducing storage in the chalk. The concept of chalk being a dual porosity system only, where the uniform matrix porosity is clearly differentiated from fissure porosity needs re-thinking since

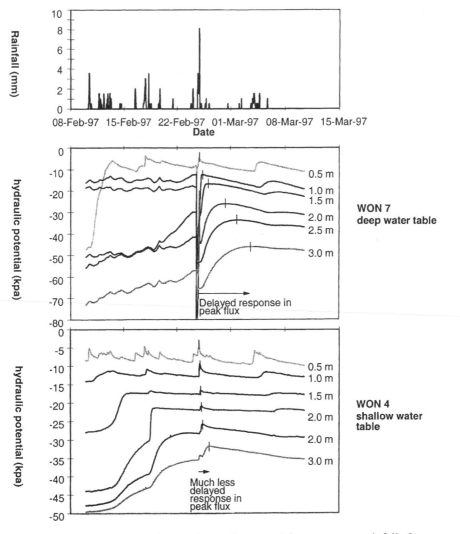

Figure 2. Time series data of hydraulic potential response to rainfall, for 0.5 m to 3.0 m depths, at WON 7 and WON 4.

clearly an intermediate, or more accurately a range of intermediate pore sizes exists. The concept is shown in Figure 3. This intermediate porosity need not be volumetrically great but it appears to be very important in providing storage sites at WON 7 which attenuate pulses of rainfall such that the resulting fluxes at lower depths are through the matrix only. At WON 4, where the intermediate porosity is largely water filled because of groundwater capillary effects, rainfall pulses quickly fill the remaining intermediate storage sites and further drainage "overflows" into the fissures. These storage sites have recently been investigated by

Price *et al.*, (2000), who identified sites on chalk block surfaces. Other possible loci of intermediate porosity may be at contact points between chalk blocks. Additionally, the profile at WON 7 may have had a bigger moisture deficit from the previous summer; at WON 4 upward gradients from the shallow water table in the summer mean the chalk here would not be as dry.

The bromide profiles (not shown) determined by coring at WON 4, described water movement through the chalk matrix, with the peak Br concentrations representing mean pore water velocities. Knowledge of chalk properties and looking at Br peak displacement enabled calculation of the flux of water through the matrix between core extractions. Using MORECS hydrometric data, and peak pesticide concentrations reaching the groundwater following rainfall, it was possible to estimate the amount of pesticide transported preferentially through the fissures for the period between core extractions. Calculations under the worst case scenario, assuming an effective matrix porosity of 0.5 v/v (Barraclough et al., 1994), predicted that 0.13% of pesticide applied reached the groundwater through the fissure system between 28th September 1996 and 22nd September 1997. More realistic estimates, assuming an effective matrix porosity of 0.85 v/v (Besien *et al.*, 2000), were between 0.04 % and 0.07 % of the pesticide applied reaching the groundwater at WON 4 through the fissure system.

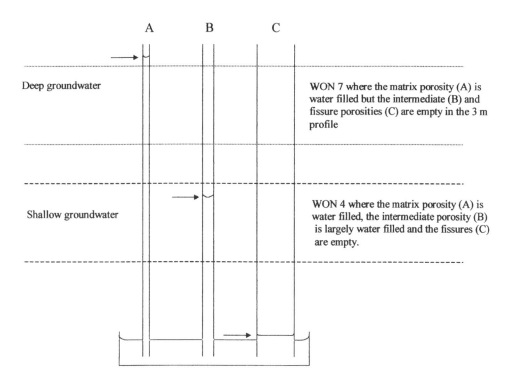

Figure 3.   Conceptual model explaining the effect of the capillary fringe in reducing storage sites in the unsaturated zone close to the water table.

CONCLUSIONS

Winter recharge processes to the Upper chalk aquifer can be very different depending on distance to the water table. At the shallow groundwater site, the near water table capillary fringe effectively reduced the intermediate storage potential in the unsaturated chalk above. Recharge fluxes very quickly wet the profile to a point where the fissures began to operate. For the same storm the recharge at the deep groundwater site was through the chalk matrix only. The resultant pesticide contamination by preferential fissure pathways was shown not to exceed 0.13% of that applied in the 1996-1997 field season. However, this value will vary depending on many factors such as the depth of the water table, rainfall patterns, pesticide used etc. The implications for winter cereal production over shallow unconfined chalk aquifers, due to the potential preferential contaminant transport to groundwaters, needs to be researched further.

ACKNOWLEDGEMENTS

The authors would like to thank T Besien and C White for assistance in the field, and to NERC for funding the project. The authors are especially grateful to A Dixon whose drilling/coring experience made this work possible. The authors also thank the British Geological Survey for assisting in the project.

REFERENCES

Barraclough D; Gardner C M K; Wellings S R; Cooper J D (1994) A tracer investigation into the importance of fissure flow in the unsaturated zone of the British Upper Chalk. *Journal of Hydrology*, **156:** 459-469.

Besien T J; Williams R J; Johnson A C; (2000) The transport and behaviour of isoproturon in unsaturated chalk cores. *Journal of Contaminant Hydrology*, **43:** 91-110.

Cooper J D; Gardner C M K; Mackenzie N (1990) Soil controls on recharge to aquifers. *Journal of Soil Science*, **41:** 613-630.

Johnson A C; White C; Lal Bhardwaj C (2000) Potential for isoproturon, atrazine and mecoprop to be degraded within a chalk aquifer system. *Journal of Contaminant Hydrology*, **44:** 1-18.

Price M; Downing R A; Edmunds W M (1993) The chalk as an aquifer. In: *The hydrogeology of the Chalk of North-West Europe*. R A Downing; M Price; G P Jones (eds) Clarendon Press, Oxford, pp. 35-58.

Price M; Low R G; McCann C (2000) Mechanisms of water storage and flow in the unsaturated zone of the Chalk aquifer. *Journal of Hydrology*, **233:** 54-71.

Wellings S R (1984) Recharge of the upper chalk aquifer at a site in Hampshire, England. 1. WaterBalance and Unsaturated Flow. *Journal of Hydrology*, **69:** 259-273.

SESSION 5

DEGRADATION

Chairman &   Dr G D Bending
Session Organiser: *HRI, Wellesbourne, UK*

Improving the exploitation of microorganisms in environmental clean-up

I P Thompson, A C Singer, M J Bailey

Centre for Ecology & Hydrology Oxford, Mansfield Road, Oxford, OX1 3SR, UK.
Email: ipt@ceh.ac.uk

ABSTRACT

There are few if any natural materials that cannot be degraded by at least one type of microorganism making microbes potentially very valuable for the clean-up of man-made chemicals introduced in the environment. This review identifies the physical and microbiological constraints to environmental clean-up processes, and describes the rationale behind manipulating the chemical and biological environment for enhanced remediation.

INTRODUCTION

Microorganisms have several important features that make them potentially very valuable for the clean-up of man-made chemicals introduced in the environment—amongst these is their extreme metabolic diversity. There are few if any natural materials that cannot be degraded by at least one type of microorganism and this is likely to be the case for most man-made compounds (xenobiotics). In many cases, only a select few microbial isolates have demonstrated the ability to metabolise a particular xenobiotic. In even fewer cases have the complex biochemistry and genes involved in the catabolic pathways been resolved. As well as being metabolically diverse, microorganisms are genetically adaptable organisms, which enables them to rapidly respond to new situations and stresses, such as pollution events. Consequently, when pollutants enter pristine environments, microorganisms that can degrade them are either already present or can "acquire" the necessary genetic capacity through mutation, gene re-assortment or horizontal gene transfer.

Despite the metabolic versatility of microbes and their wide distribution, they are not infallible, evident by the thousands of hectares of contaminated land still present. The reasons for the poor recovery of an impacted site are complex, but may be summarised as:

- The functional microorganisms or genes required for degradation are present in very low numbers or absent.
- The chemical conditions of the pollutant are unfavourable to microbial degradation - for example, the concentration of pollutant is so high it is toxic or too low to stimulate degradation.
- The environmental conditions are biologically unfavourable for microbial growth and activity – for example pH, water logging or inadequate nutrients.

Considerable attention in recent years has been given towards furthering the understanding of the microbiological and chemical component of bioremediation, however, much remains obscured by the physical complexity of the environment. The purpose of this review is to identify the physical and microbiological constraints to clean-up processes, and to describe the rationale behind manipulating the chemical and biological environment for enhanced remediation. For convenience we have divided this review into 3 sections.

1. Assessing microbial diversity and genetic potential for natural attenuation.
2. Identifying the populations responsible for attenuation and the constraints to activity.
3. Manipulating microbial communities to overcome the constraints.

ASSESSING MICROBIAL DIVERSITY AND THE GENETIC POTENTIAL FOR NATURAL ATTENUTION

We are largely ignorant of the diversity and identity of microorganisms responsible for environmental detoxification and clean-up processes. For example, we know little of the overall function or the extent of the diversity of component microorganisms involved, even in intensively studied systems such as sewage processing plants. This ignorance is largely due to the lack of suitable methods of assessing the composition and population dynamics of microbial communities. Traditionally, microbial community profiling has been based on culture-based methods that require the isolation and growth of microorganisms on artificial media. Typically, these methods qualitatively and quantitatively underestimate the composition of the microbial community. The isolation method can also be hampered by uncertainties caused by the selective enrichment procedure itself. Because of this limitation, bioremediation and natural attenuation studies have been carried out using a "black box" approach, whereby the disappearance of substrates indicates microbial degradation, with little understanding of the microbial communities responsible for the process.

An important advance in studies aimed at understanding and exploiting microbial populations for the remediation of environmental xenobiotics, has been the application of molecular biology. The foundation of recent work in environmental molecular biology has been exploitation of the differences in the nucleotide sequence of an ubiquitous set of genes within the ribosomal RNA (rRNA). A considerable database of sequences for the small sub-unit RNA, 16S rRNA, is available and is rapidly growing, thereby facilitating the identification of bacterial isolates. The analysis of 16S rRNA often elucidates the presence of previously unknown members of the microbial community, thereby contributing valuable information to an understanding of the overall attenuation picture. However, the key advance these methods bring in terms of assessing microbial diversity, is that they preclude the need for culturing and in so doing, provide a more comprehensive assessment of the composition of the microbial populations present. Two key methods, denaturing gradient gel electrophoresis (DGGE) and temperature gradient gel electrophoresis (TGGE) (Muyzer 1999) have been widely adopted for monitoring microbial diversity. These techniques generate a genetic fingerprint or community profile, based on the small differences present in the 16S rRNA sequence of specific bacteria. Total nucleic acids (DNA and RNA) are extracted from a soil sample, and amplified by PCR using primers specific to a particular gene sequence, i.e. 16S rRNA. The amplimers generated are then separated due to their sequence differences by gradient-gel electrophoresis. In a complex mixture of soil DNA, typical of an environmental sample, specific amplimers migrate to different positions down the gel matrix resulting in banding patterns similar to a bar code. The methods enable the diversity of communities to be measured and contrasted. In this way, microbial population dynamics can be followed in natural and perturbed soil environments (Torsvik et al., 1998). An improved understanding of the community composition enables directed manipulation of the microbes responsible for pollutant degradation. Members of a microbial community may be monitored for their activity and response to pollution perturbation, thereby indicating the efficacy of attenuation processes (Whitely & Bailey 2000; Whitely *et al.,* 2001). Molecular techniques have the important advantage in that they are relatively rapid to perform (Griffiths *et al.,* 2000). DGGE and TGGE have been applied by a number of groups to interrogate the dynamics of a wastewater treatment plant (Curtis & Caine 1998), and to detect, isolate and characterise the active bacteria in a sample (Watanabe *et al.,* 1998). Another key advance over previous methods is that the approach can be used to monitor specific taxonomic groups of bacteria (Stephen *et al.,* 1998), the presence of functional gene sequences (Rosado *et al.,* 1998) and identifies microbial consortia involved in specific clean-up processes (Boon *et al.,* 2001).

IDENTIFYING THE POPULATIONS RESPONSIBLE FOR ATTENUATION AND THE CONSTRAINTS TO ACTIVITY.

Molecular studies have revealed considerable diversity within microbial populations and are helping to elucidate their complex interactions with contaminants. By comparison of microbial community profiles provided by DGGE, it is possible to determine the response of specific populations to chemical and physical changes in contaminated sites. By further analysis it is possible to identify the populations responsible for the biodegradative process. The utility of 16S rRNA oligonucleotide probes enable the rapid screening of populations for the presence or absence of the selected nucleotide sequence. These probes may be fluorescently tagged, and are available at a number of different wavelengths, allowing a mixture of probes to be used simultaneously. The technique of fluorescent *in situ* hybridisation (FISH) has the advantage of both enabling rapid *in situ* detection and enumeration of microorganisms with homology to the probe. Furthermore, it is possible with the combined use of different phylogenetic probes and substrate addition, to determine the contribution of key functional groups to a particular process. This has been illustrated in systems examining phenol and metal working fluid degradation (van der Gast *et al.,* 2001; Whitely & Bailey 2000). FISH and similar methods used to interrogate remedial processes provide significant insights into the key functional bacterial groups. When used in tandem with chemical analysis, molecular probing can provide valuable information for monitoring pollution and its temporal and spatial dynamics.

The generation of probes for measuring specific gene activity (i.e. RNA rather than DNA) *in situ*, arguably, provides the most useful measure of the biodegradative potential and activity within a contaminated site. Gene probes are being used to monitor the presence of specific genes in the population and their level of expression. The true utility of this technology is when it is correlated to degradative activity as demonstrated by pollutant mineralisation. This has been particularly effective in the analysis of naphthalene degradation, associated with BTEX compounds, were *nahA* mRNA expression has been correlated to enzyme activity and [^{14}C] naphthalene mineralisation rates (Fleming *et al.,* 1993). Despite a number of similar studies with equally encouraging results, there are many cases where molecular signatures do not correlate with monitored degradation rates (Laurie & Lloyd-Jones 2000). These failures are in part due to the misleading assumption that genes identified in laboratory-derived bacterial isolates are solely responsible for the biodegradation observed in the field. To be an effective measure of attenuation, it is therefore essential that the genes to be monitored fully represent the true complement of genes responsible for the pollutant's degradation. In this respect, a novel application has been developed, stable isotope probing

(SIP), which exploits the fact that DNA from microorganisms can become ^{13}C-labelled following growth on a ^{13}C-enriched carbon source (Radajewski *et al.*, 2000). The method is elegant in its simplicity. The ^{13}C-labelled DNA of replicating organisms is heavier than DNA containing the more abundant ^{12}C. The difference in density (due to isotopic atomic mass difference) between 'heavy' ^{13}C- and 'light' ^{12}C-DNA can be resolved by equilibrium centrifugation in CsCl-ethidium bromide gradients. Thus, after purification and sequence analysis of the heavy DNA the active members of the microbial community responsible for the pollutant's degradation can potentially be identified. Theoretically, any labelled substrate can be applied, illuminating the catabolically active member(s) of the population. This will eventually lead to a better understanding of how genetically diverse groups share a common function or co-operate in the degradation of recalcitrant compounds.

Another way in which molecular biology is being used to enhance understanding of the biodegradative process is through the use of biosensors. A typical approach is the modification of an indigenous strain to express a novel phenotype, which is used to indicate the presence or absence of a chemical. The most common reporter gene used is derived from naturally bioluminescent organisms, such as fire-flies or small group of marine bacteria - yielding quantitative light emissions. The biosensors themselves fall broadly into two categories, specific and generalised. Specific sensors have been developed for the detection of one or more related compounds. The sensor utilises reporter gene constructs that are expressed from inducible promoters, which respond to the bioavailability of specific chemicals (Corbisier *et al.*, 1996). Generalised sensors have more widespread utility since they can monitor the impact of toxicity on the overall physiological state of the cell; for example, a decrease in physiological activity of the cell correlates to an increase in toxicity (Boyd *et al.*, 1997; Paton *et al.*, 1995). Reporter based biosensors are therefore a powerful tool in identifying biological and physical constraints on cellular metabolism, such as impaired bioavailability or the presence of inhibitors, elevated concentrations of toxins or the effect of co-contaminants.

MANIPULATION OF CONTAMINANTS AND MICROORGANISMS IN SOIL

Molecular and conventional bacterial isolation techniques are capable of demonstrating the presence of xenobiotic degraders in a soil. However, in a majority of the cases, these populations are either not metabolically active or too few in numbers to significantly contribute to natural attenuation. One viable solution to this problem is to relieve one of the major constraints to microbial activity, the nutrient limitation (carbon or nitrogen). Thus, when this is alleviated through the use of fertilisers (Lindstrom *et al.*, 1991), significant pollutant degradation is often observed. However, alleviating the nutrient limitation is only part of the solution. Xenobiotic biodegradation in the environment is also restricted by the accessibility of the microorganism to the pollutant, termed bioavailability.

The bioavailability of a chemical in soil is influenced by a number of factors, including concentration, solubility, type and quantity of clay and organic matter, pH, temperature, and the compound's chemical characteristics (Alexander 1999). The phenomenon of sorption and desorption, or the partitioning of a chemical from one phase to another (i.e., aqueous to solid), helps to define a chemical's location in the soil, and thus its bioavailability. Typically, as a compound's hydrophobicity, solubility and affinity to organic matter and clay increases, its bioavailability declines. Biounavailable chemicals are often sorbed within small soil pores, typically in clay particles or organic matter, where they remain largely inaccessible to microorganisms. This sorption process often entails an initially rapid and reversible phase, where the highest bioavailability can be found, followed by a period of slow sorption, which can continue indefinitely (Hatzinger & Alexander 1995). It is the remediation of the desorption-resistant fraction, which makes clean-up a significant and in some cases seemingly insurmountable challenge. It has been commonly observed that the desorption-resistant pollutant pool increases with time as the chemical remains in the soil (MacLeod & Semple 2000). The slow diffusion into and out of clay and organic matrices contributes to the phenomenon of ageing—the declining bioavailability and extractability of a pollutant over time.

It is only recently that researchers have begun to quantify the bioavailable fraction. A number of studies have demonstrated the utility of different extraction solvents and biological indicators in quantifying and qualifying the bioavailable fraction of a pollutant in soil (Reid *et al.,* 2000; Tang *et al.,* 1999). The key to improving the efficacy of bioremediation is to understand and address the factors that influence the dynamics of this bioavailable pool. The current understanding of bioavailability suggests that, if the aqueous concentration of a pollutant is increased (i.e. partitioning from the solid to the aqueous phase), a greater contact between the microbe and the pollutant can be attained, thereby increasing the pollutant's bioavailability. A primary method for increasing the aqueous concentration of a pollutant has been with the use of surface-active-agents, or surfactants (Willumsen & Karlson 1997).

A surfactant molecule typically contains two or more moieties of varying polarity, and by definition lowers the surface tension of a liquid. Surfactants are classified as cationic, anionic or nonionic, referring to the presence of a positive, negative, or neutral charge, respectively, in the molecule. Much of the experimental evidence suggests that the increase in pollutant solubility afforded by surfactants, dramatically increases the rate and extent of pollutant biodegradation (Aronstein & Alexander 1992; Mulligan *et al.,* 2001). As well as increasing the solubility of pollutants, some surfactants also act as nutrient sources for the inoculum and/or indigenous microorganisms (Lajoie *et al.,* 1992; Singer *et al.,* 2000; Singer *et al.,* 2001). In addition to the use of synthetic surfactants, a rapidly developing field is the use of bacterial species that excrete surface-active or emulsifying agents, which decrease the surface tension of water and increase the apparent solubility of the pollutant (Holmberg 2001; Willumsen & Karlson 1997). Biosurfactants are renewable resources and in some cases have been shown to be superior to synthetic surfactants in reducing the surface tension of water, a measure of a surfactant's efficacy (Yakimov *et al.,* 1995).

In addition to alleviating nutrient limitations and pollutant bioavailability, supplementing the soil with inducers and co-metabolites has also been demonstrated to dramatically improve the rate and extent of pollutant biodegradation. The introduction of readily degradable compounds with similar structure to the recalcitrant pollutant has been shown to stimulate degradation of otherwise highly recalcitrant pollutants. This practice has been termed analogue enrichment. For example, biphenyl is readily utilised as a cometabolite, serving as a carbon source and inducer for polychlorinated biphenyl (PCB) degradation. It was observed in the 1990's that non-structurally related compounds could also stimulate recalcitrant xenobiotic degradation (Gilbert & Crowley 1997; Singer *et al.,* 2000). For example, carvone and a number of other plant-derived compounds (eg. terpenes and flavones), were shown to stimulate PCB degradation at equivalent rates to that of biphenyl, the classically used cometabolite (Gilbert & Crowley 1997). Inducers are typically plant-derived compounds. Since the compound is natural and is not required at high concentrations, it is much safer to use, and has been demonstrated to be as effective as a cometabolite (Gilbert & Crowley 1997).

Future bioremediation projects will likely require the incorporation of surfactants, inducers, and/or cometabolites, as part of an integrated clean-up system. To be competitive with current remediation technologies, the system will need to be applicable to very large-scale sites. Current technologies are too cost prohibitive for large impacted sites, leaving the door open for a novel, environmentally friendly alternative. A promising new technology has taken off in recent years, which is highly suitable to large-scale contaminations; it is the use of plants to assist in stimulating biodegradation—phytoremediation. The available research has suggested planted soils significantly outperform similarly treated fallow soils (EPA 2001). Potential future avenues may lie in the application of plants to contaminated sites that produce inducing compounds, *in situ*, thereby alleviating the need for repeated inducer applications (Crowley *et al.*, 2000).

Natural attenuation and bioremediation hold great promise for efficient and cost effective means for cleaning contaminated environments. By applying methodologies that examine ecological events at their molecular level, we should improve our ability to predict the impact of pollution, the intrinsic ability of natural microbial communities to degrade the contaminant, provide a reliable estimate of recovery time, and obtain an indication of the effectiveness of remedial measures. The quality of the information we are now getting from the environment is improving, and is approaching the point of being able to determine the genes present in a contaminated site, which population contains the genes, and the factors that constrain the expression of the genes. What we now need to do is effectively combine this microbial information with the mass of data on the chemistry, hydrology and geology of a site and develop integrated predictive models. Extrapolation into the future should find us in the position where we can rapidly predict from a small sample the fate of a contaminant, the genetic potential for self-cleaning, the constraints on microbial activities, and the need for manipulations, such as the addition of surfactants or inducers.

REFERENCES

Alexander M (1999) *Biodegradation and Bioremediation.* Second Ed., Academic Press: San Diego.

Aronstein B N; Alexander M (1992). Surfactants at low concentrations stimulate biodegradation of sorbed hydrocarbons in samples of aquifer sands and soil slurries. *Environmental & Toxicological Chemistry* **11**: 1227-1233.

Boon N; Goris J; DeVos P; Verstraete W; Top E M (2001). Genetic diversity among 3-chloroaniline- and aniline-degrading strains of the Comamonadaceae. *Applied & Environmental Microbiology* **67**: 1107-1115.

Boyd E M; Meharg A A; Wright J; Killham K (1997). Assessment of toxicological interactions of benzene and its primary degradation products (catechol and phenol) using a lux-modified bacterial bioassay. *Environmental Toxicology & Chemistry* **16**: 849-856.

Corbisier P; Thiry E; Diels L (1996). Bacterial biosensors for the toxicity assessment of solid waste. *Environmental Toxicology & Water Quality* **11**: 171-177.

Crowley D E; Luepromchai E; Singer A C (2000) Cometabolism of xenobiotics in the rhizosphere. In: *Pesticide biotransformation in plants and microorganisms: similarities and divergences*. eds. J C Hall R E Hoagland & R M Zablotowitz, pp. 333-352, American Chemical Society: Washington, DC.

Curtis T P; Caine N G (1998). The comparison of the diversity of activated sludge plants. *Water Science and Technology* 37: 71-78.

EPA U S (2001) *Phytoremediation of contaminated soil and ground water at hazardous waste sites*, ed. B E Pivetz, EPA/540/S-01/500, Technology Innovation Office, Office of Solid Waste and Emergency Response: Washington, DC.

Fleming J T; Sanseverino J; Sayler G S (1993). Quantitative relationship between naphthalene catabolic gene-frequency and expression in predicting PAH degradation in soils at town gas manufacturing sites. *Environmental Science & Technology* 27: 1068-1074.

Gilbert E S; Crowley D E (1997). Plant compounds that induce polychlorinated biphenyl biodegradation by *Arthrobacter* sp. strain B1B. *Applied & Environmental Microbiology* 63: 1933-1938.

Griffiths R I; Whiteley A S; O'Donnell A G; Bailey M J (2000). A rapid method for the co-extraction of DNA and RNA from natural environments for the analysis of rDNA and rRNA based microbial community composition. *Applied & Environmental Microbiology* 66: 5488-5491.

Hatzinger P B; Alexander M (1995). Effect of ageing of chemicals in soil on their biodegradability and extractability. *Environmental Science & Technology* 29: 537-545.

Holmberg K (2001). Natural surfactants. *Current Opinion in Colloid & Interface Science* 6: 148-159.

Lajoie C A; Chen S-Y; Oh K-C; Strom P F (1992). Development and use of field application vectors to express nonadaptive foreign genes in competitive environments. *Applied & Environmental Microbiology* 58: 655-663.

Laurie A D; Lloyd-Jones G (2000). Quantification of *phnAc* and *nahAc* in contaminated New Zealand soils by competitive PCR. *Applied & Environmental Microbiology* 66: 1814-1817.

Lindstrom J E; Prince R C; Clark J C; Grossman M J; Yeager T R; Braddock J F; Brown E J (1991). Microbial populations and hydrocarbon biodegradation potentials in fertilized shoreline sediments affected by the T/V *Exxon Valdez* oil spill. *Applied & Environmental Microbiology* 57: 2514-2522.

MacLeod C J A; Semple K T (2000). Influence of contact time on extractability and degradation of pyrene in soils. *Environmental Science & Technology* 34: 4952-4957.

Mulligan C N; Yong R N; Gibbs B F (2001). Surfactant-enhanced remediation of contaminated soil: a review. *Engineering Geology* 60: 371-380.

Muyzer M (1999). DGGE/TGGE a method for identifying genes from natural ecosystems. *Current Opinion in Microbiology* 2: 317-322.

Paton G I; Campbell C D; Glover L A; Killham K (1995). Assessment of bioavailability of heavy metals using lux modified constructs of *Pseudomonas fluorescens*. *Letters of Applied Microbiology* 20: 52-56.

Radajewski S; Ineson P; Parekh N R; Murrell J C (2000). Stable-isotope probing as a tool in microbial ecology. *Nature* 403: 646-649.

Reid B J; Stokes J D; Jones K C; Semple K T (2000). Nonexhaustive cyclodextrin-based extraction technique fo the evaluation of PAH bioavailability. *Environmental Science & Technology* 34: 3174-3179.

Rosado A S; Duarte G F; Seldin L; Elsas J D v (1998). Genetic diversity of nifH gene sequences in *Paenibacillus azotofixans* strains and soil samples analysed by denaturing gradient gel electrophoresis of PCR-amplified gene fragments. *Applied & Environmental Microbiology* **64:** 2770-2779.

Singer A C; Gilbert E S; Luepromchai E; Crowley D E (2000). Bioremediation of polychlorinated biphenyl-contaminated soil using carvone and surfactant-grown bacteria. *Applied Microbiology & Biotechnology* **54:** 838-843.

Singer A C; Jury W; Luepromchai E; Yahng C S; Crowley D E (2001). Contribution of earthworms to PCB bioremediation. *Soil Biology & Biochemistry* **33:** 765-776.

Stephen J R; Kowalchuk G; Bruns M -A V; McCaig A E; Phillips C J; Embley T M; Prosser J I (1998). Analysis of α-subgroup Proteobacterial ammonia oxidizer populations in soil by denaturing gradient gel electrophoresis analysis and hierarchical phylogenetic probing. *Applied Environmental Microbiology* **64:** 2958-2965.

Tang J; Robertson B K; Alexander M (1999). Chemical-extraction methods to estimate bioavailability of DDT, DDE, and DDD in soils. *Environmental Science & Technology* **33:** 4346-4351.

Torsvik V; Daae F L; Sandaa R-A; Overeas L (1998). Novel techniques for analysing microbial diversity in natural and perturbed environments. *Journal of Biotechnology* **64:** 53-62.

van der Gast C J; Knowles C J; Wright M A; Thompson I P (2001). Identification and characterisation of bacterial populations of an in-use metal-working fluid by phenotypic and genotypic methodology. *International Biodeterioration & Biodegradation* **47:** 111-123.

Watanabe K; Teramoto M; Futamata H; Harayama S (1998). Molecular detection, isolation and physiological characterisation of functionally dominant phenol degrading bacteria in activated sludge. *Applied & Environmental Microbiology* **64:** 4396-4402.

Whitely A S; Bailey M J (2000). Bacterial community structure and physiological state within an industrial phenol bioremediation system. *Applied & Environmental Microbiology* **66:** 2400-2407.

Whitely A S; Wiles S; Lilley A K; Philp J; Bailey M J (2001). Ecological and physiological analyses of Pseudomonad species within a phenol remediation system. *Journal of Microbiological Methods* **44:** 79-88.

Willumsen P A; Karlson U (1997). Screening of bacteria, isolated from PAH-contaminated soils, for production of biosurfactants and bioemulsifiers. *Biodegradation* **7:** 415-423.

Yakimov M M; Timmis K N; Wray V; Fredrickson H L (1995). Characterization of a new lipopeptide surfactant produced by thermotolerant and halotolerant subsurface *Bacillus licheniformis* BAS50. *Applied & Environmental Microbiology* **61:** 1706-1713.

Sorption and degradation of glyphosate and dichlobenil in fractured clay

J Aamand, O S Jacobsen

Geological Survey of Denmark and Greenland (GEUS), Thoravej 8, DK-2400 Copenhagen, Denmark.
Email: jeaa@geus.dk

ABSTRACT

Sorption and degradation of glyphosate, dichlobenil and 2,6-dichlorobenzamide (BAM) were studied in a Danish topsoil (0-0.45 m) and in the underlying, fractured clayey till (0.45 - 4.10 m). Sediments from fracture walls and the adjacent matrix were carefully transferred to flasks containing dichlobenil or ^{14}C-glyphosate. Mineralisation of glyphosate was measured by trapping the evolved $^{14}CO_2$ in an alkaline solution while accumulation of BAM from degradation of dichlobenil was measured using an immunological assay. Glyphosate mineralisation was observed in all samples, but the extent of mineralisation was highly variable (6-21% CO_2 recovery) and no correlation between depth and the extent of mineralisation was seen. The highest amount of $^{14}CO_2$ was seen in experiments with fracture wall material sampled at a depth of 2.4 m. Sorption coefficients (K_d) for glyphosate ranged between 65-147 l/kg with the highest values in the topsoil and at depths below 2.8 m. Dichlobenil was transformed to BAM in samples above 0.6 m, only. Sorption of dichlobenil was high in topsoil (51 l/kg), but decreased by a factor of ten in the underlying sediment. K_d values for BAM followed the same pattern, although they were one order of magnitude lower (0.2 - 0.7 l/kg).

INTRODUCTION

Sorption of xenobiotics to soil or sediments may impede contamination of the groundwater; however, certain soils such as clay often contain fractures that may facilitate rapid transport to underlying aquifers. The only way to eliminate xenobiotic compounds from the environment is by complete degradation to CO_2, a process known as mineralisation. Glyphosate is among the most widely used herbicides, but due to its strong sorption, it is not expected to be found in groundwater. In contrast, 2,6-dichlorobenzamide (BAM) which is a product of dichlobenil degradation (Figure 1) is among the most frequently found pollutants in Danish groundwater and has caused closure of many drinking water wells.

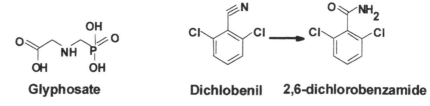

Glyphosate   **Dichlobenil**   **2,6-dichlorobenzamide**

Figure 1.   Structural formulae of pesticides studied: Glyphosate and transformation of dichlobenil to 2,6-dichlorobenzamide (BAM).

We studied sorption and degradation of glyphosate, dichlobenil and BAM in a Danish topsoil and in the underlying fractured clay sediment. The scope was to compare potential degradation and sorption in the fracture fillings and the adjacent matrix sediment.

METHODS AND MATERIALS

Topsoil and sediments were sampled from the Avedøre field site located Southwest of Copenhagen, Denmark (McKay et al., 1999). The site consists of 7-8 m of clay rich till which overlies a major chalk aquifer. The upper 3-4 m of the till is oxidized and highly fractured with widely spaced fractures persisting to at least 5 m depth. The samples were obtained from a 5 x 5 m hole dug to a depth of about 5 m below the surface (m.b.s). Matrix and fracture wall sediments were carefully sampled from different depth using a sterile spatula.

Bacterial numbers was determined by extraction of bacteria from the sediment and counted as colony forming units by plating onto R2A agar.

Transformation of dichlobenil to BAM was assessed in 10 ml vials with 2 g wet sediment and 10 ml of a mineral salt solution. Dichlobenil was added in 20 µl aliquots of aqueous solutions to reach a concentration of 25 µg/l and the vials were incubated at 10 °C. The amount of BAM produced was measured using an immunological assay (Bruun et al., 2000). Mineralisation of glyphosate was studied in small test tubes with 1 g wet sediment and 10.000 DPM ^{14}C-glyphosate equivalent to 33 µg/kg. To trap the evolved CO_2 the test tubes were placed in 10 ml scintillation vials containing 2 ml of 0.5 M NaOH. At times of sampling, the test tubes were removed to new vials and the remaining NaOH was added to 10 ml OptiPhase HiSafe scintillation fluid and were counted for 10 min on a Wallac 1409 liquid scintillation counter.

Adsorption and desorption were determined using ^{14}C-labelled herbicides. Aliquots of 1, 2 or 5 g fresh soil were transferred to 15 ml Pyrex flasks with Teflon sealed caps followed by 10 ml groundwater with 1 mg/l unlabelled herbicide and 50000 DPM labelled herbicide. NaN_3 was added to 0.1 M to prevent microbial degradation during the experiment. The flasks were incubated on a tilting table at 20°C in the dark. After a short centrifugation, water phase samples (100 µl) were collected after 2, 24, 48 and 96 h and analysed on a Wallac 1409 liquid scintillation counter as described above. The herbicide-containing groundwater was then replaced by uncontaminated groundwater and after a period of 182 h the amount of herbicide desorbed to the water phase was quantified.

RESULTS

The pH values of the sediments were in the range of 7-8 with a maximum pH at a depth of 0.45 m (Figure 2). The organic matter content was highest in the topsoil (8.5% of dry weight) decreasing to less than 1.5%, an exception being the matrix sediment from a depth of 1.5 m which had an unusual high concentration of carbon. The amount of phosphate was high in the topsoil (118-163 mg phosphate/kg soil) decreasing to almost zero below 0.5 m, an exception being the depth of 3.9 m where 162 mg phosphate/kg soil was measured. This high value is probably due to transition from oxidised to more reduced conditions at this depth, which may lead to release of bound phosphate. The carbonate content was low (<25 mg/g soil) to a depth of 0.6 m below which a stable concentration of about 200 mg/g soil was measured (Figure 2).

The number of culturable bacteria in the topsoil was in the range of $2 \cdot 10^5 - 1.1 \cdot 10^6$ cells/g soil (Figure 3). At a depth of 0.6 m fractured till became evident and was shown to support a very heterogeneous distribution of bacteria. Compared to the matrix sediments, the fracture walls contained a higher bacterial cell number, except at a depth of 2.4 m and 3.2 m where the numbers were in the same range. The highest bacterial community of $1.1 \cdot 10^6$ cells/g was obtained at the fracture wall at a depth of 2.4 m.

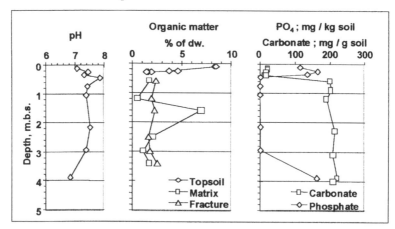

Figure 2. Analysis of groundwater chemistry. Left; pH in pore water. Middle, Organic matter measured as loss after ignition. Fractures were visible only below 0.6 meter. Right; phosphate and carbonate in bulk samples.

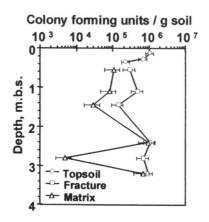

Figure 3.   Number of colony forming units.

Glyphosate was mineralised without a lag-phase in all samples from the topsoil (Figure 4). The mineralisation was most rapid during the first 5-8 days after which the rate decreased. The maximum recovery of added ^{14}C as ^{14}CO$_2$ amounted to 15.0 % and was found at the depth of 0.25-0.30 m. A potential to mineralise glyphosate was also seen in sediments from lower depths (Figure 5). The highest recovery of ^{14}CO$_2$ was obtained with sediment from the fracture wall sampled at a depth of 2.30-2.50 m. The fracture wall sediments in general, however, did not seem to have a higher potential to mineralise glyphosate compared to the matrix sediment.

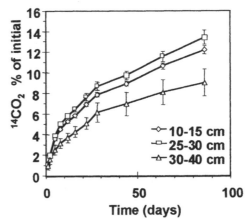

Figure 4. Cumulative ^{14}CO$_2$ from mineralisation of [P–methylene–^{14}C] glyphosate in topsoils.

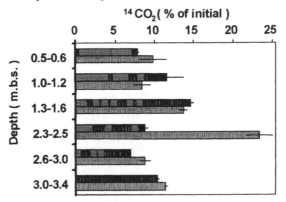

Figure 5. Recovery of ^{14}CO$_2$ from [P–methylene–^{14}C] glyphosate in sediments incubated at 10 °C for 110 d. Dark grey bars: Matrix sediments, striped bars: fracture wall sediments.

Transformation of dichlobenil to BAM was only observed in the topsoil (0.1-0.45 m) and in the matrix sediment at a depth of 0.50-0.60 m, but very large standard deviations between replicates were seen (Figure 6). BAM did not accumulate in vials with autoclaved soil, indicating that the transformation is microbially facilitated. However, more research is needed to elucidate the mechanism of dichlobenil transformation to BAM.

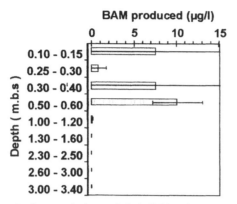

Figure 6. Accumulation of 2,6-dichlorobenzamide (BAM) in top soils and matrix sediments incubated at 10 °C for 64 d. No accumulation of BAM was seen in the fracture wall sediments (data not shown).

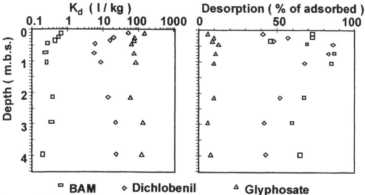

Figure 7. Kd-values and desorption percentage for dichlobenil, 2,6-dichloro-benzamide and glyphosate.

Glyphosate was the herbicide showing the highest sorption to both the clayey till and the organic topsoil. K_d-values were in the range between 65 and 147 l/kg (Fig 7). Dichlobenil also sorbed to soil, but to a lesser extent than glyphosate. K_d-values were in the range between 7 and 51 l/kg with the highest value in the uppermost soil. In practise no sorption of BAM was seen. The measured K_d-values were in the range between 0.2 and 0.8 l/kg with values decreasing from the topsoil towards the lower depths. The desorption study showed that only about 10 % of the sorbed glyphosate was released to the aqueous phase. The highest desorption was seen for BAM. Up to 87% of the sorbed BAM could be released to the aqueous phase which shows that BAM is a highly mobile compound in clayey tills (Fig 7).

DISCUSSION

The higher cell number in the fracture wall compared to the matrix sediment may be explained by bacterial growth on organic compounds preferentially transported through fractures towards the groundwater. Not all fractures are hydrological active (Vinther *et al.*, 1999) and it is possible that a thorough study identifying the active fractures would have revealed even more distinct bacterial enrichments on the active fracture walls. A potential to mineralise glyphosate was seen at all depths. In contrast previous studies have shown more rapid mineralisation of e.g. mecoprop and isoproturon in topsoils compared to deeper sediment (Larsen *et al.*, 2000). The high potential for mineralisation of glyphosate at greater depths may be explained by the relatively high biomass found at those depths. Dick & Quinn (1995) isolated several bacteria able to use glyphosate as a phosphorus source. It is possible that a preferential use of phosphate in the topsoil inhibit glyphosate mineralisation. On the other hand, the topsoil also contained much organic carbon, which may serve as a primary carbon source for the glyphosate mineralising organisms. Glyphosate showed the highest sorption of the herbicides studied and only limited desorption was seen. Slow desorption may limit the degradation of glyphosate.

Contrary to glyphosate, transformation of dichlobenil to BAM was only associated with the topsoils and the upper part of the till. The process is probably microbially mediated, but more research is needed to elucidate environmental factors governing the transformation rate. Dichlobenil is now banned in Denmark, but it has been found in large quantities in many soils. Compared to dichlobenil BAM is very mobile and is a threat to the groundwater quality for many years.

ACKNOWLEDGEMENT

The study was supported by Copenhagen Water and by the Immunalyse project (Grant No. 9901188), the Danish Research Agency.

REFERENCES

Bruun L; Koch C; Pedersen B; Jakobsen M H; Aamand J (2000). A quantitative enzyme-linked immunoassay for the detection of 2,6-dichlorobenzamide (BAM), a degradation product of the herbicide dichlobenil. *Journal of Immunological Methods*. **240:** 133-142.

Dick R E; Quinn J.P. (1995). Glyphosate-degrading isolates from environmental samples: Occurrence and pathways of degradation. *Applied Microbiology & Biotechnology* **43:** 545-550.

Larsen L; Sørensen S R; Aamand J (2000) Mecoprop, isoproturon, and atrazine in a sandy aquifer: Vertical distribution of mineralization potential. *Environmental Science & Technology* **34:** 2426-2430.

McKay L; Fredericia J; Lenczewski M; Morthorst J; Klint K E S (1999) Spatial variability of contaminant transport in a fractured till, Avedøre Denmark. *Nordic Hydrology* **30:** 333-360.

Vinther F P; Elsgaard L; Jacobsen O S (2001). Heterogeneity of bacterial populations and pesticide degradation potentials in the unsaturated zone of loamy and sandy soils. *Biol. Fertil. Soils* **33:** 514-420

The use of enantiomeric ratios to assess the fate of mecoprop in groundwater

G M Williams, I Harrison, D J Noy
British Geological Survey, Keyworth, Nottingham, UK, NG12 5GG
Email: gmw@bgs.ac.uk

O Crowley, R Kalin
The Queen's University of Belfast, Belfast UK, BT7 1NN

ABSTRACT

Disposal of the chiral phenoxyacid herbicide mecoprop into landfills in the Lincolnshire Limestone has polluted an abstraction well 2.5 km away. Differences in the biological behaviour of the two mirror image structures of mecoprop (or enantiomers), means that changes in the enantiomeric ratio (ER) can help identify the extent of biodegradation down gradient of the landfill. Deposited as a racemic mixture (i.e. 50% of each enantiomer), there has been no change in the ER in the most polluted part of the landfill plume where conditions are sulphate reducing/methanogenic, indicating no degradation. In the iron and nitrate reducing zones of the plume *(S)*-mecoprop dominates suggesting either inversion of the *(R)*-mecoprop to *(S)*-mecoprop, or faster degradation of *(R)*-mecoprop. In the aerobic aquifer the gradual increase in the ER in favour of *(R)*-mecoprop suggests faster degradation of *(S)*-mecoprop. The persistence of mecoprop in the confined Lincolnshire Limestone further down dip is explained by degradation being inhibited by sulphate reducing conditions that develop naturally.

INTRODUCTION

Mecoprop exists in two mirror image forms (Figure 1). The *(R)*- and *(S)*- enantiomers have identical chemical and physical properties but can behave differently when they interact with other chiral compounds in biological systems. Only the *(R)*-mecoprop is herbicidally active (Loos 1975), but both enantiomers are known to degrade aerobically although at different rates (Harrison *et al.* 1996). Degradation under anaerobic conditions has been reported to be slight or absent. Muller & Buser (1997) provided evidence for enantiomeric inversion in both directions and also derived the quasi-first order reaction rates for the processes shown in Figure 2 (Buser & Muller 1998). Kohler *et al.* (1999) reported enrichment of *(R)*-mecoprop down gradient from a landfill in Switzerland and ascribed it to the faster degradation of the *(S)*-enantiomer. They concluded that changes in the enantiomeric ratio of mecoprop provide useful evidence in support of its biotransformation and natural attenuation in groundwater.

In this study, the degradation of mecoprop down gradient from a landfill site in the Lincolnshire Limestone aquifer has been investigated by determining changes in the enantiomeric ratio, and in the stable carbon isotope ratios of the enantiomers, in relation to the prevailing redox zones. Stable isotope fractionation is an established technique for identifying biologically mediated reactions and leads to an increase in the proportion of ^{12}C in the products and a consequent decrease in ^{12}C (increase in ^{13}C) in the reactant (Hoefs 1973).

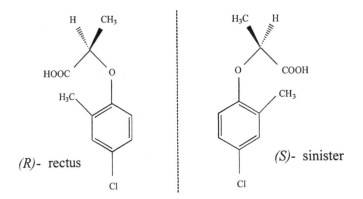

Figure 1. The enantiomers of 2-(-4-chloro-2-methylphenoxy)-
propionic acid (or mecoprop)

SITE DESCRIPTION

Three landfills which received an estimated 40 tonnes of the herbicide mecoprop as liquid
waste, are situated in former quarries in the Lincolnshire Limestone which is a fractured
highly permeable aquifer extensively used for water supply in the UK. The landfills lie just
west of a major geological fault which at one time was considered to be a barrier to
groundwater flow (Sweeney *et al.*, 1998).   East of the fault the aquifer is overlain by
relatively impermeable strata and, with increasing distance, the aquifer becomes confined
with artesian flowing wells. Up to 8 µg/l mecoprop has been detected in a public supply
borehole, 2.5 km to the east of the landfills, and the supply is treated to reduce concentrations
below the EEC recommended limit of 0.1 µg/l (EEC 1980).

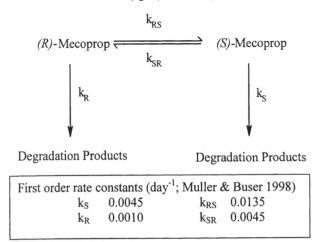

Figure 2.   Scheme for mecoprop inversion and degradation (after Buser
& Muller, 1998)

GROUNDWATER SAMPLING AND ANALYSIS

Groundwater samples from approximately 30 boreholes were analysed for major and trace inorganic species, for non-particulate organic carbon (NPOC) and for mecoprop. Mecoprop analysis differentiated between the two enantiomers and included measurement of their stable carbon isotope ratios ($\delta^{13}C$). Broad scan GC/MS was used to qualitatively identify organic compounds. Full details of the analytical methods and the compounds identified are reported in Williams *et al.*, (2001).

RESULTS AND DISCUSSION

The Piper diagram (Figure 3) is a convenient geochemical tool for displaying variations in major ion chemistry (Domenico & Schwartz 1998). The percentage equivalents of the total anions or cations are shown in the lower triangles whilst the overall composition is plotted in the trapezoid. The line joins groundwater compositions along a flow path from the landfill to the confined aquifer down dip to the east. Immediately surrounding the landfill the groundwater is highly mineralised, organically polluted, sulphate reducing and methanogenic (Zone I). With distance, the plume is diluted and disperses and redox conditions move towards iron and nitrate reducing (Zone II). Further east the aquifer becomes confined and initially contains aerobic calcium bicarbonate dominated groundwater (Zone III). Further away it becomes dominated increasingly by calcium sulphate, then becomes saline (Zone IV) as a result of sulphate reduction (Edmunds & Walton 1983).

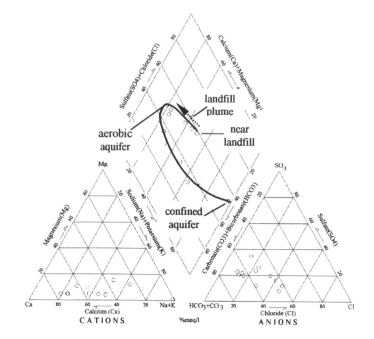

Figure 3. Piper diagram showing changes in water chemistry with distance from the landfill ('o' depicts water composition)

These four geochemical zones form a basis for comparing changes in the enantiomeric ratio (Table 1). Actually the enantiomeric fraction rather than the enantiomeric ratio is a more convenient expression to avoid infinite values (Harner *et al.* 2000). The enantiomeric fraction (EF) is defined as follows:

$$EF = [R] / ([R]+[S])$$ (1)

Where [R] and [S] are the concentrations of *(R)*- and *(S)*-mecoprop respectively.

Change in the enantiomeric fraction (EF) along the flow path from the landfill (Figure 4) show that in the most polluted methanogenic part of the aquifer (Zone I, mecoprop ≈ 7 mg/L) the mecoprop is still racemic (EF = 0.5) which suggests that no degradation has occurred within a period of 8 years since the last known disposal occurred in 1991.

With migration, dilution and dispersion, mecoprop concentrations reduce and the plume becomes more oxidising but not aerobic (Zone II). Here, at mecoprop concentrations around 500 µg/L, and total organic carbon (TOC) still above background, Fe, Mn and nitrate reducing conditions prevail, and *(S)*-mecoprop dominates. This EF could be interpreted as either inversion of *(R)*- to *(S)*- and/or faster degradation of *(R)*-. As mecoprop concentrations fall further and conditions become aerobic (Zone III), the EF rises above 0.5 as *(R)*-mecoprop dominates. This is consistent with the faster degradation of *(S)*-mecoprop under aerobic conditions, and is similar to observations by Muller and Buser (1997), and Kohler *et al.,* (1999).

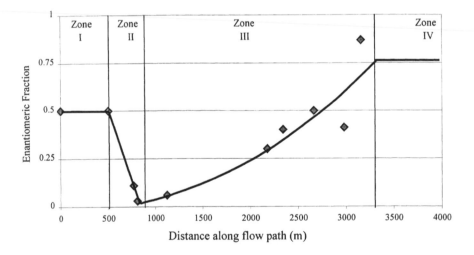

Figure 4.   Changes in mecoprop EF with distance along the flow path from the landfill

It is noteworthy that the field samples show only slight changes in $\delta^{13}C$ (<2‰), and thus provide tenuous evidence for microbial transformation. However, changes would not be expected to be large since isotopic fractionation as a result of side chain attack would be diluted by the unchanged carbon isotope ratio in the aromatic moiety. Evidence of fractionation from controlled microcosm experiments not prone to field sample variability is expected to provide a better indicator of microbial mediation.

Table 1.   Geochemical zones, changes in mecoprop EF and $\delta^{13}C$, and inferred processes

Zone	Organic C Content	Redox state	EF / $\delta^{13}C$		Inferred processes
I	Close to landfill.	High 100-1000 mg/L	Sulphate reducing/ methanogenic	EF = 0.5	No change in $\delta^{13}C$	No degradation or inversion
II	In landfill plume	Medium 10–100 mg/L	Iron & nitrate reducing	EF < 0.5	slight (?) $\delta^{13}C$ increase in R & S	• Inversion of *(R)*- to *(S)*- and/or • faster degradation of *(R)*- than *(S)*-
III	Aerobic aquifer	Low <10 mg/L	Aerobic	trend to EF > 0.5	slight (?) increase for R, more for S	faster degradation of *(S)*- than *(R)*-
IV	Confined aquifer	Low <10 mg/L	Sulphate reducing	EF constant	no $\delta^{13}C$ data	no degradation or inversion

This preliminary interpretation of the field data is presently being confirmed using laboratory microcosms to identify the conditions under which inversion or degradation occur; the rate constants; the microbial consortia present; and, if possible, the enzymes responsible for inversion/degradation. Early indications are that under anaerobic conditions *(R)*-mecoprop degrades but *(S)*-mecoprop does not. There also appears to be little evidence for inversion of *(R)* to *(S)*.

CONCLUSIONS

Change in the enantiomeric ratio of mecoprop is a useful indicator of *in situ* processes such as degradation/inversion in different redox zones. In this study the dominance of the *(S)*-enantiomer in the anaerobic landfill plume may be explained by faster degradation of *(R)*-mecoprop, or inversion of *(R)*- to *(S)*-. This is the reverse of that reported for aerobic environments where *(S)*-mecoprop degrades faster than *(R)*-. In general, the fact that enantiomers may invert means that the fate of each enantiomer needs to be assessed even if enantiomerically pure formulations are manufactured and released into the environment.

ACKNOWLEDGEMENTS

The Environment Agency (EA), the British Geological Survey and the Engineering and Physical Sciences Research Council funded this work. The authors are grateful to URS Dames and Moore, Alistair Wyness, Wayne Holden and Alison Lowick (now EA), for providing insight into the hydrogeology and for field sampling; to Jonathan Smith and Jonathan Greaves (EA); and to Tony Harte for field sampling and mecoprop analysis as part of his MSc dissertation at the Queen's University of Belfast. This paper is published by permission of the Director of the British Geological Survey (Natural Environment Research Council).

REFERENCES

Buser H R; Muller M D (1998). Occurrence and transformation reactions of chiral and achiral phenoxyalkanoic acid herbicides in lakes and rivers in Switzerland. *Environmental Science and Technology* **32**: 626-633.

Domenico P A; Schwartz F W (1998). Physical and Chemical Hydrogeology 2nd edition. Wiley: New York.

EEC Directive (1980). EEC directive on drinking water 80/778/EEC. *Official Journal of the European Communities* No L 229.

Edmunds W M; Walton N R G (1983). The Lincolnshire Limestone: Hydrochemical evolution over a 10 year period. *Journal of. Hydrology* **61**: 201 -211.

Harrison I; Leader R U; Higgo J J W; Williams G M (1998). A study of the degradation of phenoxyacid herbicides at different sites in a limestone aquifer. *Chemosphere* **36**:1211-1232.

Harner T; Wiberg K; Norstrom R (2000). Enantiomeric fractions are preferred to enantiomeric ratios for describing chiral signatures in environmental analysis. *Environmental Science and Technology* **34**: 218 – 220.

Hoefs J (1973). Stable Isotope Geochemistry. Springer: New York, Heidelberg, Berlin.

Kohler H P E; Nickel K; Bunk M; Zipper C (1999). Microbial transformation of the chiral pollutants mecoprop and dichloroprop:-the necessity of considering stereochemistry. In: *Novel Approaches for the Bioremediation of Organic Pollution* eds Fass R; Flashner Y; Reuveny S; pp 13 – 20. Kleuwer Academic/ Plenum Press: New York.

Larsen L; Aamand J (2001). Degradation of herbicides in two sandy aquifers under different redox conditions. *Chemosphere* **44**: 231-236.

Loos M A (1975). Chapter 1; Phenoxyalkanoic acids. In: *Herbicides - Chemistry, Degradation and Mode of Action* eds Kearney P C; Kaufman D D Volume 1: 2-101. Marcel Dekker, Inc: New York and Basel.

Muller M D; Buser H R (1997). Conversion reactions of various phenoxyalkanoic acid herbicides in soil. 1. Enantiomerisation and enantioselective degradation of the chiral 2-phenoxypropionic acid herbicides. *Environmental Science & Technology* **31**: 1953-1959.

Sweeney J; Hart P A; McConvey P J (1998). Investigation and management of pesticide pollution in the Lincolnshire Limestone aquifer in eastern England. In *Groundwater contaminants and their migration.* eds Mather J; Banks D; Dumpleton S; & Fermor M Geological Society, London - Special Publication **128**: 347 - 360.

Williams G M; Harrison I; Noy D J; Crowley O; Kalin R M (2001). Use of enantiomeric ratios to identify the natural attenuation of mecoprop in the Lincolnshire Limestone. *Environment Agency Research & Development Report* P 349.

Biobeds: safe disposal of pesticide waste and washings

P Fogg

Cranfield Centre for EcoChemistry, Shardlow Hall, Shardlow, Derby, DE72 2GN, UK
Email: p.fogg@cranfield.ac.uk

ABSTRACT

The presence of pesticides in environmental waters can come from a number of point and diffuse sources. However, contamination arising from non-approved use, poor practice, illegal operations or misuse of pesticides is increasingly thought to be responsible. Biobeds appear to provide a low cost system for treating pesticide waste and washings, providing a matrix to adsorb the pesticide(s) and facilitate biodegradation. Water management is crucial in terms of biobed performance, construction costs and management. Unlined biobeds appear to have a similar level of performance as more costly treatment systems.

INTRODUCTION

When used correctly according the label instructions and with the appropriate precautions pesticides should present minimal risk to the environment. However the small drips and spillages which occur as part of normal agricultural practice can result in a significant amount of surface water contamination (Mason *et al.*, 1999). In the UK washings from equipment and spray tanks should be disposed of in accordance with the Code of Practice for the Safe use of Pesticides on Farms and Holdings (1998, currently under review) and the Groundwater regulations (1998). However, due the practicalities and costs associated with the recommended procedures and lack of awareness of the legislation, it is possible that many users do not comply with these requirements. A system is therefore required that is able to treat the small drips and spills which occur as part of the normal mixing procedure as well as larger volumes of tank and equipment washings. The system must be robust in terms of its ability to retain and degrade high concentrations of pesticide mixtures applied repeatedly, simple to construct and manage and require a low technical input. Biobeds appear to offer an alternative to current methods of treating pesticide waste and washings.

In its simplest form a biobed is a hole in the ground filled with a mixture of topsoil, peat and straw (Torstennson & Castillo 1996, 1997). The biobed is covered with grass and equipped with a ramp enabling the tractor and sprayer to be driven over the bed. Studies in Sweden have demonstrated that biobeds can effectively retain and degrade pesticide waste arising from accidental spillages of prepared pesticides on concentrate. In order to be used on UK farms biobeds would also need to be able to cope with much larger volumes of waste arising from tank and machinery washings. The objective of this study was to determine whether biobeds could be used to treat pesticide spills, waste and washings arising from UK farms. A series of laboratory and semi-field experiments were performed to determine the degradability and leaching potential of pesticides in a biobed under conditions that are likely in the UK. Previous studies using lined biobeds have demonstrated that water management is crucial in terms of construction costs, management and performance. Although pesticides were effectively retained within the biobed, saturated conditions below 10 cm and poor degradation means that unlined biobeds are unlikely to work on UK farms. This paper focuses on results from a semi-field experiment.

MATERIALS AND METHODS

The degradability and leaching potential of 6 pesticides (Table 1) with a range of hydrophobicities and half lives were measured.

Table 1. Study compounds and their reported physico-chemical charactersistics

Active Substance	K_{oc} ml/g	DT_{50}	Water Solubility (mg/l)	Application rates mg/biobed Topsoil vs Biomix	Water loading
Isoproturon	100	6 - 28	65	1114	255
Pendimethalin	5000	90 - 120	0.3	800	204
Chlorpyrifos	6000	60 - 120	1.4	583	73.4
Chlorothalonil	1600 - 14000	6 - 43	0.81	653	153
Epoxiconazole	957 - 2647	60 - 90	6.6	76	51
Dimethoate	16 - 52	7 - 16	22300	244	34.7

Values taken from Wauchop et al,. (1992) and Tomilin (2000)

Pesticide leaching from topsoil and biomix

The leaching potential of pesticides in soil and biomix were compared. Two sets of four cores were prepared using unplasticised polyvinyl chloride (PVC-u) piping (20 cm diameter x 75 cm length) filled with 2-3 cm of gravel followed by 15 cm of washed sand and a 50 cm layer of either fresh biomix (50% straw, 25% peat substitute, 25% topsoil) or topsoil (69% sand, 13% silt, 18% clay, 1.95% organic matter, pH 6.15). The base of each core drained via Teflon tubing to a 2.5 l amber glass bottle. Three of the biomix filled cores and 3 of the topsoil filled cores were treated with the study pesticides. Split applications of isoproturon, pendimethalin, chlorpyrifos and chlorothalonil, epoxiconazole dimethoate were made in the autumn and spring respectively.   A bromide tracer was also applied (628 mg/core) to check the hydrological integrity of the lysimeters, as well as looking at the breakthrough timing of infiltrating water. Collection vessels were monitored after all rainfall events and the total volume of leachate recorded. Volumes in excess of 500 ml were collected and stored at (0 - 10°C) prior to analysis. Where possible, a 60 ml sub-sample was also taken for bromide analysis. At the end of the study all cores were sectioned (0-5, 5-10, 10-20, 20-30 and >30 cm), homogenised and stored at -15°C prior to analysis.

Effect of water loading on pesticide leaching

The effect of water loading on pesticide leaching behaviour was also investigated. Twelve cores containing pre-composted biomix (composted for 97 days) were prepared. Cores were again constructed from PVC-u tubing and consisted of a 50 cm layer of biomix on a 5 cm layer of course gravel draining to an adjacent collection vessel. Three hydrological scenarios were investigated. Four cores were connected using plastic guttering to 0.54 m^2 concrete slabs, four cores were connected to 0.135 m^2 concrete slabs whilst the remaining cores received only direct inputs of rainfall. The study pesticides were applied as a mixture at an application rate based on concentrations of pesticides measured in second rinse tank washings. A bromide tracer was again applied (314 mg/core). Water samples were collected once leachate volumes exceeded 200 ml and the cores were destructively sampled at the end of the study (299 DAT). All samples were frozen at (-15°C) prior to analysis.

Analytical methods

Water samples (200 ml) were extracted 3 times into 30 ml dichloromethane (DCM). The DCM fractions were filtered through anhydrous Na_2SO_4 and then evaporated to dryness. The resulting residues were re-dissolved into 2 ml of a mixture containing 10% methanol and 90% DCM. Soil and biomix samples (40 g) were mixed with 60 g anhydrous Na_2SO_4 and extracted using 160 ml of a mixture containing 10% methanol and 90% DCM. Samples were shaken for 1 h and allowed to stand until clear with a 2 ml aliquot taken for analysis. Concentrations of each pesticide were determined using GC, (Hewlett Packard HP5890) fitted with a split/splitless injector, 12 m x 0.53 mm BPX5 column (SGE) and a nitrogen-phosphorous detector.

RESULTS and DISCUSSION

Topsoil Vs Biomix

Topsoil and biomix lysimeters recieved 116% of the long term average rainfall with 13 samples of leachate being collected over a 9 month period. With one exception cumulative leachate volumes were similar between columns with approximately 10 l collected. Rapid breakthrough of bromide was observed from topsoil lysimeters with highest concentrations observed 35 DAT. Movement of bromide through biomix filled cores was much slower with maximum concentrations not being observed until 102 DAT.

With the exception of pendimethalin concentrations of pesticide in leachate from biomix filled lysimeters were significantly lower than in leachate from topsoil (for example data for isoproturon are presented in Figure 1). Considering the physico-chemical properties of pendimethalin (i.e a high K_{oc}) this result cannot be explained without further investigation. Peak concentrations of active ingredient in leachate from biomix ranged from 0.15 µg/l (epoxiconazole) to 127 µg/l (isoproturon) whereas from topsoil cores concentrations ranged from 0.47 µg/l (pendimethalin) to 3845 µg/l (isoproturon). With the exception of dimethoate in soil, no pesticide was detected in the soil or biomix matrix below 30 cm depth with the majority being retained in the top

10 cm. A mass balance was performed to determine the fate of each of the study compounds in topsoil and biomix (Table 2). This indicated that in biomix only a small proportion is leached and between 70 and 93% is degraded.

Table 2. Mass balance (*) for topsoil and biomix lysimeters

| Pesticide | TOPSOIL | | | BIOMIX | | |
	Leached %	Retained %	Degraded %	Leached %	Retained %	Degraded %
Isoproturon	1.5	0.7	97.8	0.1	7.0	92.9
Pendimethalin	0	37.4	62.6	0	28.8	71.2
Chlorpyrifos	0	14.6	85.4	0	13.1	86.9
Chlorothalonil	0.2	34.2	65.5	0	25.6	71.4
Epoxiconazole	0.3	24.7	75.0	0	30.0	70.0
Dimethoate	8.4	4.0	87.5	0	7.3	92.7

* Mass balance calculated 217 days after last application of isoproturon, pendimethalin and chlorpyrifos and 83 days after application of chlorthalonil, epoxiconazole and dimethoate

Effect of additional water loading

Rainfall between January and September 2000 was 17% above average with leachate samples collected on 28 occasions. Cumulative leachate volumes ranged from 3.4 to 5.1 l from biobeds receiving only direct rainfall, between 45.2 - 56.4 l were collected from biobeds receiving a medium water loading and between 103.7 and 177.6 l from biobeds subjected to a high water loading.

Bromide movement through biobed columns with a high water loading was rapid. Breakthrough occurred 7 DAT and coincided with mean maximum bromide concentrations. From biobeds subjected to a medium water loading, bromide breakthrough also occurred 7 DAT, however maximum concentrations were not measured until 29 DAT. Water movement through biobed columns receiving only direct rainfall was slow, and breakthrough was detected 57 DAT with mean maximum concentration not measured until 229 DAT.

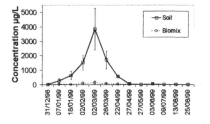

Figure 1. Mean concentrations (± 1 SE) of isoproturon in leachate from topsoil and biomix

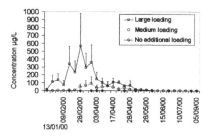

Figure 2. Mean concentrations (+1 SE) of isoproturon in leachate from biobed columns subjected to a high, medium and no additional hydraulic loadings

Maximum pesticide concentrations were measured in leachate collected from biobed columns with a high water loading. These were an order of magnitude higher than from biobeds with a medium water loading and 3 orders higher than columns receiving only direct rainfall inputs (for example results for isoproturon are shown in Figure 2.) Generally, highest concentrations were observed for the most mobile compounds, isoproturon and dimethoate. Peak concentrations ranged from 1.21 µg/l (epoxiconazole) to 1367 µg/l (isoproturon) from biobeds with a high water loading, from 0.35 µg/l (epoxiconazole) to 258 µg/l (isoproturon) from the medium loading experiment; and from 0.57 µg/l (dimethoate) to 1.65 µg/l (chlorpyrifos) from biobeds with no additional water loading. From high water loading biobeds no concentrations of pesticide were measured below 30 cm depth, with 95 - 100% retained in the top 10 cm of biomix. A similar distribution was observed for the medium loading cores. No pesticide was detected below 20 cm depth with 97 - 100% retained in the top 10 cm. From lysimeters receiving only direct rainfall inputs no concentrations of pesticide were measured below 10 cm depth. A mass balance was performed to determine the fate of each of the study compounds under each of the three hydraulic scenarios investigated (Table 3) and indicated that with a medium water loading <1% of the applied pesticide leached, with between 66 and 99% degraded within 9 months.

Table 3. Mass balance for biobed columns receiving a high, medium and no additional
hydraulic loading

	% Leached			% Retained			% Degraded		
	High	Medium	No	High	Medium	No	ligh	Medium	No
Isoproturon	6.4	0.2	0	0.1	0.1	1.2	93.5	99.7	98.8
Pendimethalin	0.1	0	0	12.8	14.9	17.2	87.1	85.1	82.8
Chlorpyrifos	0	0	0	0.4	0.7	3.5	99.5	99.3	96.5
Chlorothalonil	0.1	0	0	1.8	1.7	9.4	98.0	98.3	90.5
Epoxiconazole	0	0	0	33.5	33.9	32.8	66.4	66.1	64.1
Dimethoate	6.1	0.6	0	0	0	0.1	93.9	99.4	99.9

CONCLUSIONS

Studies using open biobeds confirmed that the biomix could retain and subsequently degrade high concentrations of pesticide. Performance of biobeds with a medium water loading was similar to other commercially available treatment systems with >99.4% of the applied pesticide retained of which >66% was degraded within 9 months. However, in order for biobeds to be approved for use in the UK performance will have to improve such that concentrations of pesticide potentially reaching ground water are <0.1 µg/l. Theoretically biobeds can achieve this target.

BIOBED DESIGN

Using the relationship between hydraulic loading expressed in l/m^3 of biomix and the mean maximum concentrations of pesticide measured in leachate, the size of biobed required to achieve 0.1 µg/l pesticide concentration in leachate can be calculated.

Assuming that two identical biobeds are operated in series (Figure 3), to treat 10000 litres of dilute pesticide waste and to achieve pesticide concentrations less than 0.1µg/l the biobeds would need to be 3 m³ in size.

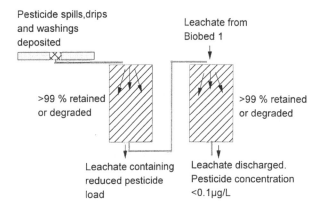

Pesticide spills,drips and washings deposited

Leachate from Biobed 1

>99 % retained or degraded

>99 % retained or degraded

Leachate containing reduced pesticide load

Leachate discharged. Pesticide concentration <0.1µg/L

Figure 3. Schematic diagram of unlined biobed system

ACKNOWLEDGEMENTS

This study was funded by the Environment Agency, the Department for Environment Food and Rural Affairs, the Crop Protection Association and Monsanto.

REFERENCES

Code of practice for the safe use of pesticides on farms and holdings (1998). Ministry of Agriculture Fisheries and Food, PB3528.

Mason P J; Foster I D L; Carter A D; Walker A; Higginbotham S; Jones R L; Hardy I A J (1999). Relative importance of point source contamination of surface waters: River Cherwell catchment monitoring study. *Proceedings of the XI Symposium Pesticide Chemistry,* 11-15 July 1999, 405-412, Cremona Italy, ISBN 88-7830-299-6.

The Ground Water Regulations (1998). Statutory Instrument No. 2746, ISBN 0 11 079799 X.

Tomlin C D S (1997). The Pesticide Manual eleventh edition. The British Crop Protection Council:Farnham.

Torstensson L; Castillo M dP (1997). Use of biobeds in Sweden to minimise environmental spillages from agricultural spray equipment. *Pesticide Outlook* **8:** 24-27.

Torstensson L; Castillo M dP (1996). Biobeds minimise environmental risks when filling agricultural spraying equipment. *Proceedings of COST 66 Workshop, Stratford-upon-Avon,* 223-224.

Wauchop R D; Butler T M; Hornsby A G; Augustjn-Beckers P W M; Burt J P (1992). SCS-ARS-CES pesticide properties database for environmental decision making *Reviews of Environmental Contamination & Toxicology* **123:** 1-164.

SESSION 6

QUANTITATIVE ASPECTS

Chairman &   Dr C D Brown
Session Organiser: *Cranfield University, Silsoe, UK*

Examining the spatial variation of environmental properties using geostatistics

Z L Frogbrook

Department of Soil Science, University of Reading, Whiteknights, Reading, RG6 6DW, UK
Email: z.l.frogbrook@reading.ac.uk

ABSTRACT

Environmental properties vary across the surface of the earth and often at many
different spatial scales. Over the last thirty years, geostatistics has been used
successfully to analyse spatial data throughout the earth sciences. This paper
gives a brief introduction to geostatistics. It describes the variogram, a model of
the spatial variation, and kriging, a method of prediction. A case study shows
how the spatial variation of soil organic matter can be explored geostatistically
within a single field. The importance of sampling intensity is examined by sub-
sampling a dense grid of data.

SPATIAL VARIATION

Soil plays an important role in determining the fate of pesticides in the environment. Soil
chemical, physical and biological properties influence the adsorption and degradation of
pesticides. Soil properties, however, like many environmental properties vary more or less
continuously across the earth's surface. The variation of these properties is complex because
of the interaction of many different processes that operate at different spatial scales.
Burrough (1983) suggested that the variation in soil properties occurs at all levels of
resolution from millimetres to hundreds of kilometres. Figure 1 shows three possible levels
of spatial variation superimposed on one another: one over hundreds of metres defined by
two classes separated by a boundary (the steep slope), an intermediate scale of variation over
tens of metres, and short scale variation over distances of less than a few metres. The latter
appears to be unstructured and locally erratic, a feature often referred to as noise. It is
important to remember, however, that what is observed as noise at one resolution can appear
as structure at another and vice versa; it depends on the scale at which the variation is
resolved (Oliver, 1999).

SAMPLING AND ESTIMATION

Information on environmental properties is often restricted to observations on small areas or
volumes of the survey area, i.e. a sample. To provide an overall view of the variation there is
a need to predict values at unsampled sites. The two main methods that have been used for
prediction are classification and interpolation.

Classification is the traditional approach to prediction where the mean value of a property is
used as the predictor at all places within the class. Conventional farm management tends to
use this approach and each field is treated as a distinct class for fertiliser applications, for
example. Classification assumes that the classes account for all of the spatially correlated
variation and that any remaining variation is random. In other words, it is assumed that there

is no statistical relation between values a given distance apart within the soil class. If this is the case then classification is a reasonable approach. The number of sample locations needed to estimate the mean values of the soil properties reliably for each class can be determined by conventional statistics for a given level of confidence (Webster and Oliver, 1990). If, as is usually so, there is spatially correlated variation remaining within the classes this represents variation that could be resolved but has not been.

Interpolation is an alternative to classification that expresses the continuity in the variation. This approach to prediction can provide the local detail that is often required for environmental management. All methods of interpolation assume implicitly that there is a statistical relation between values a given distance apart. Conventional methods of interpolation, such as inverse squared distance and nearest neighbour interpolation, provide no means of assessing this and there is a risk of predicting from data that are spatially uncorrelated. Geostatistics overcomes many of the weaknesses of traditional interpolation and has been used successfully to analyse spatial data throughout the earth sciences.

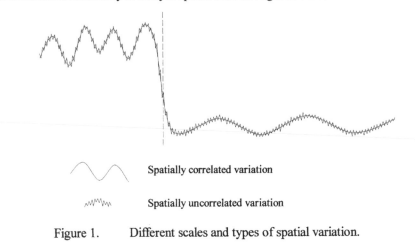

⌇⌇⌇⌇⌇⌇   Spatially correlated variation

⌇⌇⌇⌇⌇⌇   Spatially uncorrelated variation

Figure 1.   Different scales and types of spatial variation.

GEOSTATISTICS

Geostatistics has been well documented in several texts (e.g. Goovaerts, 1997; Isaaks & Srivastava, 1989; Webster & Oliver, 2001) and only a brief introduction is given here.

The *variogram* is the central tool of geostatistics. It describes the spatial structure of the variation by measuring the degree of correlation between sampling points a given distance apart. This measure is based on the notion that samples are more similar at nearby locations than at distant ones. The standard formula for computing the variogram is:

$$\hat{\gamma}(\mathbf{h}) = \frac{1}{2M(\mathbf{h})} \sum_{i=1}^{M(h)} \{z(\mathbf{x}_i) - z(\mathbf{x}_i + \mathbf{h})\}^2 \tag{1}$$

where $\hat{\gamma}(\mathbf{h})$ is the estimated semivariance, $z(\mathbf{x}_i)$ and $z(\mathbf{x}_i + \mathbf{h})$ are the measured values of Z at any two places $\mathbf{x}_i$ and $\mathbf{x}_i + \mathbf{h}$ separated by $\mathbf{h}$, a vector having both distance and direction known as the lag, and $M(\mathbf{h})$ is the number of paired comparisons at that lag. By changing $\mathbf{h}$, an ordered set of values is obtained and this is the experimental variogram. The semivariance is computed for discrete values of **h**, but the experimental variogram represents the regional variogram, which is continuous. The latter is represented by authorized mathematical functions fitted to the experimental values.

Figure 2 illustrates some of the main features of variograms. In the first example, Figure 2a, the semivariances increase initially and then reach an upper limit, or bound. This maximum is known as the *sill* variance and it estimates the *a priori* variance of the process. The distance at which the sill is reached is the *range*, denoting the limit of spatial correlation (or spatial dependence); sampling locations separated by distances greater than this are spatially uncorrelated. The variogram in Figure 2b appears to increase indefinitely; it is unbounded. It suggests that the full extent of the spatial variation has not been encompassed at the scale of investigation. Both variograms meet the ordinate at a positive value, known as the *nugget variance*. This is common when the experimental semivariances are extrapolated to the origin. For continuous properties the nugget variance encompasses any measurement error and spatial variation occurring within the shortest sampling interval, i.e. the unresolved spatial variation. The latter is usually the larger of these (Oliver & Frogbrook, 1998). Sometimes the variogram appears to be flat, it is pure nugget, Figure 2c. For continuous properties this usually means that the sampling has failed to resolve the spatial variation present and that all of the spatial structure is contained within the smallest sampling interval. The spatial structure can only be identified by more intensive sampling.

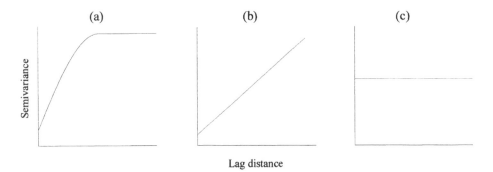

Figure 2.   Forms of variogram (a) bounded (b) unbounded (c) pure nugget.

The method of prediction embodied in geostatistics is known as *kriging*, which is a general term that embraces several types of prediction. The most commonly used form is *ordinary kriging*. Kriging is a method of local weighted moving averaging of the sample data within the neighbourhood of the point to be predicted. The weights depend on the variogram and the configuration of the sampling points, and are allocated in such a way as to minimize the kriging variance and to ensure that the estimates are unbiased. Kriging is optimal in this sense (Webster & Oliver, 2001). Kriged estimates can be made for points (punctual kriging) or over areas (block kriging). Punctual kriging is an exact interpolator and the kriged prediction at a sampling site is the observed value there and the kriging variance is zero. Block kriging results in smoother estimates and smaller kriging variances overall.

$$\hat{Z}(B) = \sum_{i=1}^{n} \lambda_i z(\mathbf{x}_i),$$
(2)

where n usually represents the data points within the local neighbourhood, A, and is usually much less than the total number in the sample, and λ_i are the weights. The weights are chosen to sum to 1 to avoid bias and to minimise the kriging variance:

$$\sum_{i=1}^{n} \lambda_i = 1. \tag{3}$$

The kriging variance of $\hat{Z}(B)$ is:

$$\sigma^2(B) = E\left[\left\{\hat{Z}(B) - Z(B)\right\}^2\right]$$
$$= 2\sum_{i=1}^{n} \lambda_i \bar{\gamma}(\mathbf{x}_i, B) - \sum_{i=1}^{n} \sum_{j=1}^{n} \lambda_i \lambda_j \gamma(\mathbf{x}_i, \mathbf{x}_j) - \bar{\gamma}(B, B) \tag{4}$$

where $\gamma(\mathbf{x}_i, \mathbf{x}_j)$ is the semivariance between points $\mathbf{x}_i$ and $\mathbf{x}_j$, $\bar{\gamma}(\mathbf{x}_i, B)$ is the average semivariance between data point $\mathbf{x}_i$ and the block B, and $\bar{\gamma}(B, B)$ is the within block variance.

Some properties are sampled sparsely because they are expensive or difficult to measure and the predictions obtained from them are likely to be unreliable. In this situation, the predicted value might be improved by using the spatial relation, or coregionalization, between other better sampled properties that are cheaper or easier to measure. This procedure is known as *cokriging*. McBratney & Webster (1983) took this approach to improve the prediction of topsoil silt using the better sampled subsoil silt and sand. Frogbrook and Oliver (2001) used this to improve the predictions of soil organic matter content.

In agriculture many management decisions, such as the application of lime, are made using critical thresholds. For example, a farmer might decide that lime is needed only in areas of the field where the soil pH is 5.5 or less. One approach would be to map the kriged predictions of soil pH and from this map identify regions where an application of lime is required. However, the kriged values are estimates only and as such they are subject to error. In areas where the predictions are much less than or much greater than this threshold the decision as to whether to act is easy but when predictions are close to the threshold this decision is harder to make. To aid this decision an estimate is required of the probability that the threshold is, or is not, exceeded (Oliver et al.,1996). This can be determined by *indicator kriging* or *disjunctive kriging*. The former is a non-parametric approach to kriging where the data are transformed to a binary variable (indicator). Disjunctive kriging is also based on an indicator approach but allows all of the information of the original variable to be retained. Webster & Oliver (1989) used disjunctive kriging to determine areas where phosphate was required on Broom's Barn Experimental Station, England.

SAMPLE DESIGN

To describe reliably the variation within a field, the sampling intensity should relate to the scale at which most of the spatial variation occurs. Otherwise the sampling might be more intensive than necessary or, more seriously, too sparse to provide spatially correlated data for any method of interpolation. The sampling intensity might need to be different for different properties or for different regions. For example, Figure 3 shows that soil *A* varies over shorter distances than soil *B*; the peaks and troughs are closer together. To resolve the variation in soil *A* a smaller sampling interval would be required than that for soil *B*. If the sampling interval for *B* were used for *A*, as illustrated in Figure 3, the variation would appear as noise. However, for soil *B* the sampling intensity used for *A* would result in wasted effort.

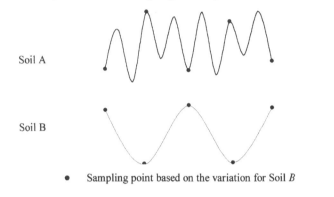

Soil A

Soil B

• Sampling point based on the variation for Soil *B*

Figure 3. Location of sampling points for two soil types.

If there is no information on the likely scale of variation a nested survey may be a sensible starting point. This allows several magnitudes of spatial scale to be investigated in a single analysis. Price *et al.,* (2001) gives an example of a nested sampling design. If there is some prior knowledge of the scale of variation, transects or grid surveys can be used.

Case Study

The study site is an arable crop field at the Centre for Dairy Research (CEDAR), Berkshire, south central England. The soil in the field is predominately a clay loam. Soil samples were taken at the nodes of a 20-m square grid, giving a total of 160 sample points. The samples were analysed for soil organic matter content (OM).

The variogram is based on variances and, therefore, the statistical distribution of the data can affect the reliability of the semivariances. Geostatistics also assumes some degree of stationarity. When local trend or drift, or large scale variation exists in the study area the data may not be stationary. This violates the assumptions of geostatistics. An exploratory data analysis showed that the OM data were normally distributed with no evidence of trend.

The experimental variogram was computed and an exponential model fitted (Figure 4). The variogram shows a clear structure with a small nugget variance, which suggests that the sample design was adequate to identify the variation within the field. To examine the spatial variation of OM, predictions were made at 5 m intervals on a square grid by ordinary block kriging using blocks of 20 m by 20 m, which relate to management units. These values were mapped (Figure 4). The map shows that the variation is patchy, some areas have large values and other areas small values. Such patchy distributions are the transition feature that give rise to bounded variograms; the average extent of the patches generally relates to the range of the variogram.

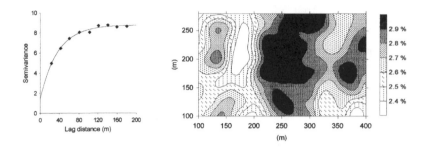

Figure 4.   Variogram and map of kriged estimates for organic matter at CEDAR.

Sampling on a 20-m grid is likely to be too costly for most routine surveys. To explore the effect of the sampling interval, the original data on the 20-m grid were sub-sampled to produce data on 40-m (40 points), 60-m (24 points) and 100-m (8 points) grids. These subsets contain fewer than 100 data points, which is generally considered the minimum for producing a reliable variogram (Webster & Oliver, 1992). Variograms were computed to illustrate the effects of few data, and where possible models were fitted (Figure 5). These variograms show how the sampling intensity affects the form of the variogram. Even when a 40 m sampling interval is used there is a change in the structure of the variogram. For the 100-m subset the variogram has only one point and it is not possible to determine whether the data are spatially dependent.

The variogram and data for each subset were used for prediction by ordinary kriging. This could not be done for the 100-m subset and predictions were made using inverse squared distance. The maps of the predictions for OM are shown in Figure 5. They show how the detail in the variation is lost as sampling becomes increasingly sparse. This loss occurs even for data on the 40-m grid, although the main areas of small and large values are still evident. The map for predictions from data on the 60-m grid loses more detail and identifies only the patch of large values in the centre of the survey area. The map of predictions using data on the 100-m grid shows that the OM content is over- and under-estimated in many regions of the field and the original pattern is lost. The maps of kriging variance from data on the 20-m, 40-m and 60-m grids show that the values increase as the sampling interval increases; the predictions become less reliable (Figure 6).

Soil sampling and analysis are costly and time consuming, but unless they provide information that is reliable for the purpose then any effort is wasted. The results from this field illustrate the effect of increasingly sparse sample information on the reliability of the experimental variogram and accuracy of the predicted values. They show that maps made from such predictions can be an unreliable representation of the variation. Depending on the level of detail required, a 40-m or 60-m grid might be adequate for this field. For a different field, however, a different sampling intensity might be required to reflect the spatial scale of variation. Careful planning is required at the outset to ensure that the sample design is suitable for the study site. Some guidance on the spatial variation of soil properties can be gained from ancillary data, data that are cheaper to obtain but which are related to the soil in some way. This may include aerial photographs, electro-magnetic inductance (EMI) surveys or yield maps.

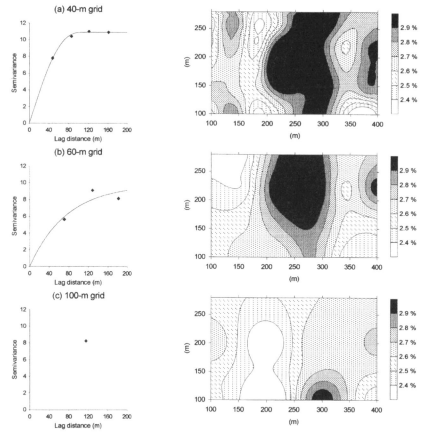

Figure 5.   Variograms and maps for organic matter at CEDAR for the sub-sampled data.

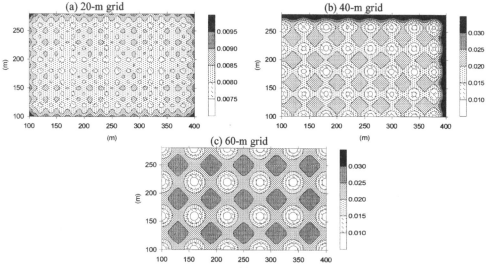

Figure 6.   Maps of the kriging variance for data on a 20-m, 40-m and 60-m grid.

CONCLUSION

Environmental properties, such as soil properties, vary in a complex way. Geostatistics provides a suite of methods that are suitable for analysing the spatial variation of these properties. The variogram describes the structure and spatial scale of the variation and kriging uses this model to predict the values of a property at unsampled places. An important part of any survey is the sample design. To describe the variation reliably the sampling intensity should relate to the scale of spatial variation that needs to be resolved. This might be different for different soil types or different landscapes. The case study illustrates the use of geostatistics and the effect on the predictions when sampling is too sparse.

Once the spatial variation within a study area in known it is possible that this information can be incorporated into pesticide models. This would allow the fate of pesticides to be predicted at unsampled locations across the field. In areas where properties vary considerably this would be a more accurate approach than using a single value for prediction.

REFERENCES

Burrough P A (1983). Multiscale sources of spatial variation in soil. I. The application of fractal concepts to nested levels of soil variation. *Journal of Soil Science*, **34**: 577-597.

Frogbrook Z L; Oliver M A (2001). Comparing the spatial predictions of soil organic matter determined by two laboratory methods. *Soil Use and Management*. In press.

Goovaerts P (1997). *Geostatistics for natural resources evaluation*. Oxford University Press, New York.

Isaaks E H; Srivastava R M (1989). *An introduction to Applied Geostatistics*. Oxford University Press, Oxford.

McBratney A B; Webster R (1983). Optimal interpolation and isarithmic mapping of soil properties. V. Co-regionalization and multiple sampling strategy. *Journal of Soil Science*, **34**: 137-162.

Oliver M A (1999). Exploring soil spatial variation geostatistically. In: *Precision Agriculture '99, Proceedings of the 2nd European Conference on Precision Agriculture*, ed J.V. Stafford, pp. 3-17. Sheffield Academic Press, Sheffield.

Oliver M A; Frogbrook Z L (1998). Sampling to estimate soil nutrients for precision agriculture. The International Fertiliser Society. Proceedings No 417.

Oliver M A; Webster R; McGrath S P (1996). Disjunctive kriging for environmental management. *Environmetrics*. 7: 333-358.

Price O R; Walker A; Wood M; Oliver M A (2001). Using geostatistics to evaluate the spatial patterns in pesticide/soil interactions at the field scale (These proceedings).

Webster R; Oliver M A (1989). Optimal interpolation and isarithmic mapping of soil properties. VI. Disjunctive kriging and mapping the conditional probability. *Journal of Soil Science*, **40**: 497-512.

Webster R; Oliver M A (1990). *Statistical Methods in Soil and Land Resource Survey*, Oxford University Press, Oxford.

Webster R; Oliver M A (1992). Sample adequately to estimate variograms of soil properties. *Journal of Soil Science,* **43**: 177-192.

Webster R; Oliver M A (2001). Geostatistics for Environmental Scientists. J. Wiley & Sons Chichester.

Using geostatistics to evaluate spatial variation in pesticide/soil interactions

O R Price, A Walker
HRI, Wellesbourne, Warwick, CV35 9EF, UK
Email: Oliver.Price@hri.ac.uk

M Wood, M A Oliver
University of Reading, Soil Science, Whiteknights, Reading, RG6 6DW, UK

ABSTRACT

The scale and structure of the spatial variation in degradation of isoproturon, chlorpyrifos and chlorothalonil were quantified. Degradation rates of the three pesticides all showed similar structures in their spatial variation and their persistence was shown to be strongly correlated with both pH and microbial activity estimated by dehydrogenase activity.

INTRODUCTION

It is well known that soil properties vary in space and this variation appears to be random but spatially dependent. Flury (1996) commented that in terms of pesticide fate modelling, aspects of spatial variation in pesticide-soil interactions have generally been ignored, and that there is little information concerning the structure and scale of variation in pesticide fate. Recent work has shown that significant spatial variation occurs in isoproturon (IPU) degradation rates (Walker *et al.*, 2001; Wood *et al.*, 2001) and sorption (Lennartz, 1999) within a single field. There is a need to evaluate the significance of this spatial variation in degradation and sorption in terms of pesticide performance at the field scale and the assessment of environmental fate. Novak *et al.*, (1997) investigated the variation in sorption of atrazine within a field, and used geostatistical techniques to quantify the scale and structure of the variation observed. Richter *et al.*, (1996) reviewed the role of geostatistics in the modelling of pesticide fate.

The method of geostatistical estimation is known as kriging. The main aim of the present work was to use kriging to identify the spatial patterns in pesticide degradation rate and sorption across a specific study area. A secondary objective was to define an approach for soil sampling that would be suitable to estimate the behaviour of pesticides within a single field.

METHODS AND MATERIALS

Field site and sampling strategy

The study area was Deep Slade field at Horticulture Research International, Wellesbourne (grid ref: 426820,255600). The soil was classified as a sandy loam of the Wick Series.

In January 2000, a 240 m x 240 m grid was located in Deep Slade field with nine main grid nodes at 120 m intersections, which were located using an electronic distance measurement machine (Geodimeter 400). The grid covered most of the study site with a boundary of 30 m around the edge of the field. The sampling scheme was an unbalanced nested design, and a hierarchical analysis was used to estimate the components of variance associated with different scales and minimise the number of samples required (see Webster & Oliver, 2001). The scheme covered a range of distances in a single analysis with a minimal number of samples. A sampling interval of 1 m was chosen for the lowest stage as this was expected to encompass most of the small scale variation. The other intervals followed an approximate three-fold geometric progression with further samples at 3, 9 and 27 m, with two further stages at 60 and 120 m. Although the position of the nine main nodes was predetermined (120 m spacing), the positions of all other sampling points were located on random orientations. In total 108 soil samples were collected with 12 samples from each node (Figure 1).

In January 2001, a 180 m x 180 m grid was relocated in Deep Slade field to cover an area within that sampled in the previous year. A soil sample was taken every 20 m along the horizontal and vertical lines of the grid to give a total of 100 soil samples from the study area.

Soil analyses

Individual soil samples of about 1 kg were collected from each sampling position in both years. Precautions were taken to minimise cross contamination between samples (Walker *et al.*, 2001). The soil samples were left to air-dry overnight before being sieved to 2 mm. The sieves were cleaned with ethanol and dried in an oven at 110°C between successive samples to further minimise microbial cross-contamination. Soil pH was measured using a glass electrode in a 1:2.5 suspension of soil/distilled water and organic matter content was estimated by loss on ignition at 450°C (Rowell, 1994). Soil dehydrogenase activity was measured as outlined by Tabatabai (1994) and microbial biomass was estimated by the fumigation-extraction method (Mele & Carter, 1996).

Soil incubations and pesticide residue analysis

Soil samples taken in January 2000 from the nine main grid nodes were used to measure the average maximum water holding capacity (MWHC) and the average moisture content at 40% MWHC was then derived. Four sub-samples (25 g) from each of the 108 samples were weighed into glass jars (125 ml). All sub-samples were treated with an aqueous suspension of a commercial formulation of isoproturon (Arelon SC) to give an initial concentration of 15 mg IPU/kg soil. Soil moisture contents were adjusted to 40% of the average MWHC. A treatment check was carried out after every 50 samples dosed to ensure constant application rates. All soil samples were incubated at 15°C and moisture contents were maintained by addition of sterile distilled water when required (usually once a week). Samples were extracted at 7, 14, 21 and 35 days after application, and four extractions immediately after application were made with soil from each of the nine main grid nodes. After the first day of incubation, all samples were shaken gently to thoroughly mix the IPU throughout the soil. Isoproturon residues were extracted by shaking the soil samples with 30 ml of acetonitrile/water (90/10 v/v) in the 125 ml glass jars on a wrist shaker for 60 minutes.

The average MWHC for the soil samples collected in January 2001 was determined as above. Three sub-samples (25 g) from each of the 100 soil samples were weighed into glass jars (125 ml). The soils were dosed individually to obtain 15 mg/kg of IPU, chlorpyrifos or chlorothalonil. They were incubated as before and the pesticide residues were extracted as above at 21, 35 and 69 d for chlorothalonil, IPU and chlorpyrifos, respectively.

Pesticide concentrations were measured by high performance liquid chromatography (hplc) using Kontron Series 300 equipment. The column used was a Lichrosorb RP-18 (25 cm x 4 mm i.d., Merck). The solvent system used for isoproturon and chlorothalonil was acetonitrile:water:orthophosphoric acid (75:25:0.25 by volume) at a flow rate of 1 ml/min. Detection of these two pesticides was by UV absorbance at 240 nm and 235 nm, respectively. Chlorpyrifos was analysed at 240 nm using a mobile phase of 85:15 acetonitrile:water.

RESULTS & DISCUSSION

The relationship between soil pH and IPU remaining after 21 days was non-linear (Figure 2). Soil samples with pH less than 6.7 generally contained high residues of IPU and those with pH greater than 7.0 had considerably lower IPU residues. Similar relationships were observed between IPU residues and total microbial biomass, with high IPU residues in soil samples with less than 100 mg microbial C/kg.

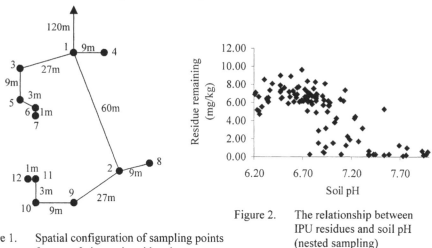

Figure 1.   Spatial configuration of sampling points for one of nine main grid nodes

Figure 2.   The relationship between IPU residues and soil pH (nested sampling)

The accumulated components of variance for the soil properties and IPU residues were plotted against distance on a logarithmic scale as a first approximation to the variograms. Generally the results indicated that the components of variance for the five lower stages accounted for at least 60% of the total variance i.e. a large proportion of the variation occurred at less than 60 m (e.g. IPU residues; Figure 3a). An exception was soil pH (Figure 3b) where stage 1 (120 m) accounted for 55% of the total variation. The sampling scheme generally accounted for much of the variation observed. A larger interval (>120m), however,

235

would begin to explain the unresolved variation observed above 60 m. Walker *et al.,* (2001) measured the variation of IPU degradation at sampling intervals of 50 m. The data in Figure 3a show that 50% of the variation observed in degradation occurred at less than 27 m, indicating that a smaller sampling interval would be optimal for the measurement of IPU degradation. However, sampling for soil pH at a spacing of less than 60 m would be a waste of resources and time as only 27.6% of the variation is accounted for at less than 27 m.

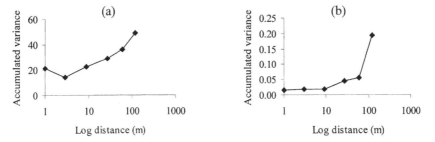

Figure 3. Accumulated components of variance plotted against distance on logarithmic scale: for: (a) IPU residues and (b) soil pH first approximation to variogram (nested sampling)

A 20 m interval was chosen for sampling in the second experiment to ensure that most of the variation in IPU persistence observed in the field would be accounted for. Most of the variates had near-normal distributions. Natural log-transformations were used to reduce skewness on data sets that were not normally distributed. Experimental variograms were computed from the data as described by Webster & Oliver (2001). Variogram models were fitted to the experimental values by weighted least squares approximation. The models that minimised the sums of squares were chosen. All the variables measured showed some evidence of spatial dependence. The nugget variances, i.e. the positive intercept on the ordinate were small suggesting that the sampling had resolved the variation well (with the exception of that for chlorothalonil). This embraces measurement error, but mainly variation associated to distances less than the sampling interval used. All of the variograms were bounded and had ranges varying between 60 m and 90 m, e.g. chlorpyrifos residues (Figure 4a) and dehydrogenase activity (Figure 4b). Using the appropriate variogram model and data for each variable, the kriging equations were solved to obtain estimates at 10 m intervals and the associated estimation errors for a block size of 10 m.

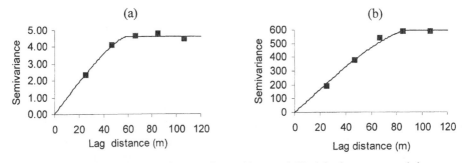

Figure 4. Variograms for: (a) chlorpyrifos residues and (b) dehydrogenase activity (grid sample)

The kriged estimates of the soil properties and pesticide persistence were contoured and mapped so that their patterns of variation could be examined (Figure 5a-5d). The maps of all of the variables show a distinctly patchy distribution in the values. The maps of dehydrogenase, soil pH (data not shown) and residues of the three pesticides all show similar distribution patterns. The variogram models for the pesticides and the soil properties were also similar with ranges of approximately 70 m. The northern part of Deep Slade field showed high values for dehydrogenase activity and soil pH and these correspond well with small values of pesticide residues. The extremes of this relationship are shown well in the contoured maps, Figure 5.

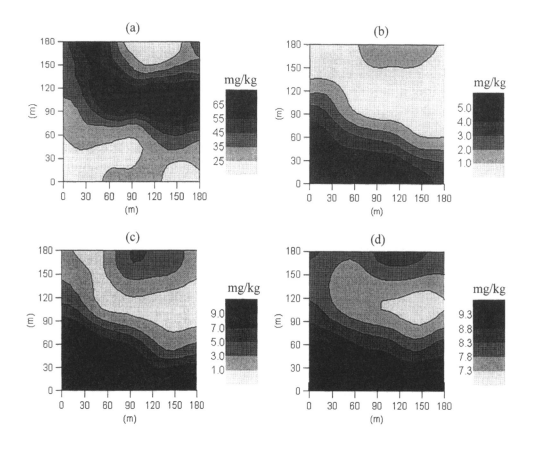

Figure 5   Map of kriged estimates for: (a) soil dehydrogenase activity, (b) IPU residues (35 days), (c) chlorpyrifos residues (69 days), (d) chlorothalonil residues (21 days). Based on laboratory measurements on samples from Deep Slade field (2001). The quantities of pesticide are expressed as residues remaining from an initial concentration of 15 mg/kg.

For the modelling of the environmental fate of pesticides, geostatistics has the potential to describe the variation accurately. It has been shown to provide an insight into the scale at which variation in pesticide degradation rate (and sorption) occurs within the study site. It has enabled conclusions to be drawn concerning the effect of soil properties on pesticide degradation even when conventional correlation analysis does not suggest significant relationships. The data can be used to indicate areas at high risk with respect to pesticide leaching. After running the LEACHP model for 208 sub-sites within a single field Oliver *et al.,* (1999) concluded that significant leaching losses of atrazine would occur from only 10% of the 9 ha site, and the contribution through leaching to groundwater from the other 90% would be negligible. The data presented here indicate that small areas of Deep Slade field (where persistence is greater) would contribute more to possible leaching losses and that there is large within-field variation in the variables controlling pesticide availability.

ACKNOWLEDGEMENTS

Thanks go to the Environmental Dynamics of Pesticides group at HRI and to colleagues in the Soil Science Department at Reading University, (particularly Dr Zoe Frogbrook) for their help and guidance. The research work was financially supported by the Natural Environment Research Council (NERC), Environmental Diagnostics Programme.

REFERENCES

Flury M (1996). Experimental evidence of transport of pesticides through field soils – A review. *Journal of Environmental Quality.* **25**: 25-45.

Lennartz B (1999). Variation of herbicide transport parameters within a single field and its relation to water flux and soil properties. *Geoderma.* **91**: 327-345

Mele P M; Carter M R (1996). Estimation of microbial biomass by ninhydrin-reactive N using liquid chloroform. *Canadian Journal of Soil Science.* **76**: 37-40.

Novak J M; Moorman T B; Cambaradella C A (1997). Atrazine sorption at the field scale in relation to soils and landscape position. *Journal of Environmental Quality.* **26**: 1271-1277

Oliver M A; Simmonds L P; Wood M (1999). Use of geostatistics to determine spatial variation in pesticide leaching - preliminary findings. Proceedings of XI Symposium Pesticide Chemistry, pp. 551-559.

Richter O; Diekkruger B; Nortersheeuser P (1996). Environmental Fate Modelling of Pesticides: From the Laboratory to the Field Scale. VCH Publishers Inc., New York. USA.

Rowell D L (1994). Soil Science: Methods and Applications. Longman Group UK Limited, Essex, England.

Tabatabai M A (1994). Soil Enzymes. In: '*Methods of Soil Analysis: Part 2 Microbiological & Biochemical Properties,* ed RW Weaver *et al.*, pp. 903-947. SSSA, Madison, Wisc.

Walker A; Jurado-Exposito M; Bending G D; Smith V J R (2001). Spatial variability in the degradation rate of isoproturon in soil. *Environmental Pollution*, **111**: 407-415.

Webster R; Oliver M A (2001). *Geostatistics for Environmental Scientists.* J. Wiley & Sons, Chichester.

Wood M; Issa S; Albulquerque M; Johnson A C (2001). Spatial variability in herbicide degradation in the subsurface environment of a groundwater protection zone. *In Press.*

Sources of uncertainty in pesticide fate modelling

I G Dubus, C D Brown, S Beulke

Cranfield Centre for EcoChemistry, Cranfield University, Silsoe, Beds MK45 4DT, UK
E-mail: i.dubus@cranfield.ac.uk

ABSTRACT

Current risk assessment procedures for estimating the possible environmental impact of crop protection products do not explicitly account for uncertainty in exposure estimates and ecotoxicological endpoints. The level of protection provided by the use of safety factors in the risk quotient approach is unknown. Probabilistic risk assessment is considered as a possible refinement to procedures in place and Monte Carlo approaches have been proposed to obtain more realistic assessments of exposure. A number of scientific challenges need to be met for the approach to be robust and useful with regard to risk assessment. These include: i) attributing probability density functions to input parameters and choosing how much uncertainty to include in the analysis; ii) addressing correlation between parameters; iii) dealing with sources of uncertainty which are not covered by Monte Carlo simulations; and, iv) making decisions on the basis of probabilistic information. Effective risk communication is essential for probabilistic risk assessment to be accepted by all stakeholders.

INTRODUCTION

Current environmental risk assessment procedures for pesticide registration in the EU rely on the comparison between exposure and ecotoxicological endpoints (surface waters) or a legal threshold concentration (groundwater). A tiered approach is implemented to focus on those compounds which might be harmful to the environment and not penalise those which pose little threat. Relevant ecotoxicological endpoints are typically derived by laboratory tests using a range of representative organisms although a range of relationships between ecotoxicity and compound properties may also be used in the early stages of the risk assessment. In contrast to the derivation of effect concentrations, the estimation of predicted environmental concentrations for exposure (PEC's) relies heavily on the use of predictive models, especially at higher tiers.

For surface waters, the ratio between PEC's and ecotoxicological endpoints is calculated (termed TER for Toxicity:Exposure Ratio) and compared to threshold values which are dependent on the target organism considered (typically 10 or 100). A compound is considered to pose little threat to surface water organisms if TERs exceed the relevant threshold. For groundwater, PEC's for the parent are compared to a limit concentration of 0.1 µg a.i./l, irrespective of the toxicity and ecotoxicity of the compound.

Current risk assessment procedures are likely to be subject to significant uncertainty originating from both the exposure and the effects side. Uncertainty is indirectly taken into account in the process through the use of TER threshold values which act as safety factors. The level of protection provided by these safety factors is unknown and a number of initiatives are currently underway to try to quantify associated safety margins. Uncertainty in the derivation of ecotoxicological endpoints may arise, for instance, from not knowing the most sensitive species or from the use of constant concentration in laboratory tests. A range of initiatives have been proposed to make ecotoxicological endpoints more realistic, including the establishment of species sensitivity distribution, the refinement of experimental conditions and the use of microcosm/mesocosm studies. Uncertainty on the exposure side may be addressed using probabilistic modelling.

The present paper presents the different sources of uncertainty in the assessment of PEC's and discusses the appropriateness of methods proposed to deal with uncertainty in exposure.

SOURCES OF UNCERTAINTY IN PESTICIDE FATE MODELLING

"Uncertainty" is a capacious term used to encompass a multiplicity of concepts (Morgan and Henrion, 1990). According to these authors, uncertainty in empirical quantities may be classified according to the different sources from which it can arise: random error and statistical variation, systematic error and subjective judgement, linguistic imprecision, variability, randomness and unpredictability, disagreement, and approximations. Uncertainty may also originate for other reasons, for instance from the fact that environmental models only provide an incomplete description of reality. For the purpose of clarity, we use a classification of sources of uncertainty based on their occurrence in relation to the modelling.

Uncertainty arising prior to any modelling activity

Although a number of input parameters in pesticide leaching models have no physical basis and cannot be determined experimentally, values for most inputs can be estimated on the basis of field or laboratory measurements. Examples include model input related to soil and that related to pesticide sorption and degradation properties. The field environment is inherently variable in space and time and this variability will introduce uncertainty into the modelling. Wood et al., (1987) reported Koc values varying from 66 to 1445 l/kg in a 4-ha field (coefficients of variations 17-47%) while Elabd et al., (1986) reported a CV of 38% for the Koc of napropamide in a 0.6-ha plot. Walker et al.,(2001) found large variation of isoproturon degradation in 30 samples taken from a 5-ha field (DT50 6.5 to 30 days). Apart from natural variations at the field scale, variability arising prior to modelling may originate from the use of different sampling techniques in the field, differences in sample storage and preparation (e.g. frozen vs. refrigerated soil samples; air dried vs. moist soil samples), the use of different procedures for analytical measurements or different environmental conditions in the laboratory.

Uncertainty arising from model parameterisation

One of the most important stages in modelling is the attribution of a value to each input parameter of the model. Although experimental data can be directly fed into the model in some instances (e.g. rainfall and temperature data, molecular weight of the compound), model parameterisation traditionally requires manipulation of field or laboratory measurements. Uncertainty may arise because of the variety of procedures in deriving an input value from experimental data. The derivation of a DT50 value from a set of laboratory degradation data is a typical example. Leake et al., (1995) used a degradation dataset (decrease in pesticide concentrations over time) and calculated DT50 values using a range of equations and fitting packages. Resulting DT50 values ranged between 4 and 93 days (mean 27.9 days; median 21.0 days). Uncertainty in the selection of a DT50 value may then arise from the selection of a representative value (typically mean or median) from a range of values derived for different soils or different environmental conditions. Where data are missing or cannot fully support the selection of input values, the model is parameterised using established numerical relationships (e.g. pedotransfer functions) or expert judgement. These estimation methods which are likely to introduce uncertainty into the modelling are also used for attributing values to parameters which do not have a physical basis and cannot be determined experimentally.

Other types of uncertainty

Other significant sources of uncertainty which are less well documented are: i) the influence of model selection on risk assessment results; ii) the influence of the modeller on modelling results (user subjectivity); iii) the fact that models only provide an inaccurate description of field behaviour (model inaccuracy); and, iv) the individual subjectivity in decision making on the basis of probabilistic results. All these sources of uncertainty related to non-empirical quantities are typically ignored in probabilistic modelling.

METHODS TO INCORPORATE UNCERTAINTY INTO THE MODELLING

Methods available

A number of methods are available for taking into account the uncertainty associated with empirical quantities. These include *stochastic modelling* where model input and output are expressed probabilistically, *interval analysis* which is applicable where few assumptions on the form of the parameter variation can be made, *Monte Carlo simulations* where a number of input parameterS are attributed a statistical distribution reflecting their uncertainty and a large number of model runs are carried out, *first-order uncertainty analysis* where Taylor series expansion for key model equations is used, and *fuzzy logic* which describes imprecision in a non-probabilistic framework.

The Monte Carlo approach to integrating uncertainty into the modelling

The Monte Carlo approach to dealing with uncertainty has been used for numerous years in different fields of science and has been proposed as an adequate method for a probabilistic framework for pesticide exposure (ECOFRAM, 1999). This versatile approach is based on numerous runs of a model. Once parameters to be included in the analysis have been selected, a probability density function is attributed to each of them. This reflects the fact that these parameters are considered uncertain and can take a range of values. Correlations between input variables may be introduced into the analysis. A large number of input values for each parameter (say, 1000 values) are sampled randomly from the probability density functions using an adequate sampling procedures and these are used to generate 1000 model input files. The model is run for all these input files and model outputs are aggregated to enable a presentation of the results in probabilistic terms. An example of output of a probabilistic assessment of PEC's for groundwater is provided in Figure 1. The chart can be used to estimate the probability of simulating a concentration above or below a particular threshold.

In Figure 1, concentrations below 0.07 µg/l are predicted in 75% of the cases and the probability of the pesticide concentration exceeding the threshold of 0.1 µg/l is *ca.* 12%.

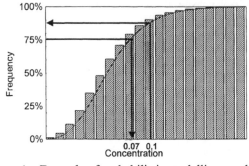

Figure 1.   Example of probabilistic modelling results.

DISCUSSION

The transfer of knowledge from fields of science where uncertainty has historically played an important role (nuclear safety in particular) to environmental risk assessment for chemicals has been extremely fast. Monte Carlo simulations are particularly used since they are easy to implement and understand by all stakeholders. Monte Carlo simulations have thus been considered the panacea for dealing with uncertainty and the challenges associated with the technique are frequently overlooked. These include i) attributing probability density functions to input parameters and choosing how much uncertainty to include in the analysis; ii) dealing with correlations; iii) integrating uncertainty other than that associated with empirical quantities (i.e. that not covered by Monte Carlo simulations); iv) making decisions on the basis of probabilistic information; and, v) communicating risk.

Attribution of probabilistic distributions to input parameters

The determining step in a Monte Carlo exercise is the description of the variation of selected input parameters using probability density functions. The attribution of these probability distributions should ideally be based on the examination of a large amount of data (say >100 datapoints). Generating so many data on the variation of input parameters of pesticide fate models for a particular situation is impractical and alternative methods have to be considered. These include the use of literature information on the likely pattern and magnitude of variations of model inputs and the use of expert judgement. These methods are likely to introduce subjectivity and uncertainty into the probabilistic approach and research is needed to estimate the influence of using different estimation methods and data sources on probabilistic results. Also, it is not clear how much uncertainty should be reflected by these probabilistic distributions. In the case of DT50 values or degradation rates, should probability density functions reflect the variation in values between different soils? the spatial variability in the field? the uncertainty introduced by differences in experimental and analytical conditions in the laboratory? that associated with the treatment of outliers? that arising with the derivation of values from a set of degradation data? that introduced by the choice of representative statistics to be used in the modelling? It is essential that the extent to which uncertainty has been considered in the analysis is specified so that regulators can assess the confidence that should be assigned to risk estimations.

Correlations

If a positive correlation exists between variables, then ignoring these correlations in a probabilistic risk assessment will result in an underestimate of the extremes in environmental impact. Conversely, if correlations between variables are negative, the result will be overly conservative (Millstein, 1995). Although correlations can be handled through Monte Carlo simulations, specifying adequate correlations between parameters remains a challenge because of the lack of associated experimental data. For instance, one would expect some sort of correlation between sorption and degradation in the modelling of the fate of pesticides since increased sorption leads to a decrease of the compound in the liquid phase and hence smaller degradation (it is assumed that degradation mainly occurs in the liquid phase). Translating this intuitive relationship into correlation coefficients is not straightforward although it is felt that this might need integrating into the modelling in some way.

Uncertainty not covered by the Monte Carlo approach

The Monte Carlo approach, in common with most other methods for probabilistic modelling, concentrates on accounting for uncertainty in the values attributed to input parameters. Sources of uncertainty other than that related to empirical quantities are numerous and are likely to be significant (a few examples of these uncertainties are provided earlier in the text). These will be ignored in Monte Carlo analyses and will affect the confidence that should be assigned to results from probabilistic assessments.

Decision making on the basis of probabilistic information

Regulators currently make decisions with regard to the placement of crop protection products on the basis of a large amount of data which are brought together in a deterministic risk assessment. Although the approach is considered to be conservative, the lack of knowledge on the level of protection involved has prompted the application of probabilistic methods to environmental risk assessment for pesticides and a number of research projects on the subject have been initiated. Probabilistic outputs will quantify the likelihood of an adverse impact occurring. As such, there will need to be a revised definition of the regulatory endpoints as absolute protection is *de facto* impossible within a probabilistic framework.

Risk communication

It is likely that the scientific community will address remaining issues in probabilistic risk assessment in the years to come. Still, the scientific challenge in this instance is surpassed by the critical importance of risk communication. With regard to uncertainty, no matter how scientifically robust the answer, it is of limited use unless it can be explained clearly to a lay audience (Hoffman *et al.*, 1999). Recent health scares demonstrate that the lay person can depict strong emotional responses to risk information. The current TER approach carries the message that there is no risk of impact even though this cannot be truly established. In contrast, the acknowledgement and quantification of risk (however small) is inherent in the probabilistic approach. The challenge is hence to communicate effectively the benefits of understanding uncertainty and the rationale for considering low levels of risk acceptable.

CONCLUSIONS

Taking uncertainty into account is being seen as a natural 'next step' for environmental risk assessment. However, a number of key issues need to be addressed before probabilistic techniques can be used with confidence in risk assessment for pesticides.

ACKNOWLEDGEMENTS

The funding of the project "Uncertainty and probabilistic approaches to pesticide fate modelling" by the Department for Environment, Food and Rural Affairs through the Pesticides Safety Directorate is gratefully acknowledged.

REFERENCES

ECOFRAM (1999). ECOFRAM aquatic report (draft), www.epa.gov/oppefed1/ecorisk

Elabd H; Jury W A; Cliath M M (1986). Spatial variability of pesticide adsorption parameters. *Environmental Science & Technology* **20**: 256-260.

FOCUS (2000). FOCUS groundwater scenarios in the EU review of active substances. Report of the FOCUS Groundwater Scenarios Workgroup, EC document reference Sanco/321/2000 rev.2, 202pp.

Hoffman F O; Chambers D B; Stager R H (1999). Uncertainty is part of decision making. *Human and Ecological Risk Assessment* **5**: 255-261.

Millstein J A (1995). Simulating extremes in pesticide misapplication from backpack sprayers. *International Journal of Pest Management* **41**: 36-45

Morgan M G; Henrion M (1990). Uncertainty: a guide to dealing with uncertainty in quantitative risk and policy analysis. Cambridge University Press, Cambridge, UK.

Walker A; Jurado-Exposito M; Bending G D; Smith V J R (2001). Spatial variability in the degradation rate of isoproturon in soil. *Environmental Pollution* **111**: 407-415.

Wood L S; Scott H D; Marx D B; Lavy T L (1987). Variability in sorption coefficients of metolachlor on a Captina silt loam. *Journal of Environmental Quality* **16**: 251-256.

Pesticide leaching potential in the Trasimeno Lake area. Assessment of uncertainty associated with the simulation process

M Trevisan, R Calandra
DISAPROV, Università di Perugia, Borgo XX Giugno 72, 06121 Perugia, Italy
Email: trevisan@unipg.it

C Vischetti, A Esposito,
CCBF-CNR, Borgo XX Giugno 72, 06121 Perugia, Italy

L Padovani
Istituto di Chimica Agraria ed Ambientale, Università Cattolica del Sacro Cuore, 29100 Piacenza, Italy

ABSTRACT

The potential leaching of atrazine in the area around Trasimeno Lake is evaluated using the PELMO model and the uncertainty associated with the simulation process is assessed. Simulation has been performed for all combinations obtained from weather (15 years), soil profile (115 different soil profiles), and pesticide properties. The amount of atrazine leached below 1 m depth is used as an indicator of the potential leaching. Two approaches are compared: stochastic and "megaplot". The stochastic approach is based on 400 simulations performed through a Monte Carlo generator simultaneously modifying key input data such as soil texture, organic carbon and pesticide properties. Megaplot is based on simulation of the 44 unique combinations of weather, soil and crop characteristics identified in the area. The uncertainty of the stochastic approach is about 62% but it is difficult to upscale to a large scale. The uncertainty of the megaplot approach ranges between 55 and 88% and upscaling to a large scale is easier.

INTRODUCTION

Potential groundwater contamination may be defined as the possibility that a given fraction of applied pesticide reaches the water table and the actual contamination depends on the meteorological conditions following application. As the measurement of pesticide concentrations in groundwater is laborious and costly, in recent years a number of pesticide leaching models, at the field scale, have been developed to predict the fate of pesticides in soil and water (FOCUS, 2000). Groundwater vulnerability to contamination depends on the various physical, chemical, and biological processes that determine the environmental fate of pesticides. The rate and importance of each process is strongly affected by various space and time dependent environmental factors (soil, weather and crop) and the properties of the pesticide itself. Then, upscaling procedures to transfer data from edge-of-field to larger scales are affected by uncertainties. Accounting for uncertainties is therefore the only way to get some insight regarding the overall reliability of a regional assessment (Soutter & Pannatier, 1996). Several procedures are proposed (Bouma et al., 1998) such as metamodels, megaplots, stochastic and analytical model methods. In this paper, the potential leaching of atrazine in the area around Trasimeno Lake is evaluated using the PELMO model, a FOCUS groundwater model (FOCUS, 2000). The uncertainty of the simulation process is evaluated for stochastic and megaplot approaches.

MATERIALS AND METHODS

Field study

The study area is located around Lake Trasimeno near Perugia (Italy). The area is of about 280 km². 115 soil profiles were taken across the whole area as representative of the landscape. Texture, hydrologic properties, organic carbon content (OC) and pH have been determined for each soil horizon (Giovagnotti et al., 1999). An analysis of correlation of soil properties has been carried out as shown in Table 1. In Table 2 are reported the descriptive statistics of those parameter values not correlated with each other and obtained by dividing the soil profiles into three depths (0-35, 35-70, 70-100 cm). The distribution of texture, OC, pH, and depth have been characterised for each depth interval.

Table 1.   Correlation matrix of soil properties

	sand	silt	clay	bulk density	field capacity	wilting point	pH	organic carbon
sand	1.000							
silt	-0.858	1.000						
clay	-0.893	0.537	1.000					
bulk density	0.348	-0.322	-0.291	1.000				
field capacity	-0.936	0.717	0.912	-0.327	1.000			
wilting point	-0.888	0.678	0.870	-0.321	0.941	1.000		
pH	-0.422	0.250	0.481	-0.231	0.496	0.474	1.000	
organic carbon	-0.184	0.256	0.080	0.314	0.154	0.126	-0.113	1.000

Table 2.   Distribution of soil profile characteristics

Profile (cm)	Properties	n	mean	max	min	Std. dev.
	Sand	115	51.6	95.2	6.1	19.0
	Clay	115	19.2	51.2	2.3	11.1
0-35	pH	92	6.7	8.2	5.3	1.1
	OC	92	2.4	19.5	0.5	2.8
	Depth	115	23.6	40.0	3.0	13.4
	Sand	115	53.2	91.3	3.7	22.2
	Clay	115	20.1	63.8	1.0	13.4
35-70	pH	92	7.1	8.3	5.3	1.0
	OC	92	1.2	6.9	0.1	1.1
	Depth	115	55.9	75.0	45	8.4
	Sand	115	46.8	91.6	0.8	26.0
	Clay	115	25.8	75.6	0.7	17.1
70-100	pH	92	7.3	8.8	4.7	1.1
	OC	92	0.8	4.2	0.1	0.7
	Depth	115	106.8	140	75	17.4

Meteorological data, collected at four weather stations situated around the lake, are available from 1980 to 1995. They include daily rainfall, minimum and maximum temperature and pan evaporation. The area is characterised by a typical Mediterranean climate with winter-dominant rainfall ranging from 700 to 900 mm/year. Potential evaporation exceeds precipitation from May to August so that irrigation is required for maize, which is the crop mainly grown in the area. For this exercise it is supposed that the whole area was cropped by maize and treated the same day with atrazine at a rate of 2 kg a.s./ha. Crop information is reported in Table 3. Koc and half-life values of atrazine were determined for nine soil profiles (Vischetti & Businelli, 1992; Table 3). Other pesticide properties are from Tomlin (1994).

Table 3.   Agronomic and pesticide information

max interception water (%)	30	date of emergence	5/05
max active root depth (cm)	80	date of treatment	1/05
max soil cover (%)	100	date of maturation	28/9
soil condition after harvest	residue	date of harvest	15/10
irrigation (mm)	300		
atrazine Koc (ml/g)	108 ± 40	atrazine half-life in soil (days)	80 ± 15

Model

PELMO is a one dimensional model simulating the vertical movement of chemicals in soil by chromatographic leaching. PELMO version 3.2 was used (FOCUS, 2000). Two strategies of simulation are compared: stochastic and megaplot. The stochastic approach is based on many simulations performed through a Monte Carlo modification of key input data such as soil texture, organic carbon and pesticide properties. Upscaling is performed by assigning the mean of the results (i.e. cumulative fluxes of pesticide below 1 m depth) over the whole area. The megaplot approach is used to simulate the potential for pesticide leaching at a large scale and to reduce the number of simulations. Megaplot is based on identification of unique combinations of weather, soil and crop characteristics. Upscaling is performed assigning the same parameter value to all profiles within the same unique combination.

Stochastic approach

Simulations were carried out for a soil profile divided into three horizons. All parameters are defined according to the FOCUS parameterisation procedure (FOCUS, 2000). Spatially distributed input data for PELMO (soil clay and sand content, soil organic carbon content, pH, horizon depth, and atrazine Koc) were statistically analysed in order to assign the type of distribution. A total of 400 values have been randomly created using a Monte Carlo generator (Poptool). The number of Monte Carlo random values could be calculated from the event probability and the confidence interval of the error. In case of a confidence interval of 95% and event probability of 50, the number of Monte Carlo random values is 400 (Snedecor & Cochran, 1989). The 400 simulations were performed for a period of 15 years randomly varying the meteorological data and considering for the analysis only the results of the last 10 years of simulation. Cumulative fluxes of water and pesticide below 1 m depth were recorded for each year of simulation.

Megaplot approach

Weather conditions are quite similar for the whole area and maize is assumed to be the only crop. Therefore unique combinations were determined using only soil profile characteristics. The actual sand, clay and organic content parameters of the first horizon were divided into five classes, as shown in Table 4. Considering all the class combinations, 44 unique combinations were found: 29 combinations included more than one profile, and the first 9 represent 45% of the profiles. Simulations for all the unique combinations were performed for a period of 15 years using fixed pesticide data (Koc = 108 ml/g, and $t_{1/2}$ = 80 days) and considering for the analysis results from only the last 10 years of simulation. Annual average concentrations of pesticide below 1 m depth were recorded for each year of simulation and the 90th percentile calculated.

Table 4.   Class distribution of spatially distributed variables of the upper soil horizon

Class	Range	n° profiles	mean	Std. deviation	Coefficient of variation
Sand					
1	0 - 24	15	15.71	7.01	44.6
2	24 - 42	22	34.04	4.66	13.7
3	42 - 60	27	51.36	5.41	10.5
4	60 - 70	20	64.21	2.81	4.4
5	70 - 100	27	78.75	6.20	7.9
Clay					
1	0 - 10	29	7.01	2.51	35.8
2	10 - 20	37	13.91	2.64	19.0
3	20 -30	17	24.94	3.02	12.1
4	30 - 40	19	34.57	2.84	8.2
5	40 - 100	9	48.79	8.81	18.0
OC content					
1	0 - 0.45	10	0.36	0.10	28.2
2	0.45 - 0.75	17	0.66	0.06	9.3
3	0.75 - 1.5	46	1.13	0.20	17.3
4	1.5 - 2.0	14	1.72	0.13	7.3
5	2.0 - 9.0	24	2.94	1.19	40.5

RESULTS AND DISCUSSION

Stochastic approach

3910 simulations were performed and the annual average concentrations of pesticide leached below 1 m depth were recorded. Descriptive analysis is reported in Table 5.

Table 5. Descriptive statistics for the stochastic and the megaplot approaches.

	AAC (µg/l) stochastic	DAC (µg/l) megaplot	AAC (µg/l) megaplot	90AAC (µg/l) megaplot
Mean	0.12	0.61	0.61	1.56
Std. Error of Mean	0.01	0.32	0.15	0.80
Median	0.00	0.09	0.002	0.25
Std. Deviation	0.61	2.13	3.10	5.30
Minimum	0.00	0.00	0.00	0.00
Maximum	13.08	14.06	43.18	34.93
90th Percentiles	0.16	1.17	1.16	2.23

AAC = annual average concentration below 1 m; DAC = 10-year average concentration below 1 m; 90AAC = 90th percentile of annual average concentration

The mean ranges between 0.10 and 0.14 µg/l (at 95% of probability). Stepwise regression indicates that spatially distributed input data and outputs from the model are not well correlated. The best model explains only 11% of variability (Table 6). Analysis of variance shows that weather conditions significantly (p=0.0026) affect the results.

Megaplot approach

440 simulations were performed (44 unique combinations for 10 years) and the annual and 10-year average concentrations of pesticide below 1 m depth were recorded. The 90th percentiles of these data were also computed to take into account the influence of weather conditions. Descriptive analysis is reported in Table 5. The mean at 95% probability of the annual average concentration of pesticide leached below 1 m ranges between 0.32 and 0.90 µg/l. The same mean of 10-year average concentration ranges between 0.00 and 1.24 µg/l. The 90th percentile of the annual average concentration of pesticide leached below 1 m weighted to take into account the unique combination frequencies is 1.28 µg/l. This value is higher than the 90th percentile from the stochastic approach (0.16 µg/l) which is a comparable result.

Table 6 summarises the results of a stepwise regression carried out to evaluate the relationship between outputs and either spatially distributed variables or the classifying variables of unique combinations. A stepwise regression builds a regression model by repeating a process that adds (probability F=0.05) and deletes (probability F=0.05) variables from a list of candidates. The stepwise process stops when no variables not already in the model meet the selection criterion and no variables in the model meet the elimination criterion. For spatially distributed variables, the model obtained explains 25% of variability and this indicates that this approach has a high level of uncertainty. For classifying variables of unique combinations, the model obtained explains 3% of the variability.

Table 6. Summary of stepwise regression of annual average concentration of pesticide leached below 1 m against all input data of the stochastic approach (A), all input data of unique combinations (B) and classifying variables of unique combinations (C).

	Predictors	R^2	SE of the Estimate
A	CL2, CL3, DAY80, KOC, OC1, OC2, OC3, PH2, PROF3	0.111	0.574
B	CL2, CL3, DAY80, OC3, PROF1, SA2, SA3	0.243	2.712
C	OC1	0.026	9.342

CL2=clay content 2nd horizon; CL3=clay content 3th horizon; DAY80=total rainfall in the first 80 days; OC1=Organic carbon content 1st horizon; OC2=Organic carbon content 2sd horizon; OC3=Organic carbon content 3th horizon; PH2= pH 2sd horizon; PROF1=depth of 1st horizon; PROF3=depth of 3th horizon; SA2=sand content 2nd horizon; SA3=sand content 3th horizon.

Uncertainty evaluation

Due to the lack of correlation with spatially distributed data, upscaling of results from the stochastic approach to a large scale is possible only by assigning the same value to the whole area. The uncertainty related to this procedure could be assumed to be the standard error of the mean (0.12 ± 1.96*0.01, where 1.96 is the value of t for probability=0.05 and degrees of freedom = ∞). In this case the uncertainty (at 95% of probability) is approximately 14%. The uncertainty is also affected by weather conditions: this effect could be assumed to be the standard error of the annual mean grouped by weather condition and the uncertainty related is approximately 25%. Then the total uncertainty becomes approximately 40%.

The megaplot approach allows upscaling by assigning the same value to profiles belonging to the same unique combination. The uncertainty related to this procedure could be assumed to be the error encountered during the process of selection of unique combinations. As indicated in Table 7, only organic carbon content describes the variability of the results. It is possible to calculate the uncertainty deriving from the definition of unique combinations definition from the coefficient of variation of organic carbon content (Table 4): it ranges from 7 to 40% depending on the class. The uncertainty related to the weather conditions could be the same as the previous approach and the total uncertainty of the megaplot approach ranges between 32 and 65%.

The combination of the two approaches seems to be very interesting. Then the stochastic variation of input data for each unique combination increases the knowledge of uncertainties linked with the process of classification and simultaneously the megaplot approach allows to upscale to a large scale. The time of simulation could be reduced, for example, by decreasing the number of Monte Carlo runs (Snedecor & Cochran, 1989) or by using a latin hypercube generator (Soutter & Pannatier, 1996).

ACKNOWLEDGEMENTS

Work funded by EU–FP5 contract n° EVK1-CT-1999-00028 project PEGASE

REFERENCES

Bouma J; Finke P A; Hoosbeek M R; Breeuwsma A (1998). Soil and water quality at different scales: concepts, challenges, conclusions and recommendations. *Nutrient Cycling in Agroecosystems* **50**, 5-11.

Giovagnotti C; Calandra R; Giovagnotti E (1999). Risorse naturali ed attività dell'uomo. Suolo. In: *Sviluppo agricolo sostenibile del bacino del Lago Trasimeno*, eds. A Boggia & F Pennacchi, pp. 124-162. Regione Umbria, Università Perugia: Città di Castello, Italy

FOCUS (2000). FOCUS groundwater scenarios in the EU plant protection product review process. *Report of the FOCUS Groundwater Scenarios Workgroup*, pp. 197, EC Document Reference Sanco/321/2000.

Snedecor G W, Cochran W G (1989). Statistical methods. Eighth edition, pp. 503, Iowa State University Press, Ames, Iowa, USA.

Soutter M; Pannatier Y (1996). Groundwater vulnerability to pesticide contamination on a regional scale. *Journal of Environmental Quality* **25**, 439-444.

Tomlin C (1994). The Pesticide Manual. Tenth Edition, pp. 1341, BCPC: Farnham, UK.

Vischetti C; Businelli M (1992). Simulazione del movimento e della persistenza di alcuni erbicidi s-triazinici nei suoli umbri. *Annali della Facoltà di Agraria dell'Università di Perugia* **54**, 547-562.

FOCUS surface water scenarios: influence of soil degradation and sorption parameters on simulated losses of pesticides via drainflow and runoff in step 1, 2 and 3 scenarios

R Allen[1], P I Adriaanse, M Balderacchi, C Beigel, E Capri, B Erzgraeber, V Gouy, B Gottesburen, M Greener, J Hollis, A Huber, N Jarvis, B Jene, M Klein, J B H J Linders, P. Lolos, W-M Maier, S J Maund, C Pais, G Reinken, M H Russell, D Schaefer, H Schaefer, J L Teixeira, S Vizantinopoulos, D A Yon
on behalf of FOCUS Working Group on Surface Water Scenarios (under the auspices of European Commission's DG Health and Consumer Protection).
[1] *Aventis CropScience, 2 TW Alexander Drive, Research Triangle Park, NC 27709, USA*
Email: Richard.Allen@Aventis.com

ABSTRACT

The influence of soil degradation and sorption parameters on simulated losses of pesticides via drainflow and runoff in FOCUS surface water Step 3 scenarios were investigated in a collaborative project. Losses via drainflow in six standard scenarios were simulated using MACRO, whilst losses via runoff in a further four scenarios were simulated with PRZM. Further evaluation of these results will be used to develop appropriate losses via drainflow or runoff at earlier steps (1 and 2) of the proposed procedure and will be compared with measurements from field studies and monitoring data.

INTRODUCTION

The FOCUS Surface Water Scenarios Working Group proposes a stepwise procedure for the determination of exposure of pesticides in surface water. Exposure scenarios will be used to determine PEC_{sw} and PEC_{sed} as part of the aquatic risk assessments conducted by the EU rapporteur member states for consideration of the inclusion of plant protection products on Annex 1.

Entry routes from drift, runoff and drainage are considered. At Step 1, loadings from drift and runoff or drainage occur simultaneously. At Step 2, runoff or drainage occurs four days after the last application. At Step 3 deterministic models (MACRO and PRZM) are used to derive runoff and drainflow concentrations from predefined scenarios of soil, crop and weather. These are inputs (together with drift events) into TOXSWA, which simulates the fate of agrochemical products in standardized water bodies (ditches, streams and ponds). Descriptions of this process and the scenarios have been previously reported (Linders, 2001)

The proposed introduction of ten "Step 3" scenarios, representative of vulnerable agro-climatic areas of Europe is a new development within the EU exposure assessment process. This paper summarises a collaborative effort to evaluate the influence of pesticide soil degradation and sorption parameters on the flux and concentrations in surface runoff and drain flow. The results of these Step 3 tests will be used to derive generic losses from runoff or drainage for the Step 2 scenarios. This feedback mechanism ensures that the PEC_{sw} and PEC_{sed} values calculated at Step 2 are in the range of the highest values calculated at Step 3. A comparison of the runoff and drainage losses at Step 3 and Step 2 is presented.

MODEL SIMULATIONS

Test compounds

Model simulations were conducted with a series of eight test compounds. These are not real compounds but cover the typical range of half-life and adsorption values influencing losses of pesticides to surface water via runoff and drainage. Koc values ranged from 10 to 1000 L/kg; soil degradation half-lives (at 20°C and −10kPa soil moisture content) ranged from 3 d to 300 d (Table 3). A ninth possible combination of Koc (10) and half-life (300 d) was not evaluated as this was considered an unrealistic combination of parmaters. Other environmental fate parameters were kept constant. The Freundlich exponent (1/n) was assumed to be 1, water solubility was set as 1 mg/litre and all compounds were assumed to be non-volatile (vapour pressure = 1×10^{-7} Pa).

MACRO Simulations with Step 3 Scenarios

Losses of the test compounds to surface water via drainflow were simulated with a β-test version of the shell program "MACRO in FOCUS" which utilises MACRO v4.2. This shell program includes the Step 3 drainage scenarios (each a function of soil, crop and weather) defined by the FOCUS working group. The Step 3 evaluation consists of a sixteen-month assessment period. Pesticide applications (100g a.i./ha) were made for seven consecutive years (six-year warm-up period followed by 16-month assessment). The pesticides were assumed to be applied to a winter wheat crop as this was a crop common to all six drainage scenarios. The impact of application timing on losses was evaluated for each test substance. Simulations were performed following application pre-emergence (September to November, depending upon Scenario), early post-emergence (February to May) and late post-emergence (March to July).

PRZM Simulations with Step 3 Scenarios

Losses of the test compounds to surface water via runoff were simulated with a β-test version of the shell program "PRZM in FOCUS" which utilises PRZM v3.12. The procedures were similar to those described for the drainage scenarios above. A total of 96 simulations were performed (8 test substances x 4 scenarios x 3 application dates). However, only results for the water balance are presented here.

Runoff/Drainage Losses using "Steps1-2 in FOCUS"

At Step 2, runoff/drainage inputs to surface water represent the 'worst-case' loss from a rainfall event occurring 4 days after the final application of pesticide. The amount of pesticide entering surface water is a function of the season of application (autumn, spring or summer), region (Northern or Southern Europe), crop interception factors and pesticide fate properties. Currently losses via runoff or drainage can range from 1% to 4% of the pesticide residue remaining in soil at the time of the discharge to surface water, although the amount entering in the dissolved phase is a function of soil adsorption. In the current version of the steps1-2 in FOCUS calculator, the maximum losses are:
4% - Autumn, N Europe
2% - Spring, S Europe
1% - Spring, N Europe; Summer, N and S Europe

RESULTS AND DISCUSSION

Water balance

Tables 1 and 2 show the water balances predicted by MACRO for the six drainage scenarios and by PRZM for the four runoff scenarios respectively. Drainage predicted by MACRO varies between 115 mm/year at Scenario D4 (Skousbo) weather to 264 mm/year at Scenario D3 (Vredepeel weather). As an example the drainflow at scenario D5 (La Jalliere weather for 1978) is shown in Figure 1. At all locations the pattern of drain flow for the selected assessment years is similar, with little or no drainflow through the summer months.

However, selection of appropriate assessment years for runoff is more complex as runoff events are generally a response to periods of intense rainfall, sometimes only one day (or less) in duration. Therefore a different calendar year was selected for each scenario depending upon the timing of the first application of the pesticide (Table 2). For example, a pesticide applied in March for scenario R1 was assessed using the weather data for 1984 from Weiherbach (the 50th percentile year for runoff during the period March to May) whereas for a pesticide applied in June, weather data for 1987 is used. The 50th percentile runoff for the scenarios range between 11-110 mm during the selected season and between 32-184 mm per year. These represent between 4-24% of all precipitation received during the year. In general the order of runoff risk was: summer = spring < autumn.

Pesticide Balance and Drainflow/Runoff Concentrations

Figure 2 presents the simulated average daily drainflow concentrations for Pesticide D (Koc = 10, half-life = 30 d) for scenario D5 following application to a winter wheat crop in Autumn (19 October), Spring (14 March) and Summer (31 May). The product of these concentrations and the drainflow allow the daily flux to receiving water bodies to be calculated. The peak concentration for test compound D following application in the autumn in Scenario D5 was 6.83 ppb and occurred on 24 January near the start of the evaluation period. This occurred on a day with the equivalent of 10.9 mm of drainflow and corresponded to a peak daily flux of 0.74% of each annual application. This value together with maximum daily fluxes for the eight test compounds for all six drainage and four runoff scenarios are presented in Table 3. This table also includes the % of applied pesticide calculated to be lost at Step 2 in runoff or drainage and entering the water phase of a receiving water body.

The maximum daily fluxes from the drainage scenarios varied from < 0.01% to 7.63% of applied pesticide depending upon pesticide fate properties, scenario and timing of application. In general simulated losses for any one compound were greater from scenarios D1, D2 and D6 than D3, D4 and D5. Losses were greater following autumn and spring applications than summer. For compounds with a Koc value of 1000, maximum daily fluxes of greater than 1% of applied pesticide were only predicted for compound I (half-life of 300 days) in 1 scenario (D6, autumn application). Maximum daily fluxes of greater than 1% were predicted for compounds with a Koc of greater than 10 following autumn and spring applications in scenarios D2 and D6.

In most cases the maximum fluxes of pesticides were less than corresponding losses calculated at Step 2. Of the 144 drainage simulations only 20 values at Step 3 exceeded the calculated losses at step 2 and most were associated with compounds with a long degradation half-life (300 d).

CONCLUSIONS

Results from these tests have helped in an understanding of the relative vulnerability of the ten Step 3 scenarios. Further evaluation of these simulations is needed. The model outputs will be used as loading inputs into the TOXSWA model. This will allow comparisons of predicted environmental concentrations in surface water at each of the steps and the scenarios to be made in order to assess relative vulnerability and define appropriate inputs for runoff or drainage losses in the earlier Steps 1 and 2.

REFERENCES

Linders (2001). The Development and Status of the FOCUS Surface Water Scenarios within Directive 91/414/EEC. *proceedings of the SETAC Conference, Madrid, Spain*

Table 1. Water balances predicted by MACRO for the drainage scenarios for winter wheat. All figures are in mm, for the last 12 months of the 16-month simulation (1/5 to 30/4).

Scenario	Weather Station	Precipitation	Drainage	Percolation	Evapo-transpiration	Runoff
D1	Lanna	534	159	20	344	0
D2	Brimstone	623	260	15	354	0
D3	Vredepeel	818	319	0	523	0
D4	Skousbo	706	145	39	521	12
D5	La Jailliere	626	199	0	429	3
D6	Thebes	733	300	22	433	0

Table 2 Water balances predicted by PRZM for the runoff scenarios for winter wheat (except for R2, maize). All figures are in mm, for each four-month period.

Scenario	Weather Station	Season for First Application	Selected Year (50th %ile for runoff)	Precipitation	Runoff
		Mar to May	1984	817	40
R1	Weiherbach	Jun to Sep	1987	778	32
		Oct to Feb	1975	807	39
		Mar to May	1977	1906	184
R2	Porto	Jun to Sep	1989	1370	178
		Oct to Feb	1977	1906	168
		Mar to May	1977	688	85
R3	Bologna	Jun to Sep	1977	688	95
		Oct to Feb	1986	969	64
		Mar to May	1992	1000	164
R4	Roujan	Jun to Sep	1985	573	122
		Oct to Feb	1985	573	136

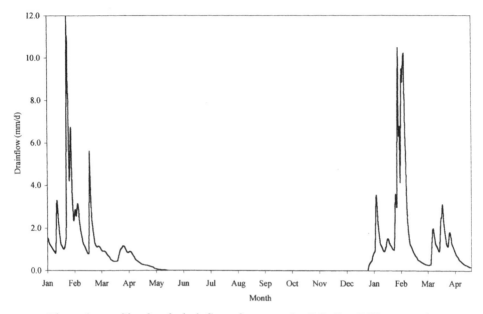

Figure 1.   Simulated drainflow for scenario D5 (La Jalliere weather
             January 1978 to April 1979) under a winter wheat crop.

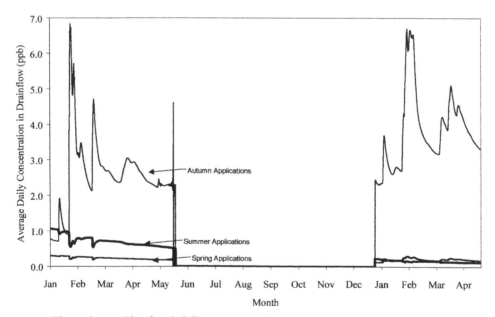

Figure 2.   Simulated daily concentrations in drainflow for scenario D5
             (La Jalliere weather January 1978 to April 1979) under a
             winter wheat crop following application of test compound D

255

Table 3. Simulated maximum daily fluxes (% of applied) via drainage for the six Step 3 drainage scenarios and two Step 2 scenarios following applications of test compounds in Autumn, Spring and Summer.

Scenario	Application time	Test compound							
		A	B	C	D	E	F	H	I
	Koc (L/kg)	10	100	1000	10	100	1000	100	1000
	DT50 (d)	3	3	3	30	30	30	300	300
D1	Autumn	0.10	0.04	0.01	0.67	1.1	0.10	2.05	**0.85**
	Spring	<0.01	<0.01	<0.01	0.05	0.37	0.02	0.73	**0.46**
	Summer	0.01	<0.01	<0.01	0.07	0.26	0.03	0.23	**0.21**
D2	Autumn	1.39	0.58	0.01	**3.84**	1.53	0.15	**2.79**	**0.92**
	Spring	**1.51**	**0.38**	0.01	**2.17**	**1.66**	0.02	**2.3**	**0.6**
	Summer	<0.01	<0.01	<0.01	0.11	0.32	0.01	0.3	**0.15**
D3	Autumn	<0.01	<0.01	<0.01	0.04	<0.01	<0.01	0.11	<0.01
	Spring	<0.01	<0.01	<0.01	0.01	<0.01	<0.01	0.09	<0.01
	Summer	<0.01	<0.01	<0.01	0.01	<0.01	<0.01	0.02	<0.01
D4	Autumn	<0.01	<0.01	<0.01	0.53	0.21	0.02	0.87	0.17
	Spring	<0.01	<0.01	<0.01	0.05	0.02	<0.01	0.50	0.12
	Summer	<0.01	<0.01	<0.01	0.03	0.05	0.01	0.14	0.04
D5	Autumn	<0.01	<0.01	<0.01	0.74	0.29	0.02	1.26	0.17
	Spring	<0.01	<0.01	<0.01	0.03	0.01	<0.01	**0.60**	0.12
	Summer	<0.01	<0.01	<0.01	0.07	0.04	<0.01	0.24	0.06
D6	Autumn	0.09	0.22	0.01	1	0.82	0.43	2.19	**1.67**
	Spring	**2.00**	**4.43**	0.05	**7.63**	0.53	<0.01	**6.14**	**0.87**
	Summer	<0.01	<0.01	<0.01	0.01	<0.01	<0.01	0.44	**0.38**
Step 2, N.Europe	Autumn	1.48	0.96	0.20	3.42	2.19	0.48	2.38	0.52
	Spring	0.37	0.24	0.05	0.85	0.55	0.12	0.59	0.13
	Summer	0.37	0.24	0.05	0.85	0.55	0.12	0.59	0.13
Step 2, S.Europe	Autumn	1.48	0.96	0.20	3.42	2.19	0.48	2.38	0.52
	Spring	0.74	0.48	0.10	1.71	1.09	0.24	1.19	0.26
	Summer	0.37	0.24	0.05	0.85	0.55	0.12	0.59	0.13

Values in bold indicate maximum daily flux at Step 3 is greater than loss in corresponding scenario at Step 2

SESSION 7
POSTER SESSION B

Session Organisers: Dr C D Brown
Cranfield University, Silsoe, UK

Dr A Carter
ADAS Rosemaund, Hereford, UK

and

Dr N MacKay
Cambridge Environmental Assessments,
Cambridge, UK

Volatilisation: an important route reducing pesticide leaching and persistence in soil

E Capri, M Nicelli, M Trevisan
Istituto di Chimica Agraria ed Ambientale, Università Cattolica del Sacro Cuore, Via Emilia Parmense, 84 – 29100 Piacenza, Italy.
e-mail: chimiv@pc.unicatt.it

M Larsson
Department of Soil Sciences, SLU, Box 7014, S-750 07 Uppsala, Sweden

ABSTRACT

Pesticide losses by volatilisation during and after application may represent an important dissipation factor. To assess the rate of volatilisation of malathion, ethoprophos and procymidone a field experiment was carried out using the *Theoretical Profile Shape* method and monitoring residues in the air continuously 2-3 weeks after the pesticide application. A bare silty loam soil was sprayed with the pesticides during Spring, Autumn and Winter. All pesticides volatilise as a function of air temperature and soil humidity, but solar energy during the day represents one of the main factors increasing the flux from the top soil to the atmosphere. In the winter experiment an estimated 0.2-15 % of the dose applied volatilised; during the autumn-spring experiment this rate increased enormously reaching the 60 % of the dose applied. The obvious consequence of this losses is a reduction in soil persistence and potential leaching of the pesticide studied.

INTRODUCTION

Pesticide dissipation via volatilisation from soil and plant surface as well as drift after the normal agricultural applications may be an important process. Most of the field measurements carried with different techniques report very intensive volatilisation sometime higher than 20 % from fallow soil (Willis G H *et al.*, 1972; Harper L A *et al.*, 1976; Glotfelty D E *et al.*, 1984; Glotfelty D E et al, 1989). Volatilisation losses of this magnitude may influence the air quality and the pesticide persistence in field.

The rate and the nature of the pesticide which pass into the air are influenced by different factors such as the pesticide physico-chemical properties, the application techniques, the meteorological conditions and dissipation processes. The nature of the surface treated and the season of the application can also have an important impact. The volatilisation from soil surface may also be influenced by the soil organic matter and the mineralogical particles with which the pesticide is associated.

In this paper we report the results of the three field experiments carried out in different periods of the year where the volatilisation rate of three pesticides from fallow soil was monitored.

METHODS AND MATERIALS

Measurement of volatilization in the field

The experiment was conducted at the Rhône-Poulenc experimental station in the Emilia-Romagna region outside Bologna, lat. 44°31'N, long 11°17'E. The field is situated on a flat alluvial plain in the Po valley. Soil is silty loam with a 1.8 % content in organic matter and pH 7.8.

The volatilization rate from the soil surface is calculated according to:

$$V = \frac{\left[u(t)c(t) \right]}{\Omega} \Bigg|_{Zinst}$$

where $u(t)$ is the wind speed and $c(t)$ is the pesticide concentration in the air at the sampling height Z_{inst}. The ratio of the horizontal to vertical flux Ω, can be obtained with the 'trajectory simulation method' (Wilson, 1982). This ratio depends on the surface roughness, Z_0, and the upwind fetch distance (i.e. the radius of the treated surface). The roughness length was estimated by measurements of the wind speed at three heights two weeks prior to the sampling events. The roughness length was then obtained from the logarithmic wind profile where Z_0 is the intercept with the z axis. A value of 0.8 cm was obtained for both the sampling events (Capri et al., 2000).

With the 'theoretical profile simulation', the hypothetical movement of the particles in the atmosphere are tracked from the source to the point of measurement. Since the height profiles of the theoretical position of the volatilised pesticides cross each other for stable and unstable atmospheric conditions, it is possible to identify a single height, Z_{inst}, were measurements can be performed for all atmospheric conditions. The value of Z_{inst} was calculated to be 67 cm with a corresponding value of 7.0 for Ω.

Pesticide application

Ethoprophos, Procymidone, Malathion were applied three times in December 1998, April and October 1999; Pyrimethalin was applied only in September 1999 (Table I). The pesticide application was performed with a hand carried sprayer with a boom of 5-m width in a quasi circle with 25 m diameter and an area of 495 m^2 (Figure 1). The air sampling started about 15 minutes after application and lasted 2 weeks in the experiment of December and April, 3 weeks in October.

The field measurements of volatilization in Bologna were performed with samplers consisting of a glass tube of 10 mm diameter containing a plug of polyurethane foam (PUF). These were connected with Teflon tubing to air sampling pumps (SKC LTD 224-PCEX4) which were operated with an air flow of 2 l/min. The PUF sampling plugs were positioned at the centre of the circular plot at Z_{inst} height. Replicate samples were collected, but with differing sampling intervals. After exposure, the plugs were returned to their sample jars and kept frozen until analysis.

An automatic weather station on the field recorded hourly values of temperature, wind speed, wind direction, precipitation, air humidity, and solar radiation. Hourly values of soil surface temperature were also recorded with two sensors covered by a thin layer of soil and protected against direct sunshine.

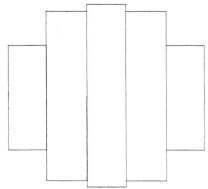

Figure 1. Representation of the pesticide treated area in Bologna. The pesticides were applied in 5 m segments (rectangles) with a total area of 495 m² reproducing a quasi-circle (dashed line) with an area of 491 m².

Validation of the air sampling procedure

For the measurement of airborne pesticide, the sampling equipment consisted of a glass tube of diameter 10 mm containing a plug of polyurethane foam (PUF), as described previously, which were operated with an air flow regulated at 2 L/min. The extraction procedure of PUF was carried using a triple extraction with acetone (50 mL for each extraction) by ultrasonic bath, followed by filtration with 10 g of anhydrous sodium sulphate. This was then concentrated under vacuum, and finally blown down to a volume of 1 mL under nitrogen flow. This 1 mL extract was used for the final GLC-ECD and HPLC analysis. Detection limit were 0.01 µg/L for ethoprophos, malathion and pyrimethalin and 0.1 µg/L for Procymidone. The air sampling system adopted for the field study was developed by evaluating a number of different procedures following the air sampling methodology reported by the American Society for Testing Materials (ASTM, 1988). Recovery tests were also evaluated for each procedure as reported in Capri *et al.,* (1999).

RESULTS

The air temperature in December was on average 1.9 °C (−3.3 °C to 12.7 °C); in April 12 °C (3.5 °C ÷ 19 °C); in October was 15.0 (8.0 °C to 20.0 °C). Total rainfall was 34 mm and 35 mm in December and April respectively; in October we measured 57 mm between the 12 to 21 days after the pesticide application. On average the wind velocity was 0.6 m s^{-1} and 1.4 m s^{-1} in all the experiments.

Pesticide volatilisation showed a large variation between the night and morning in the first three days after the application, with the highest rate in the early afternoon where the temperature is high and lowest rate at night (Figure 2). The energy balance of the soil-atmosphere regulate the fluxes between the soil layer and volatilisation losses.

The total rate seems to follow a two-phase kinetic: the first short and fast where diffusion and convection are the most important processes; the second slow where the soil-water relationship, f.i. sorption and degradation, become important (Figure 3). However the volatilisation correlated well with the pesticide vapour pressure (Pa m^3 mol^{-1}): the rate was Procymidone > Ethoprophos > Malathion $\cong$ Pyrimethalin where the Henry constants respectively are 20.46, 0.015, 0.00114 and 0.0036.

Increased soil moisture also increased the volatilisation, particularly when the soil was re-wetted. These results confirm that in fallow soil the climatic condition and the properties of the pesticide drive the rate of volatilisation: soil-pesticide processes such as adsorption and degradation becomes more important later.

The season had a strong effect as in Spring and Autumn the volatilisation was higher than in Winter due to the effect of the temperature.

Table 1. Total volatilisation in the experiments.

	Dose applied (g/m^2)			Amount volatilised (µg)		
	12/1998	04/1999	10/1999	12/1998	04/1999	10/1999
Ethoprophos	100	133	100	3.745	28.653	10.990
Malathion	64	82	64	1.386	22.770	6.611
Procymidone	75	77	75	1.87	14.20	9.99
Pyrimethalin			20			0.42

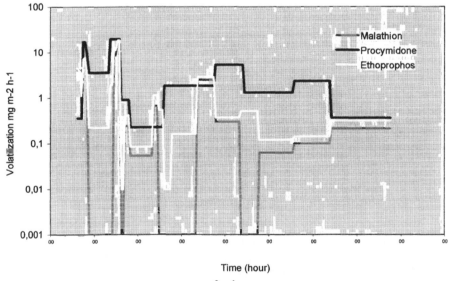

Figura 2.   Pesticide in air (mg m^{-2} h^{-1}) in the week 12 to 19 in April 1999.

More than 90 % of the volatilisation is occurred out in the first few days after the pesticide application.

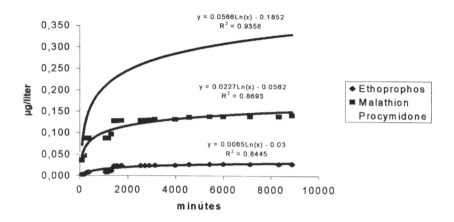

Figure 3. Cumulated volatilization of Ethoprophos, Malathion and Procymidone duringthe Spring experiment.

Total amount of pesticide in the air was 3.8 to 28.7 µg for Ethoprophos, 1.4 to 22.8 µg for Malathion, 1.9 to 14.2 µg for Procymidone, 0.4 µg for Pyrimethalin. The volatilisation rate calculated via TPS was very high and comprised between 0.5 to 60 % of the applied dose. If we exclude the leaching as a dissipation process (field capacity was never reached in the field measurement) and the transformation in the first week would be low for some of the pesticide studied (data not reported), we can argue that most of the pesticide dissipation in the experiment would be due to the volatilisation (Table 3).

These results confirm the need to measure the volatilisation in air for both pesticide leaching assessment in field and for the model validation. In fact as volatilisation reduces the pesticide dose available for leaching, this process represents a form of mitigation to be taken into the risk assessment procedure. Also field data sets used for model validation purposes should contain the measurement of this process to avoid over-estimation of the mobility in soil (Garratt *et al.*, 2001; Boesten *et al.*, 2000).

ACKNOWLEDGEMENTS

Part of this work was supported by CNR national project "Ambiente e Territorio", subproject "Valutazione dell'impatto ambientale di antiparassitari dopo trattamenti al suolo con particolare riferimento all'aria e alle colture vegetali".

REFERENCES

Boesten J J T I; van der Pas L J T (2000). Movement of water, bromide and the pesticides ethoprophos and bentazone in a sandy soil: the Vredepeel data set. *Agricure, Water and Management,* **44:** 21-42.

Capri E; Alberici R; Glass C R; Minuto G; Trevisan M (1999) Potential operator exposure to procymidone in greenhouses. *Journal of Agricultural and Food Chemistry,* **47**: 88:1123-1132.

Capri E; Larrsson M; Trevisan M; Nicelli M; Del Re A A M (2000). Studi di volatilizzazione di antiparassitari dal suolo: misure e previsioni. In: Atti XVII Convegno nazionale della Società Italiana di Chimica Agraria, 231-239.

Garratt J A; Capri E; Trevisan M; Errera G; Wilkins R A (2001). Parameterisation, evaluation and comparison of pesticide leaching models in a Bologna field environment. Submitted to *Pesticide Science Management.*

Glotfelty D E; Leech M M; Jersey J; Taylor A W (1989). Volatilization and wind erosion of soil surface applied atrazine, simazine, alachlor and toxaphene. *Journal of Agricultural Food Chemistry,* **37**: 546-551.

Glotfelty D E; Taylor A W; Turner B C; Zoller W H (1984). Volatilization of surface-applied pesticides from fallow soil. *Journal of Agricultural Food Chemistry,* **32**: 638-643.

Harper L A; White A W; Bruce R R; Thomas A W; Leonard R A (1976). Soil and miroclimate effects on trifluralin volatilisation. *Journal Environmental Quality,* **1, 3**: 236-242.

Willis G H; Parr F; Smith S; Carroll B R (1972). Volatilization of dieldrin from fallow soil as affected by different soil water regimes. *Journal Environmental Quality,* **1, 2**: 193-196.

Wilson J D (1982) Turbulent dispersion in the atmospheric surface layer. *Boundary Layer Meteorology,* **22**: 399-420.

A spatially distributed assessment for pesticide exposure in surface waters via drainflow

C D Brown, I G Dubus

Cranfield Centre for EcoChemistry, Cranfield University, Silsoe, Beds MK45 4DT, UK
Email: c.brown@cranfield.ac.uk

C Gustin

Monsanto Company, 800 N Lindbergh Boulevard, St-Louis, Missouri 63167, USA

ABSTRACT

There is no consensus on the approach to estimating exposure at higher tiers of environmental assessment. Step 1 calculations conducted for a novel herbicide did not exclude the potential for the compound to exhibit effects on higher aquatic plants following transport in drainflow. In a higher tier approach, a model was first validated against field data and then used for distributed modelling for 15 environmental scenarios with 30-year simulations for each. Predicted concentrations of the herbicide for the 15 scenarios were weighted according to their relative abundance within wheat-growing areas. The resulting 450 model outputs were ranked to assess risk and the probability of impact at the national scale.

INTRODUCTION

A step 1 risk assessment for a winter wheat herbicide proposed for use in the UK indicated a potential for effects on higher aquatic plants following transport in drainflow. The compound is acidic, impersistent and relatively mobile. There is currently no consensus on the approach to estimating exposure at higher tiers of environmental assessment. Here, a deterministic model (MACRO) is applied in a distributed manner to predict concentrations of herbicide in a small ditch. The approach is a pragmatic attempt to assess the distribution of exposure concentrations within the limitations of current knowledge and tools. It ignores much of the uncertainty in modelling which may only be addressed through the further development of probabilistic procedures and, in the longer term, true stochastic models.

MATERIALS AND METHODS

Field drainflow study

A field drainflow study was carried out to investigate the potential for movement of the herbicide to drains and a receiving water body. The compound was applied on 16 May 2000 to a 7.7-ha winter wheat field situated in Northamptonshire in the UK. The effective drainage at the site (plastic pipes and mole drains), the texture of the soil (Hanslope series; clay loam over clay), its alkaline pH (7.1-8.5) and low organic carbon content (1.2% in the topsoil) made the field experiment a worst-case for the transfer of acidic compounds to drains. Transport of pesticides via preferential flow can be significant on such soils. Water collected by the drainage system left the field via a single outfall with water moving directly into a receiving ditch. The experimental site was monitored continuously following application, with water samples collected from both the drain outfall and the receiving water body. Collection of water samples for analysis of herbicide concentrations was triggered in response to drainflow. An automatic weather station was erected on site to record rainfall, air and soil temperatures, wind speed, humidity and solar radiation.

Model selection and validation

The MACRO model (www.mv.slu.se/bgf/macrohtm/~ macro.htm) was selected for the work as it simulates both drainflow and preferential flow. MACRO is a physically-based model with the soil porosity divided into two flow systems or domains (macropores and micropores), each characterised by a flow rate and solute concentration. Richards' equation and the convection-dispersion equation are used to simulate soil water flow and solute transport in the soil micropores, whilst a simplified capacitance-type approach is used to calculate fluxes in the macropores. Additional model assumptions include first-order kinetics for degradation in each of four 'pools' of pesticide in the soil (micro- and macropores, solid/liquid phases), together with an instantaneous sorption equilibrium and a Freundlich sorption isotherm in each pore domain. Version 4.1 of the model was used in this study.

In order to support the use of the model in predictive mode for the distributed assessment, data from the field drainflow study were simulated without any calibration ('blind simulation'). No site-specific data were available for DT50 or Koc, so mean data from a range of soil types were used for the blind simulation and predictive work.

Spatially distributed assessment

The first phase of the distributed assessment of herbicide entry into surface waters via drainflow was to divide England and Wales into environmental scenarios comprising discrete classes of soil type and climate. The study sought to cover the range of soil and climatic conditions within the major wheat cultivation areas of England and Wales. Just over 50% of the area cultivated with wheat in England and Wales is estimated to be artificially drained. The soil series making up the drained wheat area were divided into six broad classes (Figure 1) based on vulnerability for leaching of the acidic herbicide via drainflow (principally clay content and pH). A representative soil was selected for each class. Non-drained soils and those with peaty topsoils were considered to have no vulnerability for leaching via drainflow, so that five soil classes were considered by the modelling, each typified by a single soil profile.

Three weather datasets were taken from the SEISMIC database (Hollis *et al.*, 1993) to represent 'dry', 'medium' and 'wet' conditions (Figure 1). Average annual rainfall for the three classes was 588, 713 and 815 mm, respectively. Wheat rarely accounts for more than 5% of land in the parts of England and Wales with >850 mm rain per annum and no modelling was thus carried out for these areas. A 30-year run of weather data was compiled for each climate class.

The model was run for the 15 scenarios (i.e. 5 soil x 3 climate classes) assuming annual applications of the test compound in the spring of each of 30 years. A simple approximation of dilution within a small receiving water body was undertaken on the basis of drainflow from a 1-ha field entering a ditch 100 m long, 1 m wide and with a water depth of 30 cm (equivalent to 3 mm water distributed across 1 ha). The maximum daily concentration in the ditch for each of the 450 years simulated was extracted and ranked in a frequency distribution.

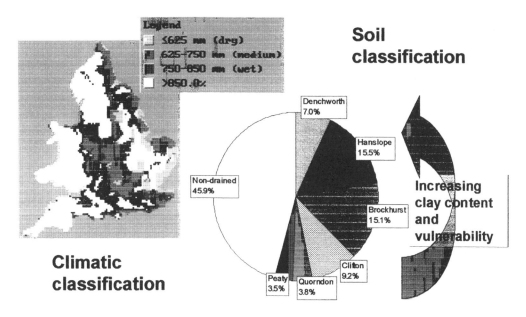

Figure 1.   Division of the wheat growing areas into climatic and soil classes

RESULTS

Concentrations in field drainflow

Drainflow was measured on an hourly basis with the frequency of sampling for herbicide determined by the automatic sampling. Peak concentrations were short-lived, lasting only a few hours. Figure 2 shows drainflow and herbicide concentrations for an event commencing 10 days after treatment (DAT). The first sample collected in response to this drainflow contained the largest concentration of herbicide (2.3 µg l^{-1}), which is indicative of the importance of preferential flow phenomena for the transfer of pesticide to drains at the experimental site.

Flow and concentrations of herbicide were also monitored regularly in the ditch receiving drainflow from the field. Concentrations of the compound were <LOQ (0.05 µg l^{-1}) apart from a single sample collected 12 DAT which contained 0.06 µg l^{-1}. This indicates a dilution factor for pesticide concentrations between raw drainflow and ditch water of approximately 100 or greater.

Model validation

Figure 2 also compares observed concentrations of herbicide in the first significant drainage event after application with values from the blind simulation by MACRO. The simulated peak concentration in drainflow was within 12% of that observed. The shape of the chemograph was well matched although the decline in concentrations from peak values was under estimated. This suggested that output from the model in predictive mode would be conservative with respect to actual concentrations under the conditions of use.

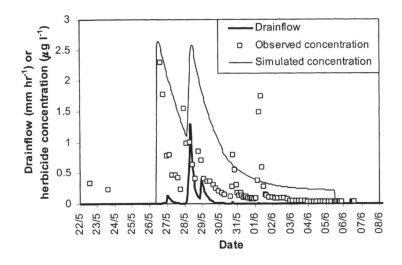

Figure 2. Flow for a drainage event commencing 10 DAT and comparison between observed concentrations of herbicide and those predicted by MACRO

Distributed risk assessment

The model was run for the 15 scenarios assuming annual applications of the test compound in each of 30 years. Daily concentrations of herbicide in the ditch are shown in Figure 3 for the worst-case scenario (heavy clay soil with high pH in the wet climatic region). Concentrations were again indicative of preferential flow with a transient pulse of the chemical predicted to move to surface water in the first significant drainflow event after application. Concentrations and losses were largest where drainflow was initiated soon after application in spring.

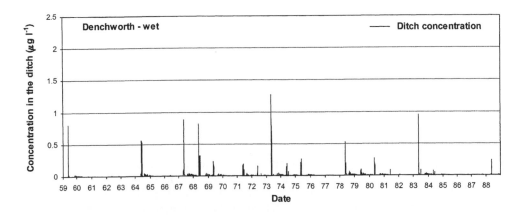

Figure 3. Herbicide concentrations in the receiving ditch predicted for a heavy clay soil in a wet climatic zone

The maximum daily ditch concentration for each of the 450 years simulated was extracted and ranked in a frequency distribution (Figure 4). A maximum daily concentration of 1.1 µg l^{-1} was derived for the field study by taking a flow-weighted average of residues in samples taken over each day. This maximum placed the field study on the 97th percentile of the distributed assessment, thereby confirming its worst-case character. Results for each scenario were weighted according to the abundance of the soil-climate combination. Maximum daily concentrations were then compared with deterministic effects endpoints for *Lemna gibba* (EC50 1.0 µg l^{-1}; recovery within 14 days for all concentrations up to 7.0 µg l^{-1} and exposure periods up to 4 days) to generate a semi-probabilistic risk assessment. *Lemna gibba* was previously shown to be the most sensitive from five species of higher aquatic plant (Davies *et al.*, 2001). Results summarised in Table 1 indicate that there will be no impact on *Lemna gibba* across 98.9% of the scenario/year combinations. There may be a potential for a temporary effect in 1.1% of instances, but recovery can be expected in all cases.

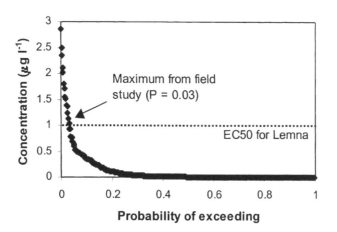

Figure 4. Frequency distribution for the annual maximum of daily concentrations of herbicide in the receiving ditch (based on 450 individual predictions)

Table 1. Summary statistics for the distributed assessment of risk to *Lemna gibba*

Maximum exposure concentration (µg l^{-1})	Potential for effect	Potential for recovery	Relative abundance (% of wheat area)
<0.1	Negligible	-	91.8
0.1 - 1.0	Very unlikely	Very high	7.1
1.0 - 7.0	Possible	High	1.1
>7.0	Possible	Low	0

DISCUSSION

The approach adopted moves forward from a simple worst-case assessment to cover a realistic range of conditions under which the herbicide is proposed to be used. However, a number of worst-case assumptions are retained and provide an additional element of environmental protection. Most notably, dilution of drainflow concentrations within the standard EU ditch (almost always less than a factor of 2) was very much smaller than that observed in the field study (a factor of 100 or greater).

There are established procedures for exposure estimation for surface waters at lower tiers of environmental assessment and these will soon be strengthened by the introduction of the FOCUS surface water scenarios (Russell, 2000). However, there is no consensus on the approach to be adopted when a lower tier assessment indicates a potential for risk. The environment into which pesticides are released is inherently variable both spatially and temporally and techniques based on probabilistic modelling and/or landscape analysis offer the best potential for more realistic exposure assessment at higher tiers. The approach presented here is a pragmatic attempt to assess the distribution of exposure concentrations within the limitations of current knowledge and tools. The technique applies deterministic models in a distributed manner and has relatively low data and time requirements compared to more sophisticated approaches. As such, the methodology may prove useful whilst the research and development necessary to implement more sophisticated approaches is being undertaken.

The main shortcoming of the approach is that it ignores much of the uncertainty associated with the modelling process. This uncertainty may partially be addressed using probabilistic procedures currently under development, but eventually will require the development and adoption of true stochastic models such as those based on the transfer function approach (Grochulska and Kladivko, 1994; Jury et al., 1996). In addition, the method described here takes no account of the intensity of occurrence of a particular scenario in a particular location. This could be overcome through the use of GIS technology to replace the national scenario statistics used here.

REFERENCES

Davies J; Tencalla F G; Honnegger J L; Brain P; Newman J R; Pitchford H F (2001). Toxicity of sulfosulfuron, a novel sulfonylurea herbicide, to aquatic plants. In Abstracts of the SETAC Europe meeting, Madrid 6-10 May 2001, pp. 144-145.

Grochulska J; Kladivko E J (1994). A two-region model of preferential flow of chemicals using a transfer function approach. *Journal of Environmental Quality* 23: 498-507.

Hollis J M; Hallett S H; Keay C A (1993). The development and application of an integrated database for modelling the environmental fate of herbicides. *Proceedings of the BCPC Conference - Weeds 1993*, 3: 1355-1364.

Jury W A; Sposito G; White R E (1996). A transfer function model of solute transport through soil. 1. Fundamental concepts. *Water Resources Research* 22: 243-247.

Russell M H (2000). Advances in surface water modelling in the USA and Europe. *Proceedings of the BCPC Conference - Pests and Diseases 2000*, 1: 77-84.

Modelling pesticide behaviour at the catchment-scale – the TERRACE project

N Kannan, S White, S P Anderton
School of Engineering, The University of Durham, Science Laboratories, South Road, Durham, DH1 3LE, UK

F Worrall
Dept. of Geological Sciences, The University of Durham, Science Laboratories, South Road, Durham, DH1 3LE, UK

J M Hollis
Soil Survey and Land Research Centre, Cranfield University, Silsoe, Bedford, MK45 4DT, UK

ABSTRACT

This paper presents the work of the TERRACE project (Terrestrial Runoff modelling for Risk Assessment of Chemical Exposure). The project seeks to develop and test models for assessing the movement of pesticides at the catchment scale as part of the development of new pan-European risk assessment tools for the evaluation of the environmental fate of new chemicals (the GREAT-ER project). TERRACE seeks to adapt existing models of pesticide, and other diffuse source pollutants, to spatial scales larger than those presently covered by the FOCUS model scenarios. In parallel to the selection and adaptation of suitable models the project will apply these models to field data.

INTRODUCTION

The GREAT-ER project (Geography-referenced Regional Exposure Assessment Tools for European Rivers) is a pan-European project to develop risk assessment tools for new chemicals sponsored by CEFIC (European Chemicals Industry Federation) and ECETOC (European Centre for Ecotoxicology and Toxicology of Chemicals). The project is now in its second three-year phase. In the first three-year phase the project focused on the development of a modelling system of point-source pollution in the river environment, especially the release of detergent compounds from sewage treatment works (Feijtel *et al.*, 1998). This system incorporates spatially-distributed, steady-state models that produce distributions of predicted environmental concentration (PEC) via an Arcview interface, and was designed to work at the regional catchment scale across the whole of Europe. The package has been tested for catchments in the UK, Italy and Germany.

In the second three-year phase of the project the model is to be expanded to include chemical behaviour in three further environments – the atmosphere, estuaries and terrestrial runoff. These three components are to be combined to give predictions of chemical transport and persistence throughout the environment. The terrestrial runoff component of this model is being considered by the TERRACE project (TErrestrial Runoff modelling for

Risk Assessment of Chemical Exposure). TERRACE focuses on the modelling of diffuse source pollution in regional scale river catchments (i.e. at much larger scales than the FOCUS model scenarios). The first phase of the project is to review and select suitable existing models rather than create new model. The project will go on to evaluate selected models using catchment scale data.

The TERRACE project is examining a range of diffuse source pollutants, including pesticides. Pesticides reach water sources in either dissolved or bound form, posing health risks to human beings and aquatic species. The greatest contribution to the overall pesticide pollution of waters comes from agriculture (Bach et al., 2001). Important risk and management decisions regarding control of such pollution are made based on rough estimates of agricultural pollution, which do not consider interaction between climate, crop soil and hydrology (Thorsen et al., 1996). Collecting data and conducting field experiments to assess this kind of pollution is becoming prohibitively expensive and so there is a need for appropriate tools to predict this pollution. Accurate representation of the processes responsible for transport and transformation of pesticides is crucial for the tools to give desired results.

Numerous models have been developed to date to predict the environmental fate of pesticides. Some catchment scale hydrological models also have modules in them to predict pesticide runoff. The amount of pesticide loss via runoff water is a complex function of rainfall timing, the hydrologic and soil characteristics of the field and the chemistry, formulation and persistence of the chemical itself (Wauchope & Leonard, 1980).

In reviewing models for inclusion in the TERRACE project a number of criteria were considered:
1. the capability for application to large-scale catchments (> 100's km^2).
2. the capability for interface with a GIS system.
3. a physically reasonable representation of hydrological and contaminant transport processes.
4. input data requirements that allow the model to be applied in a wide variety of European situations.
5. A readily available model that could be made available as part of a freely accessible package.
6. a model validated for pesticides, preferably in a European setting.

Initial review identified three models suitable for further exploration. ANSWERS 2000 (Bouraoui & Dillaha, 2000), SWATCATCH (Hollis et al., 1996), and SWAT (Neitsch et al., 2001). ANSWERS-2000 represents an event-based model with a high data requirement, and SWATCATCH an empirical model with little input data requirement. However, our first choice model is SWAT which represents a trade off between physical complexity and input data requirement that we believe could be achieved across Europe. As a first step in testing these models SWAT was applied to predict pesticide runoff for a catchment in Bedfordshire, UK.

THEORY

The Soil Water Assessment Tool (SWAT) is a basin scale model developed by the United States Department of Agriculture-Agricultural Research Service to predict the impact of land management practices on water, sediment and agricultural chemical yields. It is a distributed continuous simulation model. A number of earlier USDA models CREAMS (Chemicals, Runoff and Erosion from Agricultural Management Systems, Knisel, 1980), GLEAMS (Groundwater Loading Effects on Agricultural Management Systems, Leonard et al. 1987) and EPIC (Erosion-Productivity Impact Calculator, Williams et al., 1983) contributed significantly to the development of SWAT.

Surface runoff

SWAT divides the catchment into Hydrologic Response Units (HRU) based on land use and soil type. Surface runoff is simulated by two methods. 1. Modified SCS curve number method and 2. Green & Ampt infiltration method.

Pesticide Degradation and Transport

The equations used to model movement of pesticides are adopted from GLEAMS. Simulated processes include wash-off, degradation, leaching and transport.

Wash-off

Wash-off of pesticides is estimated as a function of plant morphology, pesticide solubility and the timing and intensity of rainfall event.

Degradation

Pesticide degradation in each soil layer is governed by first order kinetics. SWAT allows different half-lives for foliar and soil degradation. Soil half-life is a lumped parameter, which takes care of the net effect of volatilization, photolysis, hydrolysis, biological degradation and chemical reactions in the soil.

Partitioning

Partitioning of pesticide between the solute and sorbed phases is defined by the soil adsorption coefficient for the pesticide (K_{oc}). This coefficient is calculated from the adsorption coefficient normalized for soil organic carbon content (K_{oc}) and the percentage of organic carbon in the soil.

Transport of pesticides in solution

The amount of pesticide removed in surface runoff is calculated as a function of concentration of pesticide in mobile water, the volume of surface runoff and a pesticide percolation coefficient.

Transport of sorbed pesticide

Sorbed pesticide attached to soil particles may be transported by surface runoff to the main channel. Sorbed transport rates are related to the concentration of pesticide sorbed onto sediment, HRU area, the pesticide enrichment ratio and the sediment yield on a given day.

Pesticide lag

SWAT has a storage feature to lag surface runoff and pesticide in surface runoff reaching the main channel for large basins.

GIS Interface

The interface takes a digital elevation model as input and delineates the catchment and sub-catchments automatically. Additional outlets can also be added manually to increase the number of sub-catchments. The interface then divides the sub-catchment into hydrological response units based on land use and soil information and parameters for routing water are derived simultaneously. Land management information supplied by the user is used to simulate crop growth and pesticide applications, based on the information available in the SWAT-Arc View Interface database. Weather input parameters entered by the user are coupled with other available information and flow and pesticide routing is carried out (Figure 1).

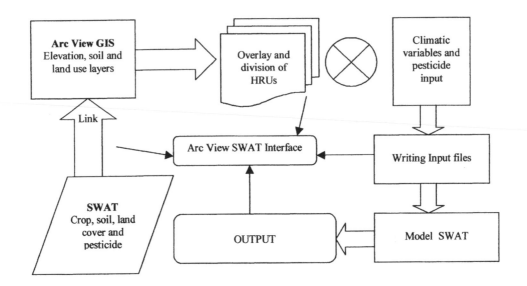

Figure 1.   Methodology for modelling pesticide runoff.

STUDY AREA

The study area is located in Sharnbrook, Bedfordshire, UK (in an area bounded by National Grid References 495000,263000 and 499000,263000). The total area is about 140 ha. The predominant soil series is Hanslope, consisting of a clay loam soil over stony, calcareous clay. A group of eight fields forming approximately half of the catchment area is directly controlled by Unilever and a rotation of wheat, oil seed rape, grass, linseed, beans and peas is grown. All eight fields are underdrained by means of tile drains.

DATA COLLECTION AND PROGRESS

Runoff, and pesticide and nutrient concentrations in runoff have been monitored at the outlet of the catchment since October 1999. Using Arc View GIS, A Digital Elevation Model (DEM) of the study area was prepared by digitising the contours from Ordnance Survey maps and using Arcview GIS. Automatic delineation of the catchment and its sub-catchments was carried out using the tools available in the SWAT-Arcview Interface. Land use and soils maps were overlaid and the catchment was divided into HRUs (hydrological response units) Relevant soil, crop and pesticide data were obtained and appended to the existing database in SWAT. Calibration of the model is currently being carried out with one year of collected data with the coming year's data to be used for validation of the model.

CONCLUSIONS

The TERRACE project aims to provide risk assessment for new chemicals at the regional river basin scale (a spatial scale not previously considered in the risk assessment process). The project has identified three models with varying input requirements which have the potential for inclusion in the TERRACE system. The first choice model is SWAT which is currently being evaluated for pesticide and nutrient transport using data from a UK catchment.

ACKNOWLEDGEMENTS

This work is supported by CEFIC and N Kannan is supported by Unilever.

REFERENCES

Bach M; Huber A; Frede H G (2001). Input pathways and river load of pesticides in Germany-a national scale modelling assessment. *Water Science and Technology* **43**: 261-268.

Bouraoui F; Dillaha T A (2000). ANSWERS-2000: non-point source nutrient planning model. *J. Env. Eng.* **126**: 1045-1055.

Feijtel T; Boije G; Matthies M; Young A; Morris G; Gandolfi C; Hansen B; Fox K; Matthijs E; Koch V; Schroder R; Cassani G; Schowanek D; Rosenblom J; Holt M (1998). Development of a geography-referenced regional exposure assessment tool for European rivers – GREAT-ER. *J. Hazardous Materials* **61**: 59-65.

Hollis J M; Brown C D; Thanigasalam P (1996). SWATCATCH: A catchment scale model for predicting weekly river flows and pesticide concentrations. SSLRC Report to the Environment Agency, TAPS Centre, SSLRC, Silsoe, UK.

Knisel W G (1980). CREAMS, a field scale model for chemicals, runoff and erosion from agricultural management systems. USDA, Research Report No. 26.

Leonard R A; Knisel W G; Still D A (1987). GLEAMS: Groundwater Loading Effects of Agricultural Management Systems. *Trans. Amer. Soc. Agric Engrs.* **30**: 1403-1418.

Neitsch S L; Arnold J G; Kiniry J R; Williams J R (2001). *Soil and Water Assessment Tool User's Manual*, Version 2000. Grassland, Soil and Water Research Laboratory, USDA Agricultural Research Service, Temple, Texas.

Thorsen M; Feyen J; Styczen M (1996). *Agrochemical modelling, **Chapter** 7, Distributed Hydrological Modelling*. Kluwer Academic Publishers, The Netherlands.

Wauchope R D; Leonard R A (1980). Maximum pesticide concentrations in agricultural runoff: a semi-empirical prediction formula. *J. Environ Qual* **9**: 665-670.

Williams J R; Renard K G; Dyke P T (1983). EPIC: a new method for assessing erosion's effect on productivity. *J. Soil and Water Cons.* 38: 381-383.

Cost-effective risk assessment of pesticide leaching at field scales: quality versus quantity of information

D C Lambkin, M Wood, L P Simmonds
Department of Soil Science, The University of Reading, PO Box 233, Whiteknights, RG6 6DW, UK
Email: d.c.lambkin@reading.ac.uk

ABSTRACT

This paper addresses the issue of how to obtain effectively and efficiently the information needed as the input parameters for pesticide leaching models, in the context of risk assessment at the field scale. A key question is the extent to which low-cost/less-accurate information at a number of locations in the field is more useful than high-cost/more-accurate information on a few (even single) samples. An example is presented which considers the balance between quality and quantity of information for several soil properties, including soil texture, soil organic matter, adsorption and degradation, based on the spatial variation in the predicted leaching losses of isoproturon from a sandy loam soil in southern England.

INTRODUCTION

It is not feasible to assess pesticide leaching at the field scale by integrating direct measurements of leaching from all parts of the field. Instead, conclusions are reached by studying sub-samples taken from the field, either by direct experiment (e.g. using lysimeters) or by modelling. Simulation models have become indispensable research tools for describing movement of water and solutes into and through the unsaturated zone (Wösten *et al.*, 1990) and are increasingly used in pesticide registration procedures.

Geostatistics optimises the interpolation between sampling sites, providing a powerful tool for predicting values of a soil property at points where no observations have been made, or over larger areas of land (Oliver *et al.*, 1996). As a result, fewer sampling sites are needed to achieve the same level of precision (Di *et al.*, 1989). An obvious next step is the application of geostatistical techniques to field measurements, generating inputs to solute transport models, and carrying out distributed modelling to predict spatial patterns of leaching within the field.

Oliver *et al.*, (1999) used the LEACHP model, in combination with geostatistics, to predict leaching of atrazine at the field scale. The simulation results predicted that significant losses of atrazine below 1 m depth would have occurred from just 10% of the field and that the contribution from the rest of the field was negligible. They concluded that, when pesticide leaching is marginal, most of the pesticide leached at the field scale is likely to be contributed by vulnerable zones that comprise a relatively small proportion of the total land area.

The identification of vulnerable zones within fields requires spatially distributed sampling involving large numbers of samples, and this has severe logistical implications. For example, pesticide transport models require parameterisation of adsorption, degradation and soil hydrodynamic properties. Since soil hydrodynamic properties are difficult to measure in the field, pedotransfer functions (PTFs) have been developed to estimate the properties from measurements of soil organic matter (SOM), bulk density (BD) and particle size distribution (PSD) (Brooks & Corey, 1964; Mualem, 1976; Van Genuchten, 1980; Hutson & Cass, 1987; Tietje & Tapkenhinrichs, 1993).

Such an approach simplifies the measurements to be made but does not decrease the amount of data required. For example, prediction of soil hydrodynamic properties in a single field using PTFs can require three measurements (PSD, SOM, BD) at three depths at each point. Geostatistics requires at least 100 data points (Oliver et al., 1996) giving a total of 900 laboratory determinations.

Therefore the laboratory measurements need to be reduced to minimise the total workload, but not at the expense of predictive accuracy. It can be argued that, where the variability of soil properties is high or a high level of precision in interpolation is desired, the number of sampling sites cannot be substantially reduced (Scheinost & Schwertmann, 1995). However, although spatial variation of a given parameter may be great, solute transport models may not be sensitive to that variation and it may be possible to reduce the number of measurements or use a single, average value for the field. When the parameter varies spatially, and the model is sensitive to that variation, the combined use of surrogate measurements at many locations and empirical relationships to transform the data may prove a better alternative. Therefore design of cost-efficient sampling strategies for risk assessment of pesticide leaching at the field scale must include consideration of model sensitivity to parameter variation.

Oliver et al., (1999) concluded that spatial variation in SOM content (associated with pesticide sorption and degradation) was very much more important in influencing the leaching of atrazine than was spatial variability in the soil hydrodynamic properties controlling the downward movement of pesticides via matrix flow. Similar results were reported by Soutter & Musy (1999). Therefore, it may be feasible to reduce the number of points where soil hydrodynamic properties are estimated and still be able to identify those zones within a field that are vulnerable to leaching.

Dubus et al., (2000) tested four pesticide leaching models for sensitivity to input parameters and concluded that the most important criteria are: the adsorption parameters (Freundlich coefficient and exponent); pesticide half-life; SOM content and bulk density. This paper investigates the effect of spatial variation in these properties on the spatial variation in the predicted leaching losses of isoproturon from a sandy loam soil in southern England.

MATERIALS AND METHODS

The study site was a 9 ha arable field situated on a river terrace adjacent to the River Thames near Reading. The soil is Sonning Series, a freely-draining light sandy loam overlying alluvial gravel. The field was surveyed in 1998 and a total of 90 samples were collected from the top 0-15 cm using a 5-stage unbalanced nested sampling scheme as described by Oliver & Webster (1986). Pesticide leaching losses from the top 30 cm were predicted using the pesticide leaching model SWAP (version 2.0.7d, January 2000). The input data were either measured (PSD, DT_{50}, Kd) or calculated using PTFs (SOM, BD).

Particle size distribution was determined on the 2 mm fraction by laser granulometry. Pesticide degradation rate (DT_{50}) was estimated by incubation with isoproturon (IPU) for 7 and 28 days. Duplicate samples of fresh soil (equivalent to 30 g oven dry soil) were weighed into glass jars. A suspension of commercial formulation of IPU (Alpha isoproturon 500, 46.4% a.i.) in water was added to produce a dose concentration of 13.2 mg/kg. The soil was incubated at $20^{\circ}C$ and the moisture content was maintained at 50% maximum water holding capacity. The samples were extracted with 90 ml acetonitrile:water (70:30 mix), a small aliquot was passed through a 0.2 µm membrane filter and analysed by hplc (Zorbex ODS; 5 µm column; flowrate 0.8 ml/min; detection by u.v. at 240 nm).

Loss on ignition (LOI) was determined by ignition of oven dried soil at $450^{\circ}C$ for 24 h. SOM was estimated from LOI using a field-specific PTF following the procedure described by Frogbrook & Oliver (2001). Geostatistical techniques were used to produce a map of LOI. Nine samples (three each from the high, medium and low LOI areas) were identified for determination of soil organic carbon (SOC) using the modified Walkley-Black procedure (MAFF, 1986). The nine LOI and SOC determinations were used to produce a PTF for SOM.

Kd was determined for all samples by equilibrium with 0.02M $CaCl_2$ containing 5 mg/l IPU (5 g soil:20 ml solution), assuming linear adsorption. The Freundlich exponent was kept constant at 1.0 because adsorption experiments on four samples showed that adsorption was linear in the range of concentrations modelled. Bulk density was calculated using a PTF for ploughed topsoils (Chen, 1998):

$$BD = 1.483 - 0.447C + 0.141S - 3.97SOM$$

where C = mass fraction of clay
S = mass fraction of sand
SOM = mass fraction of soil organic matter

Water release characteristics were calculated using a PTF within the model using the analytical function option (Mualem-van Genuchten equation) and PSD, SOM and BD.

Weather data (12 months) were selected from long-term measurements at the Reading University weather station (Sonning, Berkshire, UK). Potential evapotranspiration was calculated outside the model using the Penman-Monteith formula. The weather data were repeated to give a simulation run of three years, providing 2 years to allow the soil water status to stabilise. A crop (SWAP standard maize data) was used (sown 1 May, harvest 15 October each year). Pesticide was applied at the rate of 2.5 kg a.i./ha on 15 March of the third simulation year.

RESULTS AND DISCUSSION

The model was run six times for each of the 90 field locations. The first run was the base scenario where all spatially variable input parameters (Table 1) were as measured or calculated. For each of the subsequent runs one of the parameters was held constant at the field average value.

The model accounted for between 99.92 and 100% of the pesticide applied (Table 2). At the end of the three year simulation all the pesticide had gone from the top 30 cm of the profile, except for three of the 90 locations which had slow degradation rates (DT_{50} more than 30 days).

Table 1.   Spatial variability in the input data for the pesticide leaching model, SWAP

	%Clay	%Silt	%Sand	SOM%	Kd ml/g	DT_{50} days	BD g/cm^3
Maximum	15.04	30.93	70.91	4.092	2.14	37.37	1.4819
Minimum	6.45	21.05	54.03	1.677	0.48	8.70	1.3828
Mean	8.46	25.74	65.81	2.728	1.25	20.54	1.4297
Median	7.69	25.50	66.78	2.767	1.26	20.75	1.4283
Std Dev	1.92	2.16	3.97	0.492	0.35	4.85	0.0278
Skew	1.22	0.13	-0.76	0.322	0.35	0.65	-0.1721

Table 2.   Spatial variability in leaching of IPU (g/ha) at 30 cm predicted using SWAP for six scenarios, with all parameters varying (base scenario) or substitution of the mean value for one parameter

	Base Scenario	Mean PSD	Mean Bulk Density	Mean Organic Matter	Mean Kd	Mean DT_{50}
Maximum	318	317	315	317	312	261
Minimum	0	0	0	0	0	0
Mean	47	46	46	46	43	43
Std Dev	49	48	48	48	52	37
CV%	104.2	104.2	103.9	104.2	121.1	87.6
Skew	2.46	2.48	2.50	2.47	3.39	2.47
RMSE		1.64	2.37	1.23	53.7	46.9

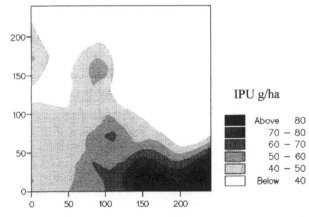

IPU g/ha

Above 80
70 – 80
60 – 70
50 – 60
40 – 50
Below 40

Figure 1.   Predicted spatial variation in leaching at 30 cm (base scenario)

In the base scenario the average amount leached at 30 cm was 47 g/ha, representing 1.9% of pesticide applied. Analysis of the variation in leaching between the locations shows that 50% of leaching was accounted for by 72 out of 90 locations and 50% by 18 locations. This confirms the bias in leaching toward a small number of locations within the field (Figure 1).

Substituting the field mean value for PSD, BD or SOM had little effect on the mean or range of amount leached. All three scenarios accounted for between 98.3% and 99.4% of the aggregated leaching of the 90 locations. The mean DT_{50} and Kd scenarios accounted for 91.7% and 92.8% of the aggregated leaching respectively. This indicates that the total predicted leaching from the field could probably be estimated from field average values of these parameters, on condition that the measured value is a true estimate of the field mean. The number of samples (n) required to estimate the field mean depends on the within-field variation (standard deviation, σ), the model sensitivity to parameter (tolerance required, L) and the confidence level required for the result (Student's-t, Z):

$$n = (Z * \sigma)^2/L^2$$

The model is very sensitive to variation in DT_{50} and Kd, and these parameters also had the greatest within-field variation. Therefore, for accurate estimation of the average field leaching, it would be more effective to take many (23) measurements of DT_{50} and Kd within the field compared with few (2) measurements of particle size distribution.

Prediction of leaching vulnerable zones within the field shows similar sensitivity to DT_{50}. There was no significant difference (R > 0.98) between the first four scenarios in Table 2 as indicated by the small differences in range, mean, standard deviation and skew. By using the mean DT_{50} much of the variation in predicted leaching was removed, resulting in a narrower range of values.

The root mean square error (RMSE) was calculated (Table 2) to compare the accuracy of each of the predictions compared with the base scenario. Comparison of RMSE shows that the accuracy depends on Kd > DT_{50} >> BD > PSD > SOM and that the RMSE for DT_{50} and Kd is an order of magnitude greater than for the other parameters. These results differ somewhat from those reported by Dubus *et al.* (2000), who predicted that the relative importance of the parameters decreased in the order Kd > DT_{50} > SOM > BD > PSD for a similar compound and soil type.

CONCLUSIONS

These results indicate that spatial variation in pesticide half-life and adsorption are the most important parameters for the estimation of total pesticide leaching and spatial variation in leaching. But the results should be treated with caution: firstly, they are the results from only one model that utilises a simplified pesticide fate routine. They refer to results for only one pesticide and one field. Two parameters have been ignored that were identified as significant by Dubus *et al.*, (2000), namely the Freundlich exponent and preferential flow. Work is currently in progress to investigate how these vary at the field scale.

ACKNOWLEDGEMENTS

This work was funded by the NERC Environmental Diagnostics Programme. The authors thank Mr O R Price for the use of his data.

REFERENCES

Brooks R H; Corey A T (1964). Hydraulic properties of porous media. Hydrology paper No. 3. Colorado State University, Fort Collins, CO, 27p.

Chen Y; Tessier S; Rouffignat J (1998). Soil bulk density estimation for tillage systems and soil textures. *Transactions of the ASAE*, **41**: 1601-1610.

Di H J; Trangmar B B; Kemp R A (1989). Use of geostatistics in designing sampling strategies for soil survey. *Soil Science Society of America Journal*, **53**: 1163-1167.

Dubus I G; Brown C D; Beulke S (2000). Sensitivity analysis for leaching models used for pesticide registration in Europe. SSLRC report for MAFF PL0532, Silsoe, Beds., UK, 85p.

Frogbrook Z L; Oliver M A (2001). Comparing the spatial predictions of soil organic matter determined by two laboratory methods. *Soil Use and Management*. In press.

Hutson J L; Cass A (1987). A retentivity function for use in soil-water simulation models. *Journal of Soil Science*, **38**: 105-113.

MAFF (1986). *MAFF Reference Book 427: The analysis of agricultural materials*, 3rd edn, HMSO: London.

Mualem Y (1976). A new model for predicting the hydraulic conductivity of unsaturated porous media. *Water Resources Research*, **12**: 513-522.

Oliver M A; Webster R (1986). Combining nested and linear sampling for determining the scale and form of spatial variation of regionalized variables: *Geographical Analysis*, **18:** 227-242.

Oliver M A; Webster R; Mcgrath S P (1996). Disjunctive kriging for environmental management. *Envirometrics*, **7**: 333-358.

Oliver M A; Simmonds L P; Wood M (1999). Use of geostatistics to determine spatial variation in pesticide leaching – preliminary findings. In: *Human and environmental exposure to xenobiotics.* eds. A.A.M. Del Re, C. Brown, E. Capri, G. Errera, S.P. Evans & M. Trevisan. pp 551-559. Proceedings of the XI Symposium Pesticide Chemistry, Sept 1999, Cremona, Italy.

Scheinost A C; Schwertmann U (1995). Predicting phosphate adsorption-desorption in a soilscape. *Soil Science Society of America Journal*, **59**: 1575-1580.

Soutter M; Musy A (1999). Global sensitivity analyses of three pesticide leaching models using a Monte-Carlo approach. *Journal of Environmental Quality*, **28**: 1290-1297.

Teitje O; Tapkenhinrichs M (1993). Evaluation of pedotransfer functions. Soil *Science Society of America Journal*, **57**: 1088-1095.

Van Genuchten M Th (1980). A closed-form equation for predicting the hydraulic conductivity of unsaturated soils. *Soil Science of America Journal*, **44**: 892-898.

Wösten J H M; Schuren C H J E; Bouma J; Stein A (1990). Functional sensitivity analysis of 4 methods to generate soil hydraulic functions. *Soil Science Society of America Journal*, **54:** 832-836.

Metamodeling to assess pesticides leaching on a wide scale

L Padovani, E Capri
Istituto di Chimica Agraria ed Ambientale, Università Cattolica del Sacro Cuore, Via Emilia Parmense, 84 – 29100 Piacenza, Italy. Email: chimiv@pc.unicatt.it

M Trevisan
DISAPROV – Università degli studi di Perugia – Borgo XX Giugno, 72 - 06121 Perugia, Italy

ABSTRACT

A simplified meta-model methodology has been applied to assess the spatial distribution of potential groundwater contamination from pesticides. The approach is based on a one-dimensional leaching model (LEACHP) linked to a geographic information system (GIS). A statistical technique to summarise the model input-output relationships (stepwise regression procedure) in order to upscale the estimated concentrations. The potential for atrazine leaching was estimated for the agricultural area of Piacenza province (Northern Italy).

INTRODUCTION

In the last decades an increasing number of mathematical models to predict environmental fate of pesticides have been developed, with particular attention to pesticides leaching. However, because of the amount of input data and the large numbers of simulations required to cover large areas (regional/national), these physically based techniques are generally time-consuming and economically unfavourable. Thus, it is required a methodology to extrapolate results from local scale to a nation-wide scale taking into account at the same time the geographic variability of the model input parameters.

We developed an approach based on a one-dimensional leaching model (LEACHP) linked to a geographic information system (GIS) and a statistical technique to summarise the model input-output relationships (stepwise regression procedure) in order to upscale the estimated concentrations. The resulting frequency distributions map of the pesticide leaching concentrations can be used in sustainable groundwater management and decision making.

MATERIALS AND METHODS

Pesticide Leaching Model

The pesticide fate and transport model LEACHP (Wagenet & Hutson, 1995) was used for this study. LEACHP is a one-dimensional finite difference model describing the water and chemical regime in unsatured or partially saturated soil profiles. All spatially-distributed parameters required as input by the model (soil type, crop type, climate and hydrology) were stored in a GIS database. Figure 1 shows the linkage between the database and the model. In this *loose coupling* (Corwin *et al.*, 1997), the GIS (ESRI ArcView, 1996) is used to create external text files consisting of input data for the model. Afterwards the output files resulting from simulations are read and processed to create leaching pesticide concentration maps.

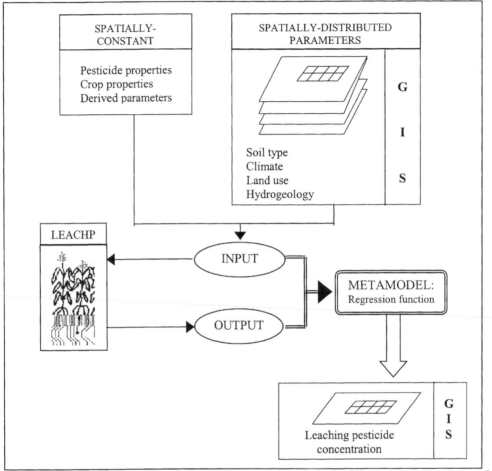

Figure 1. Link of LEACHP model to GIS and metamodel development to create map of pesticide leaching concentrations.

Study area and scenario of application

The approach developed was applied to the plain area in Piacenza Province (Po Valley, Northern Italy) covering approximately 1,100 km^2. The intensive agriculture in the area, associated with the peculiar structure of the aquifer creates a situation where the groundwater risks contamination by pollutants of agricultural origin.

The basic cartography utilised in the study was the soil map at a scale of 1:50.000 defined by 23 different types of soil units: in 40% of the area the soil texture can be classified as silty clay loam, 25.6% is silt loam, 18.5% loam, 6.5% clay and 5.4% silty clay. Soil properties were defined according to 3316 soil profiles distributed across the area. The spatial pattern of the averages of precipitation and temperature (1990-1997) was derived from daily weather data. Evapotranspiration was estimated via the Thornthwaite equation.

Atrazine was the herbicide considered in the simulations ($DT_{50} = 44$ d; $K_{oc} = 118.4$ L/kg; $K_H = 1.38E-06$) applied once per year to a maize crop at a standard dose of 1.9 kg/ha every year).

The LEACHP model was run for 306 soil sampling points selected within each cell (2 x 2 km) of a regular grid (Figure 2). Six years of simulations were performed and as model outputs we considered, according to the FOCUS procedure (FOCUS, 2000) the 80th percentiles of annual average concentration of atrazine leached below 1 meter depth.

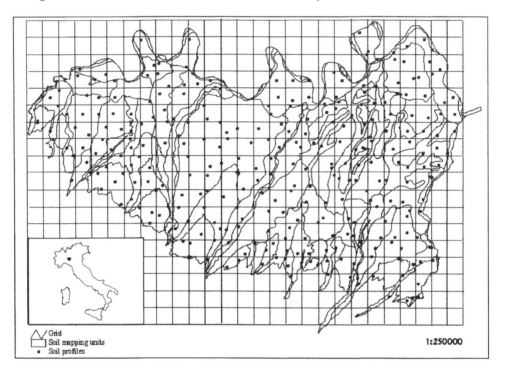

Figure 2. Study area location and selected soil profiles used to perform simulations with the LEACHP model.

Metamodel

Statistical techniques such as stepwise regression procedures are popular methods of searching for good subset models, particularly when the number of independent models is large. In this study the software STATISTIX Version 7.0 (Analytical Software, 2000) was used to summarise the model input-output relationships in order to upscale the concentrations estimated with LEACHP.

RESULTS AND DISCUSSION

A total of 306 values were determined representing the 80th percentile of the atrazine leaching concentration at 1 meter depth in 5 years. The Wilk-Shapiro test for normality suggest a logarithmic transformation of atrazine concentration (LogATR) as the data were not normally distributed. Then, independent variables (clay, bulk density, hydraulic conductivity, silt, organic matter, pH, sand) were analysed statistically with a stepwise regression (Table 1). Soil type has a clear effect on the magnitude of the maximum concentration: clay content and organic matter content are the independent variables with highest correlation with the atrazine leaching concentration.

Table 1.   Stepwise regression analysis applied to the LEACHP model output.

STEPWISE REGRESSION OF LogATR
UNFORCED VARIABLES: CLAY BD KS SILT OM PH SAND
VARIABLE(S) DROPPED FROM INITIAL MODEL BECAUSE
OF COLLINEARITY: SAND

STEP	R SQ	MSE	P	C L A Y	B D	K S	L S T	O M	P H	S A N D
1	0.8745	0.08628		A	B	C	D	E	F	.
2	0.8533	0.09169	0.2228	A	B	.	D	E	F	.
3	0.8465	0.08790	0.4926	A	B	.	.	E	F	.
4	0.8272	0.09137	0.2422	A	.	.	.	E	F	.
5	0.8001	0.09813	0.1772	A	.	.	.	E	.	.

RESULTING STEPWISE MODEL

VARIABLE	COEFFICIENT	STD ERROR	STUDENT'S T	P
CONSTANT	2.28951	0.42835	5.34	0.0001
CLAY	-0.08088	0.01525	-5.30	0.0001
OM	-1.21329	0.18444	-6.58	0.0000

CASES INCLUDED	17	R SQUARED	0.8001	MSE	0.09813
MISSING CASES	74	ADJ R SQ	0.7716	SD	0.31326

The resulting regression model ($R^2 = 0.80$) is therefore represented by the following equation:

$$LogATR = 2.28951 - (0.08088*[clay]) - (1.21329*[O.M.])$$

Considering the clay content and the organic matter content of the remaining 3010 soil sampling points, the LEACHP estimated values were extrapolated to the whole study area.

In order to create a raster overlay from the point data, a geostatistical method of interpolation (ordinary kriging) was applied by means of GS[+] software (Gamma Design Software, 1998). The results are displayed by the aid of GIS in a thematic map of the leaching concentration of atrazine at 1 meter depth in the Piacenza plain (Figure 3). It is possible to identify areas of different contamination potentials. Estimated concentrations are less than 0.01 µg/l in almost half of the area whilst in 23% of the area they range between 0.01 and 0.05 µg/l. Largest concentration (18% of the study area) of pesticide are located mainly in the Nord sector, near the Po river and in southern areas characterised by low organic matter soil contents (< 1.5%).

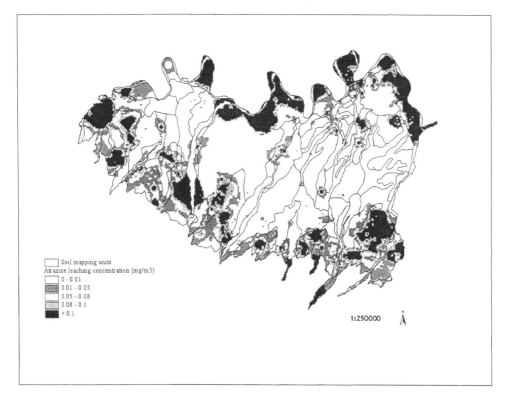

Figure 3. Atrazine leaching concentrations in the Piacenza plain estimated with the LEACHP model.

A validation of the map was carried out with analytical data of pesticide concentrations in drinking water wells. The study area includes 35 wells, which form part of a regional monitoring system. Analytical data for raw water are in good agreement with the map showing that the four wells with atrazine concentrations (average concentrations of seven years of monitoring plan) greater than 0.01 µg/l fall within areas with the largest predicted concentrations.

Results suggest that this approach can be used successfully for evaluating the contamination potential of pesticides in large areas.

REFERENCES

Analytical Software (2000). Statistix for Windows.
Corwin D L; Vaughan P J; Loague K (1997). Modeling NonPoint Source Pollutants in the Vadose Zone with GIS. *Environmental Science & Technology* **31** (8): 2157-2175.

ESRI Environmental Systems Research Institute, Inc. (1996). ArcView GIS, Version 3.0a.

FOCUS (2000). FOCUS groundwater scenarios in the EU plant protection product review process. *Report of the FOCUS Groundwater Scenarios Workgroup*, pp. 197, EC Document Reference Sanco/321/2000.

Gamma Design Software (1998). GS$^+$ Geostatistics for the Environmental Sciences, Version 3.1 for Windows.

Wagenet R J; Hutson, J L (1995). *LEACHM Leaching Estimation and Chemistry Model. A process-based model of water and solute movements, transformations, plant uptake and chemical reactions in the unsatured zone (Version 3.0).* New York State College of Agriculture and Life Sciences, Cornell University, Ithaca, (N.Y.)

Modelling pesticide input into surface waters in Germany

B Röpke, M Bach, H G Frede
University of Giessen, Department of Natural Resources Management,
Heinrich-Buff-Ring 26-32, D-35392 Giessen, Germany.
Email: *bjoern.roepke@agrar.uni-giessen.de*

ABSTRACT

A GIS decision support system (DSS) is under development for estimating the magnitude and spatial distribution of pesticide losses from non-point sources (surface runoff, tile drainage and spray drift) in Germany. The cumulative annual losses of any active ingredient (a.i.) of known half-life (DT50), adsorption coefficient normalized for organic carbon (Koc) and dosage can be calculated for approximately 400 river basins covering the territory of Germany. Furthermore, the resulting predicted environmental concentration (PEC_{sw}) can be retrieved by relating the daily input of a.i. to the daily discharge of the respective streams. Results are visualized as grid maps with a 1x1 km^2 resolution. Site-specific maps of pesticide losses and PEC frequency distributions provide a basis for regional risk assessment of pesticides.

INTRODUCTION

Pesticide use on agricultural land frequently leads to contamination of non-target areas such as ground water or surface water bodies. An essential condition for an a.i. to meet registration requirements is to rule out contamination of these non-target ecosystems. The "realistic worst-case" is the threshold to determine when a substance can be considered non-toxic for the surrounding ecosystems. The "realistic worst case" is usually determined by laboratory experiments and does not account for the probability of this threshold value being exceeded in its regional and temporal context. The DSS DRIPS follows a probability-based modelling approach on a regional scale by estimating the frequency of a set limit of contamination of a given a.i. and its spatial distribution.

MATERIALS AND METHODS

The modelled non-point sources of pesticide input into surface water bodies are surface runoff, tile drainage and spray drift. DRIPS follows a modular approach, calculating the load or PEC of an a.i. separately.

Runoff

The amount of a.i. to be translocated by runoff water essentially depends on the period of time elapsed between pesticide application and actual occurrence of a runoff-producing rainfall event (Mills & Leonard, 1984). It is assumed that rainfall events of 10 mm in 24 h or larger are sufficient to trigger surface runoff. The 'mean probability of runoff-producing rainfall occurrence' T_n with a given volume h_N and duration in a certain period is determined by the Gumbel-Distribution (Gumbel, 1958).

$$Tn = exp((h_N - u_l)/w_l)$$ [1]

The Gumbel-parameters u and w are provided by the German Meteorological Service (DWD) with a resolution of 8.5 x 8.5 km². Distribution function parameters of 60 min and 24 h duration are currently implemented in the DSS, the latter with separate datasets for summer and winter. According to Mills & Leonard (1984), the probability of a runoff-producing rainfall event Tn can also be expressed as a probability density function $f(t)$:

$$f(t) = aT \cdot e^{(-aT \cdot t)} \qquad t \geq 0$$ [2]

with aT as the reciprocal value of Tn [cf. 1] and t as the time interval between pesticide application and first runoff-producing rainfall event. A seasonal variation factor Vt_i was added to equation [1] to account for the more variable frequency of rainstorm occurrences in the summer season (Auerswald, 1996).

The calculation of the 'runoff volume' Qd_t caused by a runoff-producing rainfall $Pevent$ is based on the USSCS's curve-number-method (SCS, 1990). The curve numbers were modified according to Lutz (1984) in order to adapt the SCS-CN-method to Central European conditions.

$$Qd_t = (Pevent - Ia) \cdot Dc + \frac{Dc}{\alpha}\left(e^{-a(Pevent - Ia)} - 1\right)$$ [3]

Land use and hydrological soil group of the land parcel in question determine the drainage coefficient Dc (Anderl, 1975; Auerswald & Haider, 1996). Land use data are provided by CORINE land-cover (Statistisches Bundesamt, 1997). The hydrological soil groups were derived from a soil map (BGR, 1996) by Huber *et al.*, (1998) conforming to the SCS-CN methodology.

$$Ia = 0.76 \cdot \left(\frac{10}{Dc} - 10\right)$$ [4]

The initial abstraction Ia comprises the processes of interception, initial infiltration rate and surface storage for the time interval passing since the beginning of a rainstorm event until surface runoff starts to occur. Current soil saturation at the time of a rainstorm event is another important factor to be accounted for to calculate the runoff volume. The proportionality coefficient α of Lutz (1984) relates the current soil saturation to seasonal variation.

$$\alpha = P_1 \cdot e^{(-P_2/WZ)} \cdot e^{(-P_3/QB)}$$ [5]

According to Lutz, the base flow Qb of a catchment is the representative factor of its hydrological condition at the beginning of a runoff event. The seasonal variation of the base flow is characterized by week numbers WZ. $P1$-$P3$ are calibration factors (Grunwald, 1997). The mean annual precipitation $Pyear$ is provided nationwide by the DWD.

The 'pesticide concentration in runoff water' at the beginning of a rainstorm highly depends on the substance's decay as well as the retention capacity of the crop and soil it was applied on. Degradation can be expressed with a first-order decay function (Mills and Leonard, 1984):

$$W(t) = W_{dosage} \cdot e^{(-Bw \cdot t)} \qquad t \geq 0$$ [6]

where $W(t)$ is the fraction of a pesticide's initial load W_{dosage} left after degrading during the time-interval t since application. Decay is controlled by the breakdown coefficient B_w depending on the a.i.'s half-life $DT50$.

By merging equations [6] and [2], a probability density function can be derived (cf. Mills and Leonard, 1984) for the fraction of the initial load $W(t)$ available on the soil surface for translocation by runoff water of a rainstorm occurring t days after substance application with the probability of $f(t)$ (eq. [2]). Within the DSS DRIPS, mean values (probability = 0.5) of a.i. losses with runoff are assumed (Leonard et al., 1987)

$$W_{0Soil} = 0.5^{\frac{Bw}{aT}} \cdot W_{dosage} \cdot (1 - BG_{i,j}) \qquad [7]$$

Naturally, the full quantity of W_0 is not actually transported by runoff water. A share of it is withheld by the current plant cover of the area the pesticide was applied on. It is assumed that only the portion reaching the soil is available for translocation by runoff. $BG_{i,j}$ is an index representing the degree of soil cover of crop(j) in a specific climatic zone at a certain stage of maturity (i) (Bach et al., 2000). W_{0Soil} is the runoff-available pesticide load in the surface soil layer.

Only a portion of the runoff-available pesticide load W_{0Soil} is expected to be found in the runoff-suspension during a rainstorm event. That is the fraction of the a.i. subject to desorption processes within the first centimeters of the topsoil. Consequently, the model only calculates pesticide displacement for the liquid phase. Erosion is not taken into account. A semi-empirical approach was adopted from GLEAMS (Leonard et al., 1987) where the soluble amount of the runoff-available pesticide load can be derived by multiplying W_{0Soil} with a desorption-coefficient D_s. An instant balance of an a.i. between the liquid and solid phase is pre-supposed. D_s can be derived empirically from the distribution coefficient Kd, which in turn can be obtained from the linear organic carbon partition coefficient and the content of organic carbon $Corg$ (CREAMS/GLEAMS: Leonard et al., 1987).

Finally, the pesticide concentration of an a.i. in solution $Csolv_{w,t}$ can be calculated from the runoff-available pesticide load W_{0Soil}, the desportion-coefficient D_s and the distribution coefficient Kd. $Csolv_{w,t}$ being the quantity of the initial dosage of an a.i. which has to be expected as surface water input as a result of a runoff-producing rainstorm event.

$$C_{solvwt} = \frac{W_{0Soil} \cdot D_s}{1 + D_s \cdot Kd} \qquad [8]$$

2.2 Leaching

Germany's registration authorities make use of the model PELMO by Klein et al. (1997) for assessing the risk of a.i. displacement via leaching. To conform to registration standards, PELMO was adopted in DRIPS as the model of choice to estimate the quantity of pesticides transported by leaching water. PELMO is used to simulate the displacement of an a.i. to 0.8 m depth. At that depth, the leachate is expected to enter a tile drainage system - if installed on the land – or be subject to further vertical translocation. In the latter case, the pesticide ultimately reaches the ground water body, if it does not fully degrade along the way. The input of pesticides into surface waters from the ground water body is considered to be negligible in Germany (Bach et al., 2000). Hence, pesticide input via leaching is only calculated for drained areas. A grid cell map of Germany's drained areas is provided by Behrendt *et al* (1999). DRIPS estimates the site-specific input $L(leach.)_{w,i,j}$ of an a.i. dosage W applied on date (i) and crop (j) via a tile drainage system.

$$L(leach.)_{w,i,j} = W_{i,j,} \cdot (1 - BG_{i,j}) \cdot \delta (PELMO)_w \qquad [9]$$

In the same manner as for the runoff path, it is presupposed that only that amount of an a.i. is transported in the leachate, which is not subject to foliage-interception but reaches the soil. Since PELMO does not consider interception, BG is introduced as an index of the degree of soil cover of crop (j) in a specific climatic zone at a certain stage of maturity(i). $\delta (PELMO)_w$ is the fraction of the initial dose of an a.i. found in the leachate at 0.8 m depth. The solution is expected to enter a tile drain at that depth leading towards a surface water body nearby.

2.3 Spray drift

Surface water input of a sprayed a.i. is expected via direct drift, for the fraction of the substance not reaching the target area but being blown into an adjacent stream. Generally, a.i. loss by drift is significantly higher for fruit- or grapevine plantations than for field crops. This is mainly due to different spraying-techniques, like the use of boom sprayers in field crops and air blast sprayers in grapevine plantations (Ganzelmeier *et al.*, 1995). DRIPS uses the drift tables published by Germany's Federal Biological Research Center for Agriculture and Forestry (BBA) as a basis for estimating the fraction of an a.i. displaced by spray drift. The tables are also used by registration authorities to set up spraying-distance requirements for pesticides. Different tables are available for 95th, 70th and 50th percentiles providing separate spray drift values $BBA\text{-}Tab(Dist)_w$ for fruit grapevine and field crops each for two phenological zones and for specific proximities of surface water and site of application.

$$L(drift)_{w,i,j,} = BBA\text{-}Tab(dist)_w \cdot W_{i,j,} \cdot A\backslash G \cdot Gd_r \cdot Gbr \qquad [10]$$

where $L(Drift)_{w,i}$ is the site-specific input of a.i. W via spray drift after application at date(i) in crop(j). $A\backslash G$ is a correction factor for the cropland/pasture ratio adjacent to rivers. In DRIPS $A\backslash G$ is set to 0.4 for cropland and 1.0 for fruit- and grapevine plantations (Bach *et al.*, 2000). The mean drainage density of the river network Gd_r was derived from the Hydrological Atlas of Germany (HAD) by Huber *et al.* (1998). It is available within DRIPS as a grid map to judge the probability of an a.i. reaching a surface water body via drift. The amount of a.i. input also depends on the width of the river Gb. Larger water bodies are susceptible to higher amounts of deposition. However, most larger streams have adequate buffer zones shielding a.i. input to some extent. Unshielded small ditches are frequently found in agriculturally used areas prone to receive frequent deposition. In DRIPS Gb is set to 0.5 m for 1st order streams (definition of Strahler, 1957) and 3 m for 2nd order and higher.

2.4 PEC

The model approaches described for runoff, drainage and spray drift estimate the expected load of pesticides input into surface water bodies for a specific region and time. DRIPS will be fitted with a further module to estimate the initial predicted environmental concentration (PEC$_{sw}$). The module will link the three pathways calculating the a.i.'s load with hydrological data such as rivermorphology and flow duration. The basic river network to be used is provided by Behrendt *et al.* (1999). The network will be classified into approximately six regions *(r)* of similar drainage density and rivernet-morphology. Also, all surface water bodies will be classified *(g)* according to their volume of discharge. Significant combinations of both classes *(r)* and *(g)* such as drainage density of 2nd order streams in a certain region will be used as model variables. An evaluation of gauging station data will produce discharge values for every class on a daily basis. The ratio of the mean daily input (E) of an a.i. via runoff, drainage and spray drift into various types of surface water bodies characterized by their daily discharge (Q) yields the predicted environmental concentration of the respective surface water body.

$$PEC_{sw} = E/Q \hspace{5cm} [11]$$

RESULTS AND DISCUSSION

The model described above will be fully integrated into a GIS-shell with an easy to use graphical interface. The DSS DRIPS is set up as a user-friendly risk assessment tool for estimating the PEC_{sw} of a.i. in surface water bodies. Results will be available with fairly high temporal (eg. daily discharges) and spatial (1x1 km^2) resolution. The DSS offers a time- and cost-effective method to assess the probability of pesticide contamination of surface waters and the resulting initial concentration of the a.i. in surface water bodies. Relatively few parameters have to be specified by the user, such as dosage, DT50, Koc, crop and date of application. Spatially discriminated maps are produced as model results visualizing the hazard potential for the territory of Germany with its varying soil and climatic conditions. Authorities could use these maps as a basis to encourage field campaigns for specific substances at sites where high contamination is expected.

Figure 1. Map of results from DRIPS

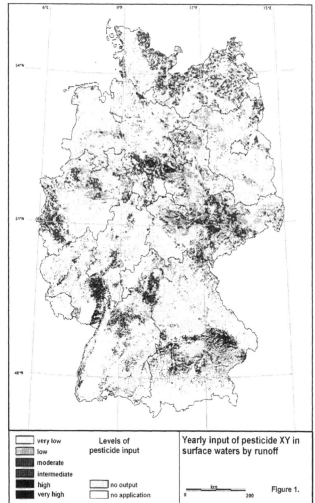

Figure 1.

ACKNOWLEDGEMENTS
This project is funded by the Federal Environmental Agency (UBA), Berlin:
UBA-FE-Project 299 24 272

REFERENCES
Anderl B (1975). *Vorhersage von Hochwasserganglinien aus radargemessenem Regen.* Mitt. Inst. für Wasserbau 7, Karlsruhe.

Auerswald K (1996). Jahresgang der Eintrittswahrscheinlichkeit erosiver Starkregen in Süddeutschland. *Z. Kulturtechnik und Landentwicklung* **37**: 81-84.

Auerswald K; Haider J (1996). Runoff Curve Numbers for Small Grain under German Cropping Conditions. *J. Environ. Management* **47**: 223-228.

Bach M; Huber A; Frede H G; Mohaupt V; Zullei-Seibert N (2000). Schätzung der Einträge von Pflanzenschutzmitteln aus der Landwirtschaft in die Oberflächengewässer Deutschlands. *UBA-Berichte 3/00*, E.Schmidt-Verlag, Umweltbundesamt, Berlin, 274 pp.

Behrendt H; Huber P; Kornmilch M; Opitz D; Schmoll O; Scholz G; Uebe R; Pagenkopf W; Bach M (1999) Nährstoffbilanzierung der Flussgebiete Deutschlands. , *UBA-Texte 99/75*, Umweltbundesamt, Berlin.

BGR (1996) Bodenübersichtskarte 1:1 Mio. (BÜK1000) der Bundesrepublik Deutschland. Bundesanstalt f. Geowissenschaften und Rohstoffe, Hannover.

Ganzelmeier H., Rautmann D., Spangenberg R., Streloke M., Herrmann M., Wenzelburger H. J., Walter H F (1995). Studies on the Spray Drift of Plant Protection Products-Results of a Test Programme Carried Out Throughout the Federal Republic of Germany. *Mitteilungen aus der Biologischen Bundesanstalt für Land- und Forstwirtschaft* **305**, Berlin, 111pp.

Grunwald S (1997). GIS-gestützte Modellierung des Landschaftswasser- und Stoffhaushalts mit dem Modell AGNPSm. *Boden u. Landschaft Bd.* **14:** Giessen, 170pp. (PhD thesis, Univ. Giessen).

Gumbel E J (1958). Statistics of the Extremes. Columbia Univ. Press, New York, 375pp.

Huber A; Bach M; Frede H G (1998). Modeling pesticide losses with surface runoff in Germany. *The Science of the Total Environment* **23**: 177-191

Klein M; Müller M; Dust M; Görlitz G; Gottesbüren B; Hassink J; Kloskowski R; Kubiak R; Resseler H; Schäfer H; Stein B; Vereecken H. (1997). Validation of the Pesticide Leaching Model PELMO Using Lysimeter Studies Performed for Registration. *Chemosphere* **35** (11): 2563-2587

Leonard R A; Knisel W G; Still D A (1987). GLEAMS: Groundwater Loading Effects of Agricultural Management Systems. *Trans. ASAE* **30** (5): 1403-1418

Lutz W (1984). Berechnung von Hochwasserabflüssen unter Anwendung von Gebietskenngrößen. *Mitt. Inst. f. Hydrol. und Wasserwirt.* 24, Karlsruhe, 221pp.

Mills W C; Leonard R A (1984). Pesticide Pollution Probabilities. *Trans. ASAE* **27**: 1704-1710

SCS (1990). Estimating Runoff for Conservation Practices. *Texas Eng. Techn. Note* No. 210-18-TX5. Soil Conservation Service. U.S. Dept. of Agriculture, Washington D.C., 47p

Statistisches Bundesamt (ed.) (1997). CORINE-Land-Cover, Digitale Bodenbedeckungsdaten der Bundesrepublik Deutschland. Statistisches Bundesamt, Wiesbaden

Strahler A N (1957). Quantitative Analysis of Watershed Geomorphology. *Trans. Am. Geophys. Union* **38** (6): 913-920

Characterisation of the structure of spatial variability for initial pesticide concentration in a field trial

C Vischetti, L Scarponi, A Esposito
Centro di Studio sulla Chimica e Biochimica dei Fitofarmaci del CNR., Borgo XX Giugno 72, 06121 Perugia, Italy
Email:vischett@unipg.it

M Vianello
Dip. Agronomia Ambientale e Produzioni Vegetali, Agripolis, 35020 Legnaro (Padova), Italy

G Zanin
Centro di Studio sulla Biologia ed il Controllo delle Piante Infestanti del CNR, Agripolis, 35020 Legnaro (Padova), Italy

ABSTRACT

The spatial variation in the concentration of four herbicides in two trials with maize (metolachlor, terbuthylazine) and winter wheat (pendimethalin, isoproturon) was assessed during the treatment, using classical statistical and geostatistical techniques. Spray trap and soil samples were collected immediately after the treatment to evaluate the herbicide concentration when the solution reaches the soil and the initial herbicide soil concentration, respectively. The results show that the values of the herbicide concentration at the moment of treatment are lower than expected, indicating that under field conditions only a part of the pesticide reaches the soil during the distribution. A decrease of CV in spray traps in winter wheat trials is partially explainable by the greater accuracy used in treatment planning and the better weather conditions. Geostatistical analysis was undertaken on the herbicide concentration in the spray traps, as 80 samples per herbicide were collected, while there were not enough samples for initial soil concentration to perform this kind of analysis. The data showed a spatial correlation only for maize herbicides. The data are discussed in order to establish a more efficient soil sampling strategy.

INTRODUCTION

One of the main problems in field studies of pesticide dissipation is the high variability in pesticide application (Wauchope *et al.*, 1977; Vischetti *et al.*, 1997). The application of pesticides under normal farming conditions is often done with little attention to the factors which can generate spatial variability in the pesticide concentration. In many field experiments carried out following standard farming practices, without any kind of interference, high variability in the initial distribution of pesticides has been found (Vischetti *et al.*, 1995; Vischetti *et al.*, 1998). Among other factors, uneven soil preparation, wind speed at the time of treatment, irregular speed of the spraying equipment and changing pressure at the nozzles, determine spatial variability in pesticide distribution. Together with the high variability, the loss of pesticides at the moment of treatment almost always happens in field experiments on pesticide fate. The loss can be high and not only explainable with the action of some factors such as wind speed or low recoveries of pesticides from soil samples (Vischetti *et al.*, 1998).

Geostatistics is a technique used to determine the spatial variability of some soil properties such as organic matter content and texture (Webster & Burgess, 1980; Vieira et al., 1981), but this technique has only been used in a few cases to characterise the spatial variability of pesticide concentration in fields (Rao & Wagenet, 1985; Vischetti et al., 1997). A possible use of geostatistics is to characterise the structure of the spatial variability in order to establish an experimental design for further trials on pesticide dissipation studies, namely the number of samples that should be taken depending on the variability and field size.

The first aim of this study was to assess the spatial variation in the concentration of four herbicides under field conditions; the second was to compare the herbicide soil concentration (initial concentration) with the herbicide concentration in glass spray traps before the solution reaches the soil.

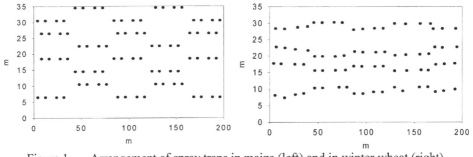

Figure 1.   Arrangement of spray traps in maize (left) and in winter wheat (right)

MATERIALS AND METHODS

Field study

Table 1.   Field information

Soil properties						
Depth	pH	Organic Matter	Clay	Silt	Sand	CEC
0-50 cm	8.11	0.92%	11.8%	44.9%	43.3%	12.87 meq/100 g

Weather conditions during herbicide application *							
Wind speed (m s^{-1})		Air humidity (%)		Temperature °C		Sun radiation (W h m^{-2})	
maize	wheat	maize	wheat	maize	wheat	maize	wheat
Mean	0.7	2.1	66.3	85.2	21.5	15.0	492.1	236.1
Min	0.2	0.8	61.0	75.0	20.6	13.0	209.3	62.8
Max	1.2	3.5	75.0	98.0	22.5	16.8	676.8	425.6

*   The application duration was 30 minutes

The study was done during 2000 on the Padova University Experimental Farm (45°12' N, 11°58' E) in north-eastern Italy. The experimental field (200 x 31.5 m) was cropped with maize and winter wheat, following standard agronomic practices. The herbicides used were metolachlor (M) and terbuthylazine (T) in maize; isoproturon (I) and pendimethalin (P) in winter wheat; the herbicides were applied 28/10/2000 (maize) and 27/10/2000 (winter wheat) as tank and ready-mix in the two crops, respectively, at the following rates: M 2200 g a.s. ha^{-1}

and T 1100 g a.s. ha⁻¹, I 900 g a.s. ha⁻¹ and P 950 g a.s. ha⁻¹. Herbicides were applied using a tractor-mounted Hardy LY-HY sprayer equipped with a 16 m boom and 4110-16 fan nozzles. Before spraying, 80 spray traps of 113 cm² with a filter paper at the bottom were placed on the soil surface to determine herbicide concentration when the solution reaches the soil. A map of the traps is shown in Figure 1: trap layout consisted of eight rows, four for each sprayer pass, along the longer field axis. Within 5 minutes of application, the traps were covered and stored at 4°C until analysis. After spraying (1-2 h), soil samples were taken to assess concentration of herbicide in soil: 20 soil samples were collected in maize, eight in winter wheat at a depth of 0-5 cm. Soil properties and weather conditions during the trials are given in Table 1.

Herbicide extraction and analysis

Spray trap samples were washed with methanol and soil samples with 100 mL of a 50/50 methanol/water mixture. The analysis of M, T and P was performed by gas chromatography while the analysis of I was performed by HPLC. The retention times where 14.1 min for M, 12.2 min for T and 15.5 min for P, and the sensitivity was 1 µg kg⁻¹ for T and P and 2 µg kg⁻¹ for M. The retention time for I was 10.5 min and the sensitivity was 8 µg kg⁻¹.

Geostatistical analysis

The GS+ Program (Gamma Design Software, 1992) was used for geostatistical analysis. The program calculates the semivariance γ(h) as follows:

$$\gamma(h) = 1 / [2N(h)] \cdot \sum_{i=1}^{N} [z(i) - z(i+h)]^2$$

where N(h) is the number of pairs z (i), z (i + h) of samples that are separated by a lag distance of h. A plot of γ versus h is called a semivariogram. Although, by definition, γ (h) = 0 when h = 0, it is often found in practice that as h approaches 0, γ (h) approaches a positive finite value, which is commonly called the nugget effect, C_0. As h increases, γ (h) often increases up to some value, say a, after which it remains approximately constant. The plateau value of γ (h) at this point, referred to as the sill C, is equal to the total variance of the data and the distance a is called the range and represents the separation distance beyond which the parameter values are unrelated, that is, spatially independent. When the semivariogram shows complete discontinuity at the origin, then γ (h) = C and there is a pure nugget effect.

RESULTS AND DISCUSSION

The range of the herbicide concentration (CV) in spray traps was between 9.5 and 31.3%; the high values of CV for M and T are in agreement with other reports of field experiments in farming scenarios.The CV for I and P was 9.5% and 17.7% respectively, which was much lower that those found for other pesticides in real farming conditions (Walker & Brown, 1983; Vischetti et al., 1998). This low variability is partially explainable by the accuracy used in planning the treatment and the more favourable weather conditions: the soil was well prepared in order to have an even seed bed and the herbicides were distributed with great attention, controlling the speed of the tractor, the pressure of the nozzles and the boom oscillations. The higher relative air humidity and the lower temperatures contributed towards reducing the vaporisation losses between the herbicide application and the closing and collecting of the traps. The wind speed during the application was very low in both experiments, particularly the first, so this variable does not seem to have influenced the application uniformity.

Table 2. Mean concentration for application rate and initial soil concentration for the four herbicides and relative statistical parameters

Application Rate	Terbuthylazine	Metolachlor	Pendimethalin	Isoproturon
Number of samples	80	80	80	80
Mean (g ha^{-1}) ± s.d.	481.0±150.6	2202.6±682.4	466.0±82.8	576.6±54.8
Min (g ha^{-1})	145.7	522.4	309.9	470.8
Max (g ha^{-1})	818.7	3765.4	628.3	679.3
C.V. (%)	31.3	30.9	17.7	9.5
Initial soil concentration				
Number of samples	20	20	8	8
Mean (g ha^{-1}) ± s.d.	285.4±105.1	654.8±193.5	189.9±114.8	648.7±378.5
Min (g ha^{-1})	132.8	624.5	62.3	304.4
Max (g ha^{-1})	511.5	1015.3	395.3	1499.6
C.V. (%)	36.8	29.5	60.5	58.3

The mean values of both herbicide concentration in the spray traps and initial soil concentration were lower than expected. The differences could be ascribed to the fact that at the end of the treatment the sprayer might still contain some pesticide in the distribution circuit. This was not checked in the experiment. The initial soil concentration of the four herbicides in the two experiments was lower than the application rate and this can mainly be ascribed to the extraction and handling of the soil samples and to the analytical method that allowed recoveries lower than 100% and led to an initial concentration value lower than that determined in the spray traps where the recoveries were always around 100%. According to Otto *et al.,* (1998), the volatilisation processes may be divided into two phases with very different loss rates. During the first phase, before reaching a partition equilibrium in the soil, volatilisation rates are very high, reaching in a similar environment, levels of about 10% of the amount in the soil per day for terbuthylazine. The delay in soil sampling could at least partially explain the discrepancy between the herbicide concentration in the traps and the soil. Geostatistical analysis was undertaken on the herbicide concentration in the spray traps where 80 samples per herbicide were collected, while the samples for initial soil concentration were not sufficient to perform this kind of analysis. Data from the geostatistical analysis showed a spatial correlation for maize herbicides (M and T) and provided the sill, nugget and range values, while the data for wheat herbicides (I and P) showed a pure nugget effect, namely a lack of structure of variability (Figure 2). Geostatistical parameters for M and T are reported in Table 3. The spherical model described the data variability well in both cases with p<0.01. The sill values were similar to the total variance of the experiment and that of M was noticeably higher. The nugget effect was about 40% of the total variance for both herbicides, thus indicating a variability in the samples coming from sites quite close to one another. The range was 37.6 m for M and 40.1 m for T and this indicates that the variability remains constant over these distances. The wheat herbicides showed semivariograms with a complete discontinuity at the origin, with a pure nugget effect that corresponds to a total lack of structure of variability. In this case variability is present from point to point and there is an absence of spatial correlation, at least at the sampling scale used. The sill is very low in both cases and indicates the accuracy in preparing the experiment.

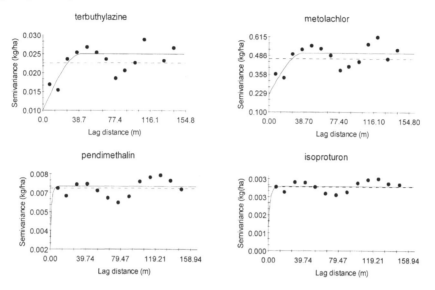

Figure 2.   Semivariograms for herbicide concentrations in boxes.

Table 3.   Geostatistical parameters for maize herbicides

	Isotropic				
	Model	Nugget	Sill	Range	r^2
Metolachlor	spherical	0.217	0.503	37.20	0.405
Terbuthylazine	spherical	0.010	0.025	40.90	0.418
	Anisotropic				
	Model	Nugget	Sill	Range	r^2
Metolachlor 0°	linear	0.378	1.134	696	0.431
Metolachlor 90°	linear	0.303	1.057	241	0.431
Terbuthylazine 0°	linear	0.017	0.054	536	0.436
Terbuthylazine 90°	linear	0.015	0.051	241	0.436

Analysis of the anisotropic semivariograms allows the effect of the treatment application on the data variability to be considered. The semivariograms at 0 degrees were performed with the vector only in the direction of the x-axis and indicate the variability between the rows where the spray traps were positioned. The semivariograms at 90 degrees were performed with a vector perpendicular to the x-axis and indicate the variability within the row. The semivariograms for maize herbicides are reported in Figure 3. The increase of variability in the semivariograms indicated that the mode of treatment strongly influences the variability in herbicide concentration. The 0 degrees variograms presented only three points because the number of traps was insufficient for a larger number of points, and the steep slope indicates a large increase in variability between rows. Under these conditions it is quite impossible to define a range. The 90 degrees variograms also showed an increasing of variability but lower than that at 0 degrees. In all cases the linear model describes the trend well, indicating that under the experimental conditions, the sampling strategy was not sufficient to estimate a range; in particular along the axis perpendicular to the main field one, the number of traps was insufficient to estimate spatial variability.

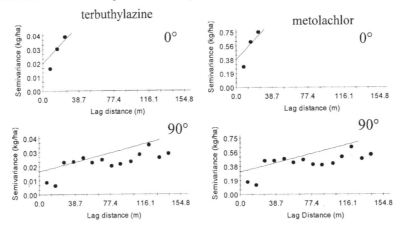

Figure 3.   Anisotropic semivariograms (0° and 90°) for metolachlor and terbuthylazine

REFERENCES

Davis B N K; Williams C T (1993). Principles of droplet drift and safe distances. In: *The environmental effects of pesticide drift*, ed Cooke A S, pp. 9-18. English Nature, Northminster House, Peterborough PE1 1UA, UK.

Gamma Design Software (1992). GS+ Geostatistics for the environmental sciences. P O Box 201, Michigan, 49080, USA.

Otto S; Vighi M; Zanin G; Finizio A; Sandroni D (1998). Losses of terbuthylazine and alachlor from agricultural fields part I: volatilization processes. *Fresenius Envir Bull*, 7:272-277.

Rao P S C; Wagenet R J (1985). Spatial variability of pesticides in field soil: methods for data analysis and consequences. *Weed Sci* 33 (Suppl 2): 18-24.

Vieira S R; Nielsen D R; Biggar J M (1981). Spatial variability of field-measured infiltration rate. *Soil Sci Soc Am J* 45: 1040-1048.

Vischetti C; Businelli M; Marini M; Merlini L (1995). Comparison of PRZM-2 computer model predictions with field data for napropamide and pendimethalin. *Eur J Agron* 4: 355-361.

Vischetti C; Businelli M; Marini M; Capri E; Trevisan M; Del Re A A M; Donnarumma L; Conte E; Imbroglini G (1997). Characterization of spatial variability structure in three separate field trials on pesticide dissipation. *Pestic Sci* **50**: 175-182.

Vischetti C; Perniola M; Scarponi L; Tarantino E (1998). Field and lysimeter study on the leaching of bromide ion and the herbicides imazethapyr and bentazone in a clay loam soil in southern Italy. *Fresenius Envir Bull* 7 (7a-8a, Special Issue): 641-648.

Walker A; Brown P A (1983). Spatial variability in herbicide degradation rates and residues in soil. *Crop Prot* **2**: 17-25.

Wauchope R D; Chandler J M; Savage K E (1977). Soil sample variation and herbicide incorporation uniformity. *Weed Sci* 25: 193-196.

Webster R; Burgess T M (1980). Optimal interpolation and isarithmic mapping of soil properties. I. The semivariogram and punctual kriging. *J Soil Sci* 37: 315-331.

Predicting atrazine transport into subsurface tile-drained soil using the HYDRUS-2D model : lysimeter study

G Abdel-Nasser

Faculty of Agriculture – Saba Bacha, Bulkily P.O. 21531, Alexandria, Egypt
E-mail: nasser@globalnet.com.eg

ABSTRACT

This study was made to compare the measured with the predicted transport of atrazine into subsurface tile-drained soil through lysimeters using the HYDRUS-2D model. The HYDRUS-2D model was able to predict atrazine movement through the soil profile. The results obtained demonstrate the ability of computer simulation models to predict the potential for groundwater pollution. Thus, we can modify our agricultural management practices to reduce contamination.

INTRODUCTION

Tile drains are commonly used in many agricultural fields to remove excess water from the vadose zone, to maintain optimum soil water contents for crop production, and to maintain a low level of soil salinity or sodicity. Likewise, tile drains have been used to study field-scale transport of solutes (Hallberg *et al.*, 1986). Nitrate or pesticide leaching losses from soils have been evaluated using many methods such as tile drains (Bergstrom, 1987), pan lysimeters (Fermanich *et al.*, 1991), monolith lysimeters (Owens, 1987) and soil columns (Allepalli & Govindaraju, 1994).

Increasing concern over pesticides in surface and ground water has required the evaluation of their mobility as a basis of risk analysis. Lysimeters offer good possibilities to conduct such tests, because they constitute closed systems, and they permit control of water movement through the soil (Bergstrom, 1990; Hance & Fuhr, 1992). Drainage lysimeters, both with and without tension, have been used to study agrochemical leaching and water movement (Tyler & Thomas, 1977; Bergstrom, 1990; Bergstrom & Johansson, 1991).

The objectives of the present study were: 1) measuring atrazine transport in tile-drained soil lysimeters, 2) evaluating the HYDRUS-2D model for predicting atrazine transport in the lysimeter systems; and 3) comparing observed versus simulated data for atrazine transport.

MATERIALS AND METHODS

Soils

Three types of soils were used in the present study, namely, clay loam (CL), sandy clay loam (SCL), and sandy loam (SL). Some properties of the soils are given in Table 1.

Table 1. Soil properties

Soils	Particle size distribution, %			ρ_b	O.M.
	sand	silt	clay	Mg m^{-3}	%
Clay loam	41	20	39	1.27	1.8
Sandy clay loam	46	27	27	1.35	0.5
Sandy loam	55	33	12	1.48	1.2

Herbicide

Atrazine (2-chloro-4-(ethylamino)-6-(isopropylamino)-s-triazine) was selected for the present study. It has a water solubility of 33 mg L^{-1} and half-life of 64 days (Singh et al., 1990).

Lysimeters

PVC columns 70 cm long and 15 cm in diameter with closed bottoms were used. The base of the lysimeters was tightly sealed with silicone adhesive. The bottom 5 cm layer in the columns comprised coarse gravel (drainage layer). A perforated plastic tube of 2.5 cm diameter was fitted into the drainage layer to collect the drainage water. The lysimeters were hand-packed with air-dried soil to the desired bulk density by gently tapping. The subsurface–tile drain was fitted at 60 cm below the soil surface.

Water and atrazine application

Water was added to the soil until steady-state water flow conditions were established. Each lysimeter unit was connected to a suction pump and subjected to –340 cm water tension (-33 kPa; field capacity condition). Atrazine was applied at a rate of 50 µg cm^{-3} using CaCl$_2$ (0.001 M) as a background solution at 2.0 cm d^{-1} with a pulse period of 1 day. Water flow then continued for 100 days at a constant rate of 2.0 cm d^{-1}. The suction heads (h) in the lysimeter soils were monitored periodically during the application period using small mercury tensiometers located at 5, 10, 15, 20, 40 and 60 cm below the soil surface. Lysimeters were monitored daily for drainage. Collected drainage water was weighed and expressed as volume per surface area of the lysimeter.

Extraction and analysis of atrazine

At the end of the experiment, soil samples were collected from the lysimeters at above-mentioned soil depths for atrazine analysis. Samples were extracted three times (3 x 20 ml) using analytical grade hexane. The extract was filtered and atrazine was analyzed by gas chromatography. Samples of drainage water were also analyzed for atrazine at different periods. Atrazine concentration was expressed as µg cm^{-3}.

Soil hydraulic parameters

The hydraulic properties of soils were described by Mualem-van Genuchten parameters (Mualem,1976; van Genuchten, 1980) and are given in Table 2.

Table 2.   Parameters of hydraulic functions used in the numerical simulation

Soils	θ_r $cm^3 cm^{-3}$	θ_s $cm^3 cm^{-3}$	α cm^{-1}	n	K_s	ι
Clay loam	0.0797	0.4429	0.01941	0.2451	11.8	0.5
Sandy clay loam	0.0560	0.4777	0.02864	1.1100	21.2	0.5
Sandy loam	0.0641	0.4010	0.01320	1.4445	36.2	0.5

θ_r = soil water content, θ_s = saturation soil water content, α and n = shape parameters
K_s = saturated hydraulic conductivity (LT^{-1}), ι = pore connectivity parameter (Mualem, 1976)

Solute transport parameters

For atrazine, the transport parameters were taken from the literature (Nicholls, 1994; Allepalli *et al.*, 1994) as shown in Table 3, assuming a linear chemical non-equilibrium reaction and a linear Freundlich adsorption isotherm.

Table 3.   Atrazine transport parameters used in the simulation

Parameters	Symbol	Units	Values
Longitudinal pore scale dispersivity	D_L	cm	0.5
Transverse pore scale dispersivity	D_T	cm	0.1
Ionic or molecular diffusion coefficient in free water	D_w	$cm^2 d^{-1}$	1.2
Adsorption isotherm coefficient	β	-	1
First order rate constant for degradation in dissolved phase	μ_w	d^{-1}	0.02
Henry's constant		d^{-1}	1.3E-07
Pulse time	t_p	d	1
Applied concentration	$C_\circ$	μg	50
Steady state water flux	q	$cm\ d^{-1}$	2

Modelling

The HYDRUS-2D numerical model (Simunek *et al.*, 1999) was used to simulate water flow and atrazine transport in the different soils and the predicted data were compared with those observed.

RESULTS AND DISCUSSION

Figure 1 shows the observed values of atrazine flux at the drain boundary of the three soils. The data show that the timing of the peak flux differed according to soil texture. The sandy clay loam soil reached a maximum flux at 30 days after application, followed by the sandy loam soil at 45 days, then the clay loam soil at 60 days. The maximum value of atrazine flux (0.56 μg cm^3 d^{-1}) was attained with the sandy clay loam soil, followed by the sandy loam soil (0.31 μg cm^3 d^{-1}), then the clay loam soil (0.27 μg cm^3 d^{-1}).

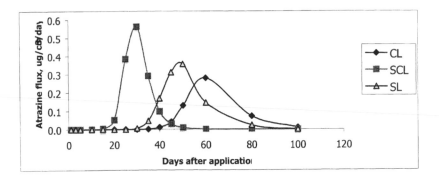

Figure 1.   Observed atrazine flux at the drain boundary in the three soils.

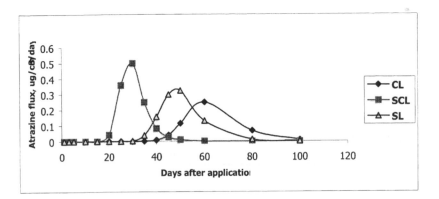

Figure 2. HYDRUS-2D simulations of atrazine flux at the drain boundary in the three soils.

The observed values were, generally, greater than those predicted (Figure 2), but the differences were small. Macropore flow may be an important reason for the differences (Hoffmann & Johansson, 1999). These differences may be attributed to the pore size distribution. At pore-scale, the variations of water and solute flux may be due to the different velocities of water and solute as a result of pore groups in soil. This is an important factor in structured soils with different pore groups, in which bypassing or preferential flow of water and solute transport can occur (Dyson & White, 1987).

Thus, the HYDRUS-2D model successfully predicted atrazine leaching in these experiments (r-values between observed and predicted data ranged between 0.96 and 0.99). The differences among the three soil textures tested may be attributed to their structures, partition coefficients (k_d), and organic matter contents (OM). The arrival times for atrazine transport to tile drains were about 15, 30 and 30 days after application for sandy clay, sandy clay loam and clay loam soils, respectively, under the conditions of these experiments. The differences in local advection velocity of atrazine transport may be attributed to the spatial variability of macropore soil hydraulic properties (Bowman & Rice, 1986; Abdel-Nasser, 2000).

The present experiment technique is useful for assessing relative behaviour of atrazine in different soils, but may not be suitable for describing chemical transport in the field scale soil profile, since it does not account for many chemical processes occurring under natural field conditions.

REFERENCES

Abdel-Nasser G (2000). Numerical simulation of water flow and solute transport into subsurface tile drains. Progress report. Dept. of Crop & Soil Sciences, Washington State University, Pullman , WA 99164, USA, September 2000.

Allepalli P K; Govindaraju R S (1994). Modeling fate and transport of atrazine in the saturated-unsaturated zone of soil. *Water Research* **28:** 1199-1205.

Bergstrom L (1987). Nitrate leaching and drainage from annual and perennial crops in tile-drained plots and lysimeters. *Journal of Environmental Quality* **16:** 11-18.

Bergstrom L (1990). Use of lysimeters to estimate leaching of pesticides in agricultural soils. *Environmental Pollution* **67:** 325 – 347.

Bergstrom L; Johansson R (1991). Leaching of nitrate from monolith lysimeters of different types of agricultural soils. *Journal of Environmental Quality* **20:** 801– 807.

Bowman R S: Rice R C (1986). Transport of conservative tracer in the field under intermittent flood irrigation. *Water Resources Research* **22:** 1531-1536.

Dyson J S; White R E (1987). A comparison of the convection-dispersion equation and transport function model for predicting chloride leaching through an undisturbed structured clay soil. *Journal of Soil Science* **38:** 157-172 .

Fermanich K J; Daniel T C; Lowery B (1991). Microlysimeter soil columns for evaluating pesticide movement through the root zone. *Journal of Environmental Quality* **20:**189 - 195.

Hallberg G R; Baker J L; Randall G W (1986). Utility of tile-line effluent studies to evaluate the impact of agricultural practices on groundwater, paper presented at Agricultural

Impacts on Ground Water Conference, National Water Well Association, Dublin, Ohio, USA.

Hance R J; Fuhr F (1992). Methods to study fate and behavior of pesticides in the soil. In: Fuhr F; Hance R J (eds). Lysimeter Studies of the Fate of Pesticides in the Soil. *British Crop Protection Council Monograph 53*, pp. 9-21.

Hoffmann M; Johansson H (1999). A method for assessing generalized nitrogen leaching estimate for agricultural land. *Environmental Modeling and Assessment* **4**: 5-44.

Mualem Y (1976). A new model for predicting the hydraulic conductivity of unsaturated porous media. *Water Resources Research* **12**: 513 – 522.

Nicholls P H (1994). "Physicochemical Evaluation: The Environment" An expert system for pesticide preregistration assessment. *Proceedings Brighton Crop Protection Conference - Pests and Diseases* **3**: 1337-1342.

Owens L B (1987). Nitrate leaching losses from monolith lysimeters as influenced by nitrapyrin. *Journal of Environmental Quality* **16**: 34 – 38.

Simunék J; Sejna M; van Genuchten M Th (1999). HYDRUS-2D/MESHGEN-2D, Simulating Water Flow and Solute Transport in Two-Dimensional Variably Saturated Media. U.S. Salinity Laboratory, USDA/ARS, Riverside, California – distributed by International Ground Water Modeling Center, Colorado School of Mines, Golden, CO 80401, USA.

Singh G; Spencer W F; Cliath M M; van Genuchten M Th. (1990). Sorption behavior of s-triazine and Thiocarbamate herbicides on soils. *Journal of Environmental Quality.* **19**: 520 - 525.

Tyler D D; Thomas G W (1977). Lysimeter measurement of nitrate and chloride losses from soil under conventional and no-tillage corn. *Journal of Environmental Quality* **6**: 63-66.

van Genuchten M Th (1980). A closed–form equation for predicting the hydraulic conductivity of unsaturated soils. *Soil Science Society of America Journal* **44**: 892–898.

Pesticide trends in raw and treated drinking water

D C Hillier, S L White
Thames Water Utilities Ltd, Clearwater Court, Vastern Road, Reading RG1 8DB, UK
Email: dinah.hillier@thameswater.co.uk

ABSTRACT

Since 1990 when the water industry in England and Wales was privatised, water companies have invested around £1 billion to remove pesticides from sources of drinking water. New treatment processes have produced a substantial reduction in the number of drinking water samples exceeding the national and European pesticide standard of 0.1µg/litre. Local voluntary action by users, stewardship activity by the agrochemical industry and intervention by regulators have also played a part. Understanding the success of these measures requires the analysis of raw water sources, often over long periods. This paper draws together pesticide monitoring data collected by Thames Water over the past 10 years and examines trends over time. In some cases measures to protect drinking water sources have produced clear improvements. In other cases regulatory action is needed to deal with contamination that other approaches have failed to address.

INTRODUCTION

The Water Supply (Water Quality) Regulations 1989 (Anon. 1989) formalised the arrangements for monitoring and reporting the quality of drinking water in England and Wales. The Regulations incorporated the standards required by the European Drinking Water Directive 80/778/EEC and included the standards for individual and total pesticides of 0.1µg/litre and 0.5µg/litre respectively. These two standards were retained in a recent revision of the European Directive (Council Directive 98/83/EC).

In the Thames Water area approximately 75% of the drinking water that is supplied to customers is derived from the river Thames and its tributaries. The remaining 25% comes from groundwater sources. Intensive agriculture, urban development and highways mean that pesticides are widely used in water catchment areas. Contamination of rivers and groundwater by agricultural and non-agricultural pesticides is commonplace. As a result of this, Thames Water has long had a problem with failures of the pesticide standards in treated water (Table 1).

Table 1. Contraventions of drinking water quality standards in the Thames Water supply area during the period 1992 to 2000

Year	Total number of contraventions - all parameters	Percentage of contraventions due to failure of the pesticide standards (%)
1992	27,532	93.8
1994	9,141	84.9
1996	1,939	36.1
1998	602	2
2000	405	0

Much of the improvement in pesticide compliance is due to the installation of new treatment technologies, such as ozone and granular activated carbon, to break down and adsorb the pesticides that are not removed by conventional treatment processes. Installing these new processes was expensive, costing £10 million or more for a single treatment works. Today the majority of these schemes have been completed, however, the operational and environmental cost of removing pesticides continues: production of ozone and the periodic regeneration of granular activated carbon consume of a lot of energy and increase the amount of carbon dioxide produced by the water industry, when other industries are reducing emissions.

The other approach to improving compliance with the drinking water pesticide standard has been to work with a variety of different organisations to minimise pesticide contamination of raw water sources. This approach is consistent with the 'polluter pays principle' and is essential where water treatment works do not have equipment to remove pesticides. Even where such facilities exist they cannot guarantee compliance. The physical and chemical properties of some pesticides may make them less amenable to treatment and spikes of pesticides can overwhelm plant designed to deal with lower levels. These facts have provided common ground for the water and agrochemical industries, often in conjunction with the users of pesticides, to support each other on several initiatives to minimise the impact of pesticides on water quality (White & Pinkstone, 1993, Davies *et al.*, 1993, Court *et al.*, 1995, White *et al.*, 1997).

This paper considers four pesticides that are among the most problematic for Thames Water in respect of complying with the drinking water standard. These pesticides are all weed-killers (herbicides) and have uses within the agricultural and/or the amenity and industrial sectors.

ATRAZINE AND SIMAZINE

In the early 1990s the majority of pesticide failures of the drinking water standard in the Thames Water region were attributable to atrazine and simazine. As traditional methods of water treatment are unable to remove pesticides, the levels measured in drinking water were indicative of those in the raw water. In Figure 1 the atrazine and simazine concentrations in the final water of a treatment works that abstracts from the river Thames are shown. Treatment that could remove both pesticides was installed in 1995. However concentrations of pesticides were already decreasing. This can be explained by the banning of atrazine and simazine for weed control on roads, railway lines and similar industrial/amenity uses. In May 1992 it was announced that from September 1993 the approval for the non-agricultural usage of atrazine and simazine would be revoked 'to reduce residues in drinking water' (MAFF/HSE, 1992).

Following the installation of pesticide removal technology it became more important to monitor the raw water sources themselves in order to identify and understand trends in pesticide concentrations. Monitoring of the Thames has shown that although concentrations of atrazine and simazine generally declined following the non-agricultural ban, both herbicides are still regularly detected at concentrations above 0.1µg/litre (Figure 2). This suggests that ongoing uses in agriculture, forestry and perhaps, home garden sectors, continue to contaminate water sources. Increased use of atrazine on maize, and applications of simazine in formulated products applied to winter wheat and barley, may explain the seasonal peaks seen in the Thames. Atrazine and simazine have also been found in groundwaters. At one groundwater source, remote from (historical) non-agricultural sources, but located close to farmland where maize has been grown, atrazine levels in the raw water initially decreased, only to increase again as crops were rotated (Figure 3). Groundwaters can take years to recover from contamination by pesticides, as is shown in Figure 4. This groundwater is situated in a rural area, but a railway line adjacent to the borehole was suspected as the source of atrazine contamination. In order to protect this borehole from contamination an agreement was reached with British Rail (and has continued with Railtrack) whereby atrazine, and latterly diuron, were not to be used on the stretch of railway line close to this groundwater source. As a consequence of this and the non-agricultural ban, levels of atrazine at this site have slowly declined, falling below the drinking water standard in 1999.

DIURON

In anticipation of and following the non-agricultural ban of atrazine and simazine, a number of amenity and industrial users of pesticides switched to diuron. As diuron is poorly adsorbed onto hard surfaces this produced an immediate impact on concentrations of diuron in surface water sources. Fig 5 shows the concentration of diuron measured in the Thames at a raw water abstraction point to the west of London. Co-operation between water companies, the agrochemical companies and users of non-agricultural pesticides has, in general, ensured that concentrations of diuron did not reach the levels of atrazine and simazine seen in the early 90's. Concentrations of diuron in the Thames are regularly greater than $0.1\mu g$/litre between May and September. Further work is needed to reduce amounts reaching water. The annual mass of diuron (concentration multiplied by river flow) at the West London abstraction points has remained at around 120kg. This is equivalent to 2-5% of the total amount used in the upstream catchment. With a fixed input the diuron concentration is largely dictated by river flow. Diuron also poses a threat to groundwater but early working with Railtrack to protect vulnerable sources close to railway line appears to have, in general prevented a rising trend in diuron in groundwaters as concentrations of atrazine have fallen (see Figure 4). That said diuron is now regularly detected, at below $0.1\mu g$/litre, in a few groundwaters in urban areas. This suggests that action to reduce use on roads and pavements is needed in these catchments. The introduction of residual acting pesticides that are less mobile than diuron would be one way forward.

ISOPROTURON

Isoproturon (IPU) is the most problematic agricultural pesticide in the Thames Water area with concentrations at abstraction points routinely exceeding $0.1\mu g$/litre during December to April. Despite considerable stewardship activity by the agrochemical industry and further restrictions on application rates and timing the amounts of IPU reaching the river Thames has not decreased (Table 2).

Table 2. Summary of data relating to the monitoring of isoproturon in the river Thames

Crop Year*	Total river flow $(x10^{12}$litres)	Total mass of IPU (kg)	Number of days exceeding the $0.1\mu g$/litre standard
1996/97	0.4	39	46
1997/98	1.2	305	113
1998/99	1.9	423	140
1999/00	1.7	885	161
2000/01	3.4	612	149

* For these calculations the term crop year refers to the period 1 October to 11 May.

The total mass of IPU that reaches the Thames does vary from year to year, but appears to be very dependent on the weather. For example, in the 1996/97 cropping year when relatively little IPU reached the Thames, the weather was particularly dry, which is reflected in the low value for the total river flow. However, in wetter years, particularly when the rainfall occurs in late autumn after IPU has been applied, much larger amounts of IPU are detected in the Thames and there are many more days when the drinking water standard is exceeded.

Whilst the stewardship activity has lead to a greater understanding of how pesticides might reach water *e.g.* from filling and washing sprayers (Aventis, 2000), voluntary actions, changes to recommended rates and new rules on when IPU can be applied have not protected water sources. It would appear that the only way to produce a substantial reduction in the amounts of IPU reaching water sources, in both wet and dry years, would be a significant, >90%, decrease in IPU usage.

CONCLUSIONS

The contamination of drinking water sources by agricultural and non-agricultural pesticides continues to be a problem in some areas. For certain pesticides the establishment of protection zones close to the water source has proved sufficient to reduce pesticide contamination. However, pesticides which are soluble, mobile, applied in large quantities within the catchment and used by many within a short time-frame will require stronger measures if concentrations in drinking water sources are to be reduced.

ACKNOWLEDGEMENTS

The authors would like to thank Thames Water's Director of Environment and Technology, Mr J Sexton for his permission to publish this paper.

REFERENCES

Anon (1989) The Water Supply (Water Quality) Regs 1989. Statutory Instrument No 1147.

Aventis (2000) Keeping pesticides out of surface water - Practical stewardship solutions for spray operators to reduce water contamination, CD and leaflet.

Council Directive 98/83/EC of 3 November 1998 on the quality of water intended for human consumption. *Official Journal of the European Communities.*

Court A C; Breach R A; Porter M J (1995) Pesticides in drinking water - catchment protection or water treatment? *BCPC Monograph No 62*, 381-389, BCPC, Farnham.

Davies A B; Noble J; Joice R; Banks J A; Jones R L (1993) A strategy for protecting UK water quality through a concerted diuron stewardship programme. *Proceedings of the Brighton Crop Protection Conference - Weeds*, **1**, 375-380, BCPC, Farnham.

MAFF/HSE (1992) *The Pesticides Register No 8*, 7-11, HMSO.

White S L; Hillier D C; Evans J C; Hewson R T; Higginbotham S (1997) A stewardship programme for isoproturon and water quality - a tale of two industries. *Proceedings of the Brighton Crop Protection Conference - Weeds*, **3**, 1107-1116, BCPC, Farnham.

White S L; Pinkstone D C (1993) Amenity and industrial uses of herbicides: The impact on drinking water quality. *Proceedings of the Brighton Crop Protection Conference - Weeds*, **1**, 363-368, BCPC, Farnham.

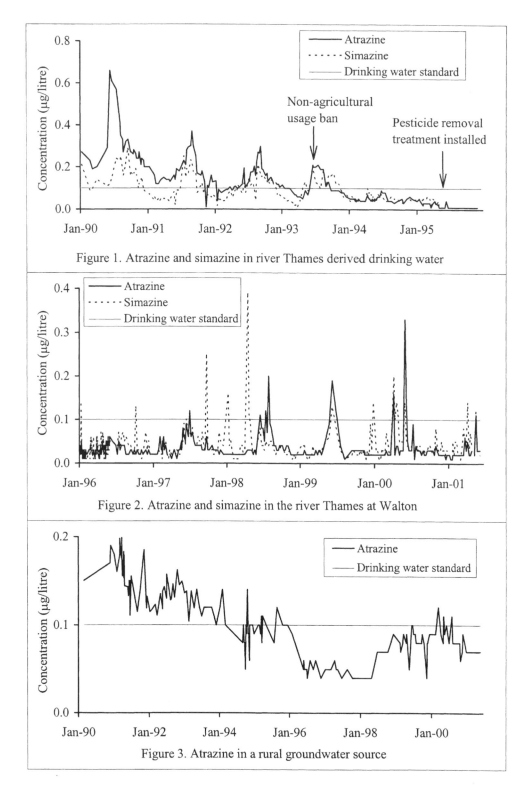

Figure 1. Atrazine and simazine in river Thames derived drinking water

Figure 2. Atrazine and simazine in the river Thames at Walton

Figure 3. Atrazine in a rural groundwater source

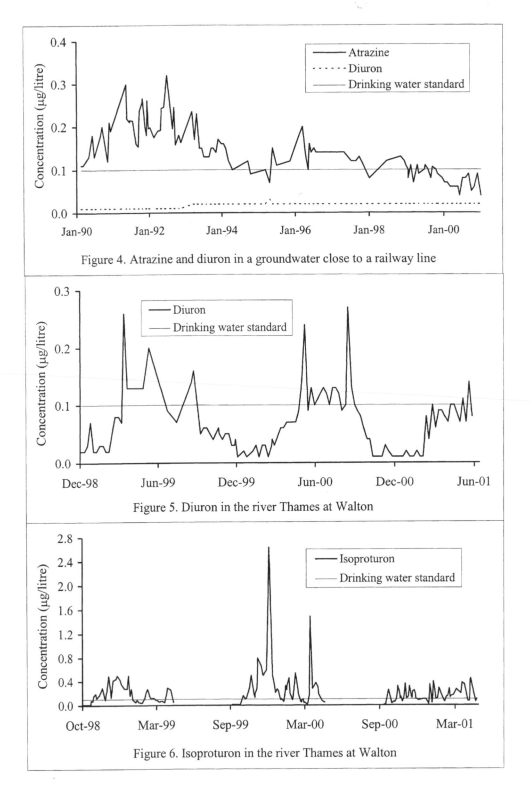

Figure 4. Atrazine and diuron in a groundwater close to a railway line

Figure 5. Diuron in the river Thames at Walton

Figure 6. Isoproturon in the river Thames at Walton

Watershed monitoring to address contamination source issues and remediation of these contaminants

P L Barnes
Agricultural Engineering, Kansas State University, Manhattan, Kansas 66506 USA
Email: lbarnes@ksu.edu

D L Regehr
Agronomy, Kansas State University, Manhattan, Kansas 66506 USA

ABSTRACT

The Big Blue River Basin is located in southeastern Nebraska and northeastern Kansas and consists of surface water in the Big Blue River, Little Blue River, Black Vermillion River, and various tributaries draining 24,968 square kilometers. Approximately 75% of the land area in the basin is cultivated cropland. The Big Blue River flows into Tuttle Creek Reservoir near Manhattan, Kansas. Releases from the lake are used to maintain streamflow in the Kansas River during low flow periods, contributing 27 percent of the mean flow rate of the Kansas River at its confluence with the Missouri River. Tuttle Creek Reservoir and the Kansas River are used as sources of public drinking water and meet many of the municipal drinking water supply needs of the urban population in Kansas from Junction City to Kansas City.

Elevated concentrations of pesticides in the Big Blue River Basin are of growing concern in Kansas and Nebraska as concentrations may be exceeding public drinking water standards and water quality criteria for the protection of aquatic life. Pesticides cause significant problems for municipal water treatment plants in Kansas, as they are not appreciably removed during conventional water treatment processes unless activated carbon filtering is used. Pesticides have been detected during all months of the year with concentrations ranging up to 200 µg/L. If high concentration in water is associated with high flow conditions then large mass losses of pesticides can flow into the water supplies in this basin. This paper will investigate the use of a monitoring program to assess the non-point source of this atrazine contamination. Several practices have shown ability to remediate or reduce these impairments.

INTRODUCTION

Atrazine herbicide (2-chloro-4-ethylamino-6-isopropylamino-s-triazine) has been used widely in Kansas and Nebraska since the 1960s for selective control of broadleaf and grass weeds in corn (*Zea mays* L.) and grain sorghum (*Sorghum vulgare* (L.) Moench). Another factor along with atrazine effectiveness is the low cost on a per-hectare basis. It provides effective weed control when applied to fields under a wide range of practices that includes conventional tillage with limited residue cover as well as fields with residue levels near complete cover with no tillage. Added benefits include application flexibility, which might include the herbicide applied at an early preplant, preplant incorporated, crop preemergence, or postemergence. The impact of atrazine use in agriculture on water quality is a growing public concern.

During 1992, the U. S. Environmental Protection Agency (EPA) established a new drinking water standard for atrazine, which prior to that date had been proposed to be 150 µg/L. This new standard called the maximum contaminant level (MCL) was set at 3 µg/L. The MCL is calculated based on an annual average of available monitoring data. Limited monitoring data in Kansas indicated that a majority of the state surface water in streams and lakes exceeded the new MCL. An audit of the monitoring data during 1998, showed that only six (6) Kansas lakes continued to show impairment from atrazine.

The Big Blue River Basin is located in southeastern Nebraska and northeastern Kansas and consists of surface water in the Big Blue River, Little Blue River, Black Vermillion River, and various tributaries draining 25,900 square kilometers. Approximately 75% of the land area in the basin is cultivated cropland. The Big Blue River flows into Tuttle Creek Reservoir near Manhattan, Kansas. Releases from the lake are used to maintain streamflow in the Kansas River during low flow periods, contributing 27 percent of the mean flow rate of the Kansas River at its confluence with the Missouri River (Dugan et al., 1991). The largest population centers in Kansas are supplied by surface water from the Kansas River. Clean Water Act monitoring for this water supply has consistently exceeded the drinking water standard for atrazine. This monitoring requires at least an annual quarterly sample to be taken for these drinking water supplies. These data would indicate that in most cases quarterly monitoring does not accurately represent conditions in the water supply.

This paper will investigate the use of a monitoring program to assess the non-point sources of this atrazine contamination. Several practices will be examined that have shown ability to remediate or reduce these impairments.

MONITORING METHODS

The objectives of this study will provide information that can be used to, (1) determine seasonal and annual concentrations of atrazine, (2) determine seasonal and annual loading of atrazine, and (3) rank locations in the watersheds based on their contribution to the TMDL. The project objectives will be met by collecting and analyzing water samples from 10 stream sites in the Big Blue River Basin. Table 1 describes these sampling locations.

Elevated concentrations of atrazine in the Big Blue River Basin are of growing concern in Kansas and Nebraska as concentrations have been shown to exceed the public drinking water standards and water quality criteria for the protection of aquatic life. Atrazine causes significant problems for municipal water treatment plants in Kansas as it is not appreciably removed during conventional water treatment processes unless activated carbon filtering is used (Miltner et al., 1989). Atrazine has been detected during all months of the year in the Big Blue Basin with concentrations ranging from 0.1 to 166 µg/L in Nebraska from 1987 to 1992 (Frankforter, 1994). More recently, in the Recharge Lake watershed near York, Nebraska, atrazine concentrations as high as 854 µg/L were detected following a May 1995 runoff event (Upper Big Blue NRD, 1995).

Table 1. Blue River Basin sampling locations and characteristics.

Station Number	Location	Drainage Area (km²)	Percent of Basin
1	Crete, Nebraska (Big Blue River)	7034	28
2	Beatrice, Nebraska (Big Blue River)	9919	39
3	Barneston, Nebraska (Big Blue River)	11318	45
4	Marysville, Kansas (Big Blue River)	12372	49
5	Deweese, Nebraska (Little Blue River)	2535	10
6	Fairbury, Nebraska (Little Blue River)	6086	24
7	Hollenberg, Kansas (Little Blue River)	7127	28
8	Barnes, Kansas (Little Blue River)	8609	34
9	Frankfort, Kansas (Black Vermillion River)	1061	4
10	Manhattan, Kansas (Tuttle Creek Reservoir)	24968	100

Sample collection included a protocol of grab sampling when stream flows were at or below normal base flow. Grab samples were collected at each site on a stratified fixed-frequency basis. Grab samples were collected instead of width-depth integrated samples because grab samples greatly reduce sample time and effort and were considered equivalent to depth-width samples in representing stream water quality conditions if the stream can be assumed to be well mixed. Grab samples were collected on a weekly basis from April through September during the runoff season when atrazine concentration variability is the highest, and on a monthly basis from October through March when concentration variability is low.

Automated runoff samplers collected additional samples when stream flows were above base flow conditions. These samplers were set to take discrete samples at uniform times during the runoff hydrograph. To determine the mean atrazine concentration for a particular runoff event, selected discrete samples of runoff that were collected by the automated sampler were composited into a single discharge-weighted sample. Discrete samples were selected to adequately define variations in flow rate and atrazine concentration. The method of computing the discharge-weighted value of each discrete sample to be included in the composite sample was based on the mid-interval method (Porterfield, 1977). Each sampling site was located at an existing United States Geological Survey (USGS) gage station or will have continuous flow meters equipped with the samplers.

MANAGEMENT PRACTICES METHODS

The objective of this part of the study will provide information that can be used to evaluate management practices success in reducing seasonal and annual concentrations and loading of atrazine.

The movement of atrazine from crop fields is determined by the chemical properties of the herbicide and mechanisms that led to its transport. Water quality concerns involve primarily atrazine transport by runoff to surface water and leaching to ground water. The most important chemical characteristics that influence atrazine loss from fields are adsorption and persistence. Solubility of atrazine also plays a role in atrazine losses.

Weakly adsorbed pesticides tend to leave the field in the water and not with soil particles lost in soil erosion. Atrazine is soluble in water and weakly adsorbed in soils, which leads to its loss in water leaving the field and not with eroding soil particles. It has been felt for a number of years that if soil erosion could be reduced that herbicide loss would also be reduced but that is not the case for atrazine (Baker and Laflen, 1979; Hall et al., 1972; Olsen et al., 1998). Because atrazine moves with runoff water leaving the field, the closer the rainfall occurs following atrazine application, the greater the atrazine loss. May through July are the months that have the greatest potential for runoff losses in the Big Blue Basin.

The term persistence refers to how long it takes for a herbicide to break down from chemical decomposition or microbial degradation. The longer a herbicide persists, the longer a herbicide can control weeds. However, the longer a herbicide is present in the environment, the greater the chance it will run off with surface water or leach into the ground water. Atrazine has a half-life of approximately 60 days (Olsen et al., 1998), which means that half the atrazine applied in April or May will be available to the peak runoff periods in the Blue River Basin. These factors are being considered as the primary causes for atrazine concentration in Nebraska and Kansas drinking water. This paper will examine practices that avoid these factors. Application timing, herbicide incorporation, and the use of vegetative buffers are practices that farmers in the Big Blue Basin are using to reduce surface water impairments.

MONITORING RESULTS

During 1998, the sampling stations (Table 1) had an average of 42 samples taken per station. The daily atrazine concentration was calculated by interpolating between discrete sampled concentrations. If the daily concentrations are averaged for the year the annual average concentration for atrazine at Station 1 is 2.84 µg/L, which is slightly below the drinking water MCL (3.0 µg/L).

These concentration peaks occur during the same time frame that represented the peak stream flows. If the daily flowrate is multiplied by the average daily concentration, then multiplied by a factor (0.005383), the result gives the daily atrazine load in kilograms.

The data from all the monitoring stations in the Big Blue River Basin are presented in Table 2. The data for the Big Blue River is near or above the drinking water MCL. These data would also suggest that a majority of the atrazine loading is coming out of the Big Blue River part of the basin. The Big Blue River at Marysville, Kansas represents 49 percent of the drainage area but produces 80 percent of the atrazine loading. If we examine the load per area for the Big Blue River, Station 4 at Marysville, Kansas exceeds the upper stations along the Big Blue River by as much as 1.5 times. Another surprise can be seen if the outflow versus inflow atrazine loading for Station 10, Tuttle Creek Reservoir is considered. The total inflow atrazine load is 11,509 kg while the outflow is reduced to 4,506 kg. This would indicate that Tuttle Creek Reservoir reduces the atrazine loading into the Kansas River by 61 percent.

Table 2. Blue River Basin sampling locations and atrazine annual mass loss (1998).

Station No.	Location	Atrazine Mass Loss (kg)	MCL	Percent of Total
1	Crete, Nebraska (Big Blue)	3819	2.84	33
2	Beatrice, Nebraska (Big Blue)	5333	3.78	46
3	Barneston, Nebraska (Big Blue)	7491	4.20	65
4	Marysville, Nebraska (Big Blue)	9241	4.55	80
5	Deweese, Nebraska (Little Blue)	256	1.46	2
6	Fairbury, Nebraska (Little Blue)	473	1.96	4
7	Hollenberg, Kansas (Little Blue)	791	1.88	7
8	Barnes, Kansas (Little Blue)	1665	2.31	14
9	Frankfort, Kansas (Black Vermillion)	603	2.24	5
10	Manhattan, Kansas (Tuttle Creek Reservoir)	4506	1.27	39

MANAGEMENT RESULTS

If atrazine losses are examined for each of the sampling stations, it was found that over 90 percent of loading occurs during the months of May and June. A number of studies have been performed to examine the application timing of atrazine to avoid the loss window. Farm surveys have shown that most farmers in the Big Blue Basin apply their atrazine in or near the May-June period that is showing the greatest loss potential. Application times examined included fall application, early spring application, and post application. Fall application should be made after harvest during the months of October or November before the ground is frozen. Early spring application should be made in the spring after the soil has thawed and before the primary runoff periods in May and June. The post application would be made after the crop has emerged and before the crop reaches labeled crop height. Post application is made at a quarter of the labeled atrazine rate and requires a chemical weed burn down at planting time, which has a higher cost. Alternative application timing can reduce atrazine runoff losses by 60 to 90 percent.

Chemical incorporation is another practice that farmers have used to apply their herbicides. The problem with this practice is that as the tillage tool incorporates the herbicide it also incorporates the residue cover needed to reduce soil erosion. If tillage is used prior to planting corn or grain sorghum atrazine losses can be reduced by 90 percent.

Vegetative buffer strips along the edge of fields are zones that can contain various forms of vegetation such as grass and trees. The purpose of these buffers is to reduce the runoff flow rate from the field to allow deposition of sediments and nutrients contained on the sediments (Dillaha et al., 1986, 1988; Cooper and Gilliam, 1987). Limited data is available on the effectiveness of these buffers ability to reduce herbicides in the runoff water (Arora et al., 1995). It is important to realize that the vegetation in the buffer does not remove the pesticide from the water passing through the buffer. It is the proportion of the herbicide-containing water that infiltrates into the buffer that reduces the herbicide runoff. Vegetative buffers used in the Big Blue Basin have reduced atrazine loss in runoff from fields by 30 percent.

CONCLUSIONS

This monitoring research suggests that additional management practices are needed in a portion of the Big Blue River Basin. Reducing runoff leaving fields with vegetative buffers combined with proper timing and application method can bring these parts of the Basin into compliance with the current water quality standards.

REFERENCES

Arora, K; Mickelson S K; Baker J L (1995). Evaluating vegetative buffer strips for herbicide retention. *Trans. Am. Soc. Agric. Eng.,* Paper No.95-2699.

Baker J L; Laflen J M (1979). Runoff losses of surface-applied herbicides as affected by wheel tracks and incorporation. *.J. Environ. Qual.,* **8**: (3), 602-607.

Cooper J R; Gilliam J W (1987) Phosphorous redistribution from cultivated fields to riparian areas. *Soil Sci. Soc. Am. J.* **51**: (2), 1600-1604.

Dillaha T A; Sherrard J H; Lee D; Shanholtz V O; Mostaghami S; Magette W L (1986). Use of vegetative filter strips to minimize sediment and phosphorous losses from feed lots: Phase I experimental plot study, Bulletin 151. Virginia Water Resources Research Institute, Virginia Tech University, Blacksburg, V A.

Dillaha T A; Sherrard J H; Lee D; Mostaghami S; Shanholtz V O (1988). Evaluation of vegetative filter strips as a best management practice for feed lots. *J. Water Pollut. Control Fed.* **60**: (7) 1231-1238.

Dugan J T; Engberg R A; Jordan P R (1991). Description of the lower Kansas River Basin. In: *Surface water quality assessment of the lower Kansas River Basin,* P R Jordon; J K Stamer (eds.), U S Geological Survey Open-File Report 91-75, pp.10-20.

Frankforter J D (1994) Compilation of atrazine and selected herbicide data from previous surface-water investigations within the Big Blue Basin, Nebraska, 1983-92. U S Geological Survey Open-File Report 94-100, 69p.

Hall J K; Pawlus M; Higgins E R (1972) Losses of atrazine in runoff water and soil sediment. *J. Environ. Qual.* **1**: (1), 172-176.

Miltner R J; Baker D B; Speth T F; Fronk C A (1989). Treatment of seasonal pesticides in surface water. *J. American Water Works Ass.* **81**: (1),43-52,

Olson B L; Regehr D L; Janssen K A; Barnes P L (1998) Tillage system effects on atrazine loss in surface water runoff. *Weed Tech.* **12**: (4) 646-651.

Porterfield G (1972) Computation of fluvial-sediment discharge. U S Geological Survey Water-Resources Investigations Book 3 Chapter C3. 66p.

Regehr D L; Devlin D L; Barnes P L; Watson S L (1996) Reducing atrazine runoff from crop fields. Cooperative Extension Service, Kansas State University. MF 2208.

Wischmeier W H; Smith D D (1978) Predicting rainfall erosion losses-a guide to conservation planning. U S Department of Agriculture, Agriculture Handbook No. 537. 58p.

Catchment scale risk-mitigation experiences – key issues for reducing pesticide transport to surface waters

J Kreuger
Swedish Univ. Agric. Sci., Dept. Soil Sci., POBox 7072, SE-750 07 Uppsala, Sweden
Email: Jenny.Kreuger@mv.slu.se

E Nilsson
VISAVI AB/SYDEK, Glimmervägen 6, SE-224 78 Lund, Sweden

ABSTRACT

A monitoring project was initiated in 1990 aimed at investigating pesticide sources, pathways and occurrence in stream water within an agricultural catchment. The work was carried out in close co-operation with the farmers operating in the selected area. Since 1995, farmers in the catchment have received extensive information regarding best management practises for pesticides adapted to local conditions on the farm. The program has continued during the entire 1990's. The results demonstrate a considerable reduction in overall pesticide findings in the stream, with concentrations down by more than 90%. The most notable decrease in concentration levels and transported amounts occurred in 1995, coinciding with the onset of the site specific information efforts. The decreasing levels of pesticides in stream water from the catchment area can primarily be attributed to an increased awareness amongst the farmers on better routines for the correct handling of spraying equipment and application procedures, including the practice of total weed killing on farmyards.

INTRODUCTION

The occurrence of pesticides in Swedish aquatic environments was initially observed during the mid-1980's, when monitoring studies first revealed the frequent findings of agricultural pesticides in streams and rivers (Kreuger & Brink, 1988). The findings were more frequent and the concentrations higher than had been anticipated based on earlier laboratory and field studies. As a result, a great deal of attention during the late 1980's focused on diffuse pollution of pesticides from agricultural fields to ground- and surface waters.

To explore the reasons for pesticide contamination in stream water it was decided to initiate a monitoring program, working beyond the well-controlled conditions (e.g. laboratory, lysimeters, field plots) under which, for good reasons, many environmental fate studies are done. The intention was to investigate pesticide sources, pathways and occurrence in stream water within a small agricultural catchment. The work was carried out in close co-operation with the farmers operating in the selected area. The program was started in 1990 and has continued during the entire 1990's. In this paper we describe risk-mitigation efforts implemented in the catchment since 1995 and present the results of pesticide occurrence in stream water leaving the catchment during a 10-year period.

MATERIAL AND METHODS

Monitoring program

The Vemmenhög catchment is located in the very south of Sweden with undulating topography and glacial till-derived soils. The total catchment area is 9 km² (900 ha) consisting of 95% arable land, with four major crops constituting ca 95% of the cropped area (winter cereals, spring cereals, winter oilseed rape, sugar beets). None of the crops are irrigated. Sandy loam and loamy soils dominate the catchment. The climate in the region is maritime with mean annual temperature and precipitation being 7.2°C and 662 mm, respectively. Extensive drainage systems have been installed in the catchment collecting tile drainage and also runoff water from surface runoff inlets, which are often used as inspection wells and located in the lowest-lying positions in the landscape along the tile drains in the field. Surface runoff inlets can also be found along roads and in some farmyards.

Information on crops, pesticide handling and usage within this area were collected annually through interviews with the farmers. The total amount applied each crop rotation was, on average, 1300 kg of active ingredient (AI) and has been quite constant for the past seven years (Figure 1). About 35 different substances were used each year and ca 90% (by weight) of these were included in the analyses (Figure 1). Since 1990, an automatic water sampler collected time integrated water samples during May-September/November at the outlet of the catchment. Also, at different sites within the catchment, samples have been collected to assess point sources. The analyses included up to 50 different pesticides. A more detailed description of the catchment, pesticide usage, data collection and analytical methods has been reported elsewhere (Kreuger, 1998).

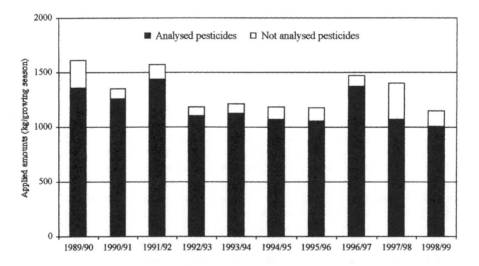

Figure 1. Total amount of pesticides applied in the catchment area during the growing seasons 1989/90-1998/1999. The columns are divided to show the distribution between pesticides included and not included in the analytical procedures.

Mitigation efforts - Implementation of best management practices for pesticides

General measures

In 1997, new legislation was introduced with stricter demands regarding pesticide use and application. The legislation included requirements for spray-free buffer zones, regulations concerning the use of pesticides in water protection areas and compulsory book-keeping of pesticide applications. Also in 1997, an information campaign called "Safe Pesticide Use" was launched on initiative of the farmers organisations in a joint collaboration with five other organisations and authorities. The focus was to raise the awareness amongst farmers of the environmental and health risks when using pesticides.

During 1998-1999, a program named "Sustainable conventional agriculture" was launched with EU and national money giving, mainly, small and mid-sized farmers economical compensation during a 5-year period when agreeing to comply with risk reduction measurement within agriculture. This included, for example, demands for the farmers to have spray-free buffer zones, a safe place for filling and cleaning the sprayer (i.e. on a biobed, on a concrete area with collection of the liquid or in the field on active arable soil) and inspection of the sprayer.

In 1999, the Swedish sugar-beet growers and the sugar industry agreed to introduce an Environmental Management System as an integrated part of the contract for growing sugar-beets in order to improve all environmental aspects of sugar-beet growing, including the safe use of pesticides. These two last programs were aimed at giving growers an economic incentive to minimise risks when using pesticides.

Site-specific measures

In late 1994 a meeting with farmers operating in the catchment was first held giving practical advice on the safe use of pesticides and risk reduction strategies. The advice was primarily focused on explaining to the farmers possible sources for the contamination and giving positive formulated examples how to decrease them. Farmers attending the meeting were offered, free of charge, a personal visit on the farm.

Shortly following the meeting, about one third of the farmers was visited. The farmers were guaranteed secrecy to make it easier to discuss problems. The advises were adjusted to local conditions on the specific farm, directed to safe storage of pesticides, how to avoid point sources when filling and cleaning sprayers and appropriate parking ground for the sprayer. Moreover, information about buffer zones to wells, drainage wells and open ditches when filling and spraying as well as a discussion about spraying herbicides on farmyards and other areas with low organic matter took place. The voluntary inspection of sprayers in use was also encouraged to reduce the risks for point sources caused by leaking hoses and dripping nozzles.

Moreover, in early 1995, staff involved in this work met with salespeople selling plant protection products to farmers in the region, providing them with information and practical training on the safe use of pesticides. Since these people often meet with the farmers out on the farm it was equally important to give them the same kind of information as the farmers.

Meetings with the farmers in the area have continued, providing them with feedback of the results of the monitoring program as well as new knowledge and recommendations regarding sources of contamination and practical solutions. Also, other farmers operating in the area were visited during the following years. All visits by the staff were made only on request by the farmer.

RESULTS AND DISCUSSION

A total of 39 pesticides (31 herbicides, 4 fungicides and 4 insecticides) and 3 herbicide metabolites have been detected in stream water samples collected during the 10-year period, with ca 10 pesticides having a detection frequency of >50% during individual years. Monitoring results obtained during the first years revealed elevated concentrations (up to 200 µg/l for single pesticides) and also pesticide residues entering the stream without preceding rainfall clearly a result of accidental spillage when filling or cleaning the spraying equipment on surfaces with drainage in direct connection to the stream. Investigations also demonstrated very high concentrations (up to 2000 µg/l) in run-off water entering surface water inlet wells on farmyards close to areas where filling of sprayers had taken place and, also, where the farmyard had been treated with herbicides to keep it free of weeds. Calculations showed that pesticide application for weed control on farmyards alone contributed to ~ 20% of the overall pesticide load in stream water. A more detailed presentation of the results have been reported elsewhere (Kreuger, 1998).

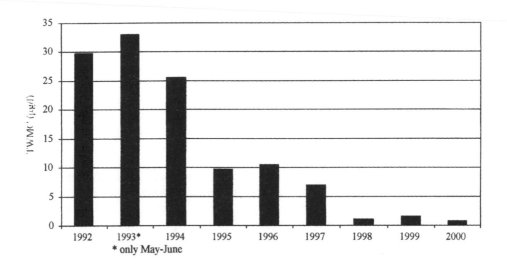

Figure 2. Time-weighted mean concentration (TWMC) for the sum of pesticides in stream water during May-September 1992-2000.

During recent years there has been a decrease in pesticide concentrations in stream water. The results demonstrate a considerable reduction in overall pesticide findings in the stream, with concentrations down by more than 90% (Figure 2). Also, transported amounts have declined significantly during the past 10 years (Figure 3). The most notable decrease in concentration levels and transported amount occurred in 1995, coinciding with the onset of the information efforts that first took place in the area before the 1995 application season.

The decreasing levels of pesticides in stream water from the catchment area can primarily be attributed to an increased awareness amongst the farmers on better routines for the correct handling of spraying equipment and application procedures (including the practice of total weed killing on farmyards). During late 1998, the first biobed (Torstensson & Castillo, 1997) was constructed in the catchment and since 2000 all farmers use either a biobed, a concrete area with collection of liquid or active arable soil when filling and cleaning the sprayer. The use of all kinds of herbicides on farmyards, also those not registered for application on yards and hard surfaces, has discontinued and today only mechanical methods and glyphosate (which is registered for those purposes) is used on these areas.

However, there has also been a slight change to the usage of pesticides active at lower doses, although, as can been seen in Figure 1, the total amount used in the area has been quite constant for the past seven years. Moreover, the number of farmers applying pesticides in the area has gradually decreased (ca 50% since 1990), resulting in fewer possible point sources.

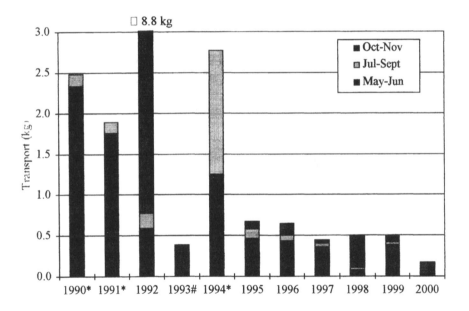

Figure 3. Total amount of pesticides transported in stream water during 1990-2000. The columns are divided to show different time periods.
* Sampled only during May-September.
# Sampled only during May-June.

Another factor is the increased use of glyphosate, both in the field and as a total weed killer on farmyards, which has more than doubled and is not reflected by the monitoring results since glyphosate has not yet been included in the analytical procedures.

CONCLUSIONS

Based on the study results it can be concluded that the occurrence of pesticides in surface water was a result of (*i*) natural processes influenced by soil and weather conditions, together with the intrinsic properties of the compound, as well as (*ii*) point sources such as spills and non-agricultural application (e.g. in farmyards).

In order to reduce the level of pesticides in streams and rivers, more effort should be directed towards education and information to those using pesticides with the aim of minimising applied quantities (e.g. by better calibrated spraying equipment and dose adjustment) and to avoid unintentional misuse and spillage.

The farmers were more willing to "accept" information when given personally and adjusted to site specific conditions than when received through general letters and pamphlets.

Essential to involve the farmers in the work and give them regular positive feed-back on the progress.

The implementation of agricultural best mamagement practices appears to have a positive effect on water quality in this area. However, both stream and ground water monitoring will be continued for several years to assess more definitively the changes in water quality.

ACKNOWLEDGEMENTS

This study was supported through funds provided by the following organisations: Association of Swedish Plant and Wood Protection Industries, County Government Board in Scania county, DuPont de Nemours (Agro) A/S, Environmental Foundation of the Scania county council, European Union, Federation of Swedish Farmers, Swedish Board of Agriculture, Swedish Environmental Protection Agency and Swedish National Chemicals Inspectorate.

REFERENCES

Kreuger J (1998). Pesticides in stream water within an agricultural catchment in southern Sweden, 1990-1996. *The Science of the Total Environment* **216:** 227-251.

Kreuger J; Brink N (1988). Losses of pesticides from agriculture. In: *Pesticides: Food and Environmental Implications*. IAEA/FAO International Symposium on Changing Perspectives in Agrochemicals, 24-27 Nov. 1987, pp. 101-112. IAEA: Vienna.

Torstensson L; Castillo M dP (1997). Use of biobeds in Sweden to minimize environmental spillages from agricultural spraying equipment. *Pesticide Outlook* **8:** 24-27.

The effectiveness of a stewardship campaign in Severn Trent Water

G Hankinson, G Welland

QES, Severn Trent Water Ltd, Sheldon, Birmingham, B26 3PU, UK

ABSTRACT

Many water companies as part of their commitment to environmental protection have introduced stewardship campaigns. These schemes encourage farmers to consider how their working practices impact on the environment and the measures that can be taken to prevent pollution. It has always proved difficult, given that many factors will impact on a campaign, to evaluate how effective such schemes have been in mitigating the negative impact of farming practices on the environment. This study has chosen to monitor the level of pesticides in a catchment and has used any significant changes as an indicator of the effectiveness of such a stewardship campaign.

In 1999, the levels of pesticide in a catchment were monitored. The results of this monitoring were presented to farmers in the area and advice on how to reduce the levels of pesticides entering the water given. The following years monitoring showed a reduction in general levels of pesticides, however there still remained some high peaks of pesticide believed to be from point source pollution events such as drips or spillage. The results were again presented to the farmers and further advice on better practice given.

This year's study has continued to monitor the area and has also included the monitoring of an adjoining catchment of similar size, with a similar farming regime but where at present no advice has been given to the farmers. This study will allow a direct comparison between the two areas which will show how effective our farmsafe campaign has been and additionally whether or not such campaigns are viable methods to use to reduce pesticide losses to water. The study will allow us to consider ways in which the campaign can be improved with a view to extending the scheme to other problem areas within other catchments.

INTRODUCTION

Many raw drinking water resources in the UK have shown a range of pesticides to be present including atrazine, simazine, isoproturon (IPU), diuron, mecoprop and bentazone. To maintain the drinking water standard such residues are removed by expensive treatment. Clearly a reduction of contamination levels would lower these costs and present the need for new treatment. A number of projects targeted at the end-user aim to reduce contamination by encouraging best practice. These have had limited success. The experience gained has shown that to further reduce and sustain low levels of contamination requires stronger incentives and full participation of all users.

Severn Trent Water (STW) have a comprehensive monitoring programme which gathers information on pesticide usage in their catchments and measures levels at abstraction points.

The company has developed and implemented a Farmsafe stewardship campaign, in collaboration with ADAS, EA, FWAG and NFU, to encourage best practice in areas where potential or actual problems have been identified. Despite these efforts pesticides are still being found in some raw waters at unacceptable levels.

Campion Hills Treatment Works, Leamington Spa has the highest pesticide loading of all STW's surface water works. Therefore Severn Trent chose this catchment to evaluate the effectiveness of the Farmsafe campaign. Several recent studies have investigated the appearance of IPU, a residual herbicide, in water. Less is known about Mecoprop, a more soluble herbicide identified as relatively difficult to remove from water. Therefore this campaign was targeted to the application period of Mecoprop. Comparison of results with previous IPU studies will help to identify factors common to pesticide applications in general and thus indicate areas where improvements may be particularly effective.

The Leam catchment covers 373km^2 with one of the highest agricultural coverages in the STW region. Many crops are planted in close proximity to the river on soils with high runoff potential and susceptibility to flooding increasing possible pesticide losses to water. The full catchment was considered too large for a detailed study of pesticide usage so in 1999 a pilot investigation commenced along the River Itchen, a tributary of the Leam. The Itchen catchment is about 37% of the Leam catchment and its land use and topography is typical of the whole area. The pilot study identified an area of the Itchen where high levels of pesticide had occurred and therefore this was a suitable target for a Farmsafe presentation the following year. Local farmers were invited to meetings (with a choice of dates) where the monitoring results were presented and advice on reducing the levels of pesticide loss to water was given. Pesticide levels in the Itchen were monitored during the following season's applications. Pesticide levels were generally reduced. However, some peak concentrations in water remained. These were probably from point sources such as drips or spillage, with the overall reduction mainly reflecting lower contamination from diffuse sources (leaching). These results were presented to the farmers with further advice on good practice.

In 2001, the monitoring study in the Itchen catchment was continued but farmers were not reminded of Farmsafe. As a further comparator monitoring was extended to the upper Leam catchment (upstream of the confluence of the Leam and the Itchen at Marton). The upper Leam comprises 2 distinct legs which join to the south of Draycote Water. Sample points along both these legs allowed comparisons of the specific contribution of each. In addition, information from this 'new' area, which has a similar topography and land use, was compared with the current and previous data from the Itchen, to evaluate the relative success of the Farmsafe campaign.

METHODS

Sample points

9 sample points were chosen for monitoring across the Leam catchment. These were chosen to represent conditions over the full length of the river, taking into account differences in land use and crop species. Consideration was also given to access, safety and repeatability of sampling. All points were on bridges across the river allowing midstream samples to be taken.

Sampling period

The study was timed to coincide with the application period for Mecoprop, expected to approximate to the months April and May. However, this years application period was uncertain due to prolonged wet weather during winter and early spring and because of problems for spray contractors due to Foot and Mouth Disease precautions. A sample plan, covering late March to early June, was updated weekly based on information from the Met Office, spray contractors, farmers and visual evidence in the catchment. This ensured samples were taken when pesticides were most likely applied.

Sampling Technique

Midstream samples were collected from each point in 1-litre glass bottles. After direct delivery to the analytical laboratory, samples were stored in refrigerators.

Sample Analysis

Samples were analysed by Severn Trent Laboratories using the System for the Automated Monitoring of Organic Substances (SAMOS). This equipment allowed simultaneous analysis of 10 compounds.
Turnaround time, no more than 1 week, was reduced towards the end of the study to allow the decrease in pesticide levels to be monitored closely.

The integrity of the SAMOS analysis was measured using conventional laboratory analysis of 3 additional samples taken from one of the sample points each week for Triazines, Sub Ureas and Acid Herbs. Results were compared to those produced by SAMOS.

RESULTS

Pesticides were recorded at all sample points during the study. IPU, Mecoprop and Simazine were most prevalent. IPU and Mecoprop levels were similar to previous years but Simazine was found at much higher levels in the Itchen. MCPA and Chlorotoluron were recorded at low levels at some sample points but are not presented. The graphs in Figure 1 show the levels of IPU, Mecoprop and Simazine at each sample point.

Figure 1: Graphs showing pesticide levels in the Leam Catchment

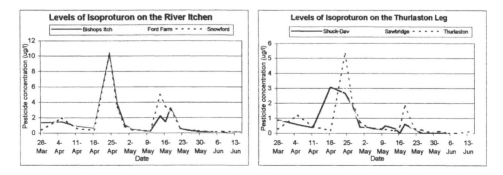

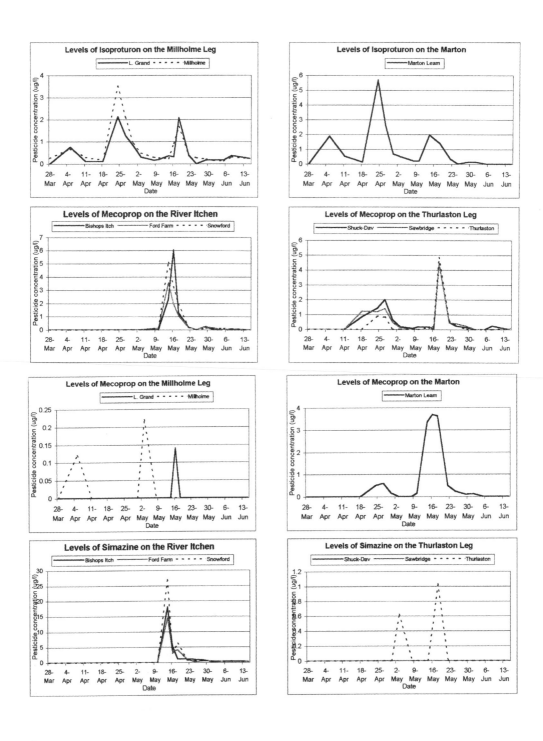

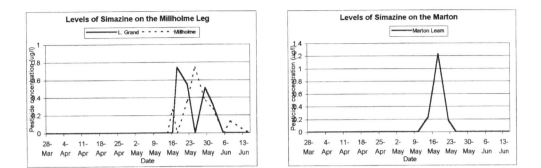

DISCUSSION

The approval period for pesticide usage can result in a limited window for application. One of the most critical factors to consider before application is rainfall, therefore this was the main tool used to decide when to take samples. There were three dry spells in mid April, early May and late May (see figure 2) when applications may have occurred. Information from farmers and contractors confirmed that the periods in mid April and early May included the majority of pesticide application, with the later dry spell being too late for application to many of the crops. The two application periods were both followed by heavy rainfall and thus runoff from the field is the probable origin of pesticides seen as peaks in graphs 1 – 12.

IPU

IPU occurred at all sample points at similar times. The levels in the Itchen were higher than in the rest of the catchment.

The small peak of IPU on 5th April is thought to be residue from the Autumn application as rainfall figures indicate that conditions were not suitable for spraying before this date.

The second peak on 24th April is most likely to be from Spring application. This occurred early in the season following the first application opportunity. Farmer concerns at being

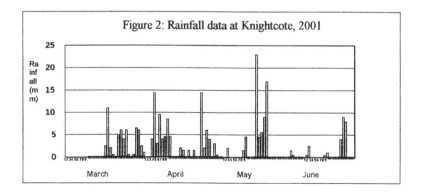

unable to spray in the Autumn may have resulted in an application when conditions were less than ideal resulting in a large peak in surface water following the subsequent rainfall.

The third lower peak in mid May is likely to be secondary to the April application.

Mecoprop

Mecoprop was detected sporadically throughout the catchment but only in mid May in the Itchen. The herbicide has a relatively short half life in the field so this pattern almost certainly reflects the time of application which is related to the growth stage of the crop. Levels were generally similar to previous years but the peak concentrations were lower. This may indicate reduced contamination from point sources.

Unusually, concentrations were similar throughout the catchment, with little evidence for flow dilution downstream. This may indicate a number of diffuse sources within the catchment, or an unusual flow pattern in the river at this time. It is notable that ADAS predicted an increased use of Mecoprop this season and this was confirmed by farmers and contractors. As increased use has not resulted in higher levels in water, it is evident that contamination is not an inevitable consequence of all uses.

Simazine

Simazine was found at higher levels than previous years in the Itchen catchment Following difficulties in drilling winter cereal in the Autumn, Spring beans had been sown as an alternative crop. The increased area of beans resulted in increased use of simazine. Cropping patterns showed large areas of beans in the Itchen catchment area with few in the upper Leam. Some of the beans were on land alongside the river with steep slopes. These have a high potential for runoff and hence are probable pollution sources.

CONCLUSIONS

The results indicate that the Farmsafe campaigns had limited impact. Following the presentations, pesticides were still found in surface waters at levels above those allowed for drinking water. A major problem with all such campaigns is to ensure that the target audience is reached. Even when all relevant farmers in a catchment are contacted and the presentation arranged at a local venue, take up tends to be low and those farmers who do attend are generally already committed to good practices.

Thus, the events are probably most suitable for disseminating new information and reinforcing the importance of existing advice. If local contractors are involved, the event may help to avoid them being put under pressure to spray in unsuitable conditions to meet specific needs. Although there may be value in continuing with similar campaigns the use of alternative methods should also be investigated.

Levels of Simazine and IPU were found in the Itchen at higher levels than the upper Leam and Mecoprop at similar levels. In the Itchen catchment pesticides were recorded at similar levels to previous years. However, in 2000 it was observed that pesticides were at similar levels at all the sample points (no flow dilution, suggesting diffuse sources) and this year the very sharp peaks attributed to point source pollution, were not seen.

This may be a consequence of the Farmsafe presentation, and in particular an application of the findings from the 'Cherwell Catchment Study' project which illustrated the importance of point sources in the contamination of water courses. At least one local contractor decided to fill his equipment in the field rather than on hard standing as previously recommended. Examples of spray drift/bad practice were also recorded in previous years. These included typical signs of phenoxy herbicide damage to weeds in a ditch.

This suggested a need for further education of spray users and/or poor practice by a (possibly small) proportion of users. As the proportion of applied pesticide which finds its way into surface waters is generally < 1% a few examples of poor technique, even if related to minor use, could account for the observed contamination. Not all users attended the Farmsafe presentation but it is possible that indirect communication has contributed to the lack of any similar observations this season.

The "Cherwell Valley" project was instrumental in demonstrating the potential importance of point source contamination in surface waters. This used IPU to exemplify the problems. IPU is a residual herbicide and dissolves relatively slowly. Similar investigations with a more soluble and shorter-lived herbicide such as Mecoprop would provide useful additional information on the relative importance of leaching and point source contributions to the burden in surface water. This is important, as different strategies are required to combat contamination from the two routes. Observations suggest that both routes may be important in this catchment and therefore alternative approaches will need to take account of this.

Such approaches which may be considered include: the adoption of uncultivated "buffer strips" along major waterways; review of the buffer zones required; modified equipment to reduce spray drift; improved training/licensing of applicators and reduced application rates. It is believed that some pesticides may leach at significant levels even when applied according to best practice and therefore in such circumstances alternative products should be considered. If such approaches are adopted it will be important to ensure full compliance to maximise the benefits, as a few, apparently minor, infringements of good practice can result in very significant additional contamination of surface waters.

ACKNOWLEDGEMENTS

We thank Dr Geoff Pigott and Robert Joice for their technical assistance during the study and in the preparation of this paper.

REFERENCES

Beeken M (1999). Campion Hills pesticide monitoring project (Internal Document)
Whitehead J (2000). Pesticides in the River Itchen – an evaluation of Farmsafe (Internal Document)

Catchment monitoring for pesticides – Unilever Colworth sustainable agriculture project

T J Pepper, S J Groves
ADAS Gleadthorpe Research, Meden Vale, Mansfield, Nottinghamshire, NG20 9PF, UK
Email: tim.pepper@adas.co.uk

D J Pendlington
Unilever Research, Colworth House, Sharnbrook, Bedford, MK44 1LQ, UK

ABSTRACT

Agrochemical concentrations, including pesticides, were measured at a number of automatically sampled drainage and streamflow monitoring stations established within a 60 ha arable sub-catchment on the Colworth estate, Bedfordshire, UK. Monitoring was conducted as part of an integrated programme evaluating the arable system impact on the environment, with the aim of developing a sustainable management policy by adoption of new cropping and cultivation practices. In this first year little pesticide was detected in leachate from the study area before spring pesticide applications to the mainly winter wheat crop. Pesticide concentrations in spring runoff events measured at the catchment outlet were highest for the conazole fungicide tebuconazole ($1.3\mu g\ L^{-1}$), and for the herbicides terbuthylazine and terbutryn ($0.21\mu g\ L^{-1}$ to $0.91\mu g\ L^{-1}$) applied to a single field of peas. In early autumn drainage events, the diazinone herbicide bentazone, and the triazine herbicide cyanazine (applied the previous spring) were detected in leachate at concentrations $6.0\mu g\ L^{-1}$ and $1.4\ \mu g\ L^{-1}$ respectively, with total losses of 1.4 and 2.0% of active substance applied.

INTRODUCTION

The Unilever Colworth Sustainable Agriculture Project was established as part of Unilever's global sustainable agriculture initiative (see http://www.unilever.com). This approach is being undertaken utilising an existing well established farming system where the maintenance of stable crop yields to maintain profitability was an important factor, whilst seeking to reduce the overall environmental impact of the farming operation. Water quality sampling stations were established in support of the project in October 1999. In the first year of monitoring (1999 – 2000), baseline water quality data were collected from a number of monitoring points with the objective of characterising nutrient and pesticide losses within the study area, and quantifying losses originating from outside the study area. In subsequent years management of agrochemical inputs within individual fields will be modified to include sustainable treatments aimed at lowering environmental impacts and thereby the associated water clean up costs. These treatments, although not organic, are intended to be beyond current UK integrated crop/pest management (ICM, IPM) practices. The sustainable treatments will be paired with normal good agricultural practice (GAP) management within a split field approach. This paper reports the first year results from the baseline pesticide monitoring.

METHODS AND MATERIALS

Site

The 76 ha study area formed part of the Colworth estate, (Bedfordshire, UK) and consisted of a group of 8 arable fields, predominantly in winter wheat, but including one field of oilseed rape and one field of peas within the rotation. The predominant soil series was Hanslope, consisting of a clay loam soil over stony, calcareous clay. All the study fields had extensive under-drainage systems, with secondary drainage treatments consisting of either mole drainage or subsoiling. All field drains eventually discharged into a main stream running through the centre of the study area, which represented approximately 50% of the total catchment area draining to this stream, the remainder consisting of a mixture of arable, woodland, and concrete/grass areas within the Santa Pod raceway to the west of the site.

Sampling

Two monitoring stations were established to measure and sample runoff generated from within the study area, with a further three stations at points where runoff had been identified as entering from outside. These additional positions were designed to quantify this external runoff component, and assess leachate movement in order to obtain nett values for the study area.

The automatic flow recording and sampling system installed at each of the monitoring locations consisted of a Wessex flume and an ultrasonic water depth probe linked to an electronic data capture system based on a Campbell Scientific CR10 datalogger, with data transfer by mobile telephone link. Water samples were collected during drainage events using EPIC automatic wastewater samplers, with flow related sampling controlled by the datalogger program. These systems collected drainage water directly as it either entered or left the study area, providing a sensitive method of monitoring leaching losses to surface waters.

Pesticides studied

Initially, (October 1999 to February 2000) water samples were analysed for a wide range of pesticides in order to determine which substances may be impacting the main stream from outside the study area, and if there had been any "carry over" from pesticide use within the study area in previous years. This analysis suite of pesticides is listed in Table 1.

Table 1. Pesticide analysis suite – October 1999 to February 2000

Acephate	Diflufenican	hosalone
Azinphos-methyl	Tebuconazole	Phosmet
Carbophenothion	Azoxystrobin	Phoshamidon
Chlorfenvinphos	Isoproturon	Pirimiphos-methyl
Chlorpyrifos	MCPA	Pyrazophos
Chlorpyrifos-methyl	MCPB	Quinalphos
Diazinon	Bentazone	Triazophos
Dichlorvos	Parathion-ethyl	Terbuthylazine
Dimethoate	Parathion-methyl	Pirimicarb
Ethion	Malathion	Terbutyrn
Etrimfos	Methacrifos	Cyanazine
Fenchlorphos	Methacrifos	Metazochlor
Fenitrothion	Methamidophos	Fluazipop-butyl
Heptenophos	Methidathion	Mevinphos
Omethoate	Monocrotophos	

From March 2000 samples were only analysed for pesticides which had been applied to the study fields, although analytical methods for some of these active substances were not available at the laboratory undertaking the analysis. Pesticides applied to the study area are listed in Table 2.

Table 2. Pesticides applied to the study area from autumn 1999 to January 2001

Active substance	Analysis	Date applied
IPU	Yes	10/3/00
MCPB	Yes	14/5/00
Terbutyrn	Yes	1/4/00
Terbuthylazine	Yes	1/4/00
Tebuconazole	Yes	1/4/00
Trinexapac-ethyl	Yes	8/5/00
Bentazone*	Yes	14/5/00
Trifluralin	Yes	10/3/00
Epoxiconazole	Yes	8/5/00
Chlormequat	Yes	8/5/00
Clodinafop-propargyl	No	3/5/00
Metasulfuron-methyl	No	6/5/00
Fluroxypyr	No	6/5/00
Cyanazine	Yes	14/5/00
Kresoxim-methyl	No	20/5/00

RESULTS

Very few pesticide detections were made during winter 1999-2000, before the majority of pesticides were applied at the site during spring 2000 (Table 2). Of the chemicals listed in Table 1, MCPA/MCPB was detected at low concentrations (maximum $0.15\mu g\ L^{-1}$) in drainage entering from outside the study area in late October 2000. Isoproturon was occasionally detected in flow entering from outside the study area in concentrations up to $0.37\mu g\ L^{-1}$ throughout the winter period, although no detections were made at the catchment outlet, suggesting that dilution in the main stream had brought levels to below the detection limit of $0.05\mu g\ L^{-1}$.

The spring of 2000 was characterised by periods of heavy rainfall, with drainage continuing into the early summer (Figure 1). A number of the pesticides applied to the study fields during this period were detected in runoff at the catchment outlet. These included the conazole fungicide tebuconazole (maximum $1.3\mu g\ L^{-1}$), and the herbicides terbuthylazine and terbutryn ($0.21\mu g\ L^{-1}$ and $0.91\mu g\ L^{-1}$), the latter applied to the single field of peas.

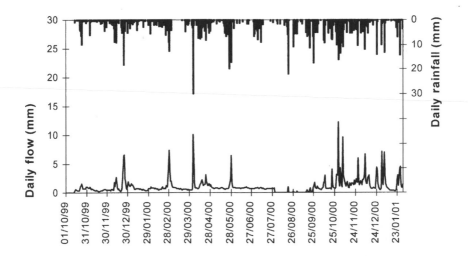

Figure 1 Rainfall and runoff at the catchment outlet – October 1999 to January 2001

The application of the diazinone herbicide bentazone, and the triazine herbicide cyanazine to the pea field in late May (Table 2) occurred towards the end of the drainage season, giving little opportunity for leaching to surface water over the summer when little or no drainage occurred. However, with an early commencement of drainflow in September 2000, as a result of the extremely wet autumn, these two chemicals were detected at the catchment outlet at concentrations of 6.0 and 1.4 $\mu g\ L^{-1}$ respectively, declining to 0.08 and 0.12 $\mu g\ L^{-1}$ by January 2001.

Leaching losses of pesticides from the study area were calculated from the measured concentrations and flow volume from each runoff event, and are presented in Table 3. The highest estimated pesticide leaching loss was for cyanazine, amounting to 2.0% of the total pesticide applied. With the exception of isoproturon, none of the chemicals monitored at the catchment outlet were detected entering the study area from the wider catchment, therefore it is most likely that the losses reported were a result of pesticides leaching from the study fields only.

Table 3. Pesticide losses – calculated at the catchment outlet

Pesticide (active substance)	Maximum concentration ($\mu g\ L^{-1}$)	Total loss (g/ha)	% loss of applied
Bentazone	6.0	0.79	1.4
Cyanazine	1.4	0.21	2.0
Terbuthylazine	0.21	2.83	1.3
Tebuconazole	1.3	0.67	0.4
Terbutyrn	0.91	5.08	1.0
Isoproturon	0.18	0.15	0.02
Trifluralin	0.15	0.07	0.007

DISCUSSION

During the first year of this study information on the leaching of pesticides from the arable system was quantified to provide a baseline for the future sustainable management programme. Monitoring of runoff originating from outside the study area confirmed that losses recorded at the catchment outlet could be attributed to pesticide applications made to the study fields, while measurement of runoff volume allowed the accurate estimate of individual pesticide losses.

Several of the pesticides applied during spring 2000 were detected at the catchment outlet soon after application at concentrations above the EC drinking water limit of $0.1\mu g\ L^{-1}$. The detection of the herbicides terbuthylazine (K_{oc}=278) and terbutryn (K_{oc}=1089) was significant as they had been applied to a single field of peas, representing only 15% of the total study area. It was probable that concentrations at the field drain would have been greater than the $0.21\mu g\ l^{-1}$ to $0.91\mu g\ l^{-1}$ measured at the catchment outlet when dilution factors were considered. Although these two chemicals may be regarded as having only a moderate leaching potential (Gustafson, 1993), application took place during an unusually wet spring, with extensive drainage occurring soon after application (Table 2, Figure 1). These conditions probably represented a "worst case" in terms of leaching risk (Jones et al., 2000). Total losses of terbuthylazine and terbutryn were influenced by the extensive drainage recorded in April/May 2000, with runoff continuing much longer than the average for this area of the UK (MAFF 1984). The presence of the herbicides bentazone and cyanazine in leachate following the early resumption of drainage in September 2000 was an indication of the relative

2000). Total losses of terbuthylazine and terbutryn were influenced by the extensive drainage recorded in April/May 2000, with runoff continuing much longer than the average for this area of the UK (MAFF 1984). The presence of the herbicides bentazone and cyanazine in leachate following the early resumption of drainage in September 2000 was an indication of the relative persistence of these chemicals (Hollis 1991), in addition to their high leaching potential. The total losses of between 1.4% and 2.0% of active substance applied were again influenced by the extreme weather patterns which characterised this period, with autumn drainage occurring some 4 to 6 weeks in advance of the normal patterns historically observed in this area.

In contrast to the pesticides applied to the pea crop, losses of isoproturon (high leaching potential) applied to the winter wheat crop during March 2000 were much less (0.02% of applied), with no detections from some of the sampled events during the spring period. The reason for this was not apparent, although the relatively dry three week period between application and the first significant drainflow may have been an important factor. Conversely, the conazole fungicide tebuconazole, applied at the beginning of the much wetter month of April, was detected in leachate for the remainder of the drainage season. The triazole fungicide epoxiconazole, with similar leaching characteristics, but applied in drier conditions six weeks later, was not detected in the final spring sampling event at the end of May 2000, perhaps emphasising the complexity of the processes observed at the site, and the importance of the timing of pesticide applications on leaching losses in this monitoring year. The observations reported here are supported by recent results from the pesticide leaching experiment at Brimstone Farm (in preparation), where long-term monitoring results have demonstrated the importance of soil moisture status to the mobility of pesticides including isoproturon in the period immediately following application.

REFERENCES

Gustafson D I (1993). *Pesticides in Drinking Water* published by Van Norstrand Rheinhold, New York, 241 pp.
Hollis J M (1991) Mapping the vulnerability of aquifers and surface waters to pesticide contamination at the national/regional scale. *British Crop Protection Council Monograph No 47, Pesticides in Soils and Water,* 165-174. BCPC, Farnham, UK.
Jones R L; Arnold D J S; Harris G L; Bailey S W; Pepper T J; Mason D J; Brown C D; Leeds-Harrision P B; Walker A; Bromilow R H; Brockie D; Nicholls P H; Craven A C; Lythgo C M (2000). Processes affecting movement of pesticides to drainage in cracking clay soils. *Pesticide Outlook.* October 2000, 174-177.
MAFF (1984). The agricultural climate of England and Wales. *Reference Book 435. HMSO London.*

A method for a diagnosis of the risk of pesticides transfer at field scale: principles, implementation and first results in Bretagne (Brittany)

F Laubier
Direction Régionale de l'Agriculture et de la Forêt, Service Régional de la Protection des Végétaux (DRAF / SRPV), BP 60116, 35701 Rennes Cedex 07, France
Email : florence.laubier@agriculture.gouv.fr

ABSTRACT

The presence of pesticides in the rivers of Brittany was underlined at the beginning of the nineties. This pollution was found to be persistent, especially for a few herbicides used on grain crops. As the CORPEN (the national committee on water and pesticides) developed a plot scale method to minimise the transfer risk of pesticides in water, the CORPEP (a regional group on water and pesticides) finalised a specific method intended to the watersheds of the « Bretagne Eau Pure » program. The two methods, however, have the same object and scientific basis. The CORPEP method is specific to the region, in relation to its hydrological and geological characteristics, and the large area of its application. It is based on five factors which are taken into account simultaneously to give a final rank to the plot. The ranks are divided into three classes of transfer risk. The principles of the method and the implementation of the diagnosis are described. An evaluation of the method is laid: progress report in Brittany and first results on water quality.

INTRODUCTION

In Brittany, the monitoring of pesticides in surface water began in 1990. These last ten years, both surfaces of maize and cereals represent around 25 percent of total agricultural surface, and the grasslands around 40 percent (Agreste, La statistique agricole). As a result, the most frequent pesticides found in raw water are atrazine, the major herbicide used on maize, and isoproturon, the major one used on cereals. Frequencies of detection and maximal values since 1990 are presented below for atrazine (Table 1).

Table 1.   Atrazine: Monitoring data from the CORPEP rivers network
(samplings after a minimum 10mm rainfall event within 24 hours)

Year	Number of water samples	Rate of detection	Rate of concentrations $>0,1\mu g.L^{-1}$	Maximum value $(\mu g.L^{-1})$ (day/month)
1990	28	93%	79%	6.8 (25/06)
1991	20	80%	70%	3.1 (09/07)
1992	24	88%	83%	14.7 (01/07)
1993	15	100%	100%	14.8 (10/06)
1994	24	88%	79%	11 (18/07)
1995	17	100%	88%	5 (03/07)
1996	63	94%	86%	8.4 (17/05)
1997	51	100%	96%	29 (16/06)
1998	62	94%	81%	4.1 (10/06)
1999	70	93%	66%	6.3 (19/05)
2000	77	94%	60%	11.1 (10/05)

For each year, the frequency of detection is high and the maximum value can reach several micrograms per litre. The pollution of surface waters by pesticides involves specific and expensive treatments to deliver water in accordance with the national regulations.

To minimise the impact of pesticides in water, the choice is made to manage the transfer risk instead of banning some of them. A method is elaborated, consisting in controlling the transfer risk of the most frequent herbicides used on crops and found in water: atrazine and isoproturon.

THE DIAGNOSIS AT THE FIELD SCALE

Historic

The CORPEP method is specifically designed for the hydrological context of Brittany. It is developed at the end of the nineties to decrease the maximum concentrations occurring during a flood, after herbicide applications (Cann, 1995; Gascuel & Molenat, 2000). As a consequence, the method takes into account the rapid water flows in the watershed, which may have an impact on the water quality downstream: surface runoff, superficial water tables, and flows along the sides through drains and ditches.

The CORPEP research indicated that the mobility and the persistence of herbicides on one hand and the field characteristics on the other hand, determine the potential for herbicide pollution (Gillet, Clement et al., 1995). Experiments of the « Service Régional de la Protection des Végétaux » (SRPV) on a small watershed underlined the specific contribution of a few fields to water pollution downstream (Gillet, 1999). Therefore, a method for a diagnosis at the field scale was chosen.

The watershed approach

The method was designed initially for the watersheds of the programme «Bretagne Eau Pure» (1995-1999). Nineteen watersheds (from 2000 to 40000 hectares) were selected in 1995, with a common objective: to restore the water quality towards pesticides and nitrates.
As the CORPEP method is designed for watersheds, unvarying factors at this physical scale are considered not relevant. This is the case for the time separating the treatment and the first rainfall event, and for geology.

As those watersheds cover around 10 percent of the Brittany surface, the scope of the programme requires a method easily implemented by a large number of farming consultants, and a permanent diagnosis (independent of yearly conditions: crop, soil characteristics, weeds development). Nevertheless, the diagnosis is based on field observations. It needs a rigorous and systematic analysis of the water path into the field.

The five factors

Five factors are selected for the diagnosis. They characterise the field topography (within the field, and inside the watershed) and the agricultural and landscape planning at the field scale. The main factors are physical factors. They have an effect on surface runoff (slope and distance to waterway) and subsurface runoff (drains). The other factors are anthropogenic (length of slope, buffer zone at the bottom of the plot). As these last ones can change, they contribute to adjust the physical factors.

For each factor, a criterion and the classes relating to the criterion are selected (Table 2). The classes are established according to the CORPEP's research (Gascuel-Odoux & Aurousseau, 1999).

Table 2. Factors, hierarchy, criterions and classes for the final rank of the field

Factor	Criterion	class
Distance	On the water path, the distance between the downstream point of the field and the hydrographic network. Hydrographic network: waterways (permanent or temporary) and ditches (in circulation at least three months during winter time)	3 classes: < 20m from 20 to 200m > 200m
Slope	On the water path: slope between the upper point and the lower point	3 classes: < 3% from 3 to 5% > 5%
Drainage	Agricultural drain underground	2 classes: presence / absence
Length of slope	On the water path: distance between the upper point and the lower point	3 classes: < 50m from 50 to 150m > 150m
Protection downstream	Presence of a continuous and long-lasting protection, avoiding any direct transfer: grassed or wooded buffer strips larger than 20m, hedges	2 classes: presence / absence

The final rank

The combination of the five factors is based on the SIRIS method, used by the French ministries of environment, of health and of agriculture (Vaillant *et al.*, 1995). The SIRIS method forms into a hierarchy the five factors. The method takes them into account simultaneously to assign a final rank to the field. Ranks range from 0 to 100 and are divided into three classes of transfer risk of pesticides: low, medium or high risk. The higher the rank is, the higher the transfer risk is. Two tables (depending on whether the field is drained or not) enable the farming consultant to determine the class of each criterion. The reading is possible in lines or in columns and leads to the final rank by a process of elimination (Table 3).

Table 3. Determination table for the SIRIS rank of drained fields

		Distance								
		> 200m			20 – 200m			> 20m		
	Length of slope	Slope < 3%	Slope 3 - 5%	Slope > 5%	Slope < 3%	Slope 3 - 5%	Slope > 5%	Slope < 3%	Slope 3 - 5%	Slope > 5%
With protection	< 50m	6	13	20	22	31	41	38	50	63
	50 –150m	9	17	24	27	37	48	46	59	72
	> 150m	11	20	29	32	43	55	54	68	82
Without protection	< 50m	9	17	26	30	41	52	51	65	79
	50 –150m	12	22	31	36	48	60	60	75	90
	> 150m	16	26	37	42	55	68	69	84	100

22	Low risk	22	Medium risk	22	High risk

IMPLEMENTATION AND USE OF FIELD DIAGNOSIS

Implementation

The farming consultant is chosen by the farmer and realises the diagnosis with him. Every field is analysed separately. The consultant observes the water path and fills the different classes of criterions using the farmer's information when necessary (drain). At the end of the diagnosis, both of them get a map where the fields appear coloured in green, yellow or red (respectively low, medium or high risk).

The guidelines for a prevention of risk of water pollution by pesticides

The second step consists in adapting the agricultural practises to limit the diffuse pollution risk by pesticides. In each watershed, a charter signed by the farming consultants and the herbicides suppliers, defines the guidelines to protect water quality from pesticides. The charter gives recommendations to reduce the risk level by agricultural planning (grassed buffer strips, hedges). If the risk level cannot be changed, it can be managed by a combination of mechanical and chemical weeding or an exclusively mechanical weeding, and by substituting molecules with a more favourable environmental profile for worse environmental behaviour molecules.

As atrazine and isoproturon are the most frequent pollutants found in water, substitution recommendations focus on those two herbicides. The aim is to choose molecules according to the risk level of the field (Table 4). Therefore, molecules are classified into three groups according to their rate, their mobility (K_{OC}) and their persistence (DT_{50}). The first group gathers herbicides which have a low potential for mobility; the second group, herbicides with low persistence but with a high potential for mobility; and the third group, the herbicides with high persistence and mobility.

Table 4.   Correspondence between groups of herbicides and risk levels of fields

	Risk level		
	Low risk	Medium risk	High risk
Group 1	Yes	Yes	Yes
Group 2	Yes	Yes	No
Group 3	Yes	No	No

For example, alachlore belongs to the third group; it can be applied only on low risk fields. This filling is based on physical and chemical properties of herbicides, but is corrected every year according to the monitoring data by a CORPEP commission. Monitoring data come from a regional « surveillance network » of water quality and from every « Bretagne Eau Pure » watershed.

RESULTS AND DISCUSSION

A specific test of the charter guidelines is conducted in 2000 on one of the « Bretagne Eau Pure » watershed. On a small surface watershed (lower than 50 ha), the farming consultants and the farmers are supplied with a financial aid. The complete respect of the charter is required to get the subsidy (it is not the case in the other watersheds).

The test demonstrates that, if the charter is respected, it is possible to control the water pollution by maize herbicides.

From 1999 to 2000, maize surfaces increased on this watershed from 15 to 23 hectares. It is still possible to apply atrazine on more than 10 hectares (instead of less than 6 hectares in 1999). In spite of that, atrazine concentrations in water remain under 0,22µg.L⁻¹ in 2000 (Figure 1), which means more than six times lower than the 1999 maximum concentrations. At the exit of the entire watershed, he monitoring reveals that none of the other maize herbicides used are found in the water at upper concentrations than 0,1µg/l.

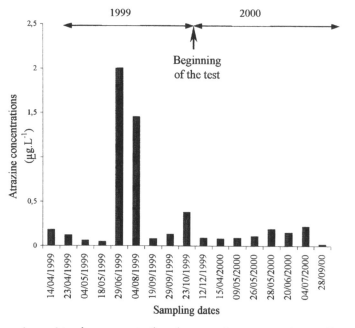

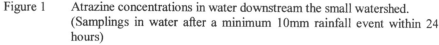

Figure 1   Atrazine concentrations in water downstream the small watershed. (Samplings in water after a minimum 10mm rainfall event within 24 hours)

These first results are confirmed in a few watersheds of the « Bretagne Eau Pure » programme, where water quality regarding atrazine is improving. On those watersheds, both frequencies of concentrations above 0,1µg.L⁻¹ and maximum concentrations of atrazine are decreasing. The same results are still expected for isoproturon.

CONCLUSION AND PROSPECTS

The test indicates, at the scale of a watershed, that it is possible to reduce the atrazine pollution in surface water by adapting the use of pesticides according to the specific transfer risk of the field. It also indicates that the pollution control requires a complete respect of the charter by all the farming consultants and all the farmers of the watershed. For a complete validation of the substitution process, a rigorous monitoring of water is absolutely necessary. It is a security, especially regarding to the molecules used for substitution. Today (beginning of 2001), 300 consultants are trained to implement the CORPEP method and the transfer risk diagnosis concerns more than 30000 hectares. The method will probably develop in the Brittany Region: with the « Bretagne Eau Pure » 2000-2006 programme concerning around

40 percent of the Brittany region, and with the new dispositions developed by the French ministry of agriculture to promote sustainable agriculture. In the rest of France, diagnosis of the transfer risk of pesticides at the field scale are also developing. They are based on the CORPEN method which implies an agronomic section but can be applied everywhere. Like in Brittany, they are designed for watersheds selected for their contribution to pollution.

REFERENCES

AGRESTE. La statistique agricole – Tableaux de l'agriculture bretonne, résultats années 1990 à 1999, Direction Régionale de l'Agriculture et de la Forêt de Bretagne.

Aurousseau P; Gascuel-Odoux C (1998). *Un indicateur de risque parcellaire de contamination des eaux superficielles par les produits phytosanitaires.* Contrat Bretagne Eau Pure – Etude CORPEP 98/3.

Aurousseau P; Gascuel-Odoux C; Squividant H (1998). Elément pour une méthode d'évaluation d'un risque parcellaire de contamination des eaux superficielles par les pesticides. In: *Etude et gestion des sols*, **5**: (3), 143-156.

Aurousseau P; Squividant H; Baqué M C; Simon F (1996). *Analyse des facteurs de risque de transferts de pesticides dans les paysages. Etablissement d'une hiérarchie de ces risques: application au calcul d'un indice de risque par bassin versant et par parcelle.* Rapport de contrat pour l'Agence de l'Eau Loire-Bretagne, 22 pp. 12 cartes, 12 tableaux, 6 figures.

Cann C (1995). Le transfert des triazines vers l'eau, *Actes du colloque " Qualité des eaux et des produits phytosanitaires: du diagnostic à l'action "*, Rennes 1995, 107-115.

CORPEN (1999). *Désherbage – Elements de raisonnement pour une maîtrise des adventices limitant les risques de pollution des eaux* . Groupe PHYTOPRAT. Juin 1999. 161 p.

CORPEP. Etudes de la contamination des eaux superficielles de Bretagne par les produits phytosanitaires, années 1990 à 2000

Gascuel-Odoux C; Molénat J (2000). Etude de la dynamique hydrochimique des nappes superficielles en vue de déterminer les temps de réponses des hydrosystèmes à des mesures agri-environnementales : cas des nitrates et des pesticides. *Water in Celtic world : managing Resources for the 21st Century, 2nd Inter-Celtic Colloquium, University of Wales Aberystwyth, 3-7 July 2000 : BHS Occasional Paper*, **11**: 311-318.

Gillet H; Clement M; Choisy A.M; Seux R (1995). Evaluation du niveau de contamination des eaux de surface par les produits phytosanitaires,. In: *J. Eur Hydrol* **26**: fasc 1, pp. 5 -82 .

Gillet H; Ferron O; Bazile E; Clisson O; Carrel V; (1999). Transfert de produits phytosanitaires à l'echelle d'un bassin versant : le Pouliou. In: *Actes du programme Systèmes Terre et Eau* 1994-1999, 107-111

Vaillant M. *et al.*, (1995). A multi-criteria estimation of the environmental risk of chemicals with the SIRIS method. In: *Toxicology Modelling*, **1**: (1), pp. 57-72.

Herbicide flow from two types of hard surfaces in urban areas: first results for glyphosate and diuron

G Angoujard, N Le Godec
FEREDEC Bretagne, BP 79128, 35079 Rennes Cedex 7, France

L Lefevre, P Blanchet
DRAF Bretagne, Service régional de la protection des végétaux, BP 60116, 35079 Rennes Cedex 7, France

ABSTRACT

An experiment has been established in a mini-watershed to determine the contribution of urban areas to water pollution. The idea was to collect run-off from two man-made surfaces : concrete (impermeable) and compacted sandy soil (permeable). Both surfaces can be considered as hard ones if compared with agricultural soils. The losses of glyphosate and diuron sprayed at 3000 g ha^{-1} were monitored for 10.5 months after application. For diuron, 33.3% of the applied quantity is transferred to the water from concrete surface and 39.5% from the sandy zone. For glyphosate, the rates are respectively 8.5% and 12.8%. These very high results are to be compared with the data for agricultural use of herbicide indicating an average range of 0.1% to 1% loss of the applied quantity. 5 or 3 mm rainfall are enough for the leaching of 50% of the total loss of glyphosate and diuron from concrete surface. The regulatory process should be improved regarding urban uses of pesticides and herbicides with the less possible loss encouraged. A new impetus has to be given to the research of non-chemical methods in urban areas, which could be the ultimate environment friendly solution on hard surfaces.

INTRODUCTION

Extensive research has been carried out on pesticide losses from agricultural plots and fields. But the losses from hard surfaces in urban areas are an underestimated source of diffuse pollution (Shepherd & Heater 1999). This situation has been emphasized by the monitoring of surface water in Bretagne (Brittany). There, diuron is a major pollutant although not used in agriculture as orchards and vineyards are lacking in this part of France (Gillet 1995).

An experimental mini-watershed has been designed to improve our understanding of the role of herbicides leaching from hard surfaces in the surface water pollution. To provide preliminary data, glyphosate and diuron have been investigated as a local diuron ban increased the use of the further.

MATERIALS AND METHODS

The experimental design is located in Pacé near Rennes, the capital city of Brittany. An existing lane (ten years old) is chosen for its conditions similar to common weeds control practice. This design is different from the one used with new surface material by Shepherd &

Heather (1999). It has a 3.8 % slope and is divided in two parts : one with an impermeable concrete surface (47m x 4 m) , the other with a permeable sandy compacted man-made soil (47m x 6.8m). There are referred thereafter as CZ (concrete zone) and SZ (sandy zone). Both surfaces are considered as hard ones if compared to agricultural soil. Each plot is protected from the other and the highest ones by a ditch preventing any undesirable water transfer.

A strip in the middle of each plot is sprayed with glyphosate and diuron on June 9th at a rate of 3000g active ingredient per hectare with a precision sprayer (ATH company, Altkirsch). The size of the strip is adjusted to get the same 50% of the surface sprayed along each plot.

The water volume/ha is 500 litres and the nozzles are Teejet 80015 VS. Downstream each plot, a ditch equipped with automatic sampler and flow-meter collects the run-off water during the rain. An automatic weather station provides the necessary rainfall data. Herbicide concentration (diuron, glyphosate and its metabolite AMPA) of the water samples is analysed by gas chromatography in the laboratory of the *Ecole Nationale de la Sante Publique* in Rennes.

The losses of the herbicide have been monitored till 10.5 months after spraying, corresponding to 23 rain events and 78 rain days (Figure 1). 79 water samples have been analysed for diuron, glyphosate and AMPA.

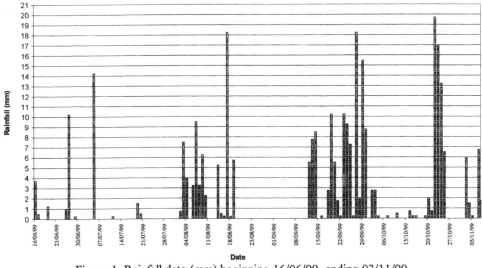

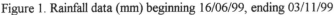

Figure 1. Rainfall data (mm) beginning 16/06/99, ending 03/11/99

RESULTS

Water run-off is observed after 0.5 to 1 mm rainfall on the impermeable zone and after 2 mm on permeable zone (Figure 2). These data confirm that the surfaces have to be considered as hard ones if compared to agricultural soils, which usually needs more than 10 mm for a significant run-off.

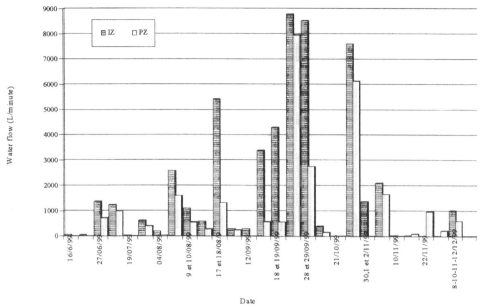

Figure 2. Relationship between rainfall and water run-off

The average concentrations for each type of surface are summarised in table 1. Data in brackets are the maximum values of the rain event.

The concentrations observed on both zones are very high during the first rains : diuron 1330 µg L⁻¹ and glyphosate 8000 µg L⁻¹. Whatever the molecule, the concentrations on impermeable surface are higher than on permeable one for the first rains. The results are inverted three months after spraying.

Table 1. Concentrations (µg L⁻¹) for each rain and type of surface (IZ, impermeable zone, PZ permeable zone). The glyphosate values are the sum of glyphosate and AMPA.

		First rain event with run-off		1 month after spraying	2 months after spraying	3 months after spraying	6 months after spraying	10.5 months after spraying
		16/06/99	27/06/99					
Glyphosate	IZ	1320		95	63	10	2	2
		(1320)		(257)	(257)	(10)	(2)	(2)
µg L⁻¹	PZ		882	255	84	69	7	2
			(1330)	(336)	(146)	(69)	(7)	(2)
Diuron	IZ	8000		387	12	0.2	0.5	0.5
		(8000)		(529)	(17)	(0.2)	(0.5)	(0.5)
µg L⁻¹	PZ		2496	1299	42	98	1	1
			(3300)	(1700)	(63)	(98)	(1)	(1)

The concentrations are presented in Figure 3 for "impermeable" zone and Figure 4 for "permeable" zone.

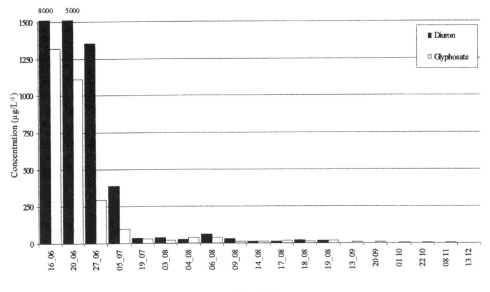

Figure 3. Evolution of the run-off water concentration for "impermeable" zone

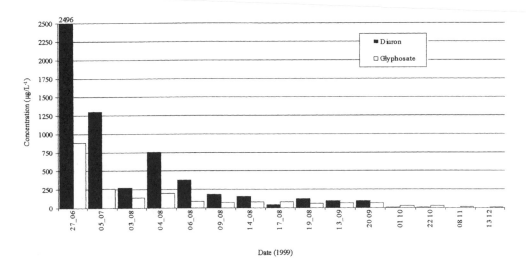

Figure 4. Evolution of the run-off water concentration for "permeable" zone

For a better understanding of the differences between the two zones, more attention has to be paid to the balance between glyphosate and its metabolite AMPA (Figures 5 and 6). On "impermeable" surface, AMPA and glyphosate are contributing roughly equally to the total glyphosate+AMPA indicating a limited degradation of the molecule. On "permeable" surface, AMPA represents about 80% of the total suggesting a higher biodegradation process.

348

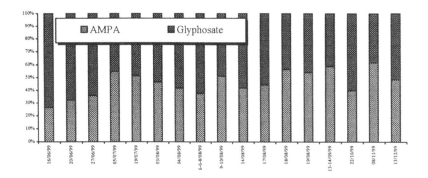

Figure 5. Evolution of the ratio glyphosate/AMPA on impermeable zone

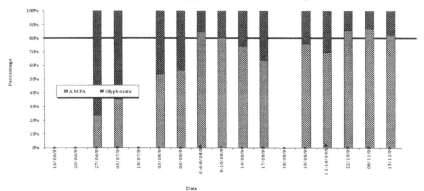

Figure 6. Evolution of the ratio glyphosate/AMPA on permeable zone.

The combination of water flows and concentrations makes it possible to calculate the active ingredient flow transferred to water for each molecule and surface. The results are as following :
- for diuron 33.3 % of the applied quantity on impermeable" zone, and 39.5 % on permeable" one,
- for glyphosate 8.5% of the applied quantity on "impermeable "zone" and 12.8% on "permeable" one.

Regarding environmental issues, the peak of flow and its relation to rainfall have a decisive influence. 5 or 3 mm are enough for the leaching of 50% of the total loss of glyphosate or diuron on "impermeable" zone (table 2).

Table 2. Rainfall necessary for the leaching of 50% and 90% of the total loss.

		percentage of the total loss	
		50%	90%
IZ	Glyphosate	5 mm	570 mm
	Diuron	3 mm	65 mm
PZ	Glyphosate	22 mm	490 mm
	Diuron	13 mm	190 mm

DISCUSSION

Most of the data concerning agricultural use of pesticides indicate that the herbicide transported to the water is in the range of 0.1 to 1 % of the applied quantity. On hard surfaces, the percentages for glyphosate (8 to 12%) and of diuron (33 to 39%) show a very different behaviour of pesticide in urban areas. The very high peak of concentration in run-off water during the first rain leads probably to unacceptable pesticide presence in surface water if not enough dilution.

With the development of urbanisation, the always-increasing acreage of hard surface could play an important role in water pollution. If up to a third of the applied herbicide sprayed on roads, pavements, car parks, etc.. is rapidly transported to surface water, the regulation process based on agricultural soils and conditions could be questionable. However, with a multiplying factor 3-4 between diuron and glyphosate flows, herbicides with a better environmental profile (high K_{OC}, very low rate/ha) should be encouraged. A new impetus has also to be given to the research of non-chemical methods in urban areas that could be the ultimate environment friendly solution for weed control on hard surface (ANGOUJARD *et al.* 2001).

The decisive influence of the first rainfall after spraying for transferring the peak of herbicide to the water should be considered to improve weed control strategies. The standard practice of spraying before the rainfall is most aggressive to the environment. If only a limited number of herbicide sprays are to be used they should be scheduled when the rainfall hazard is reduced to the minimum after application.

ACKNOWLEDGMENTS

This work was supported by the french Ministry of Agriculture and Fisheries, Direction Générale de l'Alimentation.

REFERENCES

Shepherd A J; Heather A I J (1999). Factors affecting the loss of six herbicides from hard surfaces. In : *Proceedings of the 1999 BCPC Conference, Weeds.* **2:** pp. 669 – 674.

Angoujard G ; Lefèvre L; Blanchet P J (2000). Techniques alternatives au désherbage chimique des surfaces imperméabilisées en zone urbaine. In: *Proceedings XIth International Conference on Weed Biology.*, 6-8 septembre 2000, AFPP. pp. 445-452.

Gillet H (1995). Contamination des eaux superficielles de l'Ouest de la France par les produits phytosanitaires: du diagnostic à quelques propositions d'action. In: *Proceedings of: ANPP seizième conférence COLUMA, Journées internationales sur la lutte contre les mauvaise herbes*, Reims 6,7 et 8 décembre 1995., pp.1 – 7.

Modelling pesticide residues in irrigation water: - Managing their impact on non-target cultures and the environment

R Quental-Mendes
Direcção-Geral de Protecção das Culturas (DGPC), Quinta do Marquês, Oeiras, Portugal
Email: dgpc.pest@mail.telepac.pt

T Vinhas, P Viana, M Pereira, P Antunes
Direcção Geral do Ambiente (DGA), Rua da Murgueira 9-9a, 2721- 865 Amadora, Portugal

ABSTRACT

Three compartmental models (rice paddy, canal and leaching) are being linked to simulate the flux of water and herbicides in an agricultural ecosystem in Portugal. The water-quality of drainage canals is of paramount importance in this ecosystem for further re-use in crop irrigation downstream. The application and dissipation of an active substance and its metabolites in a rice paddy and associated drainage canal are being monitored by biological and chemical means in order to assess for phytotoxicity effects on non-target cultures. The time-series will be used to calibrate and validate a mathematical model to manage the quality of water from canals for the irrigation of tomato crops downstream. This tool aims to help in decision making on the use of herbicides, to minimize the risk of soil and groundwater contamination, and to optimize agricultural practices. It works by predicting the right timing for water consumption, when the risk of phytotoxic effects to non-target crops is minimal, avoiding its use during events of herbicide contamination in the stream. This model will optimize the use and preservation of water resources.

INTRODUCTION

In Portugal, it is still common practice to re-use water from drainage canals to irrigate crops, especially in areas not yet served by a modern network of irrigation canals that bring good quality water from far-off sources. Waters from drainage canals carry herbicide chemical residues (active substance and/or metabolites) that contaminate soils and surface waters and underground waters. These waters may cause phytotoxic damage to plants and crops and are harmful to the environment and to the farmer too, because they undermine the crop production levels.

The marshland of the Paul de Magos, in the Tagus/Sorraia valley is an area where the water from drainage canals is still re-used to irrigate tomato, melon, spring beetroot and maize crops that are cultivated downstream of the rice paddies.

Bearing in mind the need for this agricultural practice and the inherent difficulty to characterize the quality of water from drainage canals, we set out to evaluate the phytotoxicity of those waters for crop irrigation.

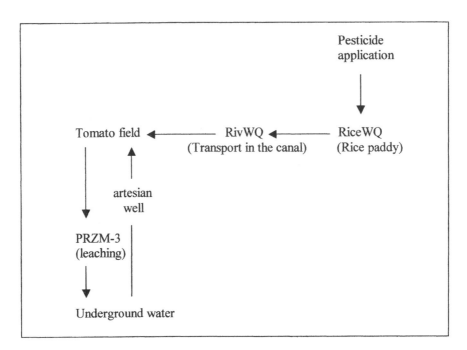

Figure 1. Diagram of the conceptual model showing the proposed linkage of existing sub-models to simulate the flow of pesticide contaminants into irrigation water used in agricultural lands.

This working tool to address pesticide contamination of irrigation water serves a practical purpose - to give advice to local farmers:

1- on the safeguard waiting time for crop irrigation. This is the time interval to be respected once the floodgate from the rice paddy is opened and before the abstraction of water from the drainage canal can begin, given the flow speed and herbicide degradation in the waters of the drainage canal.
2- on the minimum safety distance to the discharge point, for the use and consumption of water from the drainage canal.
3- on estimated phytotoxic damages to plants and crop production levels, if the farmer chooses to ignore the advice and abstracts water from the drainage canal, for crop irrigation during the safeguard waiting time.
4- on the estimated value of groundwater contamination by leaching of herbicides, if the farmer chooses to ignore the advice and abstracts water from the drainage canal, for crop irrigation during the safeguard waiting time.

The project 'Herbicides And Irrigation' has already achieved some of its aims. The three compartmental models were linked, to simulate the flux of water and herbicides in an agricultural ecosystem. The calibration and validation of this meta-model is now underway.

MATERIALS AND METHODS

An agricultural ecosystem comprising a rice paddy, a drainage/irrigation canal, a tomato field and six wells was studied from spring to autumn 2001 during the rice campaign in the Tagus/Sorraia valley.

The rice paddy was treated with molinate (4,500g a.s./ha), bentazone (2,400g a.s./ha) and propanil (3,600g a.s./ha) herbicides in standard agricultural fashion for rice crops. Five sampling points in the rice paddy and six sampling points in the drainage canal along the transect to the tomato field, were chosen for the collection of water and sediment samples. Measurements of dissolved oxygen, conductivity, pH and temperature were also taken. Biological methods for the identification, the detection and the dosage of herbicide residues in water were set-up and are being evaluated under greenhouse conditions. Furthermore, herbicide chemical residues in water from this agricultural ecosystem are being monitored by biological and chemical means. The time-series contains daily data on active substance and its metabolites for the first week after each herbicide application and weekly data thereafter. This study has been conceived in order to provide data to calibrate and validate a mathematical model for the management of those waters for irrigation purposes.

DISCUSSION

The issue of pesticide contamination of irrigation water used in agricultural lands is an ever increasing problem and needs to be addressed. Previous work on this subject has centered on monitoring programmes of pesticides in surface water (Barceló *et al.,* 2000; Azevedo *et al.,* 2000). However, the present ongoing project on herbicide application in rice paddies and their effect on the quality of surface waters and groundwater is a new approach to the problem. The core of the project is a conceptual model (Figure 1) which links three existing compartmental models (rice paddy, canal and leaching models) to simulate the flux of water and herbicides in an agricultural ecosystem in Portugal. The individual components are:

- RICEWQ (Williams *et al.,* 1999), a water quality simulation model for rice paddies that can be used to evaluate the dissipation of herbicides in an aquatic system and to predict the runoff losses of those herbicides to receiving waters;

- its companion RIVWQ (Williams *et al.,* 1999) is a transport model for pesticide contaminated water in ditch/ canals;

- PRZM-3 (Carsel *et al.,* 1998), a model to simulate the leaching processes of pesticides in soil which enables the concentration of pesticides reaching groundwater to be estimated.

The three models are used in pesticide registration studies by the US EPA.

The pesticide is applied to the rice paddy and its dissipation plus runoff losses to receiving waters, by overflow and drainage, is processed by the RICEWQ model. The drained part is transported by the RIVWQ model and is used to irrigate a farmed field (tomato, melon, beetroot or maize). The pesticide residue in this irrigation water is now transferred to the PRZM-3 model which calculates the pesticide mass reaching groundwater by leaching.

The monitoring of herbicide residues in groundwater and surface waters (in the rice paddy and canals) by chemical means has been carried-out, in order to obtain a time-series to calibrate and validate the models.

However, there are other tasks that have yet to be accomplished:

- the best strategy for herbicide application in the rice paddy using the validated model needs to be defined. It is aimed at using the water from the drainage canal with a minimal risk to non-target crops (with regard to phytotoxic effects), and to minimize the risks of groundwater contamination by improving the agricultural practice.
- the knowledge gained must be passed on to the extension advisors in the production sector .

The model is a tool that will help in decision-making on the use of new and existing herbicides. It will also help to optimize the use and preservation of water resources.

ACKNOWLEDGEMENTS

We thank Eng B Pina for allowing the use of the rice paddy for the experiment and all the staff at the Centro de Orizicultura in Salvaterra de Magos for their collaboration. Special thanks go to D Robalo; P Soares; Eng I Frazilo and J Caetano for technical assistance in the fieldwork undertaken. We thank Prof I Moreira and Eng A Franco for lending the water-quality measuring devices. We are indebted to Dr M Williams for providing the Rice WQ and RivWQ models for evaluation purposes.

REFERENCES

Azevedo D; Lacorte S; Vinhas T; Viana P; Barceló D (2000). Monitoring of priority pesticides and other organic pollutants in river water from Portugal by gas chromatography-mass spectrometry and liquid chromatography-atmospherc pressure chemical ionization mass spectrometry. *Journal of Chromatography A*, **879:** 13-26.

Barceló D; Vinhas T; Lacorte S; Viana P (2000). Advanced Monitoring Program from Portuguese Surface Waters of 132 Volatile and Semivolatile Organic Compounds included in the 76/464/EEC Directive. *Waste Water Cluster Newsletter 2000*,**3.**

Carsel R F; Imhoff J C; Hummel P R; Cheplick J M; Donigian Jr A S (1998). PRZM-3, A *Model for Predicting Pesticide and Nitrogen Fate in the Crop Root and Unsaturated Soil Zones*. Users Manual for Release 3.0.

Williams W M; Ritter A M; Cheplick J M (1999). RICEWQ: *Pesticide runoff model for rice crops*. User's manual and program documentation version 1.6.1.

Williams W M; O'Flaherty C; Cheplick J M; Singh P; Ritter A M (1999). RIVWQ: *Chemical transport model for riverine environments*. User's manual and program documentation version 2.0.

SESSION 8

RISK MANAGEMENT

Chairman &   Dr A D Carter
Session Organiser: *ADAS Rosemaund, Hereford, UK*

Predicted impact of transgenic crops on water quality and related ecosystems in vulnerable watersheds of the United States

T L Estes
Stone Environmental Inc., 519 Koerper Ct., Wilmette, IL 60091, USA
Email: estenv@aol.com

R Allen, R L Jones
Aventis CropScience, 2 T.W. Alexander Dr., Research Triangle Park, NC 27709, USA

D R Buckler
USGS-BRD, Columbia Environmental Research Center, Columbia, MO 65201, USA

K H Carr, D I Gustafson, C Gustin, M J McKee
Monsanto Co., 800 N. Lindbergh Blvd., St. Louis, MO 63167, USA

A G Hornsby
University of Florida, Soil and Water Science Dept., Gainesville, FL 32611, USA

R P Richards
Heidelberg College, Water Quality Laboratory, Tiffin, OH 44883, USA

ABSTRACT

The agricultural industry of the United States faces a challenge to reduce the loadings of pesticides into ground and surface waters. While most water resources are not impacted significantly, monitoring data show that the water quality of vulnerable watersheds can be affected when certain pesticides of high mobility and/or environmental persistence are widely used. Even in these relatively rare cases, the presence of these products in water supplies is thought to have minimal ecological impacts, but little work has focused on the potential sub-acute cumulative impacts of mixtures of these products on either individual species or entire ecosystems. Transgenic cropping systems are intended to reduce the types and quantities of pesticide necessary for production of food, feed, and fiber. Because of this decreased reliance on chemical pesticide use, such cropping systems may be anticipated to result in reduced impacts on water quality and possibly related ecosystems. In this paper, we examine the potential water quality and related ecosystem impacts of three new transgenic cropping systems: corn (maize) modified to withstand nonselective herbicides, cotton modified to combat certain lepidopteran pests through the insertion of genetic material from *Bacillus thuringiensis (Bt)*, and corn similarly modified to prevent damage from European Corn Borer and other pests. Simple screening modeling is used to examine the displacement of insecticides by two *Bt*-cropping systems. Higher tier computer modeling is used to compare impacts on drinking water quality among various herbicide treatment scenarios commonly used in conventional and transgenic, herbicide-tolerant corn. All three transgenic cropping systems are predicted to result in significantly lower pesticide concentrations in ground and surface waters, thereby reducing whatever impacts these products have on drinking water quality and related ecosystems.

INTRODUCTION

The agricultural industry of the Midwestern United States faces a challenge to reduce the loadings of pesticides into ground and surface waters (Wauchope, 1978; Leonard, 1990; Thurman *et al.*, 1991; Goolsby *et al.*, 1991; Richards *et al.*, 1993; CAST, 1994; Clark *et al.*, 1999). While observed concentrations are generally below human health and other standards intended to prevent impacts on related ecosystems, monitoring data show that vulnerable watersheds can be affected when mobile and persistent pesticides are heavily used. Detectable levels can occur in drinking water and - in the most vulnerable systems - occasionally attain concentrations above chronic human health standards and ecotoxicological standards established by the United States Environmental Protection Agency (US EPA). While these standards are highly conservative and risk assessments suggest there is a reasonable certainty of no harm to the public or related ecological systems (Richards, *et al.*, 1995), the presence of these residues has been a significant public concern. Under the Food Quality Protection Act of 1996 (US Public Law, 1996), these residues are added to the aggregate risk calculated for uses of these products. For these reasons there is an impetus to adopt practices and technologies for agriculture that offer the promise of continued production with decreased water resource impacts.

The options now available include crops that have been genetically engineered to produce their own insecticide (eg. *Bt*-corn and *Bt*-cotton) or to withstand applications of non-selective herbicides such as glufosinate and glyphosate. Growers planting the *Bt*-crops are able to avoid spraying certain chemical insecticides. Growers planting the herbicide-tolerant varieties are similarly able to avoid use of the pre-emergent herbicides known to occur in ground and surface water supplies. The glufosinate- and glyphosate-based herbicides which replace them may be expected to have a lower human risk, both because they are less toxic and because they have a lower potential to reach water resources (Shipitello *et al.*, 2000; Wauchope *et al.*, 2001). According to a recent report (Carpenter, 2001), the introduction of *Bt*-cotton varieties has reduced the amount of insecticides used by approximately 2.7 million pounds per year in the US. Corn farmers have achieved more modest reductions through the planting of current varieties of *Bt*-corn, but the introduction of new *Bt*-corn varieties engineered to resist Corn Root Worm is expected to result in more significant reductions in insecticide use in corn in the US.

In this paper, the potential water quality and related ecosystem impacts of three transgenic cropping systems are considered: *Bt*-corn, *Bt*-cotton, and herbicide-tolerant corn. The first two systems represent the complete elimination of certain insecticide applications, and the reduced edge-of-field loadings to water supplies can be modeled using simple EPA Tier 1 modeling tools. Herbicide-tolerant corn involves the replacement of certain herbicides by glufosinate and glyphosate, and determining the net impact on drinking water quality requires the use of more sophisticated computer modeling techniques. We use Tier 2 PRZM/EXAMS modeling to quantitatively compare the net impact on both ground and surface water quality in representative case study watersheds, if growers were to switch from conventional corn to transgenic, herbicide-tolerant corn. This choice of end-points (aquatic ecological impacts for the Bt cropping systems and drinking water impacts for herbicide tolerant corn) is motivated by the general sentiment that these tend to be the key regulatory drivers for these classes of materials. The insecticides used in corn and cotton are generally not regarded to have the same frequency of detection in drinking water as do the herbicides used in corn. Similarly, herbicides are not thought to have the same potential as insecticides to have short-term acute ecological impacts on aquatic organisms.

MATERIALS AND METHODS

The two *Bt*-transgenic cropping systems and the insecticides subjected to modeling are listed in Table 1. The six corn- and four cotton-insecticides were chosen based on a recent study (Carpenter and Gianessi, 2001) listing the insecticides that have had their use reduced by the greatest amount during the introduction of *Bt*-corn and *Bt*-cotton, respectively. They are all insecticides that target the same pests controlled by the transgenic crop varieties. The data source for all toxicity data used is the USEPA Pesticide Toxicity Database (Montague, 1996). The lowest EC50 or LC50 for a standard regulatory test (48-hr *Daphnia magna* or 96-hr fish) with the active ingredient was selected for each compound.

Table 1. Properties of insecticides included in ecological effects modeling

Transgenic cropping system	Insecticides displaced	Physical properties		Aquatic toxicity (μg/L)		
		Koc (L/kg)	DT_{50} (days)	48-hr *Daphnia* EC_{50}	96-hr Bluegill LC_{50}	96-hr Rainbow trout LC_{50}
Bt-Corn	carbofuran	22	50	29	88	362
	chlorpyrifos	6070	30	0.1	1.7	7.1
	λ-cyhalothrin	180000	30	0.23	0.21	0.24
	permethrin	100000	30	0.039	0.79	2.1
	tefluthrin	74000	30	0.07	0.13	0.06
	terbufos	500	5	0.31	0.77	7.6
Bt-Cotton	cypermethrin	100000	30	1	1.78	0.82
	methomyl	72	30	8.8	480	860
	profenofos	2000	8	0.93	19	21
	thiodicarb[1]	350	7	27	1470	2650

[1] *Thiodicarb is a dimer of methomyl. The properties listed here are for parent thiodicarb.*

The herbicides subjected to modeling are listed in Table 2. The first two of these herbicides (alachlor and atrazine) are representative of the many chloroacetanilide and triazine pre-emergent soil-applied herbicides that are used in the production of corn in the US and elsewhere. The other two products (glufosinate and glyphosate) are the two non-selective herbicides for which transgenic, herbicide-tolerant varieties of corn and several other crops have been developed and introduced. As discussed elsewhere (Wauchope *et al.*, 2001), these transgenic varieties can be grown using either none or significantly reduced application rates of the pre-emergent soil-applied products, such as alachlor and atrazine.

Table 2. Properties of corn-herbicides included in drinking water modeling

Herbicide	Corn Use Rate (kg/ha)	Koc (L/kg)	DT_{50} (days)	MCL (μg/L)
alachlor	4.48	170	15	2
atrazine	2.8	156	60	3
glufosinate	0.91	600	16	170[1]
glyphosate	1.66	22,300	17	700

[1] *No MCL established for glufosinate; this is the chronic DWLOC (see text).*

The physical properties and use rates shown in Tables 1 and 2 are taken directly from the literature (Hornsby *et al.*, 1995; Tomlin, 1997) and the US EPA "One-Liner" Database. The Maximum Contaminant Levels (MCL's) shown in Table 2 are those established by the US EPA Office of Water and are to be interpreted as an annual average concentration. In the US, Community Water Systems are required to monitor for those products with MCL's, and demonstrate that the specified concentrations are not exceeded. Glufosinate does not have an MCL, but EPA has recently determined a chronic Drinking Water Level of Comparison (DWLOC) for the US population to be 170 μg /L. Though not shown in Table 2, the aquatic toxicity of these herbicides to *Daphnia* and fish is significantly less than that of the insecticides. The corresponding EC_{50} and LC_{50} values range from 1-780 mg/L with a median of 140 mg/L, i.e. generally at least 3 orders of magnitude higher than those of the insecticides.

Tier 1 Surface water exposure modeling (for Bt-corn and Bt-cotton)

The US EPA computer model GENEEC (v 1.2, Parker, 1995) was used to estimate pond concentrations of the 10 insecticides. The estimated concentrations correspond to a standard, worst-case scenario of a hypothetical farm pond, 1 hectare in size, 2 m deep, receiving spray drift and runoff from an adjacent 10 hectare agricultural field. The field is intended to be in a highly vulnerable area; the model assumes a rain even occurs 2 days after each application, and that rainfall washed 10% of the insecticide remaining in the top 1 inch of soil into the pond. Besides the Koc and DT50 physical properties already presented for each insecticide, the GENEEC model utilizes water solubility and hydrolysis rates, which were both available for these products (Hornsby *et al.* 1995). An important limitation of GENEEC comes with the fact that a single site is used to represent all possible use patterns. This site represents an extreme scenario that is unlikely to occur for most applications. With this approach only the highly vulnerable farm pounds are pertained in the assessment. These farm ponds represent only a small minority of the run off scenarios in the US. Based on this extreme scenario GENEEC computes an upper bound exposure estimate taking into consideration run off and drift. Being a screening model, the algorithms within GENEEC lack many fundamental processes that are necessary to simulate the actual run off events in an accurate way. Also the processes incorporated in the model to account for the fate in the aquatic environment are rather limited.

Tier 2 Drinking water exposure modeling (for herbicide-tolerant corn)

The US EPA computer model PRZM v3.12 (Carsel *et al.*, 1998) was used to determine leachate concentrations on a vulnerable Wisconsin site and potential loadings to surface water in edge-of-field runoff in each of three vulnerable watersheds in corn growing geographical areas (see Table 3). The surface water loadings are used as input to the EXAMS v2.98.01 (Burns, 2000) model to generate distributions of estimated reservoir exposure concentrations for several application scenarios. We estimate pesticide concentrations in a reservoir using the standard Index Reservoir approach developed by US EPA (Jones *et al.*, 1998). The selected drinking water reservoir is that used at Salem, Illinois: 962 hectares in size, draining directly into a 30 hectare drinking water reservoir of 2 meter depth, with a measured corn crop area factor of 0.26 (meaning that 26% of the watershed was assumed to be treated by herbicide). Modeling was performed under the principles of Good Modeling Practices described by Estes and Coody (Estes *et al.*, 1993).

Table 3. Geographic scenarios included in PRZM modeling

Scenario class	Site name	Soil type	Weather station[1]	Mean annual precip. (cm)
Surface Water	Coshocton, OH	Cardington SiL[2]	Dayton, OH (1948-1983)	84.81
	Four-Mile Creek, IA	Tama SiL	Waterloo, IA (1961-1995)	79.48
	Salem, IL	Bluford SiL	Evansville, IN (1948-1983)	104.98
Ground Water	Central Sands, WI	Friendship LS[3]	Wausau, WI (1963-1987)	74.10

[1] *Daily meteorlogical values.* [2] *SiL = Silt loam* [3] *LS = Loamy Sand*

For all four field settings, seven pairs of agronomic scenarios were included in the modeling plan (see Table 4). The paired scenarios (eg. 1A and 1B) differ only by whether a "burn-down" application of glyphosate was included as a pre-plant application, such as would often accompany no-till or some other conservation tillage practice. The baseline agronomic scenario (1) is one in which a conventional corn variety is planted and weed control is accomplished using an early post-emergent application of the full label rates of a pre-mix of alachlor and atrazine. Scenarios 2 and 3 represent two potential conventional methods of mitigation: banding and incorporation (Baker & Laflen, 1979). The other four pairs of scenarios represent the two transgenic corn systems, Liberty Link and Roundup Ready corn. In both Liberty Link scenarios (4 and 5), the transgenic corn receives two herbicide treatments. In Scenario 4, the first application is a pre-mix of a half-rate of alachlor and atrazine, plus an application of glufosinate. In Scenario 5, both in-crop herbicide applications are glufosinate alone, at the maximum labeled rates. Scenarios 6 or 7 are identical to Scenarios 4 and 5, except that Roundup Ready corn is substituted for the Liberty Link corn, and the glufosinate applications are replaced by glyphosate treatments.

Table 4. Agronomic scenarios included in PRZM modeling

Scenario number[*]	Corn variety	Early post-emergent application	Late post-emergent application
1A, 1B	Conventional	Alachlor 4.48 kg ha^{-1} Atrazine 2.8 kg ha^{-1}	none
2A, 2B	Conventional	Alachlor 2.24 kg ha$^{-1†}$ Atrazine 1.4 kg ha$^{-1†}$	none
3A, 3B	Conventional	Alachlor 4.48 kg ha$^{-1‡}$ Atrazine 2.8 kg ha$^{-1‡}$	none
4A, 4B	Liberty Link	Alachlor 2.24 kg ha^{-1} Atrazine 1.4 kg ha^{-1} Glufosinate 0.50 kg ha^{-1}	Glufosinate 0.41 kg ha^{-1}
5A, 5B	Liberty Link	Glufosinate 0.50 kg ha^{-1}	Glufosinate 0.41 kg ha^{-1}
6A, 6B	Roundup Ready	Alachlor 2.24 kg ha^{-1} Atrazine 1.4 kg ha^{-1} Glyphosate 0.83 kg ha^{-1}	Glyphosate 0.83 kg ha^{-1}
7A, 7B	Roundup Ready	Glyphosate 0.83 kg ha^{-1}	Glyphosate 0.83 kg ha^{-1}

[*] *For each numbered scenario, "A" includes a pre-plant application of 4.1 kg ha^{-1} glyphosate as a "burn-down" chemical tillage application. Scenario "B" has no such application.*
[†] *Banded applications of the full label rate to stripped areas along the corn rows covering only 50% of the field*
[‡] *Soil incorporated such that the soil residues have a linearly decreasing concentration from 0 to 7.5 cm soil depth*

MODELING RESULTS AND DISCUSSION

Acute aquatic toxicity assessment for insecticides displaced by *Bt*-Corn and *Bt*-Cotton

The GENEEC modeling results for the 10 insecticides are summarized in Table 5.

Table 5. GENEEC modeling summary

Transgenic cropping system	Insecticide	Rate (kg/ha)	No. of applications	Interval between apps (d)	Aqueous solubility (mg/L)	Hydrolysis DT_{50} (d)	GENEEC 96-hrEEC (ppb)
Bt-Corn	carbofuran	1.12	3	14	351	288	129.7
	chlorpyrifos	2.80	3	10	0.4	29.4	19.6
	λ-cyhalothrin	0.034	4	3	0.005	none	0.031
	permethrin	0.22	3	6	0.006	none	0.24
	tefluthrin[1]	0.18	1	--	0.2	none	0.036
	terbufos[1]	1.47	1	--	5	3.3	7.35
Bt-Cotton	cypermethrin	0.11	6	3	0.004	none	0.233
	methomyl	0.56	12	6	58000	none	188
	profenofos	1.12	6	5	28	24	19.99
	thiodicarb	1.01	6	7	19.1	8.6	39.3

1. *Granular, no drift; incorporated to 2 inches. All others were ground spray (1% drift) with no incorporation.*

The distribution of risk ratios based on Tier 1 GENEEC exposure values for cotton and corn are shown in Figures 1 and 2, respectively. Values greater than 1.0, provide a preliminary indication that there is a possibility of the expected environmental concentration exceeding the LC or EC50. For corn, the probability of a risk quotient exceeding 1.0 falls from 54, with normal insecticide use, to approximately 24 for the 50% reduction-in-use scenario. The probability drops further to about 9.3 for the 80% reduction scenario. For cotton, the probability of a risk quotient exceeding 1.0 is predicted to drop from 39 to about 18 for a 50% reduction in insecticide use and to about 6.9 for an 80% reduction. Results of surveys indicate that introduction of *Bt* cotton has resulted in actual reductions in insecticide use from 12% to 61% globally (Betz *et al.*, 2000). These reductions can decrease the probability of exposure and associated risk, as described above. The magnitude of the reduction will depend on the percent of *Bt* cotton planted relative to traditional cotton in a given watershed.

The data presented in Figure 1 and 2 are from Tier 1 GENEEC modeling which uses very conservative assumptions for screening purposes. Consequently, although some of the ratios for the corn and cotton scenarios are shown to exceed 1.0, this does not indicate that a field incident will occur. More sophisticated modeling and biological effects testing would need to be considered in order to predict such an outcome. It is also important to recognize that the pond EECs in this edge-of field analysis do not change under the various reduction-in-use scenarios, since the application rate is assumed to remain the same in fields not growing *Bt* crops. Rather, the probability reflects the reduced likelihood of discrete occurrences of EECs exceeding the LC or EC50 at the watershed level, because fewer fields will be treated.

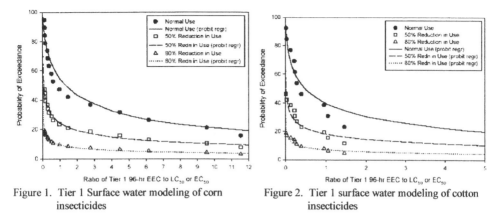

Figure 1. Tier 1 Surface water modeling of corn insecticides

Figure 2. Tier 1 surface water modeling of cotton insecticides

The distance along the vertical line segment between the curves in Figures 1 and 2 at a ratio of 1 indicates the relative area in which vulnerable sites would no longer have a potential exposure to an insecticide in excess of its LC_{50} or EC_{50}. For instance, in Figure 1 it can be seen that the area having potential exceedances from nearly 60% to less than 10% when there is an 80% reduction in corn insecticide use brought about by the introduction of *Bt*-corn to the landscape.

Chronic drinking water assessment for the herbicide-tolerant corn scenarios

Leaching Results

The results of the leaching simulations are shown in Figure 3. These results show in these vulnerable leaching scenarios atrazine applications result in average concentrations in recharge water moving 2 m would be about 1 to 2 ppb, alachlor concentrations would be negligible (0.002 to 0.004 ppb), and essentially no gyphosate or glufosinate would move below 2 m. Therefore, this simulations show that a move to transgenic, herbicide-tolerant corn would not result in increased residues of herbicides in ground water.

The simplistic nature of these simulations needs to be recognized. First, this scenario is quite extreme and in many use areas no significant leaching of any of these herbicides occur. The important transport mechanism in this scenario is chromatograph leaching. In finer-textured soils, preferential flow may result in greater movement than predicted by chromatograph leaching (however, K_{oc} is still usually an important factor affecting the amount leached). Point sources due to improper transport, storage, handling, and disposal can result in any chemical moving to ground water. Another limitation is that these simulations considered the movement of parent only (although similar results would be expected including metabolites, the additional complexity for assessing both exposure and toxicological significance is beyond the scope of this paper). Finally concentrations in recharge moving below 2 m below the soil surface is an upper bound on the concentration of ground water entering a drinking water well due to processes such as mixing, dilution, dispersion, and degradation. In spite of all of these simplistic assumptions, the conclusion that a move to transgenic, herbicide-tolerant corn would not result in increased residues of herbicides in drinking water from ground water is still valid.

363

Surface Water Results

The PRZM modeling predicts that the compounds will behave differently in the field. Alachlor and atrazine have higher edge-of-field losses, ranging as high as 8-9% of the amount applied. Glufosinate and glyphosate have lower annual losses, up to 4.8% and 2.2%, respectively. Most of the losses of alachlor, atrazine, and glufosinate are dissolved in runoff water rather than sorbed to eroded sediment. The reverse is true for glyphosate, which is bound mainly to sediment, because of its much higher soil-sorption coefficient. For the four compounds included in the simulations, the most appropriate toxicologically-relevant endpoint is the annual average concentration. The 90th percentiles of these annual average concentrations for the Illinois soil/weather scenario and all of the different agronomic scenarios are presented in Figure 4. As illustrated therein, the banding and incorporation mitigation measures reduce atrazine and alachlor concentrations by a factor of about two with little difference between the two mitigation measures. The pre-plant application of glyphosate (used to avoid the need for tillage) is not necessarily associated with Roundup Ready corn, as this application can be used with any corn variety. However, the post-emergence applications of both glufosinate and glyphosate are made exclusively to transgenic, herbicide-tolerant corn. Annual concentrations from each application of glyphosate can be added to obtain an average annual concentration, but peak concentrations are less than the sum of peak concentrations resulting from each application.

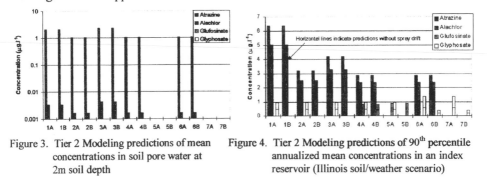

Figure 3. Tier 2 Modeling predictions of mean concentrations in soil pore water at 2m soil depth

Figure 4. Tier 2 Modeling predictions of 90th percentile annualized mean concentrations in an index reservoir (Illinois soil/weather scenario)

Interpretation of the simulation results should consider the predicted concentrations relative to their respective MCL's (which are different for each of the four compounds). The results show that the annual average concentrations expressed as a fraction of the guideline level are significantly lower for glyphosate and glufosinate than for atrazine and alachlor. This is due to three factors. First, the amount applied per unit area is somewhat less than with the conventional herbicides, making less compound available for runoff (the pre-plant application of glyphosate is not included in this statement). Second, the soil sorption of both compounds is higher, making the percent loss in runoff generally lower, for this range of K_{oc} values. Finally the permissible water quality standards are numerically larger for both glyphosate and glufosinate.

CONCLUSIONS

The simple screening modeling predicts that the displacement of insecticides by two *Bt*-cropping systems is likely to significantly reduce the potential for exceedances of aquatic toxicology threshold concentrations in vulnerable watersheds. The higher tier computer modeling predicts that herbicide treatment scenarios associated with transgenic, herbicide-tolerant corn result in lower drinking water concentrations. All three transgenic cropping systems are predicted to result in significantly lower pesticide concentrations in ground and surface waters, thereby reducing whatever impacts these products have on drinking water quality and related ecosystems.

ACKNOWLEDGEMENTS

The authors acknowledge R Don Wauchope, of the USDA-Agricultural Research Service, and Professor J L Baker, of Iowa State University, who both contributed significantly to the Tier 2 modeling work on herbicide-tolerant corn.

REFERENCES

Baker J L; Laflen J M (1979). Runoff losses of surface-applied herbicides as affected by wheel tracks and incorporation. *J Environ Qual* **8**:602-607.

Burns L (2000). Exposure Analysis Modeling System (EXAMS): User Manual and System Documentation, National Exposure Research Laboratory, Office of Research and Development, U.S. Environmental Protection Agency.

Carpenter J E (2001). National Center for Food and Ag. Policy, *Science*, **292 (5517)** :637.

Carpenter J E; Gianessi L P (2001). Agricultural biotechnology: updated benefits estimates. National Center for Food and Agricultural Policy, Washington DC, 48 pp.

Carsel R F; Imhoff J C; Hummel P R; Cheplick J M; Donigian A S (1998). PRZM-3, A Model for Predicting Pesticide and Nitrogen Fate in the Crop Root and Unsaturated Soil Zones: Users Manual for Release 3.0, National Exposure Research Laboratory U.S. Environmental Protection Agency.

CAST (Council for Agricultural Science and Technology), (1994). Pesticides in surface and ground water. *CAST Issue Paper No. 2*: April 1994, 8pp. CAST, 4420 W Lincoln Way, Ames, IA.

Clark G M; Goolsby D A; Battaglin W A (1999). Seasonal and annual load of herbicides from the Mississippi river basin to the Gulf of Mexico. *Environ Sci Technol* **33**:981-986.

Dorn, E; Goerlitz G; Heusel, R; Stumpf K (1992). Behaviour of glufosinate-ammonium in the environment - Degradation in, and effects on, the ecosystem. Hoechst C Produktentwicklung Oekologie 1, DEU. *Zeitschrift fuer Pflanzenkrankheiten (Pflanzenpathologie) und Pflanzenschutz Sonderh.* **13**: 1992, 13: 459-468.

Estes T L; Coody P N (1993). Toward the development of good modeling practices in chemical fate modeling, 14th Annual Meeting of the Society of Environmental Toxicology and Chemistry, Houston, TX.

Giesy J P; Dobson S; Solomon K R (2000). Ecotoxicological risk assessment for Roundup herbicide. *Rev Environ Contam Toxicol* **167**: 35-120.

Goolsby D A; Coupe R C; Markovchick D J (1991). Distribution of selected herbicides and nitrate in the Mississippi river and its major tributaries. *US Geol. Survey Wat. Resources Invest.* Rep. 91-4163, 35 pp.

Hornsby A G; Wauchope R D; Herner A E (1995). *Pesticide Properties in the Environment*, Springer, New York, NY, 227 pp.

Jones R D; Abel S W; Effland W; Matzner R; Parker R (1998). An Index Reservoir for use in assessing drinking water exposures, in *Proposed Methods for Basin-Scale Estimation of Pesticide Concentrations in Flowing Water and Reservoirs for Tolerance Reassessment*, presented to the FIFRA Scientific Advisory Panel, July 1998, http://www.epa.gov/pesticides/SAP/1998/index.htm.

Leonard R A (1990). Movement of pesticides into surface water, In: *Pesticides in the Soil Environment: Processes, Impacts and Modeling*. ed. by Cheng H H, SSSA Book Ser. No. 2, Madison WI, pp. 303-350.

Montague B (1996) Pesticide Toxicity Database. Office of Pesticide Programs, US Environmental Protection Agency, Washington, DC.

NASS (2000). Agricultural Chemical Usage-1999 Field Crops Summary, USDA-NASS report Ag Ch 1 (00)a, Wash., D.C., 117 pp.

Parker R D; Rieder D D (1995) The Generic Expected Environmental Concentration Program, GENEEC. Part B - User's Manual. US Environmental Protection Agency, Environmental Fate and Effects Division, Washington, D.C. .Richards R P; Baker D B (1993). Pesticide concentration patterns in agricultural drainage networks in the Lake Erie Basin. *Environ Toxicol Chem* **12**:13-26.

Richards R P; Baker D B' Christensen B; Tierney D (1995). Atrazine exposures through drinking water: exposure assessments for Ohio, Illinois, and Iowa. *Environ Sci Technol* **29**: 406-412.

Shipitalo M J; Malone R W (2000). Runoff losses of pre- and post-emergence herbicides from watersheds in a corn-soybean rotation, Annual Meetings Abstracts, American Society of Agronomy, Crop Science Society of America, Soil Science Society of America, November 9-13, Minneapolis, MN, p. 4.

Sidhu R S; Hammond B G; Fuchs R L; Mutz J-N; Holden L R; George B; Olson T (2000). The composition and feeding value of grain from glyphosate-tolerant corn is equivalent to that of conventional corn (*Zea mays* L.). *J Agric Food Chem* **48**: 2305-2312.

Thurman E M; Goolsby D A; Meyer M T; Kolpin D W (1991). Herbicides in surface waters of the United States: the effect of spring flush. *Environ Sci Technol* **25**: 1794-1796.

Tomlin C D S (1997). *The Pesticide Manual, 11th edition*. British Crop Protection Council, Farnham, Surrey, UK. 1606 pp.

United States Environmental Protection Agency (2000). Drinking Water Standards and Health Advisories, Office of Water, EPA 822-B-00-001.

United States Federal Register (1992). Establishment of maximum contaminant levels, 57 FR 31776, 17-Jul-92.

US Public Law (1996). The food quality protection act of 1996, 104-170, August 3, 1996, 110 *Stat* 1489.

Wauchope, R D (1978). The pesticide content of surface water draining from agricultural fields--a review. *J Environ Qual* **7**: 459-472.

Wauchope R D *et al.*, (2001). Predicted impact of transgenic, herbicide-tolerant corn on drinking water quality in vulnerable watersheds of the mid-western United States. Presented at IUPAC conference, Brisbane, Australia, July 4, 2001.

Evaluation of best management practices in a midwestern watershed

G F Czapar
University of Illinois Extension, PO Box 8199, Springfield, IL 6271, USA
Email: g-czapar@uiuc.edu

T J Lively, M S Cochran
Sangamon County Soil and Water Conservation Dist., 40 Adloff Lane, Springfield, IL 62703, USA

D P Tierney
Syngenta Crop Protection, 410 Swing Road, Greensboro, NC 27419, USA

J L Hatfield
National Soil Tilth Laboratory, USDA-ARS, 2150 Pammel Drive, Ames, IA 50011, USA

L L Keefer
Illinois State Water Survey, 2204 Griffith Drive, Champaign, IL 61820, USA

T M Skelly
City Water, Light and Power, Municipal Center East, Springfield, IL 62757, USA

ABSTRACT

The impact of agricultural production on water quality continues to be a major issue. Every public water supply in the United States is required to sample quarterly for regulated contaminants, including several herbicides. Best management practices (BMPs) have been shown to effectively reduce herbicide and sediment movement into surface water. The goals of this five-year project are to evaluate a range of BMPs for protecting surface water, and to assess changes on a watershed scale. The study area is a 66,000 hectare watershed in central Illinois. Surface water quality is being monitored using a network of 12 in-stream sampling stations. Automatic samplers record stream flow data and collect water samples from five to six runoff events annually. The sampling network will help identify vulnerable areas in the watershed and track changes over the course of the project. Water samples are analyzed for six herbicides, nitrate, phosphorus, and total suspended solids. On-farm demonstration plots have been established to study specific BMPs and evaluate their effectiveness on reducing runoff. In addition, a geographical information system (GIS) framework is being developed for the entire watershed to assist in project evaluation.

INTRODUCTION

National and state monitoring studies of surface water quality have helped identify the most common contaminants, and when they are most likely to occur. The extent of pesticide loss from treated fields due to surface runoff can range from less than one percent to over ten percent of the applied product (Wauchope, 1978). Several have shown that chemical losses are often greatest when heavy rainstorms closely follow pesticide applications (Thurman *et al.*, 1991).

In April 1994, a 15 cm rainstorm in a 24-hour period produced considerable runoff and resulted in high levels of atrazine in Lake Springfield. Although atrazine concentration in finished water was temporarily elevated, the public water supply never exceeded the maximum contaminant level (MCL) of 3 μg L^{-1}. The water utility was able to treat with powdered activated carbon (PAC) to successfully reduce atrazine concentrations in the finished drinking water, but it was an expensive process (Brown *et al.*, 1996).

The practice of treating with PAC has been successfully used to manage atrazine fluctuations in the lake. Figure 1 and figure 2 demonstrate the variation of atrazine concentration in Lake Springfield between 1998 and 1999, while finished water levels are kept relatively consistent.

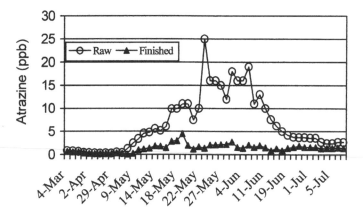

Figure 1. Atrazine concentration in Lake Springfield raw and finished water in 1998.

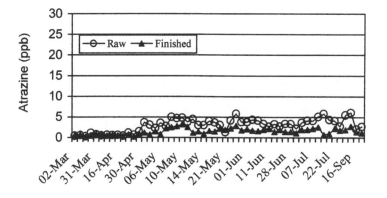

Figure 2. Atrazine concentrations in Lake Springfield raw and finished water in 1999.

Although treatment may reduce seasonally high concentrations of pesticides in water, most would agree that prevention and reducing the risk of pesticide runoff is a preferred approach. Best management practices are designed to minimize adverse impacts on surface water and groundwater quality. In addition to protecting the environment, these practices must be economically sound. Baker and Mickelson (1994) reviewed management factors such as herbicide application and timing, conservation tillage, and filter strips for minimizing herbicide runoff. Hirshi *et al.*, (1997) provided a comprehensive summary of management practices for protecting surface water.

BMPs that are specific to a watershed are likely to be more effective than treating every acre the same way. In most cases, a combination of practices will be required to achieve water quality goals, and the suggested BMPs may vary depending on soils, topography and individual farm operation.

MATERIALS AND METHODS

Lake Springfield is a 1,700 hectare reservoir with a storage capacity of approximately 66 billion liters of water. It is the public drinking water supply for over 150,000 people. The Lake Springfield watershed includes 66,000 hectares of area southwest of the actual lake. Approximately 88% of the watershed's highly productive soils are intensively cropped, with about 61,000 hectares planted each year. Historically, sedimentation has been a concern in the area, and was a major reason that a watershed resource planning committee was formed in 1990.

BMP demonstration project

The Lake Springfield Watershed project is a collaborative effort involving many different individuals and groups. It includes farmers and landowners, City Water, Light and Power, the Illinois State Water Survey, the Natural Resource Conservation Service, Syngenta Crop Protection, Inc., Sangamon County Soil and Water Conservation District, the Soil Tilth Laboratory/USDA/ARS and University of Illinois Extension.

Specific goals of the project are to; 1) evaluate the effectiveness of BMPs for protecting surface water 2) identify combinations of BMPs that can reduce off-site movement of sediments, pesticides, and nutrients and 3) provide farmers and landowners a range of alternatives that are both environmentally and economically viable.

Practices such as grass filter strips, riparian buffers, waterways, sediment control basins, conservation tillage, and integrated pest management are some of the possible solutions. Some of these BMPs will be monitored at the field and sub-watershed level.

Currently, 12 in-stream automatic samplers are installed. This sampling network will help to identify vulnerable areas in the watershed and track changes over the course of the five-year project. Automatic samplers record stream flow data during five or six major runoff events, while grab samples are periodically collected all year. Water samples are being analyzed for atrazine, simazine, cyanazine, alachlor, metolachlor, acetochlor, nitrate nitrogen, ortho-phosphorus, and total suspended solids

DISCUSSION

Over the course of this five-year project, data from over 300 runoff events will be collected. An example of one runoff event from a single station is presented. Atrazine and acetochlor concentrations from stream sample station #2 on May 4, 1998 are shown in Figure 3. During 1998, automatic samples were taken at two-hour intervals during runoff events.

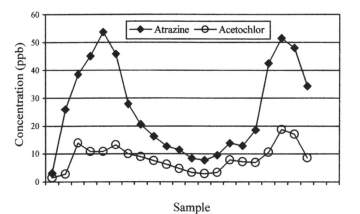

Figure 3.   Herbicide concentration at stream station #2 on May 4, 1998.

Although soil erosion and herbicide runoff are the primary water quality concerns in this project, nutrient levels in streams are also being measured. Figure 4. shows the nitrate nitrogen concentration at station #2 during the May 1998 runoff event. During rainfall events, stream stations recorded nitrate levels above the drinking water standard of 10 mg L^{-1}. However, nitrate concentration in the lake rarely exceeds 5 mg L^{-1}

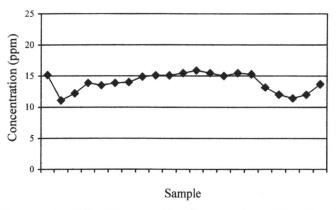

Figure 4.   NO$_3$ –N concentration at stream station #2 on May 4, 1998.

On-farm demonstrations

Working with local farmers, edge-of-field research sites were established to study specific BMPs and evaluate their effectiveness in reducing soil erosion and surface water runoff.

Practices include a disk-chisel system with and without a grass filter strip, a first year term no-till system, and a long-term no-till system. Treatments were replicated three times. Plots were 22 m long and 11 m wide and were surrounded by metal borders. Runoff was directed into a 208-liter collection reservoir that was emptied and analyzed after each rainstorm.

As shown in Figure 5, filter strips significantly reduced atrazine concentrations in runoff from small plots following a rainstorm.

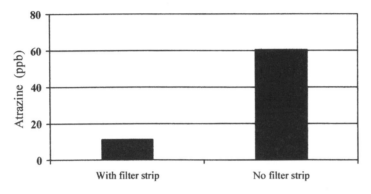

Figure 5.   Atrazine concentration in runoff on April 28, 1999.

Figure 6 shows a comparison of first year no-till plots with long term (12 year) no-till plots on April 5, 1999. Atrazine concentration in runoff was reduced by approximately 90% in the long-term no-till system compared to a field in its first year of no-till.

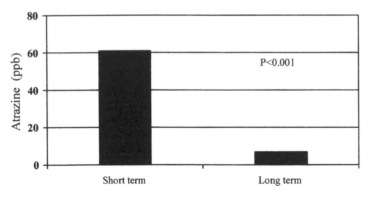

Figure 6.   Atrazine concentration in runoff on April 5, 1999.

Geographical information system (GIS) and information databases are being created for the entire watershed to assist in data evaluation. Since education is a major component of the project, regular updates and progress reports are provided to farmers, landowners, and the general public. Additional publications, field meetings, and demonstrations will continue over the course of the project.

The Lake Springfield BMP project brings together many different groups and organizations that may have individual interests, but that all share the common goal of protecting water resources. Since it is being directed at the local level, it relies heavily on the input and involvement of people living in the watershed. Finally, the experience and knowledge gained from this project can be shared with other communities in Illinois and across the country.

REFERENCES

Baker J L; S K; Mickelson (1994). Application technology and best management practices for minimizing herbicide runoff. *Weed Technology* **8:** 862-869.

Brown W A, T M Skelly, and E Hervey (1996). Powdered activated carbon treatment for the removal of atrazine and other pesticides from the Springfield, Illinois community water supply. pp. 23-32. *Proceedings of the Illinois Agricultural Pesticides Conference.* University of Illinois at Urbana-Champaign.

Hirschi M; R Frazee; G Czapar; D Peterson (1997). 60 Ways Farmers Can Protect Surface Water. College of Agricultural, Consumer and Environmental Sciences, University of Illinois at Urbana-Champaign.

Taylor A G; S Cook. (1995). Water quality update: The results of pesticide monitoring in Illinois streams and public water supplies. pp. 81-84. *Proceedings of the Illinois Agricultural Pesticides Conference.* University of Illinois at Urbana-Champaign.

Thurman E M; D A Goolsby; M T Meyer; D W Kolpin (1991). Herbicides in surface water of the Midwestern United States: The effect of the spring flush. *Journal of Environmental Science and Technology:* **25:** (10) 1794-1796.

Wauchope R D (1978). The pesticide content of surface water draining from agricultural fields - A review. *Journal of Environmental Quality* **7:** 459-472.

Management practices to minimize atrazine loss in surface water runoff

D L Regehr, P L Barnes, D L Devlin, R J Rector
Departments of Agronomy, and Biological and Agricultural Engineering, Kansas State University, Manhattan, Kansas, 66506, USA
Email:dregehr@oznet.ksu.edu

M A Hoobler
Aventis CropScience, Loveland, Colorado, 80537, USA

ABSTRACT

Atrazine herbicide remains widely used for weed management in corn (*Zea mays*) and grain sorghum (*Sorghum bicolor*). Its predominant use in the US Great Plains is soil surface application at seeding time, coinciding with the period of highest annual precipitation. On the predominately fine-textured soils of the region, this use may result in excessive atrazine loss in surface water runoff. Management options are available which reduce atrazine loss in runoff by 70 percent or more, without jeopardizing the weed control benefits. These include: 1) pre-plant soil incorporation in tilled fields; 2) fall application in no-till fields; and 3) post-emergence applications at reduced rates.

INTRODUCTION

Atrazine leads all herbicides in usage in the United States (Gianessi and Marcelli, 2000). About 80 percent of all field corn and grain sorghum acreage receives annual applications of atrazine at rates averaging about 1.3 kg/ha. After over forty years of use, it remains a key component of economical and effective broadleaf weed control, and grass suppression, in these crops.

Atrazine performs well over a broad range of application timings and rates. It has excellent residual activity in many soils at rates above about 1.5 kg/ha. Most commonly it is soil surface applied immediately after seeding corn or sorghum. However, it may also be pre-plant soil incorporated in tilled fields, or soil surface applied several weeks prior to planting, to eliminate weed establishment in no-till fields. For such soil applied situations, it is often applied with acid amide herbicides (e.g. metolachlor, acetochlor, etc.) to broaden the spectrum of weed species controlled.

In addition to its residual activity, atrazine has excellent foliar activity when applied with appropriate adjuvants. Most post-emergence herbicides for corn and sorghum benefit greatly from being applied with 0.6 to 0.8 kg/ha atrazine.

Both residual and foliar atrazine activity has been exploited in the High Plains region of the USA to help manage weeds and volunteer wheat in wheat stubble fallow, a practice called "eco-fallow." This chemical-fallow system is playing a major role in reducing soil erosion by wind and water, enhancing soil water storage, and increasing dryland corn and sorghum acreage and yields in a semi-arid region where previously the main crop was winter wheat only, alternating with 15-month long fallow periods (Dhuyvetter *et al.*, 1996).

Despite its continuing popularity with corn and sorghum producers, atrazine brings water quality concerns. It is commonly detected in streams and rivers. In 1994, the US Environmental Protection Agency announced that a maximum contaminant level for atrazine of 3 μg/Litre would be set for finished drinking water. This is an enforceable level for public drinking water systems and, according to the EPA, is a concentration that is safe to drink over a 70-year lifetime.

FACTORS INFLUENCING ATRAZINE MOVEMENT IN SURFACE WATER

Chemical properties

The chemical properties of individual pesticides influence their potential for becoming water quality problems. Atrazine is poorly adsorbed to clay and organic matter, and is relatively persistent in the environment, with a half-life of about 60 days (Ahrens, 1994). Furthermore, it is highly soluble in water. Therefore, atrazine and other weakly soil-adsorbed herbicides leave the field primarily in runoff water and not with eroding soil particles.

Soil type and site characteristics

Soil type and site characteristics are major factors influencing atrazine runoff. Soils are categorized into four hydrologic groups (A, B, C and D), based on water infiltration rates under field conditions. Many of the soils of the Great Plains are group D soils with high clay content, very slow infiltration and rapid runoff potential. Most farm fields have gradient terraces to reduce soil erosion by reducing slope length and surface drainage velocity.

Tillage practices

For many soils, no-till systems that maintain moderate to high levels of plant residue on the field surface will reduce water runoff, compared to tilled systems. Long-term no-tillage improves soil aggregate formation and plant residues hold rainwater in place longer, encouraging greater infiltration. Some soils, however, have low to very low permeability due to restrictive clay layers. Even after long-term no-till management, surfaces of such soils are often wet during spring planting when atrazine is typically applied.

Rainfall timing, intensity and duration

The surface soil moisture at time of herbicide application, the interval from application until first rainfall, and the intensity and duration of the first rainfall, greatly influence the amount of atrazine lost in surface runoff. The wetter the soil surface at the time atrazine is applied, the sooner runoff begins during a rain storm and the greater the potential for atrazine runoff. If the soil is dry at the start of a rainfall event, more water infiltration will occur, moving some atrazine below the soil surface before runoff begins.

It is well documented that atrazine is most susceptible to loss during the first runoff event following application (Hall, 1974). Figure 1 shows water runoff volume and atrazine loss from a grain sorghum field with chisel-disk (CD) and no-till (NT) management (Olson *et al.*, 1998). Note that early in the growing season, greater water runoff occurred in NT treatments, and that the pattern shifted as the crop developed. Atrazine loss from the pre-plant NT application (on

20 May) decreased with each successive event, and very little atrazine runoff loss occurred in the chisel-disk treatment where atrazine was soil incorporated.

Long-term precipitation and storm intensity records for Manhattan, KS, indicate that the highest amount and intensity of rainfall, and the period of highest potential for runoff, occur during the peak atrazine application window of May, June and July.

In summary, atrazine runoff is less when: 1) it is applied to dry soil surfaces; 2) at least 7 days time elapses between application and the first rain storm causing runoff; and 3) the first rain event after application is of low intensity.

BEST MANAGEMENT PRACTICES TO MINIMIZE RUNOFF LOSS

Atrazine is extremely versatile, with regard to application timings, both residual and foliar activity, and rates. This versatility helps account for the high volume of total use, and suggests that there should be management options that minimize off-site loss while maintaining weed control benefits (Regehr *et al.*, 1996). These best management practices should reflect regional climatic conditions, soil types, and production patterns. Three core management alternatives are presented.

Soil incorporate atrazine

This is a option for soils with moderate to poor permeability where tillage is planned. Atrazine, or an atrazine-containing product, is applied from 0 to 14 days before planting and incorporated into the top 5 cm of soil with a field cultivator.

Mechanical incorporation reduces the amount of atrazine on the soil surface where it is most vulnerable to runoff. On a poorly permeable silt loam soil with a restrictive claypan in eastern KS, pre-plant incorporation of atrazine in a chisel-disk system reduced atrazine loss in surface runoff by about 75 % over a 4-yr period, compared to soil surface applications in a no-till system (Olson *et al.*, 1998; Hoobler, 1999). On such soils, pre-plant tillage helps the soil surface to dry, and sets the stage for greater water infiltration during the first rains following herbicide application. The longer the delay of the onset of runoff in the initial precipitation event, the lower the amount of atrazine loss.

In another recent KS study (unpublished), atrazine herbicide was subjected to natural rainfall, and to natural rainfall supplemented by 6.4 cm/hr additional precipitation applied with a rainfall simulator (Swanson, 1965) at 2 and at 9 days after planting. This rate represents a one-hour storm with the frequency of occurring once every ten years (Hershfield, 1961). Averaged over the 1999 and 2000 growing seasons, soil incorporated atrazine loss was 48 % less than atrazine surface applied to tilled soils, and 61 % less than atrazine surface applied to no-till soils. Percent reductions in runoff loss were similar under both precipitation regimes. These findings show that soil incorporation can reduce atrazine runoff losses under a wide range of precipitation amounts and intensities.

The weed control efficacy of atrazine can be affected by soil incorporation. When application is followed by very limited precipitation, then efficacy is often enhanced by mechanical incorporation because less rainfall is required to activate the herbicide. On the other hand, when precipitation is high, then surface applications may give better weed control because the concentration of herbicide near the soil surface is higher. For good weed control efficacy, it is desirable that mechanical soil incorporation not exceed a depth of about 5 cm.

Use fall or early spring applications

In the western Great Plains, precipitation amounts and intensity are generally much lower during fall, winter, and early spring, than from late April through July. Atrazine has sufficient longevity that it can be applied during periods of low precipitation amounts and intensity. Fall or early spring applications are a management option for no-till fields where pre-plant incorporation is not possible. Once the atrazine has been subjected to several small precipitation events, enough product is adsorbed in the surface soil so that subsequent more intense rains cause little herbicide loss. On an eroded silty clay loam soil near Manhattan, KS, fall-applied atrazine from 1996 through 1999 averaged 1.4 % of applied, lost in runoff despite several unusual winter storm events (unpublished). These field runoff data are being used to test runoff from fall or early spring applications as predicted by the GLEAMS (Groundwater Loading Effect of Agricultural Management Systems) model.

In KS, atrazine may be applied to row-crop stubble following fall harvest, a practice analogous to the eco-fallow management of wheat stubble in the High Plains. This option is best suited to fields where soybeans have just been harvested, that will be no-till planted to corn or sorghum the following spring. Atrazine applied in fall, with crop oil concentrate and 2,4-D ester, controls a wide range of winter annual weeds including the mustards (*Cruciferae*), *Lamium amplexicaule, Conysa canadensis*, annual brome (*Bromus* spp.), *Taraxacum officinale*, etc. It reduces or eliminates the need for pre-plant burndown applications in spring. No-till farmers find that soils warm up earlier in spring when it is weed-free, and seasonal time management is improved if the number of spring field operations can be reduced.

Atrazine is not an appropriate herbicide for fall application to highly permeable soils, or in regions where winter precipitation is high. For example, in the central and eastern Corn Belt, and in the southeastern US, simazine may be a better fit for fall application. It has greater adsorptivity to clay and organic matter, is more persistent, and less soluble in water (Ahrens, 1994).

Use post-emergence atrazine applications at reduced rates

Using soil-applied acid amide herbicides for grass control, followed by post-emergence herbicides containing from 0.56 to 0.84 kg/ha atrazine, is a highly effective weed management strategy for corn and sorghum that is widely used in the US Great Plains and Corn Belt. Season-long control of broadleaf weeds such as *Amaranthus* spp., *Abutilon theophrasti, Xanthium strumarium, Ipomoea* spp, and *Helianthus annuus* is routinely achieved. The effectiveness of herbicides such as bromoxynil, bentazone, carfentrazone-ethyl, dicamba, 2,4-D, and prosulfuron is greatly enhanced by application with atrazine.

Post-emergence atrazine offers several advantages for reducing atrazine loss in runoff. Foremost is the reduction in application rates, since post-emerge tank mixtures often contain only about one-third the atrazine rate of typical planting-time tank mixtures. Hoobler (1999) showed that atrazine loss in surface runoff is proportional to the application rate (Figure 2). Low rates used in tank mixtures result in low runoff concentrations. Also, applications made to

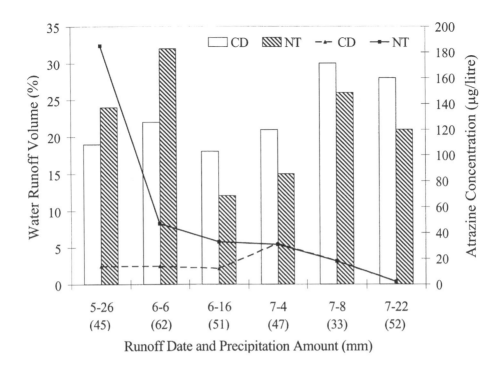

Figure 1. Percent water runoff from the six storm events that resulted in runoff during the 1996 sorghum growing season, for chisel/disk (CD) and no-till (NT) treatments, and mean atrazine concentration in runoff water (adapted from Olson *et al.*, 1998).

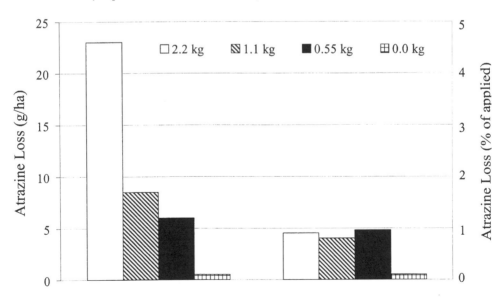

Figure 2. Effects of post-emergence atrazine rate on loss (g/ha), and percent of applied, in surface water runoff (adapted from Hoobler, 1999).

fields with growing crops and weeds would tend to have less runoff than applications to bare fields. Furthermore, soil temperatures and evaporative demand are higher during the post-emerge application time. Atrazine losses from precipitation events in a Kansas grain sorghum field in 1997 and 1998 were less than one percent of applied, whereas runoff losses from planting time applications typically run 5 to 10 % of applied, and have been documented to reach 20 % percent of applied under the most adverse conditions (Smith *et al.*, 1999).

The use of low-rate post-emerge atrazine mixed with other herbicides is effective for all tillage systems and nearly all soil types where corn and sorghum are grown. Tank-mix partners are selected to help with control of specific weed species. Even fields with coarse-textured soils can be treated because atrazine rates are low, and both corn and sorghum show excellent ability to metabolize the applied atrazine under good growing conditions.

Other best management practices to minimize atrazine loss

The core practices discussed above may be modified and/or combined in ways that further reduce atrazine loss in surface runoff. All herbicides should be used in the context of integrated weed management and crop production systems, and on fields with appropriate soil and water conservation structures. Substantial reductions in atrazine runoff loss can be achieved without sacrificing the benefits of atrazine herbicide for weed management.

REFERENCES

Ahrens W H ed (1994). Herbicide handbook. 7th ed. Champaign, IL: Weed Science Society of America, pp. 20-23.

Dhuyvetter, K C; Thompson C R; Norwood C A; Halvorson A D (1996). Economics of dryland cropping systems in the Great Plains: a review. *Journal of Production Agriculture* **9**:216-222.

Gianessi L P; Marcelli M B (2000). Pesticide use in U.S. crop production: 1997. National Center for Food and Agriculture Policy, 1616 P Street, NW, Washington, DC 20036.

Hall, J K (1974). Erosional losses of s-triazine herbicides. *Journal of Environmental Quality* **12**:336-341.

Hershfield D N (1961). Rainfall frequency atlas of the United States. *U S Weather Bureau.* Technical Paper **40**.

Hoobler M A (1999). Effects of atrazine placement, application timing, application rate, and tillage system on atrazine runoff losses. M S Thesis, Kansas State University, Manhattan, KS. 78 p.

Olson B L S; Regehr D L; Janssen K A; Barnes P L (1998). Tillage system effects on atrazine loss in surface water runoff. *Weed Technology* **12**:646-651.

Regehr D L; Devlin D L; Barnes P L; Watson S L (1996). Reducing atrazine runoff from crop fields. *Cooperative Extension Service, Kansas State University*. **MF-2208**

Smith M B; Blanchard P E; Johnson W G; Smith G S (1999). Atrazine management and water quality. *Outreach and Extension, University of Missouri-Columbia*. Manual **167**.

Swanson N P (1965). Rotating-boom rainfall simulator. *Transactions of the American Society of Agricultural Engineers* **8**:71-72.

The design of a pesticide handling and washdown facility

S C Rose
ADAS Consulting Limited, Gleadthorpe, Meden Vale, Mansfield, Notts, NG20 9PF, UK
Email: steve.rose@adas.co.uk

P J Mason, I D L Foster
Department of Geography, Coventry University, Priory, Street, Coventry, CV5 1FB, UK

A Walker
HRI, Wellesbourne, Warwick, CV35 9EF, UK

A D Carter
ADAS Consulting Limited, Rosemaund, Preston Wynne, Hereford, HR1 3PG, UK

ABSTRACT

Point source contamination of surface water by pesticides within agricultural catchments can be significant. One major source of potential contamination is the farmyard where activities involved in handling pesticides, filling sprayer equipment and washing down the sprayer after applications take place. The characteristics of the farmyard surface determine how quickly any spilt pesticide or sprayer washings reach surface waters. Impermeable surfaces which generate rapid runoff do not permit any *in situ* retention and hence degradation of pesticides to take place. Permeable surfaces and underlying material allow the pesticide residues to infiltrate into the substrate where opportunities for physical, chemical and biological degradation do exist. ADAS, Coventry University and HRI Wellesbourne are currently undertaking a collaborative research project investigating the performance of different surfaces for pesticide handling and washdown areas with a view to developing a design manual that specifies how these areas should be constructed to minimise the risk of surface water contamination by pesticides. This paper focuses on the experimental work to date.

INTRODUCTION

The pollution of water resources by pesticides can arise from a number of sources and produce a number of detrimental impacts, both environmentally and economically. Pollution of surface water can lead to a detrimental impact on water quality and aquatic ecosystems. The pollution of water resources, both groundwater and surface water, has an additional effect in terms of the quality of potential drinking water supplies at the points of abstraction. Pesticide pollution can either cause the abstraction water to be rejected as being too polluted or can require that expensive water treatment is required prior to discharge into the potable water system. This water treatment cost is passed on to the consumers of water, i.e. the whole population. There are many stakeholders involved in the use of pesticides for plant protection and the quality of water resources in the UK (e.g. agrochemical companies,

Environment Agencies, water supply companies, conservation bodies, Government). Groundwater and surface water is at risk of contamination from agricultural pesticides. In some cases this contamination is more likely to result from point sources than as diffuse sources a result of pesticide application to crops in the field. Such point sources could include areas on farms where pesticides are handled, filled into sprayers or where sprayers are washed down.

There is a range of relevant EU and national legislation, codes of practice and advisory information currently available to farm managers and pesticide users concerning the pesticide handling, and disposal of associated washings and other materials. There is also impending future legislation which will impact on 'on-farm' activities such as the Waste Framework and the Incineration Directive.

A number of monitoring projects in the UK and other countries (Carter, 2000; Mason *et al.*, 1999; Kreuger, 1998) have identified that point sources of pesticides can be responsible for a significant portion of the total amount of pesticide loading in water and can account for the peak concentrations detected. The ranges reported vary from at least 20% of the total load in a catchment but could be as high as 70% depending on catchment characteristics. The farmyard characteristics, operating practices and local conditions vary but all researchers report similar reasons for the origin of the point source contamination.

Point source contamination can range in concentration from that found in dilute washings to the concentrated, formulated active substance depending on the nature of loss. Given that point sources are largely attributable to operator error or bad practice, equipment faults and the physical characteristics of the handling/mixing area it is considered that point sources can conceivably be controlled more easily than diffuse pollution. Better training of operators and good machinery maintenance, with storage undercover, are considered to be fundamental to minimising the risk of pollution from many point sources. Another important consideration is the design and operation of pesticide handling and washdown areas on farmsteads. Traditionally these areas have been mainly on concrete pads, close to farm buildings where there is access to a mains water supply. Often these concrete pads drain to sumps which connect then direct to the nearest watercourse or soakaway. As a results direct and rapid contamination of water resources can arise from these pesticide handling and washdown operations. In 2000 a research study commenced with the objective of producing a new cost-effective design manual for pesticide handling and washdown areas which significantly reduces the risk of contamination of water resources. One aspect of this work was to test the effectiveness of various test surfaces (with underlying substrates) for retaining and degrading a range of pesticides *in situ*.

MATERIALS AND METHODS

During summer 2000 six fibreglass tanks, 1.92m long by 0.91m wide by 0.61m deep were installed at HRI Wellesbourne in holes dug into the local soil. The tanks were installed such that they protruded approximately 0.05m above the surrounding soil. The tanks were laid onto a bed of sand and tilted to give a slope of 1.5% towards the front end. Along the front edge of the tanks a 10m long by 1.5m wide x 1.5m deep instrument pit was dug and lined with wood. The floor of the instrument pit was covered with gravel. Once all the tanks and the wooden liner for the pit were in place soil was backfilled in around the tanks to ensure that a good contact was made between the tanks and surrounding soil. Each tank had a 0.06m diameter perforated drainage pipe installed running diagonally across its bottom. A hole was cut at the bottom front end of the tank to allow the pipe to carry water from the bottom of the tanks into a 27 litre removable glass leachate collector. This container was housed in a 68 litre plastic tank to enable the collection of any overflow. For each tank a 0.06m layer of pea shingle was laid in the bottom of the tank to cover the drainage pipe. This would permit all the water that infiltrated through the overlying layers to drain out of the tanks and become available for sampling. A layer of geotextile covered the pea shingle to prevent the in-wash of fine particles.

The six test surfaces investigated were:
i)   Concrete
ii)   Porous asphalt
iii)   Hardcore
iv)   Porous paving
v)   Soil with a grass turf surface
vi)   Biobed (a mixture of topsoil, straw and peat substitute) with a grass turf surface

The two surfaces likely to produce surface runoff (i.e. concrete and asphalt) also had the facility to monitor the rate of runoff and sample the runoff water.

In order to eliminate the variability of contamination arising from spray operator activities each area was 'artificially' contaminated by simulating pesticide losses based on the data for isoproturon obtained from the Cherwell project (Mason *et al.*, 1999). A grid was imposed on each surface and representative surface spots, spills, leaks and vehicle washing waste were applied in a standard manner to specific grid squares. Rainfall was simulated (when necessary) to achieve a worst case event (e.g. 25mm in 24 hours) within 48 hours of an application by adding irrigation water. Subsequent natural rainfall was allowed to fall on the test areas.

Six pesticides were chosen to be applied to the test surfaces. They represented a range of physico-chemicals properties, with three that would normally be applied in the spring period (chlorothalonil, dimethoate, epoxiconazole) and three that would normally be applied in the autumn period (isoproturon, chlorpyrifos, pendimethalin).

The first application of pesticides took place to the test surfaces in June 2000. Only the three normally spring applied chemicals were used. The application rates represented the scaled-down Cherwell project findings on spills, drips, dilute sump liquid and sprayer washings when applied to the much smaller test surfaces. For the second application (in October 2000) all six pesticides were applied at the same scaled down applications rates. The third application (in December 2000), of all six pesticides, represented the worst case scenario. All the Cherwell pesticide losses onto the full-scale farmyard were applied but they were not scaled down to the size of the test surface. One litre samples were collected from the drainage water (surface runoff and/or throughflow) discharging from the test surface tanks immediately following the artificial application of the pesticides and then subsequently after rainfall/drainage events. All the samples were kept in a cold store (2-6°C) prior to laboratory analysis.

Subsamples of the drainage water (500ml) were passed through a solid phase extraction cartridge (Envirogard C18; 1g; Merck) and adsorbed residues were eluted with 2ml acetone:hexane (50:50 v/v). The elutes were then analysed by gas-liquid chromatography with a nitrogen/phosphorus detector. The limit of detection of the method was between 0.1-0.3µg/litre for the six pesticides.

RESULTS

In order to rank the performance of the test surfaces in a way that eliminated the complications of the different amounts of drainage water (i.e. throughflow and surface runoff, where collected) it was decided to calculate the total amount of all pesticides measured as a proportion of that applied to the surface per mm of rainfall (natural or artificial) falling on the surfaces. The results are given in tables 1, 2 and 3 for each of the applications.

Table 1. Test surface performance - First application (3 spring pesticides only)

Surface	Total loss of pesticide (% applied per mm of rainfall)
Biobed	<0.001
Soil/grass	<0.001
Hardcore	0.002
Asphalt	0.130
Porous paving	0.162
Concrete	0.355

Table 2. Test surface performance - Second application (all 6 pesticides)

Surface	Total loss of pesticide (% applied per mm of rainfall)
Soil/grass	0.001
Biobed	0.001
Hardcore	0.011
Asphalt	0.013
Porous paving	0.158
Concrete	0.725

Table 3. Test surface performance - Third application (all 6 pesticides)

Surface	Total pesticide loss (% applied per mm of rainfall)
Biobed	<0.001
Soil/grass	0.024
Hardcore	0.058
Asphalt	0.097
Porous paving	0.498
Concrete	0.938

The results indicate that all the surfaces provided a significant improvement in the retention and degradation of the test pesticides when compared to the performance of the traditional concrete surface. Both the biobed and the soil/grass surfaces reduced the total pesticide loss generally by a factor of over 100 when compared to the concrete surface. Pesticide losses from these two surfaces were very low even with the worst case scenario of very high pesticide contamination during the third application. Porous paving, designed to eliminate surface runoff and provide the capacity for immediate infiltration into the substrate, allowed the rapid transport of pesticides through the test tank and into the drainage water.

Table 4. Maximum pesticide concentrations (μg/litre) in drainage water – Third application.

Pesticide	Concrete	Asphalt	Porous Paving	Hardcore	Soil/grass	Biobed
Dimethoate	46000	730	980	210	70	<0.1
Chlorothalonil	200600	2500	1970	180	50	<0.1
Isoproturon	421300	1810	9570	2170	230	<0.1
Chlorpyrifos	157600	1800	4980	160	70	<0.1
Epoxiconazole	18100	500	530	30	<0.1	<0.1
Pendimethalin	371900	6180	14140	250	290	0.2

The maximum concentration of any pesticide lost from the biobed in any single sample collected during all three application periods was 0.2μg/litre; for soil/grass it was 290μg/litre. Taking isoproturon as a typical soluble and hence very mobile herbicide as an example, all samples of drainage water from the biobed failed to have a single determination for isoproturon of above 0.1μg/litre. In comparison, the maximum concentration of isoproturon in the drainage water from the concrete surface was in excess of 420,000μg/litre during the worst case scenario third application (Table 4). For porous paving and soil/grass it was 9570μg/litre and 230μg/litre respectively.

DISCUSSION

The performance of the biobed in retaining and degrading pesticides agrees well with the results from other studies in the UK and Europe. Fogg and Boxall (1998) in the UK, Torstensson (2000) in Sweden and Henriksen et al. (1999) in Denmark, all found that the biobed matrix provided numerous opportunities for the pesticides to the adsorbed onto organic matter where thriving microbial populations (bacteria and fungi) could then degrade the pesticides in situ. Other physical and chemical degradation processes could also take place within the biobed matrix that contained areas of both aerobic and anaerobic conditions. In a similar way the microbial population resident in the soil system, together with organic matter and clay adsorption sites, produced good opportunities for pesticide retention and degradation. Careful management of the water entering these systems was seen as critical to their longer term effectiveness in treating these pesticides, as sustained periods of water saturation and anaerobic conditions would be detrimental to the well-being of the microbial populations. The results also showed that a period of 3-6 months maturing of the biobed matrix, in terms of its microbial composition and activity, contributed to its improved performance even with greatly increased pesticide contamination episodes.

Even though the other three surfaces provided a significant improvement in the retention and degradation of the test pesticides over that of the traditional concrete surface they did permit concentrations of pesticides in the drainage water to frequently exceed the 0.1μg/litre Drinking Water Standard. However, the results did reiterate the current advice on good agricultural practice to spray operators to, wherever possible, move all the pesticide handling and washdown operations away from concrete surfaces or other areas where there is a direct connection for the drainage water to rapidly reach nearby watercourses and potentially produce deleterious a environmental impact on aquatic ecosystems and downstream water users.

The next phase of this project will involve the construction and monitoring of full farm-scale pesticide handling and washdown areas that are connected to biobed and soil/grass treatment systems. The findings of this work will assist in the development of a design manual for these areas that provide farmers and spray operators with a cost-effective way of reducing the risk of polluting water resources from farmyard operations.

ACKNOWLEDGEMENTS

The authors would like to acknowledge the financial support for this project from the Environment Agency, Scotland & Northern Ireland Forum for Environmental Research and the Department for Environment, Food and Rural Affairs. They would also like to thank the various staff from ADAS and HRI Wellesbourne for the installation and maintenance of the testing facility and assistance with the laboratory analysis.

REFERENCES

Carter A D (2000). How pesticides get into water – and proposed reduction measures. *Pesticide Outlook* **11(4):** 149-157.

Fogg P; Boxall A B A (1998). Biobeds: the development and evaluation of a biological system for the disposal of pesticide waste and washings. Project JF4107. Soil Survey and Land Research Centre, Cranfield University, Shardlow, Derby.

Henriksen V V; Bider A; Nielsen M; Laursen B; Spliid N H; Helweg A; Felding G; Hensen L S (1999). Leaching of pesticides from washing-sites and capacity of biobeds to retain pesticides. Proceedings of 16th Danish Plant Protection Conference. DJF rapport, No.9, 47-63.

Kreuger J (1998). Pesticides in stream water within an agricultural catchment in southern Sweden, 1990-1996. *The Science of the Total Environment* **216:** 227-251.

Mason P J; Foster I D L; Carter A D; Walker A; Higginbotham S; Jones R L; Hardy I A J (1999). Relative importance of point source contamination of surface waters: River Cherwell catchment monitoring study. Proceedings of XI Pesticide Chemistry Conference, Cremona, Italy, September 1999. 405-412.

Torstenssen L (2000). Experiences of biobeds in practical use in Sweden. *Pesticide Outlook* **11(5):** 206-211.

Policy, practice and partnership: pragmatism or perfection in farming?

D Brightman
National Farmers Union, London, UK

A D Carter
ADAS Rosemaund, Preston Wynne, Hereford, HR1 3PG, UK
Email: andree.carter@adas.co.uk

ABSTRACT

In order to protect the environment, users of pesticides have been subject to changes in regulations, stewardship programmes, and strong consumer/political pressure to modify their usual practices. Farmers have been required to increase their own awareness of soil and water quality concerns and are now expected to fully comply with all statutory requirements, codes of practice and the guidelines or advice issued by a range of stakeholders with respect to the use of pesticides. The impact of these initiatives on farmers is difficult to assess but there has been a general acceptance of the need to protect soil and water and to co-operate with the various requirements in order to avoid inflexible legislation, revocation of active substances or other stringent restrictions. However there remains some uneasiness amongst many farmers concerning the successful implementation of measures due to conflicting advice, lack of evidence of impact, inflexibility, practicality and cost. There is also a need for regulators to acknowledge that immediate improvements in practice, which do not necessarily solve environmental problems, but do reduce impacts, are acceptable when part of the overall process of achieving a longer term objective of full compliance. UK farmers are key partners in a number of proposed initiatives which have been designed to protect soil and water quality.

INTRODUCTION

The use of pesticides is regulated to ensure that there are no unacceptable effects on the environment. As researchers, the agrochemical industry, policy makers and regulators begin to understand more about the interactions of chemicals with soil and water and their impact, a range of policies, practices or risk management strategies have evolved to mitigate any adverse effects. The farmers and growers who use these pesticides have had to respond to a number of external influences and in consequence have begun to change their systems and practices in order to comply with changes in statutory or voluntary regulations and best practice recommendations. Stakeholder interest in the way that farmers use pesticides range from the consumer, the retail supply chain, the water industry, environmental organisations, regulators of pesticides and the manufacturers/ distributors of pesticides.

Historically, concerns over the presence of pesticides in surface or groundwater are based on the risk of drinking water contamination and the ecotoxicological impact of residues on non-target aquatic organisms. In 1998, 15% of freshwater sites monitored by the Environment Agency for England and Wales failed at least one environmental quality standard (EQS) with at least 32 pesticides failing at least once. Approximately 70 incidents were due to pollution related incidents, of which 44% were attributed to agricultural activities, many of which were related to use and/or disposal of synthetic pyrethroid sheep dips. Increasingly there is also concern for the impact of pesticides on soil quality, associated terrestrial organisms and its long-term sustainability. Even though scientific evidence suggests that general agricultural practices have a greater impact on biodiversity than crop protection itself, e.g. Furse *et al.* (1995), people continue to be concerned about the effect of crop protection chemicals on wildlife and the environment. In the UK, initial investment in water treatment costs for pesticides was estimated to be £1 billion with annual running costs of £100 million (Clarke 2001). Pretty (2000) calculated that in 1996 the external costs of pesticide use, in a range of countries, was between £2.20 and £8.60 per kilogramme of active substance used. This was considered to be a substantial burden on non-agricultural sectors of economies.

The mechanisms by which farmers and growers are influenced to make changes vary widely but they can be considered as 'carrots' (incentives) or 'sticks' (penalties). The pressure to make the 'polluter pay' was highlighted by the UK Government's proposal to introduce a pesticides tax (DETR 1999). However, complex interactions in the natural world mean that it is very difficult to separate out cause and effect and as a consequence it is impossible, in some cases, to identify the required measures or provide the necessary evidence to assist the implementation of changes and ensure compliance.

POLICIES TO PROTECT SOIL AND WATER

EC Directives and statutory legislation

A number of EC Directives and schemes have been implemented within national legislation in relation to minimising the potential contamination of water by pesticides. The report of the Pesticides in the Environment Group (PEWG 2000) identified that there are however, no specific policies in the UK, which refer to the protection of soil from the impact pesticides, with the exception of the regulatory directives.

The impact of the EC harmonisation directive (1991/414/EC) for plant protection products in protecting the environment is yet to be fully determined. The process of re-registration is slow and few active substances have attained approval or Annex I listing to date. Pesticides with persistent characteristics, potential to contaminate water, toxicity to non-target organisms or the potential to bioaccumulate, have caused concerns in Member States. Manufacturers or users on the basis of agricultural need have made cases for the retention of approval of some of these active substances and consequently the regulatory authorities have been required to consider risk and benefit in detail. However, the rigorous data registration requirements of the Directive which are relevant to environmental protection have led to the withdrawal of a number of new active substances at an early stage of their development or during the re-registration process, restricting the choice available to farmers.

In the UK, the Local Environmental Risk Assessment for Pesticides scheme (LERAP) was devised in response to representations by farmers' organisations, that the prevailing pesticide buffer zone regulations were too restrictive. In addition, environmental organisations had expressed concern about the low level of compliance with pesticide buffer zones. The scheme's requirement to record spray decisions when carrying out a LERAP addressed this concern by ensuring that operators were given a framework for planning their spraying near watercourses. The scheme was implemented in March 1999 and it provided farmers with the flexibility of narrowing pesticide buffer zones for certain products but retained fixed zones for organophosphate and pyrethroid pesticides.

The implementation of the Water Framework Directive (2000/60/EC) will rationalise the existing body of water legislation established under a range of European Directives since the 1970's. It will lead to the repeal of a number of directives and provides a framework for the remaining legislation. The objectives of the Water Framework Directive are:

- Protection of aquatic ecosystems and the water needs of terrestrial ecosystems.
- Promotion of the sustainable use of water resources (contributing to the provision of adequate drinking water and water for other economic uses).

Fundamental to the directive is the prevention of deterioration in water quality and the establishment of environmental objectives for all surface waters and groundwaters. The competent authority will designate surface water catchments as the management unit. Priority substances, which include some agricultural pesticides, which impact on the aquatic environment and cause transgressions of environmental quality standards, will be targeted for remedial action or change of land use activity.

The Groundwater Directive protects underground water resources from different contaminants, and prevents or limits discharges (applicable to many pesticides) to underlying reserves. In the UK, a license is required to dispose of washings and waste pesticides to a designated area, which has been assessed by the applicant and then approved by the relevant environment agency with regards to the vulnerability of water resources to contamination.

Other proposed legislation, the Waste Framework Directive and the Waste Incineration Directive will influence how pesticide containers are disposed of (Rose *et al.* 2001). Currently non-returnable containers can be rinsed and then buried (though this is not encouraged) or incinerated on the farm. It is unlikely that the required emission standards for smoke and airborne contaminants will be met by the proposed incineration directive. Specialist waste disposal of contaminated materials, through a licensed waste contractor is prohibitively expensive at approximately £4.50/kg (BAA, 1999).

Voluntary Agreements

Many of the pollution prevention initiatives have been voluntary and have often developed to avoid inflexible legislation. Examples are listed below:
- Quality assurance schemes
- National and European promotion of integrated farm management e.g. LEAF in the UK (Linking Environment and Farming) and EIF (European Initiative for Integrated Farming).
- Codes of Good Agricultural Practice.
- Stewardship campaigns

Quality assurance schemes are mainly driven by the grower or more rigorously by the retailer and can be extremely influential (more so than legislation in some cases) in determining farming or grower practice. At present, the schemes are primarily established for competitive advantage and the need for 'due diligence', but environmental objectives are implicit in many of the requirements. Integrated Farm Management (IFM) is recognised throughout Europe and organisations like LEAF in the UK or EIF at the European level aim to achieve a sustainable agriculture whilst minimising the impact on the environment. A number of Member States have developed codes of good agricultural practice, with advice based on the outcome of previous research. In the UK revised statutory codes were issued by MAFF the Ministry of Agriculture Fisheries and Food (1998a, b, c). Separate Codes of Good Agricultural Practice for the Protection of Soil, Water and Air were distributed to all UK farmers and contain practical advice and information to help farmers and growers avoid pollution of soil, water and air. The 'Green' Code (MAFF 1998d) provides practical guidance to farmers and growers concerning all aspects of pesticide use including tank mixing, spray application and disposal.

USE OF PESTICIDES IN PRACTICE

Point sources

Rose *et al* (2001) reviewed current pesticide handling and washdown practices in the UK and identified that farmers had a restricted awareness of the water quality problems which might arise when pesticide is spilt or incorrectly disposed of in the farmyard. A number of surveys were identified concerning current practices and key issues that were identified included the lack of clear advice concerning disposal of waste and spill clean up materials. Recent data suggest that point sources might be responsible for a major portion (possibly as high as 50%) of contamination and some research is underpins validity of this hypothesis (Spiteller *et al.,* 1999; Mason *et al.,* 1999). The Groundwater Directive does not specify a *de minimus* for pesticide concentrations discharging to groundwater and in the absence of data to prove no impact, $0.1\mu g/L$ is used as a surrogate. There is currently insufficient evidence to prove the effectiveness of the use of waste treatment systems such as biobeds, constructed wetlands, and activated carbon or similar systems at the farm scale and therefore their use cannot be fully endorsed by environmental regulators. This inflexibility restricts the potential for improvement in current practice due to the difficulty in proving compliance with the Directive. Even if soil and water contamination is reduced by several orders of magnitude, users of pesticides cannot currently adopt improved practices and guarantee that their efforts will not be penalised. As an example, in England and Wales, a farmer can invest in sophisticated, expensive treatment systems which sorb most pesticides from waste and washings but he still officially requires a license to dispose of the effluent to a consented area. The resulting discharge would pose little risk to the soil or aquatic environment. Disposal of untreated waste and washings still requires the same consent procedure yet the impact could be far greater.

Diffuse Sources

Most pesticide users recognise that pesticide spray drift to surface water is the main diffuse source of surface water contamination. Spray Operator compliance with buffer zones was not actively monitored in the UK but was generally considered to be very low. A recent survey (Pesticides Safety Directorate web site - www.pesticides.gov.uk) to assess farmer's understanding of, and compliance with, the LERAP scheme highlighted the following points:

- Awareness of LERAP was high but detailed understanding was more variable. For example, some did not realise that they could reduce the buffer zone and others did not understand the star rating system for sprayer nozzles.
- Two-thirds of the farmers contacted had carried out a LERAP assessment themselves (or via contractors) before spraying areas requiring buffer zones. Most of these farmers understood the definition of the two different categories of pesticides and the correct procedure when using a mixture of the two.
- Manipulating the choice of pesticides (to avoid those restrictions) and/or the use of low-drift (star rated) nozzles was considered by most to offer the best scope for reducing buffer zone requirements under LERAPs. Reducing the dose rate of pesticides was only considered suitable by a small minority of respondents.
- Compliance with LERAPs was less than awareness of it. For example, most farmers in the survey did not have information on the width of watercourses but relied on their knowledge and observations. About a quarter did not keep the required record of the LERAP decision, 8% said they ignored the rules.
- Few of those surveyed were judged to be compliant in all aspects of LERAPs, although most were taking some steps to implement the buffer zone regulations.
- Many farmers cited various drawbacks associated with LERAPs, the most common complaint being over-complexity of the scheme and the burden of paperwork. There was a general feeling that the scheme needed to be simplified and made more practical to use.
- Many farmers would prefer the provision of LERAPs information in published form such as booklets/leaflets, letters or press articles.
- Farmers are using 2 or 3 star nozzles across the whole field, rather than just along the headland. This could have a negative effect on pest control over the field as a whole

The spray operator is currently responsible for carrying out a LERAP assessment. Incorporation into long-term farm management plans would benefit long-term water protection goals since land managers could make strategic use of set aside, countryside stewardship grants or even change cropping alongside water courses.

PARTNERSHIP

The UK Government has recently accepted a voluntary package put forward by the Crop Protection Association, the National Farmers Union and other agricultural and farming organisations (CPA 2001) which replaces the proposed pesticide tax (DETR 1999). It was estimated that the proposed tax would have cost farmers and growers £125 million a year and much of the evidence indicated that environmental benefits would have been minimal. The NFU has committed to a credible alternative to the tax and believes it will make a material difference to the environment whilst allowing farmers to continue to produce safe, affordable food. Three key goals have been proposed:
- To reduce the potential environmental effects of pesticide use
- To improve farmland biodiversity
- To prevent water contamination by pesticides

A reduction in the overall amount of pesticide applied was not seen to be a sensible way forward to achieve these goals since environmental impacts may not be minimised.

Alternatives to chemical control can also impact on soil and water quality *e.g.* steam sterilisation, flaming, mechanical weeding methods. The proposals therefore identify those aspects of crop protection which pose the greatest risk to the environment and biodiversity. Practical and effective techniques will be developed to reduce or mitigate these risks and rapid adoption of these techniques on farm through a comprehensive technology transfer programme will be essential. Three 'pillars of support' will allow implementation of the proposal:

- Survey of current practice
- Crop protection management plans
- Commitment of resource to the development of farm biodiversity

It is recognised that for implementation to be successful that all growers must learn how they can apply the measures to their advantage and the benefit of the environment. Because of the scale of measures a big challenge will be to keep the message simple to avoid confusion and overload in the minds of farmers.

A review by EUREAU the European organisation which represents the water and waste water industry reports degradation of catchments by pesticides (EUREAU 2001). Water UK, assessed the extent of contamination in the UK and identified ways of reducing pesticide leaching and identified examples of best practice in pesticide use. The report suggests problems in the UK can be resolved by collaboration with stakeholders such as the Crop protection Association, the NFU and the Environment Agency. Examples of the measures identified to address pesticide contamination of raw water included:

- Assessing the need to ban or severely restrict the use of certain pesticides
- Use of financial incentives and regulatory instruments to promote good practice
- Encouraging best practice in farming and weed control on roads, railways and everywhere
- A European task force to combat pesticide pollution whose members are the water industry, regulators, farmers, pesticide manufacturers, food retailers, consumer and environmental groups, and the European Commission.

There is a clear opportunity for all stakeholders to work together to minimise pesticide contamination at the catchment scale. The implementation of the Water Framework Directive will provide environmental agencies with regulatory tools which were previously lacking but it will also focus the attention of all stakeholders on achieving the overall objectives. The development of farm management plans and the adoption of best management practices at the catchment scale will undoubtedly lead to overall improvements in water quality.

Table 1. Measures proposed and their impact on soil and water quality

Action plan	Content	Possible implications for soil and water quality
Improving crop protection application practices	Best practice, waste disposal, nozzle selection, sprayer testing. Incorporate into crop management plans	Targeted application, minimisation of use, decrease point source losses and drift. Improved timing of application, reduced soil losses
Sprayer operator training and certification	Improved application practice, statutory training, register of operators, updates with new equipment	Improved handling and use of pesticides. Reduced point and diffuse sources of contamination
Improving farmer's own crop protection decisions	Maintenance of BASIS register and training certification for farmers who make their own decisions	Improved awareness of impact of use of pesticides on soil and water and appropriate risk management options
Sprayer testing	Independently validated, annual testing scheme for spray machinery	Correct application rates, reduction of spillages, decrease in overall loading to soil and water
Environmentally aware and BASIS registered advisers	Increase the environmental training and continuous professional development for those on professional advisory registers	Greater awareness and sensitivity for soil and water protection - influence over farmer decisions
Environmental Information Sheets	Provision of independently validated environmental information for products. Awareness of risks and their management. Training in their use	Opportunity for choice of products for soil and water protection. Ability to take into account vulnerability and site specific problems
Water industry collaboration	Working group with the water industry to develop catchment protection plans and local campaigns. Water protection will be key in the CPMP	Identification of specific problems of water contamination, local solutions and site specific solutions to leaching and run-off from fields, yards etc
Supporting research programmes	Commitment to part fund relevant research e.g. optimising spray applications	Reduction of drift

PRAGMATISM OR PERFECTION?

In 1998, 42,860,976 hectares of arable crops were sprayed or treated with pesticides in Great Britain (Garthwaite and Thomas 1999). Each arable crop received an average of 4.6 spray rounds and an average of 11.3 active substances. With such a large number of pesticide users to influence, practical, efficacious, inexpensive solutions are required which will take time and resource to implement. Complete solutions to the problem are not possible and perfection *i.e.* compliance with statutory and voluntary measures cannot be attained overnight or probably ever. Regulatory systems need to recognise that immediate improvements in practice, which do not necessarily solve environmental problems, but do reduce impacts are acceptable when part of the overall process of achieving a longer term objective of full compliance. Awareness of the natural environment in which the farm is located needs to be assessed and understood. Information on the environmental properties of products needs to be available so that choices can be tailored to specific circumstances. Table 2 identifies the different sources of pesticide contamination to water and proposes measures to reduce levels of pesticides in water for each (Carter 2000). Those highlighted in bold are the most pragmatic, most likely to have an impact, relatively easy to implement and are not considered to be expensive relative to the overall costs described by Pretty (2000).

Most on farm actions listed can be implemented quite cheaply and effectively by the farmer himself. A major task is to identify the means by which information can be transferred effectively to land managers and spray operators. Uptake, compliance and goodwill would be greater if 'carrots' or incentives were offered and a consistent, transparent approach to the interpretation of legislation agreed. In the UK, a number of regulatory authorities currently influence how pesticides are used and disposed of and there is often confusion or different interpretation of the statutory and voluntary legislation which applies at the farm scale.

The UK Pesticide Forum aims:

- to bring together all those stakeholders with interests in the use and effects of pesticides
- to identify their common interests and to assist in the dissemination of best practice, advances in technology and research and development results
- to advise government on the promotion and implementation of it's policy relating to the responsible use of pesticides.

The success of the Forum depends crucially on the efforts of its member organisations and also relies on using established channels between Forum members and the farming community. In 1998/99 UK government expenditure on the pests and pesticides research programme, totalled £8,132 million. Recent Forum efforts have focussed on the development or support of indicators to monitor impacts, to ensure that the implementation of research findings is effective in the environment.

A flexible, pragmatic approach to the environmental impact of farming is advocated. The needs of all stakeholders need to be considered and where appropriate agreements and compromises reached. The short-term objective of improvement, working towards long-term compliance is the most realistic approach which can be taken.

Table 2. Methods to reduce pesticide levels in water

Entry Route	Reduction Method
Diffuse sources	
Drainflow and interflow	• restrict flow when peak losses are anticipated to increase time for degradation • manage soil structure e.g. to optimise tilth to increase sorption/water retention • incorporate additives to soil surface e.g. organic material or stabilisers • **restricted application areas e.g. protection zones** • reduce drain intensity • **optimisation of application rates** • target timing of applications to avoid potential loss periods
Surface flow	• **buffer zones with various surface treatments e.g. grass strips** • **contour cultivations** • manage soil surface e.g. reservoir tillage, minimal tillage
Leaching	• **restricted application areas** • **restrict application to products with appropriate properties to minimise leaching** • manage soil structure e.g. create fine tilth to increase sorption and retention • incorporate additives to soil surface e.g. organic material or stabilisers
Precipitation	no specific measure
Spray drift	• **no-spray zones e.g. LERAPS** • **manage vegetation adjacent to water e.g. hedges, interception plants** • **low drift application technology** • **education of operator to choose optimal conditions**
Point	
Tank filling	• **container modifications e.g. anti-glug necks, pack size, returnable packs** • **add container rinsate to the tank mix** • **engineering solutions e.g. tank full alarm, direct injection** • **remove operations from drained impermeable areas** • biobeds • interception areas drained to waste collection site • **education of operator**
Spillages	• **remove operations from drained impermeable areas** • biobeds • interception areas drained to waste collection site • **use of sorbent pads/material to intercept spills or clean up** • use of licensed hazardous waste contractors • **immediate incineration of empty containers/store under cover** • **education of operator**
Faulty equipment	• **regular maintenance and servicing of sprayer** • **sprayer testing**
Washings and waste disposal	• biobeds • other on farm treatment systems e.g. Sentinel system • **authorised waste disposal** • **dispose of tank sump contents appropriately**
Sumps, soakaways and drainage	• requirement for licensing • diversion from direct discharge to water
Direct contamination including overspray	• **avoidance** • **education of operator**
Consented discharges	• **requirement for licensing and compliance with Environmental Quality Standards**

REFERENCES

BAA (1999). *Container management strategy.* British Agrochemicals Association: Peterborough.

Carter A D (2000). How pesticides get into water – and proposed reduction measures. *Pesticide Outlook* **11**: 149–156.

Clarke B (2001). Keeping sources safe from pesticides. *Water* **131**: 7.

Crop Protection Association (2001). *Minimising the environmental impacts of crop protection chemicals, revised proposals - February 2001*, CPA: Peterborough.

DETR (1999). *Design of a tax or charge scheme for pesticides.* DETR: London.

Environment Agency (undated). *Pesticides 1998, A summary of monitoring of the aquatic environment in England and Wales*, National Centre for Ecotoxicology and Hazardous Substances: Wallingford.

EUREAU (2001). *Keeping raw drinking water resources safe from pesticides*, Report EU1-01-56, European Union of National Associations of Water Suppliers and Waste Water Services: Brussels, Belgium.

Furse M T; Symes K L; Winder J M; Clarke R T; Blackburn J H; Gunn R J M; Grieve N J; Hurley M (1995). *The faunal richness of headwater streams: Stage 3 –impact of agricultural activity.* National Rivers Authority R&D note 392, National Rivers Authority: Bristol.

Garthwaite D G; Thomas M R (1999). Arable farm crops in Great Britain 1998. *Pesticide Usage Survey Report* **159**. MAFF: London.

Mason P J; Foster, I D L; Carter A D; Walker A; Higginbotham S; Jones R; Hardy I (1999). Relative importance of point source contamination of surface waters: River Cherwell catchment monitoring study. *XI Symposium Pesticide Chemistry, Human and Environmental Exposure to Xenobiotics*, 12-15 September 1999, Università Cattolica 'Sacro Cuore': Cremona, Italy.

Ministry of Agriculture Fisheries and Food (1998a). *Code of Good Agricultural Practice for the Protection of Soil.* MAFF Publications: London.

Ministry of Agriculture Fisheries and Food (1998b). *Code of Good Agricultural Practice for the Protection of Water.* MAFF Publications: London.

Ministry of Agriculture Fisheries and Food (1998c). *Code of Good Agricultural Practice for the Protection of Air.* MAFF Publications: London.

Ministry of Agriculture Fisheries and Food (1998d). *Code of Practice for the Safe Use of Pesticides on Farms and holdings.* MAFF Publications: London.

PEWG (2000). *Monitoring of pesticides in the environment.* E1a(99)03, report of the Pesticides in the Environment Working Group, Environment Agency: Bristol.

Pretty J (2000). Changing agricultural practices and their impact on biodiversity. *Allied Domecq Public Lecture Series, 16 March 2000*, University of Cambridge Committee for Interdisciplinary Environmental Studies. Cambridge.

Rose S; Carter A D; Basford W (2001) *Development of a design manual for agricultural pesticide handling and washdown areas, Stage 1 Desk study review report.* Technical report P2-200/TR/1 Environment Agency: Bristol, UK.

Spiteller M; Hartmann H; Burhenne J; Muller K; Bach M; Frede H G (1999). Reduction of pesticide pollution in surface water determined by LC/MS-MS. *XI Symposium Pesticide Chemistry, Human and Environmental Exposure to Xenobiotics*, 12-15 September 1999, Università Cattolica 'Sacro Cuore': Cremona, Italy.

SESSION 9

HERBICIDES IN THE ENVIRONMENT: EXPOSURE, CONSEQUENCES AND RISK ASSESSMENT – PART 1

Chairman &
Session Organisers:

D J Arnold
*Cambridge Environmental Assessments,
Boxworth, UK*

and

A Craven
Pesticides Safety Directorate, York, UK

FOCUS surface water scenario development

D A Yon
Dow AgroSciences, Letcombe Laboratory, Letcombe Regis, Wantage, Oxon, OX12 9JT, UK
Email: Dayon@dow.com

P I Adriaanse, R Allen, E Capri, V Gouy, J Hollis, N Jarvis, M Klein, J B H J Linders, P Lolos, W-M Maier, S J Maund, C Pais, M H Russell, J-L Teixeira, S Vizantinopoulos
On behalf of FOCUS Working Group on Surface Water Scenarios (under the auspices of European Commission's DG Health and Consumer Protection).

ABSTRACT

The Authorisations Directive, 91/414/EC for the placing of Plant Protection Products on the market came into force in July 1993. In the Annexes, which give substance to the Directive, there is a clear need to provide Predicted Environmental Concentrations (PECs) as part of the process for assessing the risk to non-target organisms. In the specific context of organisms dwelling in surface water, the Annexes are also clear in the need to consider **all** appropriate input routes into surface water bodies. In the dossier preparation for the first list compounds most of the Agrochemical Industry concentrated on spray drift as the main route of entry into water bodies as this was readily quantified through the use of simple "models" based on empirical "drift tables", several sets of which exist at the National level. Little emphasis was put on the entry of pesticides into surface water via surface run-off/erosion and sub-soil drainflow and what work was done was carried out in an uncoordinated and unguided manner. In 1997 the fifth FOCUS (**FO**rum for the **C**oordination of pesticide fate models and their **US**e) workgroup was created with the remit to define "standard scenarios" for surface water exposure. This paper records the advances made by the group since then and gives an overall appraisal of the timeline for the completion of the work.

INTRODUCTION

In 1992 an ad-hoc group of regulatory, industry and academic "experts" met in Brussels to lay the foundations for the FOCUS (**FO**rum for the **C**oordination of pesticide fate models and their **US**e) groups. One of the remits of these groups has been to provide guidance to the Member States, the European Commission and the Agrochemical Industry on the role of modelling in the EU registratory process. The third of the FOCUS groups met to deal with surface water models and produced a report (DOC.6476/VI/96) which included an extensive review of available models and also proposed a "stepped" approach to exposure assessment, starting with simple "back of the envelope" calculations and increasing in complexity to sophisticated mechanistic modelling. The report also highlighted the importance of run-off/erosion and drainflow as entry routes into surface waters and the need for their inclusion in exposure calculations.

In 1997 the fifth FOCUS workgroup was created with the remit to define a limited number of "standard scenarios" for surface water exposure (not more than 10), representative of commercial agriculture across the EU. The workgroup of "expert scientists" numbering 16 in total (14 at any one time) have been drawn from Regulatory, Academic and Industrial backgrounds and have relevant expertise in modelling surface water issues. They represent 8 Member State Nations as well as the European Commission.

REVISED REMIT

Whilst the original remit of the workgroup was interpreted as the need to create up to 10 standard scenarios for modelling surface water exposure ("step 3" in a four step process defined by the first FOCUS Surface water workgroup, see Figure 2), it quickly became apparent that this could not be done without reference to the two preceding steps in order to ensure that the correct level of conservatism and realism was used at each step. Consequently, as these two more conservative assessment steps had not been defined in detail, the workgroup undertook this additional task. It was agreed that the assessments should be most conservative (least realistic, highest safety margins) at step 1 and become less conservative (more realistic) through the steps. Furthermore, the range of possible predicted exposure concentrations gets wider as the user proceeds through the steps, reflective of the wider range of climates, soils and agronomic practices in the "real world". The perceived ranges of predicted exposure concentrations for the different steps, compared to "reality" are shown in Figure 1. As part of the definition of the step 1 and 2 calculations the workgroup also recognised the need to provide guidance for the calculation of exposure concentrations in sediment (PEC_{sed}).

SPRAY DRIFT

Spray drift had been perceived as the most significant entry route to surface waters for the compounds evaluated under list 1 and, therefore, was an important consideration for the workgroup. From the list 1 experiences, however, a number of shortcomings were identified; overspray was an unacceptable and illegal practice and should not be considered a realistic exposure route, drift deposition at the 95th percentile was too conservative, drift deposition for multiple applications each at the 95th percentile was extremely conservative and drift data for S. European agricultural practices (*e.g.* aerial application) was absent. The workgroup also agreed that all relevant published spray drift data should be considered for use in the new drift tables, however, when the data were evaluated only the work of Ganzelmeier *et al*, (1995) and the US Spray Drift Task Force (SDTF) AgDRIFT v 1.11 Model met the publication criteria and were used. After debate (and following the example of the FOCUS groundwater scenarios workgroup) the workgroup adopted the 90th percentile as a "realistic worst case" exposure level for drift events. The group also agreed that for multiple applications in a season, the total exposure from drift should be at the 90th percentile. To this end the drift data of Ganzelmeier *et al* were recalculated to provide 90th percentile drift values for single spray events and appropriate percentiles such that 2 to 15 sequential applications resulted in a cumulative probability of 90th percentile. Data for aerial applications were also taken from the SDTF and were included in the drift tables. However, after presentation of the workgroup concepts at a workshop held in Bilthoven in 1998 and discussions between workgroup members and scientists of the Federal Institute of the Ministry of Agriculture, Forestry and Fisheries (BBA), new official drift tables were released by BBA (2000) which included drift data for 5 crop classes (arable, vines, orchard fruit, hops and vegetables with vines and orchards further differentiated according to early and late growth stage and vegetables differentiated according to crop height) for distances of up to 250 m from the edge of the crop. Drift data were calculated at the 90th percentile for single applications and also for up to 7 sequential applications such that the cumulative probability of 90th percentile was achieved. The workgroup agreed to adopt these data rather than to create another slightly different data set based on the earlier drift data.

The final product used for estimating drift loadings within the FOCUS surface water process was an Excel spreadsheet calculator based on a regression analysis of the various drift data sets, such that the drift at user defined distances from the edge of the field can be calculated. Drift loadings for up to 25 sequential applications can be calculated (after 7 the loadings are the same) for up to 28 crops plus a no-drift option. The calculator also allows the integration of spray drift over various widths of water body as required by surface water models (eg. EXAMS or TOXSWA) and will give appropriate "width averaged" loadings. The calculator has also been included as an integral part of the scenario management tool SWASH (see later).

STEP 1 AND 2

The conceptual starting point for the step 1 and 2 calculations was the standard "EU" ditch that was used for the surface water assessments for the compounds on the first list and was a static ditch (no dilution from flowing water) of 30 cm depth. In order to allow an estimate of exposure concentrations in sediment, a 5 cm deep sediment layer was added and after much discussion the organic carbon content and bulk density of this layer was set to 5 % and 1.5 g.l^{-1}. These values cover both the requirements for the sediment used in the sediment dwelling eco-toxicology tests and the laboratory water/sediment studies. A 5:1 field scaling factor was also applied for the area of treated field impacting on the water body. These constraints were applied at both steps 1 and 2.

At step 1 the application rate was the maximum season's usage applied as single dose. One exception to this was agreed when the DT$_{50}$ in water for the compound is less than a third of the interval between treatments. In this case a single application should be assessed because there is no possibility of accumulation of residues in the ditch. As described above, spray drift was considered at the 90th percentile for a single application and varied with crop. No-spray zones between the edge of the crop and the water body were fixed at 1m for row crops and 3 m for tall crops. Run-off/erosion and/or drainflow were also considered as a single non-specific loading and was fixed at a value of 10% for all calculations. The loading to the ditch also occurred on the day of application. Clearly this reflects a very "worst case" situation! All of the compound is in the water phase for the first 24 hours and is then partitioned between the water and sediment phases. This is driven by the average soil Koc value. Degradation subsequently occurs in both the water and sediment phases. For step 2 calculations a number of refinements were included. Applications were made sequentially at rates and intervals representative of real use. This allowed degradation and partitioning to occur between applications, thus reducing the exposure in the water column. Spray drift was considered separately for each treatment but the sum of the spray drift represents the 90th percentile loading. No spray zones were still fixed as before. Four days after the last treatment, a percentage of the residue remaining on the treated field is then added to the ditch as a run-off/erosion or drainage input and is added directly to the sediment layer of the ditch. The magnitude of this loss is dependant on season and zone (North EU or South EU) of use and was set by expert judgement plus some calibration based on the results of the step 3 calculations. As with step 1, partitioning to sediment occurred after 24 hours and degradation occurred in both sediment and water phases.

The original versions of the step 1 and 2 calculators were Excel spreadsheets. It soon became apparent that these fell foul of the users PC operating system and version of MS Windows/Excel being used and, therefore, the decision was made to encode the tool in Visual Basic and this has made it much more system independent. The new tool is windows driven with drop down menus for selecting different options. Both the step 1 and 2 calculations have been encoded and both calculations can be conducted automatically and, therefore, because of the ease of conducting the more sophisticated step 2 calculations, the step 1 calculations are almost redundant. Output from the calculator is presented in tabular and graphical form which capture the input values and assumptions, calculate initial exposure concentrations as well as "time weighted average" concentrations for both water and sediment and finally present graphs of the exposure concentration with time.

STEP 3 "STANDARD SCENARIOS"

The step 3 scenarios were developed following a number of basic principles; there should be no more than 10 and these should be broadly representative of EU agriculture, the scenarios should take into account all relevant entry routes, target crops, surface water bodies, topography, soils and climates, the scenarios should reflect realistic combinations of run-off/erosion and drainage and wherever possible the scenarios should include conditions representative of a field test site with monitoring data to allow validation of scenarios. Digitised data characterising landscape, land use, climate and soils were collected together to allow a pragmatic approach to scenario selection based on available data and scientific judgement. Only arable agricultural areas were considered and land was broadly characterised into drainage (by recharge) and run-off/erosion (based on spring daily rainfall) areas. Appropriate soil type, slopes and crops were then obtained for these areas. In the absence of digitised data, dominant water bodies (ponds, ditches or streams) associated with the scenarios were determined from detailed topographic maps. At the end of this process 6 drainage and 4 run-off/erosion scenarios had been identified. The broad characteristics of the scenarios are shown in Table 1. The extent of the scenarios in European agriculture has been evaluated and found to vary between 1 and 12% of total EU agricultural land with all scenarios representing a total of 42%.

The approach to defining the water bodies was equally pragmatic given the absence of hard data and was governed in part by expert judgement, available literature references and some practical requirements from the models. The characteristics and scenario associations of the various water bodies are shown in Table 2.

Weather data associated with the scenarios was taken from Meteorology stations located near the representative field sites. Daily data for 20 years periods were obtained from the EU sponsored MARS project (Vossen & Meyer-Roux, 1995). The data were evaluated and weather years were selected which were representative of 50th percentile run-off and drainage years.

MODEL SELECTION AND PARAMETERISATION

Having defined the characteristics of the scenarios and associated water bodies, the workgroup was faced with the prospect of parameterising a wide range of possible models (*eg.* PELMO and PRZM for run-off, TOXSWA and EXAMS for surface water fate *etc.*). After much deliberation it was decided to parameterise only three models, MACRO for drainage, PRZM-3 for run-off/erosion and TOXSWA for surface water fate. This was not to state that other models were not equally applicable but rather a practical consideration to limit the workload.

The scenarios for MACRO and PRZM were parameterised based on actual field sites broadly representative of the scenarios. The field sites also generally represented national notional worst case examples for surface water exposure and included such locations as Brimstone (UK, DEFRA site), Lanna (Sweden, Swedish Land University site), Skousbo (Denmark, DEPA site), Vredepeel (Netherlands) and Roujan (France, INRA site). Data for soil properties, slope, drainage systems, cropping *etc.* were taken from these sites. For surface water fate, a new version of the TOXSWA model has been developed which has dynamic hydrology and is capable of simulating a water body of fluctuating height. This has particular importance for fast moving and seasonally dry streams associated with the run-off/erosion scenarios and also some of the drainage scenarios. This model uses the run-off and drainage losses as the driver for the water height in the water body. It also simulates an "upstream catchment" that feeds water into the water body of interest and which contains a percentage of untreated field, thus providing diluting water. The sizes of the "upstream catchments" vary between the scenarios.

All of the models are DOS based and have "user friendly" shells to improve ease of use and to present interfaces with similar styles. The shells for MACRO and PRZM were developed to select a crop first, this dictates the available scenarios which can then be run individually or in batch mode after entry of pesticide properties, use rates and timings. Output from these models can be visualised from the model shells but the most important output files are those which subsequently become input files for the TOXSWA model and these are automatically formatted. Links between PRZM, MACRO and TOXSWA are "loose" so all models exist as separate items. The TOXSWA model requires appropriate MACRO or PRZM hourly loadings files, spray drift loadings (from the drift calculator) and pesticide properties for behaviour in a water body (taken from a lab water/sediment study). Computation times for the models vary dramatically with the PRZM model completing a 30 year simulation in under 5 minutes, the MACRO model completing a 7 year simulation in 30 – 60 minutes and TOXSWA completing a 1 year simulation in 15 – 30 minutes depending on the capabilities of the computer. Output from the TOXSWA model will be in the form of peak hourly concentrations in water and sediment plus "time weighted average" concentrations (over a range of intervals) for comparison with acute and chronic eco-toxicity end points respectively.

MANAGING THE SCENARIOS

Because of the complexity of the process of step 3 modelling and the loose coupled nature of the various models, a scenario manager tool (SWASH) was developed to guide the user through scenario selection and which models to be run for which scenarios. To illustrate this further, if tobacco is selected as the target crop then only one scenario needs to be considered (R3) and only one water body (stream), so one PRZM run and one TOXSWA run need to be conducted. However, if winter cereals is chosen as the target crop then 9 scenarios need to be considered (all except R2) with 15 associated TOXSWA runs. The SWASH tool also contains a database of pesticide properties required as input for the MACRO, PRZM and TOXSWA models with the intention that this database interacts with databases in the model shells, thus ensuring that all databases contain the same information and thereby reducing potential errors from data transcription. SWASH also contains a hard coded version of the spray drift calculator and it is intended that the tool should prepare input parameter files containing drift inputs and pesticide properties for the TOXSWA model. Another function of SWASH is to prepare tables of runs to be conducted with unique run identifiers for the various simulations. These tables can be printed and simulations checked off as they are conducted and provide a written record of work done.

Table 1: Broad charateristics for surface water scenarios

Scenario	Soil	Water body	Slope %	A A Precip". mm	Av. spring & autumn temp. °C
D1	Clay	Stream Ditch	Level (0 – 0.5)	600 - 800	<6.6
D2	Clay	Stream Ditch	Gentle (0.5 – 2)	600 - 800	6.6 - 10
D3	Sand	Ditch	Level (0 – 0.5)	600 - 800	6.6 - 10
D4	Loamy	Stream Pond	Gentle (0.5 – 2)	600 - 800	6.6 - 10
D5	Loamy	Stream Pond	Moderate (2 – 4)	600 - 800	10 – 12.5
D6	Heavy loam	Ditch Pond	Level (0 – 0.5)	600 - 800	> 12.5
R1	Silty	Stream Pond	Moderate (2 – 4)	600 - 800	6.6 - 10
R2	Loamy	Stream	Steep (10 – 15)	>1000	10 – 12.5
R3	Heavy loam	Stream	Strong (4 –10)	800 – 1000	10 – 12.5
R4	Loamy	Stream	Strong (4 – 10)	600 - 800	>12.5

Table 2: Broad characteristics of surface water bodies and their associations with the scenarios.

Water body type	Ditch	Pond	Stream
Width (m)	1	30	2
Depth (m)	0.3	1	0.5
Length (m)	100	30	1000
Distance (m) from:			
top of bank to water	0.5	3	1
crop to top of bank	0.5	0.5	0.5
Average residence time (d)	50	50	0.1
Relevant scenarios	D1, D2, D3, D6	D4, D5, D6, R1	D1, D2, D4, D5, R1, R2, R3, R4

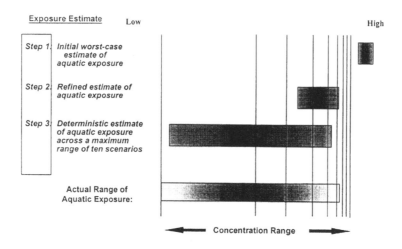

Figure 1. Relationship of predicted exposure concentrations for Steps 1, 2 and 3 calculations.

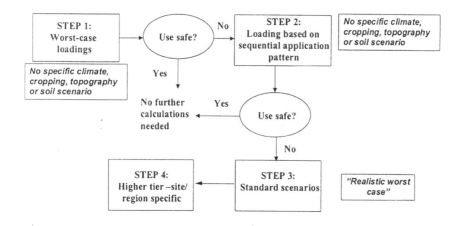

Figure 2. Inter-relationship of the four assessments steps for surface water exposure.

CONCLUSION

The preceding sections have been a quick summary of the current status of the FOCUS Surface water scenarios workgroup activities and condense the activities of four years into a hand full of pages. As of today the final report is in an advanced draft form and beta test versions of the Step 1 and 2 calculator, MACRO, PRZM and SWASH models are available and have been tested for some months. An early release version of the new TOXSWA model is also being tested. A joint FOCUS/ECPA project is underway to evaluate steps 1, 2 and 3 with a range of 9 fictitious compounds with different Koc and DT50 values in order to ensure that the relativity of steps 1, 2 and 3 is correct, with step 1 being most conservative. The results of this may be used to adjust losses for run-off/erosion and drainage at steps 1 and 2. The results of this work have also been presented in a separate presentation at this conference. Seven real example compounds are also being tested and the results from these will be compared with monitoring data to ensure reasonableness of the predicted results. Predicted exposure concentrations will also be compared with eco-toxicity end points and risk assessment conducted. Comparisons have also been made between the old surface water exposure model which was based on drift and the new step 1 and 2 calculator and for a limited set of compounds the results are not very different. This work also continues.

The current timetable for the FOCUS surface water scenarios report calls for completion of the report and all models and submission to the Commission by the end of the year. Adoption and final release is then anticipated mid-2002 after member state review and comment.

REFERENCES

BBA (2000), Bekanntmachung über die Abtrifteckwerte, die bei der Prüfung und Zulassung von Pflanzenschutzmitteln herangezogen werden. (8. Mai 2000) in : Bundesanzeiger No.100, amtlicher Teil, vom 25. Mai 2000, S. 9879.

H Ganzelmeier; D Rautmann; R Spangenberg; M Streloke; M Herrmann; H-J Wenzelburger; H-F Walter (1995). Studies on the spray drift of plant protection products. Results of a test programme carried out throughout the Federal Republic of Germany. Heft 305, Berlin.

Vossen; Meyer-Roux (1995). Monitoring Agriculture by Remote Sensing (MARS) project. Held by the Space Applications Institute of the Joint Research Centre (JRC) at Ispra, Italy.

The influence of wind speed and spray nozzle geometry on the drift of chlorpyrifos to surface water

T J Pepper, D J Arnold, C Murray
Cambridge Environmental Assessments, ADAS Boxworth, Cambridge, CB3 8NN, UK

G L Reeves
Dow AgroSciences, Letcombe Regis, Wantage, Oxon, OX12 9JT, UK

ABSTRACT

Under the Plant Protection Product (PPP) Authorisations Directive (91/414/EEC) the risk of a PPP to off-crop non-target aquatic organisms is assessed in a tiered approach. From the properties and use pattern of the product, the likely routes of entry into surface water are assessed for PPPs applied as sprays. These assessments are based upon a calculated percentage of the active substance being deposited on a static body of water, 30cm deep, related to the distance from the end of the spray boom to the edge of the water body (Ganzelmeier *et al.* 1995). For some PPPs, such as chlorpyrifos, a buffer (no spray zone) may be applied to "in use" situations to reduce drift off-crop. However, there is little data to demonstrate how well drift events with specific chemicals match Ganzelmeier data or the extent to which application factors such as wind speed and spray nozzle affect the degree and amount of drift. Using a large-scale wind tunnel, a series of controlled, replicated studies were carried out to measure the influence of two wind speeds in combination with a conventional and three star (UK) rated reduced drift nozzle on the spray drift of chlorpyrifos, applied as Dursban 4, and its deposition on to an artificial ditch, simulating a static edge of field water body, 30cm deep. Results showed a clear reduction in amounts of chlorpyrifos as distance from the nozzle increased. The combination of 3mph (low) wind speed and low drift nozzle had a significant influence in reducing drift by ca. ten-fold at 2m from the spray nozzle, and five-fold at the mid-ditch position (4.5 or 5m), as measured by polyethylene strings stretched horizontally across the path of the drift. Water concentrations were reduced by ca. half from an average of 1.11µg L^{-1} to 0.45µg L^{-1} The presence of a 50cm artificial bank had no significant influence on the concentration of chlorpyrifos in surface water. Results show that both low wind speed and low drift nozzle can contribute to risk reduction of certain PPPs in surface water.

INTRODUCTION

Environmental (ecological) risk assessment of PPPs is usually based on a tiered approach ranging from conservative assumptions at Tier 1 to more realistic scenarios at higher tiers, reflecting normal use patterns of the product. For PPPs applied as sprays, aquatic risk assessments are based upon a calculated percentage of the active substance being deposited on a static body of water, 30cm deep, related to the distance from the end of the spray boom to the edge of the water body (Ganzelmeier *et al.* 1995).

For regulatory purposes, the 95th percentile worst case figures are currently used to calculate a Predicted Environmental Concentration (PEC) which is used in conjunction with single species toxicity data LC50, EC50 or NOEC to derive a Toxicity Exposure Ratio (TER). If acute or chronic TERs are below 100 or 10, respectively, then higher tier approaches based on either less conservative assumptions or using measured data are applied to refine exposure and, consequently, effects on non-target organisms. For some PPPs, such as chlorpyrifos, a buffer (no spray) zone may be applied to "in use" situations as a risk reduction (mitigation) tool to reduce drift to edge of field water bodies. However, there is little data to demonstrate how well drift events with specific chemicals match Ganzelmeier data or the extent to which application factors, such as wind speed and spray nozzle geometry, might affect the level of drift.

Using a large-scale wind tunnel, a series of controlled, replicated studies were carried out to measure the influence of two wind speeds, in combination with a conventional and three star (UK rated) reduced drift nozzle, on the spray drift of chlorpyrifos, applied as Dursban 4, and its deposition on to an artificial ditch, simulating a static edge of field water body.

MATERIALS AND METHODS

The wind tunnel facility used in this study at Silsoe Research Institute, Silsoe, UK, was designed specifically to enable experiments using active pesticide formulations to be conducted under safe and controlled conditions (Miller 1998). The tunnel used a re-circulating design such that airborne pesticide spray material was not lost from the system during the experiment.

Following each experimental run, air was drawn into the working section of the tunnel, through the fans and airflow straightening sections, before being blown up a discharge stack to atmosphere. The complete tunnel was sited in a sealed pit in which any liquid discharge, waste or spillage drains to a sump from which could be pumped into a treatment plant. The working section of the tunnel was 3m wide and 2m high and 7m wide. Air movements within the tunnel were generated by two 15kw, 1.25m diameter axial flow fans mounted above the working section. Flow through the fans was ducted through an air straightening section, turned through 180° using vanes, into a contraction section and then into the working section. The system was designed to operate with a plug air flow down the tunnel at speeds ranging from 2 to 19mph. Humidity within the tunnel was controlled using an air-conditioning plant.

An artificial ditch, comprising a stainless steel tank 2m long, 1m wide and 35cm deep, containing 30cm deep (600L volume) tap water, was situated within the working section of the tunnel ca. 4.5m from the spray track with the water level ca. 5cm below the level of the floor of the wind tunnel.

In some experimental 'runs' a stainless steel plate, simulating a sloping (45°), 50cm high ditch bank, was fixed to either side of the ditch and the tank lowered so that the bank top was at floor level. (Figure 1). Experiments were conducted at constant relative humidity and temperature and, after each application of chlorpyrifos, the tunnel was purged for 2 minutes to remove any residual chemical from the atmosphere.

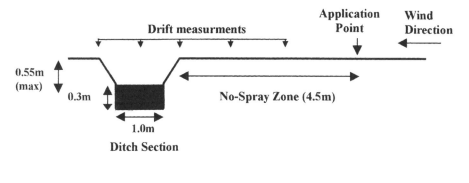

Figure 1.   Wind tunnel layout

The formulated product (Dursban 4) was applied from a single spray nozzle at a concentration calculated to represent that arriving at the end of a standard 12m boom under normal use. Spray drift was captured by 1.5m length polyethylene "strings" (diameter 1.98 mm) stretched horizontally across the path of the drift at 2, 3 and 4.5m from the spray nozzle ca. 10cm above the floor surface. Additionally, a string was placed at the centre of the ditch above the water surface at 5.0m distance where no bank was present, or 5.5m with the bank *in situ.*

Following each spray run, chlorpyrifos was removed from each "string" by slowly passing it through a glass U-tube, containing 10ml n-hexane, held in an ultra-sonic bath. Following each spray application the water in the ditch was vigorously stirred for 2 minutes using a stainless steel paddle, in order to mix the chemical, and 3x 250ml samples were collected in acid washed glass bottles. The samples were firstly acidified with pH 4 buffer to prevent hydrolysis of chlorpyrifos and then 50mL n-hexane was added to extract the compound from the water. Non-homogeneity of the formulated product in the water after mixing was evident from the variability in concentrations of chlorpyrifos in some water samples. This was improved by drilling holes in the stainless steel paddle which resulted in better mixing and more even distribution of the chemical. Analysis of chlorpyrifos was carried out by Gas Chromatography – Mass Spectrometry (GC/MS). The organic phase of the extracted sample was separated from the aqueous phase using a sodium sulphate funnel, before reducing under nitrogen and analysis using a Hewlett Packard 6890 Plus GC with Hewlett Packard 5973 mass selective detector and ZB5-MS 30m x 0.25mm x 0.25µm column.

Experimental design

The study comprised of replicated randomised treatments based on a statistical design (three factorial randomised block). The first set of experiments reported here evaluated the influence of either 3mph (low) or 6mph (high) wind speed combined with a conventional or a low drift 3 star (UK rated) nozzle, and also compared the influence of a 50cm deep ditch bank on spray drift.

RESULTS

For each treatment combination (Table 1), chlorpyrifos deposition at each of the monitoring points was calculated from the material extracted from the spray drift targets ("strings") as a proportion of the applied mass. Standard statistical methods were used to determine the significance of observed differences between the treatment combinations.

Table 1   Randomisation plan – phase 1 applications (block 1 of 3)

Application	Block	Treatment 1 Wind speed	Treatment 2 Spray nozzle	Treatment 3 Bank height
A1	1	Low	Low drift	5cm
A2	1	High	Low drift	5cm
A3	1	High	Conventional	5cm
A4	1	High	Conventional	55cm
A5	1	High	Low drift	55cm
A6	1	Low	Low drift	55cm
A7	1	Low	Conventional	55cm
A8	1	Low	Conventional	5cm

Results showed a clear reduction in amounts of chlorpyrifos as distance from the nozzle increased (Figure 2).

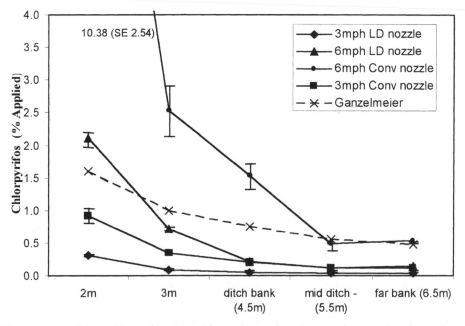

Figure 2.   Mean chlorpyrifos deposition at increasing distance from application point (with 50cm deep ditch sides in place)

The high wind speed/conventional nozzle treatment showed the greatest variance with the calculated values given by Ganzelmeier at the 2m position, although the measured and predicted values converged with distance from the application point, and were similar at the mid ditch position (5.5m).

When compared to the high wind speed / conventional nozzle treatment, the combination of 3mph (low) wind speed and low drift nozzle had a significant (p<0.001) influence in reducing drift by ca. ten-fold at 2m from the spray nozzle, seven-fold at 3m and five-fold at the mid-ditch position (Figure 2). The addition of a 50cm artificial bank on either side of the ditch had no significant influence on the deposition of chlorpyrifos at drift capture points across the 4.5m no-spray zone to the ditch section (Figure 3).

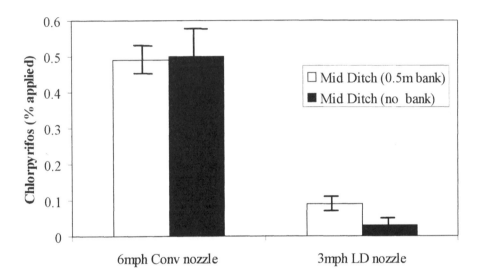

Figure 3. Spray drift deposition (as chlorpyrifos) with and without a 50cm ditch bank

Water concentrations in the initial test runs showed a large amount of variability between replicate samples, which was attributed to insufficient agitation of the ditch water causing non-homogeneous mixing of chlorpyrifos. Re-design of the stainless steel paddle and its use in later tests gave more consistent results. Concentrations were reduced by ca. half from an average of 1.11μg L^{-1} with the high wind speed / conventional nozzle combination, to 0.45μg L^{-1} under the low wind speed and low drift nozzle treatment.

DISCUSSION

The initial phase of the work described here demonstrated the value of using a large- scale wind tunnel to conduct spray drift / exposure potential investigations, as opposed to either field based or small scale laboratory experiments. Controlled conditions within the wind tunnel isolated the test system from external influences, and allowed the implementation of a replicated statistical design to test individual spray application parameters and their combinations. In addition, field scale application methods and rates could be utilised while retaining laboratory characteristics of measurement and repeatability.

Results from this first phase showed significant differences in the pattern of spray drift deposition for the combinations of spray nozzle and wind speed tested, when compared with Ganzelmeier data. Differences were most marked within 3m of the spray nozzle. In general, the data suggest that the use of both low wind speed and low drift nozzle can contribute to reductions in the amount of certain PPPs deposited on edge of field surface waters. This has significant potential for reducing initial exposure concentrations in the water body and consequent reductions in effects on susceptible non-target aquatic organisms. The issue of uneven distribution (non-homogeneity) of oily formulations in water arose in this study. It was considered that this could be due the tendency of the emulsifiable concentrate micelles to float to the surface of the water. This phenomenon could influence both the rate of loss of chlorpyrifos from surface water and exposure of organisms in the water body. Further work to investigate this issue was identified and will be reported elsewhere.

ACKNOWLEDGEMENTS

We thank Prof. P Miller and Dr S Parkin of Silsoe Research Institute for their technical assistance in this study, and for the provision of the wind tunnel facilities.

REFERENCES

Ganzelmeier H; Rautmann D; Spagenberg R; Hermann M; Wenzelburger H J; Walter H F (1995). Studies on the spray drift of plant protection products. *Mitteilungen Aus Der Biologischen Bundesanstalt Fur Land-Und Fortwirtschaft*, Berlin
Miller P C H; Campbell S (1998). When the wind blows. *Resource* pp.8 - 9

Prediction of field efficacy from greenhouse data for four auxenic herbicides

J P Wright
Dow AgroSciences, Indianapolis, IN, USA
Email: jwright@dowagro.com

A R Thompson
Dow AgroSciences, Wantage, Oxfordshire, UK

ABSTRACT

The proposed paper will compare greenhouse and field efficacy data in light of concerns for offsite movement of herbicides. A central issue of environmental concern is how well greenhouse or laboratory data collected on a few species can predict injury to a larger, more diverse set of species in the field. A retrospective analysis of four auxenic herbicides shows that most efficacy data was generated to predict, with a high degree of certainty, the application rates required to cause 90% injury. There was little rate response data generated on the same species in both the greenhouse and field sufficient to estimate the 25% or 50% injury that is the environmental endpoint for most regulatory concerns. For those species where direct comparisons could be made, the greenhouse to field injury varied from approximately equal to as much as 20X with large variations between species. For the species with the lowest EC_{25} values, the greenhouse data over predicted the field injury. Alternatively, a species sensitivity distribution uses all available data, and is predictive of injury to plant populations. Initial results suggest that the field and greenhouse data can be adequately modeled as log-normal distributions, were non-parallel, and can be used to predict the maximum application rates that are protective of 95% of species.

INTRODUCTION

Risk analysts, when attempting to judge potential impacts to the environment, have traditionally used deterministic calculations with single point estimates of injury to represent what in reality is a range of exposures and effects. Such risk assessments that use single values, i.e., the most sensitive species tested, loose information about both the extreme values and median responses and require some judgement about what information to exclude from the analysis (Cullen & Frey, 1999). In many instances, the person choosing which data to use has little or no knowledge of the underlying assumptions or range of true values. Currently, US EPA guidelines for pesticide registrations require greenhouse data on ten terrestrial species (USEPA, 1989), while German guidelines require data on six species (Füll *et al.*, 1999) for their ecological risk assessments. In both cases, the assessments are based on the single most sensitive species tested with limited or no consideration of other species or the relative sensitivity between greenhouse and field grown plants.

It is generally accepted that a higher application rate is required to cause injury to field grown plants than greenhouse grown plants because of physical and metabolic differences, dissipation/degradation of the product, plant age and structure, cuticle thickness, and other factors. From a review of published data, Fletcher *et al.* (1990) concluded that the ratios of greenhouse to field EC_{50} values ranged from 0.26 to 3.26. For 30% of the herbicide/species combinations he evaluated, the greenhouse EC_{50} values were lower than the corresponding values in the field. The remaining 70% had field EC_{50} values that were lower than those measured in the greenhouse. In Fletcher's review, it is not clear if the values were calculated from the dose response in individual studies, or from data aggregated across multiple studies. Few dose response studies have made direct comparisons between greenhouse and field grown plants under controlled conditions. In the current investigation using historical data generated during product development, it was found that a limited number of species were tested under both greenhouse and field conditions because of the nature and purpose of discovery screens and field efficacy tests. Direct comparisons of individual species gave variable conclusions. Expressing the data as species sensitivity distributions, however, demonstrated linear relationships between the EC_{25} values and the cumulative percentage of species, and revealed a non-parallel relationship between the greenhouse and field data.

METHODS

Greenhouse and field efficacy data for individual herbicides were retrieved from the archives of Dow AgroSciences LLC and used for comparison between species. Greenhouse data were derived either from studies required to meet product registration requirements or from discovery, efficacy screens. Data on the field response of species were obtained from field development reports or annual data summaries as available. Only those studies with a minimum of three application rates and injury responses that bracketed the appropriate level of injury were included. Estimates of the application rate that caused 25% visual injury (EC_{25}) were made by fitting the data for each study to a four-parameter logistic dose response model. The greenhouse to field ratios were calculated as the average greenhouse EC_{25} divided by the average field EC_{25} across all studies for each species. A species sensitivity distribution for each herbicide was constructed by ranking the EC_{25} values in ascending order and plotted against the cumulative percent of species (Newman et al., 2000; Versteeg et al., 1999). For example, if there were data on 10 species, each species would represent 10% of all species. Initial results showed that the species EC_{25} values adequately fit a log-normal distribution. A linear relationship was obtained by plotting the common log of the EC_{25} values vs. the percent cumulative species for each product. Estimates of the EC_{25} for the lowest 5% of all species were calculated by least squares linear regression and extrapolation as necessary from the regression equation.

RESULTS AND DISCUSSION

There was very little overlap between the species tested in the greenhouse and field. In this analysis, 104 EC_{25} values were obtained from greenhouse tests and 40 from field tests, that together allowed for direct comparisons between 38 data points. The lack of overlap between species probably stemmed from the different purposes for the two test systems. The greenhouse tests were designed to detect herbicidal activity using a representative set of species based on their economic importance and ability to be grown reproducibly in a greenhouse while field tests were designed to determine with high precision the application rate that caused 90% control under varying conditions. Direct comparisons showed that for 13 of the 38 data points, higher EC_{25} values were measured in the greenhouse than in the field. The greatest differences were for ABUTH and DAOTE with all four herbicides, DATST for pyridyloxy A and pyridyloxy C, and NIOTA for pyridyloxy A (Figure 1). The differences for ABUTH, DATST and NIOTA derive from a single field test and may not be representative. The remaining species had lower EC_{25} values in the greenhouse.

The ability to predict field effects from a limited amount of greenhouse data is an important concern in ecological risk assessment. The small number of species with data from both the field and greenhouse limited the comparisons that could be made. A better approach is to examine the trend using all available data instead of single species. Such an approach has been recommended by several groups including the Aquatics Dialog Group of SETAC (SETAC 1994), ECOFRAM (ECOFRAM 1999) and EPPO (EPPO 2000). Species sensitivity distributions for each of the four herbicides are presented in Figures 2 through 5. In each case, the resulting plots were linear but non-parallel between greenhouse and field data with steeper slopes for the field data. The results suggest that a smaller application rate range was required for species in the field than in the greenhouse. From such a distributional approach, it is not possible to predict the response of any given species, but instead indicates the overall population trend. The non-parallel lines suggest that plants grown in the greenhouse vs. the field behave as two separate populations, though they contain the same species. From the regression equations, application rates that would cause 25% visual injury for the lowest 5% of species, i.e. the rate that would be protective of 95% of species, was calculated. The results are given in Table 1. The differences between the field and greenhouse ranged from 3.4X for pyridyloxy D to approximately 13X for pyridyloxy B with the greenhouse values lower than the field. The use of species sensitivity distributions may provide a useful way to summarize disparate data sets and predict field responses of plant populations as part of ecological risk assessments.

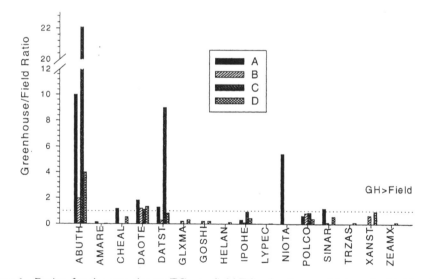

Figure 1. Ratios for the greenhouse EC_{25} to field EC_{25} for four pyridyloxy herbicides (A-D). The dotted line represents a ratio of 1 where the greenhouse equaled the field.

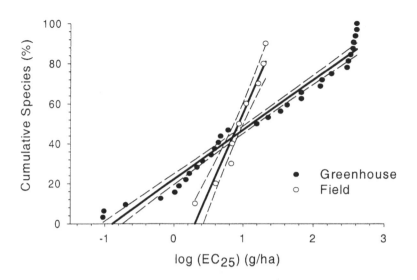

Figure 2. Species sensitivity distributions for pyridyloxy A. The dotted lines are for the 95% confidence interval around the regression lines.

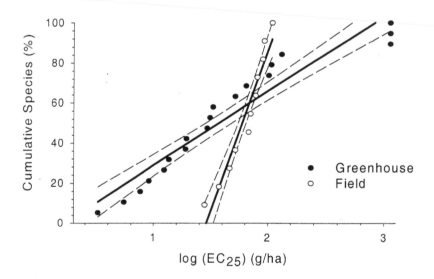

Figure 3. Species sensitivity distributions for pyridyloxy B. The dotted lines are for the 95% confidence interval around the regression lines.

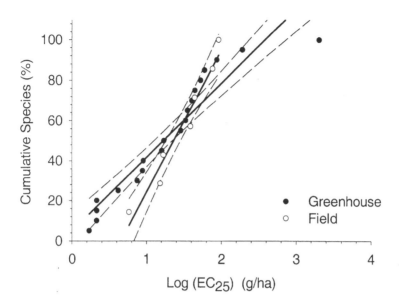

Figure 4. Species sensitivity distributions for pyridyloxy C. The dotted lines are for the 95% confidence interval around the regression lines.

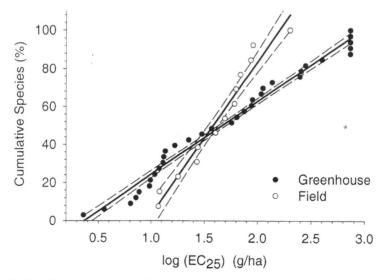

Figure 5. Species sensitivity distributions for pyridyloxy D. The dotted lines are for the 95% confidence interval around the regression lines.

Table 1. Predicted EC_{25} values for the lowest 5% of species, greenhouse vs. field data

Product	Greenhouse (g/ha)	Field (g/ha)
Pyridyloxy A	0.21	2.3
Pyridyloxy B	2.3	31.0
Pyridyloxy C	1.0	5.3
Pyridyloxy D	3.1	10.6

REFERENCES

Cullen AC; Frey HC (1999). *Probabilistic Techniques in Exposure Assessment, A Handbook for Dealing with Variability and Uncertainty in Models and Inputs.* Plenum Press, New York.

ECOFRAM (1999). The Ecological Committee for FIFRA Risk Assessment Methods, Preliminary Report, US EPA Office of Pesticide Programs.

EPPO (2000). *Decision making scheme for environmental risk assessment of plant protection products.* Chapter 13, Non-target plants. European and Mediterranean Plant Protection Organization, Paris, France.

Fletcher JS; Johnson FL; McFarlane JC (1990). Influence of Greenhouse Versus Field Testing and Taxonomic Differences on Plant Sensitivity to Chemical Treatment. *Environmental Toxicology and Chemistry* **9**, 769 – 776.

Füll C; Jung S; Schulte C (1999). Guidelines: Pesticides. Testing requirements of the Federal Environmental Agency for assessing the effects of plant protection products on terrestrial plants. Federal Environmental Agency, Division IV: Material assessment and execution, Seeckstr. 6-19, D-13581 Berlin.

Newman MC; Ownby DR; Mezin LCA; Powell TRL (2000). Applying species sensitivity distributions in ecological risk assessment: Assumptions of distribution type and sufficient numbers of species. *Environmental Toxicology and Chemistry* **19**, 508-515.

SETAC (1994). *Aquatic Dialog Group: Pesticide Assessment and Mitigation, Final Report: Aquatic Risk Assessment and Mitigation Dialog Group.* Society of Environmental Toxicology and Chemistry. Pensacola FL, USA.

USEPA (1989). Pesticide Assessment Guidelines, Subdivision J: 122 and 123, Non-target Area Terrestrial Plant Phytotoxicity.

Versteeg DJ; Belanger GJ; Carr GJ (1999) Understanding single species and model ecosystem sensitivity: Data-based comparison. *Environmental Toxicology and Chemistry* **18**, 1329-1346.

SESSION 10

HERBICIDES IN THE ENVIRONMENT: EXPOSURE, CONSEQUENCES AND RISK ASSESSMENT – PART 2

Chairman &
Session Organisers:
D J Arnold
Cambridge Environmental Assessments, Boxworth, UK

and

A Craven
Pesticides Safety Directorate, York, UK

Biodiversity, herbicides and non-target plants

E J P Marshall

Marshall Agroecology Limited, 2 Nut Tree Cottages, Barton, Winscombe, North Somerset, BS25 1DU, UK
Email: jon.marshall@agroecol.co.uk

ABSTRACT

Herbicides provide a useful tool for the farmer, grower and vegetation manager. However, they are capable of affecting non-target plants. Non-target plants may be those outside the target area, or those within the target area of conservation concern or whose control has untoward effects on biological diversity. A number of farmland birds, invertebrates and plants have shown population declines in Europe; changes in agriculture, including herbicides, are implicated. Whilst a better understanding of the impacts of weed control on biological diversity is needed, the new challenge is the development of more ecologically sustainable production, incorporating the maintenance of some weed species within crops. The first-generation genetically modified herbicide-tolerant (GMHT) crops seem unlikely to provide the required flexibility of management. For success, greater selectivity of herbicide chemistry is indicated, together with a range of risk avoidance approaches.

INTRODUCTION

Herbicides are an essential part of the farmer and grower's equipment for crop management. In addition, herbicides can play a useful role in vegetation management in a variety of non-crop situations, ranging from industrial areas to amenity sites (Marshall, 1994) and even nature reserves and conservation areas. For example, herbicides may be an essential part of control strategies for alien invasive species, such as giant hogweed (*Heracleum mantegazzianum*). Nevertheless, a range of environmental problems, including residues in water, has focussed attention on the regulatory process and the impact of herbicides in the environment. There have been a number of recent developments in approaches to risk assessment and risk avoidance for non-target effects of herbicides (Breeze *et al.*, 1999). This paper reviews the definition of non-target plants, the use of herbicides and assesses the impacts of herbicides on non-targets and biological diversity. The implications of improved understanding of functional biodiversity and of developments in new technologies are discussed. Finally, a number of requirements for the future approval and use of herbicides are proposed.

DEFINING NON-TARGET PLANTS

The movement of herbicide away from the application area will bring it into contact with plants that are by definition non-targets. This "off-field" movement may be due to droplet drift, vapour movement, leaching and erosion, as well as inappropriate disposal. An extremely wide range of plant species (the national flora) is potentially at risk to such movement. Approaches to risk assessment and risk avoidance in the UK have been reviewed by Marshall *et al.* (2001). Advances in non-target risk assessment have also been made in Europe and North America, aimed at assessing the risks to off-field flora particularly from drift events (Hewitt, 2000).

There are also within-field non-target plants that need consideration. There are two very different scenarios where herbicides are used. In most situations, a herbicide is deployed to control all the plant species present except the single crop species. In the non-crop situation, either all species are targets for total weed control, or there is a single target species and all others present are non-targets. This is a simplification, as herbicide selectivities vary and the target group necessarily may be wider. Likewise, within a crop, there may be a number of unsown plant species present forming a weed assemblage. As many of these species reduce yield, or affect harvesting, storage or crop quality, farmers regard them all as weeds worthy of removal. Nevertheless, amongst these non-crop species, there may be both target and non-target species for weed control. A number of rare weed species, such as broad-leaved cudweed (*Filago pyramidata*), are subject to conservation effort and some are included within UK Biodiversity Action Plans (BAPs), the response to the Rio Convention on Biological Diversity (Anon, 1994). These may be regarded as non-target species. Of greater significance, as they are commoner and often have significant biomass, there is a suite of species that might be targets at higher density, but may be non-targets at low population levels for biodiversity reasons. There are a number of species that are almost invariably targets for control, usually because of their competitive ability, such as wild-oat (*Avena fatua*). The consideration of non-target species within the application area brings a number of potential complications to the regulatory process and to practical management. However, against the environmental background of significant declines in farmland wildlife across Western Europe, this is a challenge to be faced.

HERBICIDE IMPACTS AND NON-TARGET EFFECTS

Agricultural and horticultural habitats do not occur in isolation in the landscape. Field systems occur as mosaics of crop and non-crop habitat (Marshall, 1988) and may be refuges for many plant and animal species. Whilst most species associated with non-crop areas do not commonly pose serious threats to adjacent crops (Marshall, 1989), these areas may be important for the conservation of biological diversity in agricultural landscapes, particularly as production methods have intensified. Extensive studies of land use change and their ecological consequences also indicate that botanical diversity is continuing to decline (Haines-Young *et al.*, 2000). Whilst the causal effects are not agreed, they are most likely to be eutrophication and disturbance. Agricultural practices, including fertiliser and herbicide applications, are implicated (Kleijn & Snoeijing, 1997).

Within agricultural systems, there have been significant declines in both population sizes and ranges of common birds in the UK (Fuller *et al.*, 1995). Likewise, there have been significant declines in some taxa of invertebrates found within fields (Aebischer, 1991). The idea that arable fields are "ecological deserts" is ill founded, as there is a range of plant and animal species specifically adapted to the habitat, for example the cornfield flowers.

Individual plant species can be affected directly by a herbicide. As part of a plant community made up of many species, a plant species can also be affected indirectly following herbicide contamination. This can be mediated by competition between species, or by affecting plant recruitment (vegetative or from seed), or by affecting herbivore pressure or symbionts. Determining the effects of herbicides on plant communities is not straightforward (Cousens *et al.*, 1988). Susceptibility of plants to herbicides is not a constant characteristic, as application variables interact with plant variables.

Non-target effects of herbicides may be caused when materials reach situations beyond the target application area and/or reach species not intended to be affected growing within the target area. The direct adverse effects of herbicides can range from outright death of a plant or population, through minor effects, to enhanced growth. The spectrum of direct effects on individuals is matched by a spectrum of indirect effects on associated fauna and flora. Direct effects on plants can appear to be insignificant, for example, reduced flowering. However, such impacts may be of major significance to species where seed production is the key element of the regenerative cycle of the plant. Effects on germination and early recruitment of plant species are believed to be of particular importance at a growth stage that is particularly susceptible to pesticides. Non-target effects may have subtle effects on plant community composition, mediated by plant competition or by effects on the water and chemical environment in the rhizosphere.

It is unclear how important the non-target effects of herbicides are. For example, it is unknown if repeated drift events, or mixtures of herbicides at low doses, can have sub lethal effects on plant recruitment. The "off-field" movements from herbicide application are likely to be the most common cause of non-target effects (Breeze *et al.*, 1999). These can result from droplet drift, mist, solid and vapour movement. Of these drift forms, droplet movement is by far the most important and common form. Following application, pesticides may also undergo secondary redistribution with a risk of non-target effects, if pesticide concentrations are high enough.

BIODIVERSITY AND ECOSYSTEM FUNCTION

The reasons for the conservation of biodiversity are moral, aesthetic, social and economic. We steward other organisms for their intrinsic value and because species may be of benefit to human society and have economic value. A culture that encourages respect for wildlife is preferable to one that does not. Biodiversity can be easily lost but is difficult to regain, particularly if species are driven to extinction. Biodiversity, including genetic diversity, may provide economic benefits. Even at the level of landscape, biodiversity may influence tourism and sense of place. Perhaps of greatest concern is that biodiversity has a role in the function of ecosystems (Tilman *et al.*, 1996). Erosion of diversity may thus ultimately result in damage to ecosystem function.

Plants are key components of terrestrial ecosystems, providing the primary production upon which food chains are built. Different plant parts provide a range of resources for associated fauna (Figure. 1). Leaves and stems may be browsed, while pollen and nectar provide resources for pollinating insects. Fruits and seeds are important food for a large number of organisms. Plants have other functions as well as providing food for herbivores. They provide cover, reproduction sites and structure within habitats. Plants also form a substrate for bacteria, fungi etc., both above ground and in the soil.

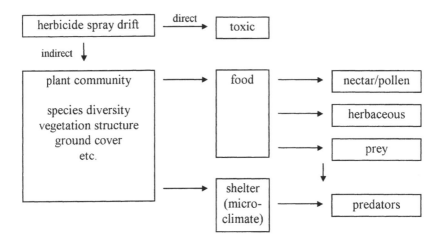

Figure 1.   Potential ecological effects of herbicide spray drift on invertebrates – from Breeze *et al.*, (1999)

Even non-crop plants or weeds may play a role in the function of the ecosystem and in supporting many other species. As an example, the grey partridge (*Perdix perdix*) requires insects as chick food during the first ten weeks of rearing. Many of these insects are associated with annual dicotyledonous weeds in cereal crops in the UK. Adult partridges also feed on plants, particularly within arable crops. Management of the crop with pesticides and herbicides is therefore likely to have had a major impact on partridge populations, explaining the major declines in population of this bird species in the twentieth century (Potts, 1991).

Interactions between weed diversity and biodiversity

A comparison of herbicide-treated and untreated plots in the headlands of winter cereal fields in southern England (Moreby & Southway, 1999) has clearly demonstrated that untreated plots had greater weed density and diversity and significantly higher numbers of many invertebrate taxa, notably those that are important in the diet of farmland birds. Studies of the insects associated with soybean in Iowa, USA, indicate that weedier fields have generally higher insect densities. Weed management in herbicide-resistant soybean generally gave fewer insects (Buckelew *et al.*, 2000). The effects were indirect, mediated through the weed flora. Several initiatives, notably for integrated crop management, indicate there are implications for biological diversity within fields from different approaches to weed control. The protection of the farmers' investment and avoidance of risk have been the driving forces for efficient weed control in the past. However, an emerging new paradigm is to match crop production with conservation of biological resources (Paoletti *et al.*, 1992) and the development of more sustainable systems. This may require the maintenance of some weeds within fields.

NEW TECHNOLOGIES FOR WEED MANAGEMENT

Genetically modified herbicide-tolerant (GMHT) crops

The introduction and testing of GMHT crops, whilst widely accepted in North America, has been opposed by many interest groups in Europe. Current work on the field-scale evaluation of the biodiversity impacts of these crops in the UK is examining the likely impact of modified herbicide use within the crop (Firbank *et al.*, 1999). The first generation of GMHT crops are engineered for tolerance to broad-spectrum herbicides, notably glyphosate and glufosinate. These *may* allow greater flexibility in weed management, but there may be effects on biodiversity as a result.

Watkinson *et al.* (2000) simulated the effects of the introduction of GMHT crops on weed populations and the consequences for seed-eating birds, using fat-hen as the model weed. They predicted that weed populations might be reduced to low levels or practically eradicated, depending on the exact form of management. Consequent effects on the local use of fields by birds might be severe, because such reductions represent a major loss of food resources. Buckelew *et al.* (2000) have shown that herbicide-resistant soybean crops tend to have lower insect population densities, associated with fewer weeds.

Whilst it may be argued that GMHT crops offer the opportunity to delay weed control, some crops, most notably maize, are particularly susceptible to early weed competition. Such crops are likely to be treated with herbicide around the time of crop emergence to eliminate weeds early in the life of the crop. The technology offers reduced risk to the farmer, with opportunities for repeated application, should this become necessary. Environmentally, the technology offers the possibility of clean crops and thus adverse biodiversity effects, as well as the unknown, if low, possibility of gene transfer to wild relatives. Nevertheless, it must be accepted that in the developing world, where weeds are the primary source of crop loss, this first-generation technology may have an important role.

Integrated weed management

Approaches to weed management over recent years have taken an holistic view of the crop rotation as a whole, rather than simply in single crops, as part of integrated crop management (ICM). ICM considers fertiliser use, targeted pesticide use, alternative control techniques, forecasting and modelling, as well as crop rotation (Jordan & Hutcheon, 1995). Economic pressures have also forced farmers and growers to consider the number of herbicide applications made and the dose of active ingredients used. Reduced dose applications have become common. Within ICM, the manipulation of crop architecture, tillage regimes, mechanical weed control, allelopathy, mulching, biological control may all contribute to "integrated weed management".

However, "*devising integrated weed management strategies that address a diversity of weed species with a diversity of life history traits is difficult*" (Mortensen *et al.*, 2000). A sound understanding of species, population and community ecology can contribute to weed management. Advances include population equilibria, density-dependent effects, crop competition models and integration with herbicide dose-response studies.

RISK MANAGEMENT

Risk management needs to address herbicide susceptibility and exposure. Exposure can be most easily manipulated, though susceptibility may be influenced, for example by protectants. The key to risk avoidance must be in targeting only those plant species or populations that require control. This means that precision in chemistry, *i.e.* selectivity of herbicide, and precision of application, *i.e.* only to the target plants, offers the most robust way forward. Aspects of dose, formulation, application timing and application technology may be usefully modified within a sound weed forecasting and decision-support framework. There may nevertheless be opportunities for spatial approaches to biodiversity maintenance. For example, conservation headlands, in which limited pesticide applications are made to the outside 6m or 12m of crop, allow sufficient weeds and invertebrates to survive for grey partridge populations to switch from decline to increase (Rands & Sotherton, 1987).

NEW DIRECTIONS FOR HERBICIDE USE AND WEED BIODIVERSITY

Ecologically, there is a requirement for greater specificity of herbicide action for minimising environmental and non-target effects. This runs against the trend for more broad-spectrum products produced by manufacturers. In order to cover the high costs of product development, manufacturers require products that will sell into global markets. This has resulted in herbicides with wide weed spectra coming to market, with more selective products rarely being commercialised. Greater herbicide selectivity is not without practical and financial difficulties. The inertia of commercial development could only be mobilised by legislative and regulatory requirements, possibly backed up by redirected farm support to growers. In addition, there could be difficulties if there are insufficient product options, e.g. herbicide resistance. Nevertheless, there could be opportunities for specialist market development, if agricultural support is redirected from production to environmental support. Non-crop vegetation management could provide a diversity of niche markets.

Clearly, where selectivity in chemistry is limited, there are opportunities for achieving selectivity by exploiting application technology and spatial methods, as well as manipulating crop phenology and growth characteristics. Further work on the opportunities for arable biodiversity areas, such as conservation headlands, is required.

Under the regulatory regimes for pesticides, there is a need to consider non-target, indirect effects that occur within the target crop area. This will require testing on a wider range of plant species representative of the diverse flora of arable and horticultural fields.

Current integrated weed management programmes might be further developed and modified to maintain adequate populations of the most important weed species for biodiversity, while controlling the most damaging. There is some possibility of relaxing weed control either rotationally or in limited areas of fields. Nevertheless, the major constraint is that the most fecund and often the most competitive weed species respond best to reduced control. Therefore, relaxed weed control would need to be managed carefully to allow the less common and less competitive species to increase, while controlling the competitive species. This may indicate a new approach to weed management, with the explicit aim of maintaining specific weed assemblages. These might be more traditional assemblages that were common 100 years ago, or tailored to maintaining beneficial invertebrate species, or for biodiversity more generally. An understanding of the selection pressures applied by management, including the use of herbicides, and their effects on diversity, ranging from genetic to community levels, is needed.

ACKNOWLEDGEMENTS

I would like to thank all the scientists with whom I have collaborated for the recent reviews written for the UK Pesticides Safety Directorate on aspects of non-target effects: V G Breeze, A Hart, V K Brown, P J W Lutman, N D Boatman and G R Squire.

REFERENCES

Aebischer N J (1991). Twenty years of monitoring invertebrates and weeds in cereal fields in Sussex. In: *The Ecology of Temperate Cereal Fields*, eds L G Firbank; N Carter, J F Darbyshire & G R Potts, pp. 305-331. Blackwell Scientific Publications, Oxford.

Anon (1994) *Biodiversity. The UK Action Plan*. HMSO, London.

Barr C J; Bunce R G H; Clarke R T; Fuller R M; Furse M T; Gillespie M K; Groom G B; Hallam C J; Hornung M; Howard D C; Ness M J (1993). *Countryside Survey 1990*. Main Report. Department of the Environment.

Breeze V G; Marshall E J P; Hart A; Vickery J A; Crocker J; Walters K; Packer J; Kendall D; Fowbert J; Hodkinson D. (1999). *Assessing pesticide risks to non-target terrestrial plants. A desk study. Commission PN0923*. MAFF Pesticides Safety Directorate.

Buckelew L D; Pedigo L P; Mero H M; Owen M D K; Tylka G L (2000) Effects of weed management systems on canopy insects in herbicide-resistant soybeans. *Journal of Economic Entomology*, **93**, 1437-1443.

Cousens, R.; Marshall, E.J.P.; Arnold, G.M. (1988) Problems in the interpretation of effects of herbicides on plant communities. In: *BCPC Monograph No.40. Field Methods for the Study of Environmental Effects of Pesticides*, eds M.P. Greaves, B.D. Smith & P.W. Greig-Smith, pp. 275-282.

Firbank, L.G.; Dewar, A.M.; Hill, M.O.; May, M.J.; Perry, J.N.; Rothery, P.; Squire, G.R.; Woiwod, I.P. (1999) Farm-scale evaluation of GM crops explained. *Nature*, **399**, 727-728.

Fuller, R.J.; Gregory, R.D.; Gibbons, D.W.; Marchant, J.H.; Wilson, J.D.; Baillie, S.R.; Carter, N. (1995) Population declines and range contractions among farmland birds in Britain. *Conservation Biology*, **9**, 1425-1441.

Haines-Young, R.H.; Barr, C.J.; Black, H.I.J.; Briggs, D.J.; Bunce, R.G.H.; Clarke, R.T.; Cooper, A.; Dawson, F.H.; Firbank, L.G.; Fuller, R.M.; Furse, M.T.; Gillespie, M.K.; Hill, R.; Hornung, M.; Howard, D.C.; McCann, T.; Morecroft, M.D.; Petit, S.; Sier, A.R.J.; Smart, S.M.; Smith, G.M.; Stott, A.P.; Stuart, R.C.; Watkins, J.W. (2000) *Accounting for nature: assessing habitats in the UK countryside*, DETR, London.

Hewitt, A.J. (2000) Spray drift: impact of requirements to protect the environment. *Crop Protection*, **19**, 623-627.

Jordan, V.W.L.; Hutcheon, J.A. (1995). Less-intensive Farming and the Environment: an integrated farming systems approach for UK arable crop production. In: *Ecology and Integrated Farming Systems* eds D.M. Glen, M.P. Greaves & H.M. Anderson, pp. 307-318. John Wiley & Sons, Chichester.

Kleijn, D.; Snoeijing, G.I.J. (1997) Field boundary vegetation and the effects of agrochemical drift: botanical change caused by low levels of herbicide and fertilizer. *Journal of Applied Ecology*, **34**, 1413-1425.

Marshall, E.J.P. (1988) The ecology and management of field margin floras in England. *Outlook on Agriculture*, **17**, 178-182.

Marshall, E.J.P. (1989) Distribution patterns of plants associated with arable field edges. *Journal of Applied Ecology*, **26**, 247-257.

Marshall, E.J.P. (1994). Amenity grass for non-sport use. In: *Natural turf for sport and amenity: science and practice*, eds W.A. Adams & R.J. Gibbs, pp. 354-376. CABI, Wallingford.

Marshall, J., Brown, V., Boatman, N., Lutman, P., & Squire, G. (2001). *The impact of herbicides on weed abundance and biodiversity. Commission PN0940.* IACR-Long Ashton Research Station.

Moreby, S.J.; Southway, S.E. (1999) Influence of autumn applied herbicides on summer and autumn food availability to birds in winter wheat fields in southern England. *Agriculture, Ecosystems & Environment*, **72**, 285-297.

Mortensen, D.A.; Bastiaans, L.; Sattin, M. (2000) The role of ecology in the development of weed management systems: an outlook. *Weed Research*, **40**, 49-62.

Paoletti, M.G.; Pimentel, D.; Stinner, B.R.; Stinner, D. (1992) Agroecosystem biodiversity - matching production and conservation biology. *Agriculture, Ecosystems & Environment*, **40**, 3-23.

Potts, G.R. (1991). The environmental and ecological importance of cereal fields. In: *The Ecology of Temperate Cereal Fields*, eds L.G. Firbank, Carter, N., Darbyshire, J.F. & Potts, G.R., pp. 373-397. Blackwell Scientific Publications, Oxford.

Rands, M.R.W.; Sotherton, N.W. (1987) The management of field margins for the conservation of gamebirds. In: *BCPC Monograph No. 35. Field Margins*, eds J.M. Way & P.W. Greig-Smith, pp. 95-104.

Tilman, D.; Wedin, D.; Knops, J. (1996) Productivity and sustainability influenced by biodiversity in grassland ecosystems. *Nature*, **379**, 718-720.

Watkinson, A.R.; Freckleton, R.P., Robinson, R.A., & Sutherland, W.J. (2000) Predictions of biodiversity response to genetically modified herbicide-tolerant crops. *Science*, **289**, 1554-1557.

Terrestrial non-target plant testing and assessment; the conservative nature of the process

J J Dulka

DuPont Crop Protection, Stine-Haskell Research Center, Newark, Delaware 19714, USA
E-mail: joseph.j.dulka@usa.dupont.com

ABSTRACT

Terrestrial non-target plant testing and assessment is an emerging topic in Europe, as it was not previously discussed under the framework of Directive 91/414/EEC in the European Union. Test methods and assessment techniques are under development and an evaluation of the conservative nature of the study design, the exposure assessment and the safety goals need to be carefully considered before implementation. Non-target plants are defined as plants outside of the agricultural unit (i.e., the treatment area, plus a defined area around the treatment area used for agriculture). For non-herbicides, safety can generally be addressed using data generated from plant safety screens and efficacy work done during the development of the product. For herbicides, draft OECD regulatory test methods exist for both soil and foliar exposure assessments. The draft test methods use a suite of domesticated species to indicate the range of response (e.g., two to three orders of magnitude in range, typically) which may be expected for other species not included in the test. This approach makes use of readily available species with well-defined growth characteristics that allow determination of reliable metrics (e.g., visual effects and biomass), and end-points (e.g., EC_{50}). Because the end-points are based on sub-lethal effects and not lethality, and the study design is biased towards a "worst-case" scenario, the approach provides a very conservative estimate of phytotoxicity. These data combined with a conservative estimate of exposure, allow for a very conservative estimate of risk to non-target plants.

INTRODUCTION

Several activities have been ongoing on both the international and national level to address safety to non-target plants. On a national level, Germany has recently included non-target plant risk assessments as part of their National requirements (Füll *et al.*, 1999). And, the European Commission has suggested the addition of terrestrial plant data as part of the dossier package for all crop protection products (CPPs) in their recent Guidance on Terrestrial Ecotoxicology (European Commission, 08.07.2000).

In the area of testing, the Organization for Economic Cooperation and Development (OECD) has been working to revise Technical Guideline 208, for the testing of Terrestrial Plants, Growth Test. The main purpose of the revision is to modify the current guideline to allow for the testing of crop protection products (CPPs) (OECD, 2000).

The European and Mediterranean Plant Protection Organization (EPPO) has developed a proposed risk assessment scheme using the data generated in evaluating product phytotoxicity leading to an estimate of potential risk (EPPO, 2000).

Exposure is predicted using the drift data described by Ganzelmeier *et al.*, (1995).

The purpose of this paper is:

- to briefly review several of these on-going activities,
- to identify those factors in the current glasshouse/laboratory test design which contribute the highest levels of conservatism to the evaluation of plant safety,
- to quantify what contribution each factor may contribute to the conservative nature of the assessment and uncertainty in a determination of the level of safety afforded non-target plants and,
- to demonstrate that current tests are performed in a conservative fashion, such that in combination with a conservative estimate of exposure a very conservative estimate of risk to non-target plants (NTPs) is attained.
-

BRIEF REVIEW OF TERRESTRIAL NON-TARGET PLANT TEST METHODS

For non-herbicides, data available from screening and efficacy studies generated by companies to address plant safety are being used to address product safety. Additionally, under Annex III, Section 6.6.1 through 6.6.3 of 91/414/EEC, data are generated to address safety to crops and the subsequent rotational crops for which a product is intended (EU Commission, 27 July 1993). This approach has been used successfully for insecticides and fungicides in general, and for herbicides to address in-field plant safety.

In screening studies, plants are sprayed at the maximum application rate of the product at plant growth stages typical of product use and assessed for visual injury. Since different companies may use different techniques and different rating systems to develop these data, the OECD has proposed guidance (OECD, 2000; Annex III) on what information should be supplied by the registrant and how the data can be normalized to provide uniformity in the hazard assessment.

For herbicides, two regulatory methods are being proposed to assess effects (OECD, 2000). One method assesses effects to seedlings via exposure through the soil, while the other assesses effects to young plants (two to four leave stage) via exposure through the foliage. In most cases, exposure via the foliage produces higher sensitivity, and for regulatory purposes, these data, rather than soil exposure data and seedling emergence, have been primarily used in Germany. There may be exceptions to this general rule, and in cases where the product may show pre-emergence soil activity, tests using soil exposure and seedling emergence may be conducted preferentially.

The test duration is between 14 and 21 days, depending upon the species and growth of the control group. Six species, 2 monocotyledon and 4 dicotyledon species, from the list of species shown in Table 1 (OECD, 2000) are used. The species used in these tests are intended to provide a range of response, similar to other ecotoxicological tests and not to act as taxonomic surrogates. Therefore, several species that are known to be sensitive to the herbicide are tested, as well as a tolerant species. In this fashion, inter-species response may vary as much as a factor of 1000-fold plus, from the most sensitive to the most tolerant species tested.

At the end of the test, the plants are assessed for visual injury (e.g., chlorosis, leaf curling, shoot height, etc.) and biomass (fresh or dry weight). Since a plant species is tested at several concentrations, an EC_{50} and/or EC_{25} are determined. The most sensitive species end-point is then used for the safety assessment.

Table 1.   List of species recommended for use in plant tests

Family	Species	Common names

DICOTYLEDONAE

Family	Species	Common names
Chenopodiaceae	*Beta vulgaris*	Sugar beet
Compositae (Asteraceae)	*Lactuca sativa*	Lettuce
Cruciferae (Brassicaceae)	*Brassica alba*	Mustard
Cruciferae (Brassicaceae)	*Brassica campestris* var. *chinensis*	Chinese cabbage
Cruciferae (Brassicaceae)	*Brassica napus*	Oilseed rape
Cruciferae (Brassicaceae)	*Brassica oleracea*	Cabbage
Cruciferae (Brassicaceae)	*Brassica rapa*	Turnip
Cruciferae (Brassicaceae)	*Lepidium sativum*	Garden cress
Cruciferae (Brassicaceae)	*Raphanus sativus*	Radish
Cucurbitaceae	*Cucumis sativa*	Cucumber
Leguminosae (Fabaceae)	*Glycine max (G. soja)*	Soybean
Leguminosae (Fabaceae)	*Phaseolus aureus*	Mung bean
Leguminosae (Fabaceae)	*Pisum sativum*	Pea
Leguminosae (Fabaceae)	*Trifolium ornithopodioides*	Fenugreek/Birdsfoot trefoil
Leguminosae (Fabaceae)	*Trifolium pratense*	Red Clover
Leguminosae (Fabaceae)	*Vicia sativa*	Vetch
Solanaceae	*Lycopersicon esculentum*	Tomato
Umbelliferae (Apiaceae)	*Daucus carota*	Carrot

MONOCOTYLEDONAE

Family	Species	Common names
Gramineae (Poaceae)	*Avena sativa*	Oats
Gramineae (Poaceae)	*Hordeum vulgare*	Barley
Gramineae (Poaceae)	*Lolium perenne*	Perennial ryegrass
Gramineae (Poaceae)	*Oryza sativa*	Rice
Gramineae (Poaceae)	*Secale cereale*	Rye
Gramineae (Poaceae)	*Secale viridis*	Rye
Gramineae (Poaceae)	*Sorghum bicolor*	Grain sorghum
Gramineae (Poaceae)	*Sorghum vulgare*	Shattercane
Gramineae (Poaceae)	*Triticum aestivum*	Wheat
Gramineae (Poaceae)	*Zea mays*	Corn
Liliaceae (Amarylladaceae)	*Allium cepa*	Onion

THE CONSERVATIVE NATURE OF TERRESTRIAL NON-TARGET PLANT EFFECTS TESTING

Key in any assessment, is the reliability of the data and the uncertainty which may exist in extrapolating laboratory data to the environment. In conducting non-target plant tests in the glasshouse/laboratory, there are numerous factors that make this test very conservative in nature and subsequently the assessment as well. The factors to consider and the contribution each factor may contribute to an overly conservative estimation of effects in the environment are as follows (GCPF NTP Work Group, 2001) and are summarized in Table 3. Overall, a 100 to 6000 over estimate of effects is expected based on current test methods.

Exposure (spray drift versus drench application)

Non-target plant testing is conducted to assess the safety of crop protection products (CPP) to plants growing outside the agricultural unit (*i.e.*, the treatment area, plus some small area around the field (EPPO, 2000). However, there is a significant discrepancy between the exposure used in the glasshouse test and potential exposure in the real world via spray drift. In the glasshouse study, plants are treated using some form of sprayer that normally simulates overhead hydraulic spraying as provided by a field tractor spray and utilises normal application spray volumes – approximately 200 L/ha.

Although a range of active ingredient dose rates is tested, no variation in spray volume is used. For example, if the predicted spray drift in the field for ground applications were estimated to be 1% of the application rate, a predicted spray drift of 2L/ha would be expected. It is possible therefore that the greenhouse testing procedure provides for a worse case situation whereby the use of higher spray volumes in the glasshouse results in better spray coverage and therefore an overestimate of activity which may be due to drift. Limited data (GCPF NTP Work Group, 2001) indicate that by using reduced volumes to simulate drift injury can be over estimated using standard high volume techniques by a factor of 2 to 10. More research is needed to develop an understanding of the relationship between plant response from high volume exposures versus drift exposures.

Comparison of lethal and non-lethal effects

While the EC_{25} or EC_{50} may be used to assess plant safety, a 50 or 25% effect does not mean that plant survival will be impacted. Using available regulatory data, a determination of the ratios between an EC_{25}, EC_{50} and EC_{80} was made. The slope was determined and an estimated treatment rate necessary to produce mortality (e.g., LC_{50}) versus a transient effect (EC_{50}) (GCPF NTP Work Group, 2001). This comparison was made for both seedling emergence studies and vegetative vigour studies (Table 2) indicating that the EC_{80}/EC_{25} ratio is between 10 and 20. The EC_{80}/EC_{50} ratio as well as the EC_{50}/EC_{25} ratio for these endpoints is about 3.

These results indicate that if the EC_{80} is representative of a lethal effect, the safety provided between a regulatory evaluation end-point (e.g., EC_{50}) and the lethal effect level can be as large as a factor of 10 to 20.

Table 2. Comparison of EC_{25}, EC_{50} and EC_{80} (lethality estimate) for several products

Seedling Emergence

Endpoint	EC_{80}/EC_{25}	No. of Chem.	EC_{80}/EC_{50}	No. of Chem.	EC_{50}/EC_{25}	No. of Chem.
Survival	31	2	2.2	2	9.9	3
Visual	9.9	4	3.2	4	2.5	4
Emergence	3.9	1	2.1	1	1.9	1
Plant Ht	24	13	5.4	14	3.3	15
Plant Wt	12	14	3.2	14	3.1	14
Mean	16.2		3.2		4.1	

Table 2. Continued

Vegetative Vigour

Endpoint	EC_{80}/EC_{25}		EC_{80}/EC_{50}		EC_{50}/EC_{25}	
Survival	4.6	6	2.2	6	2.1	6
Visual Emergence	8	6	2.9	6	2.3	6
Plant Ht	10	18	3.2	18	2.7	18
Plant Wt	9.6	23	3	23	2.7	23
Mean	8.1		2.8		2.5	

Effect of soil pasteurization on non-target plant test results

Soil Pasteurization is sometimes used by researchers, *in lieu* of fungicide seed treatments, to reduce the potential for soil- or water-borne pathogens to cause bacterial, fungal or viral infections of plant seedlings resulting in either mortality or damping-off effects of the test plants. While this may have less of an effect on the results of a vegetative vigour study where test material exposure to the plant is through the foliage, it can have significant effects on plant responses observed in the soil emergence study.

For those test materials which are degraded primarily by microbial or extra-cellular enzyme degradation mechanisms, the observed plant responses can be overly conservative, especially if plant exposure at a given soil concentration must be prolonged to produce the observed effect. Therefore, using un-Pasteurized soil could reduce the level of effect by a factor that is related to the rate of product bio-degradation, but a fungicide may be required to prevent pathogenic effects.

Greenhouse versus field effects

Various studies have shown that greenhouse-grown plants are more susceptible to herbicide injury than plants grown in the field, i.e., a higher application rate is required to cause injury to field grown plants (Fletcher, *et al.*, 1990; De Ruiter *et al.*, 1994; GCPF NTP Work Group 2001). The difference in susceptibility has been attributed to physical and metabolic differences between plants raised in the greenhouse and field, differences in dissipation/degradation characteristics of the product in greenhouse versus field conditions, plant age and structure, cuticle thickness, and other factors. Based on these studies an over estimate can range from 2 to 30 fold (GCPF NTP Work Group, 2001).

Decreasing sensitivity to herbicides based on increasing plant age/size

Regulatory testing requires the use of an early plant growth stage. This, in part, is because smaller plants allow for uniform coverage of the test plants with the spray solution, provide reproducible plant growth stages, allow for rapid production of plants for testing, test a growth stage sensitive to the CPPs and represent the worst-case condition (Brandt, 2000). Several studies (Klingaman *et al.*, 1992; Blackshaw, 1991; Wicks *et al.*, 1997; Rosales-Robles *et al.*, 1999) have shown that differences in plant age compared to very early growth stages can account for a 3- to 5-fold higher sensitivity in younger plants.

Table 3. Summary of factors contributing to the conservative nature of non-target plant tests

Test component	Factor
Exposure (drench in test versus drift in field)	Sophisticated tests to evaluate this are limited, but early indications suggest that a study performed using drift type exposure (patchy exposure of mainly the upper plant parts) exhibits half the level of effect as a study where there is thorough coverage of the complete plant. A factor of 2 or more.
Non-lethal (EC_{25}) versus lethal (EC_{80}) end-point	In going from an EC_{25} to an EC_{80}, an 8- (mean for vegetative vigour tests) to 16-(mean of seedling emergence tests) fold higher rate is needed. However, an EC_{80} is not equivalent to a lethal dose. It's justified to suppose a factor of 10 to 20 for the difference between the observed non-lethal endpoint and a lethal endpoint as used for all other groups of organisms in basic risk assessments for ecotox.
Greenhouse versus field	Between 3- and 30-fold, in order for the same level of effect shown in the greenhouse to be observed in the field.
Plant age	Between 3- and 5-fold less sensitive at later plant growth stages.
Total range of factors	180 to 6000

Inter-species differences

It is generally assumed that an uncertainty factor must be attached in any assessment due to differences in species and the question of whether on not the most sensitive species has been tested. However, based on a review of 11 herbicides, representing 9 different chemistries and 8 modes of action, it was demonstrated that use of the most sensitive crop species from regulatory tests provides an adequate margin of protection for all of the other non-crop species tested with that herbicide (McKelvey, *et al.*, 2001).

As such, the regulatory tests conducted using crop species provides an indication of the range of response that could occur in the field on non-target species. Additionally, using the current approach suggests that an uncertainty factor of 1 can be used to provide an adequate level of protection in performing a risk assessment. A typical case for one product for both pre-emergence and post-emergence tests is shown in Figures 1 and 2.

EXPOSURE

Risk is a function of both hazard and exposure and the more important component of risk assessment is exposure assessment as it can be modified by changes in how the product is used.

Any risk assessment proposal needs to focus on the exposure assessment. For terrestrial plants, there is no currently accepted EU method of exposure estimation, however, the EPPO risk assessment (EPPO, 2001) proposes to use the data generated by Ganzelmeier *et al* (1995) or the data by Rautman (2000) which takes into account drift reduction technology.

As mentioned earlier, consideration of the type of foliar exposure used in the laboratory versus the type of exposure that a plant may encounter (i.e., drift) needs to be considered in higher tiers of a risk assessment. Additionally, it needs to be considered that every application will not necessarily drift off-target and interception by the three dimensional nature of plants will diminish the amount of CPP potentially drifting much faster with distance than is predicted by the Ganzelmeier or Rautman exposure tables. These factors will add to the conservatism of the risk assessment.

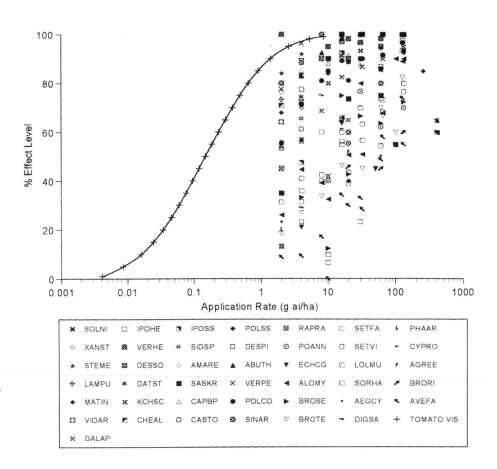

✖	SOLNI	▫	IPOHE	◣	IPOSS	◆	POLSS	⊠	RAPRA	▫	SETFA	↓	PHAAR
✤	XANST	▣	VERHE	#	SIDSP	▫	DESPI	⊙	POANN	▫	SETVI	⌐	CYPRO
★	STEME	⊠	DESSO	◇	AMARE	▲	ABUTH	▼	ECHCG	▫	LOLMU	⌐	AGREE
✢	LAMPU	✳	DATST	■	SASKR	✕	VERPE	◀	ALOMY	▫	SORHA	⌐	BRORI
◆	MATIN	✖	KCHSC	△	CAPBP	●	POLCO	▶	BROSE	·	AEGCY	⌐	AVEFA
▫	VIOAR	◪	CHEAL	○	CASTO	⊠	SINAR	▽	BROTE	⌐	DIGSA	+	TOMATO VIS
✖	GALAP												

Figure 1.   Pre-emergence data comparison for a sulfonylurea herbicide between the response for the most sensitive regulatory species (line) and several non-domesticated plant species (symbols)

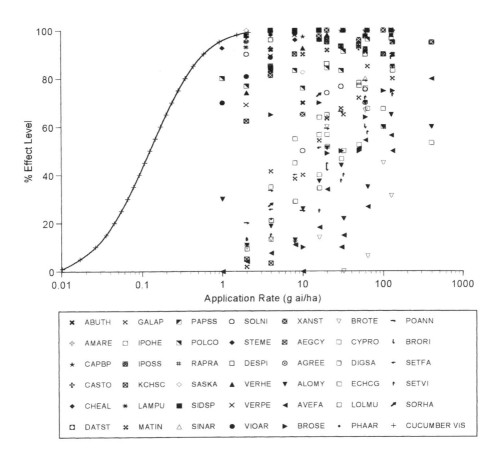

Figure 2.   Post-emergence data comparison for a sulfonylurea herbicide between the response for the most sensitive regulatory species (line) and several non-domesticated plant species (symbols)

CONCLUSIONS

Proposed terrestrial non-target plant tests are designed to be conservative in nature, and it is estimated that the effects observed in laboratory tests versus the field will be overly conservative by a factor of 100 to 6000 depending upon the product. A comparison of sensitivities for several typical domesticated species used for proposed regulatory tests to non-domesticated species indicates that the most sensitive regulatory species from those tests is as sensitive as any of the non-domesticated species tested. This comparison plus the conservative test design and the assumptions used in the exposure assessment suggests that an uncertainty factor of one or less should provide adequate protection to non-target plants.

REFERENCES

Blackshaw R E (1991). Control of downy brome (Bromus textorum) in conservation fallow systems. *Weed Tech.* **5**:557-562.

Brandt S (June, 2000). Effects of cultivation measures, particularly the use of pesticides on non-target plants in off-crop areas. IVA publication. Frankfurt, Germany.

European Commission (08.07.2000). Guidance Document on Terrestrial Ecotoxicology. 2021/VI/98 rev. 7.

European Commission (27.07.93). Amendment 93/71/EEC to Directive 91/414/EEC, Efficacy and Non-target Safety.

European and Mediterranean Plant Protection Organization (EPPO) (2000). Decision Making Scheme for the Environmental Risk Assessment of Plant Protection Products, Chapter 13, Non-target plants.

Fletcher J S; Johnson F L; McFarlane J C (1990). Influence of Greenhouse versus Field Testing and Taxonomic Differences on Plant Sensitivity to Chemical Treatment. *Environmental Toxicology and Chemistry*, **9**, pp769-776.

Füll C; Jung S; Schulte C (1999). Guidelines: pesticides. Testing requirements of the Federal Environmental Agency for assessing the effects of plant protection products on terrestrial plants. Federal Environmental Agency, Division IV: Material assessment and execution, Seecktstr. 6-19, D-13581 Berlin.

Ganzelmeier H; Rautman D; Spangenberg R; Streloke M; Herrman M; Wenzelburger H; Walter H (1995). Studies on the Spray Drift of Plant Protection Products. Blackwell Wissenschafts – Verlag, GmbH Berlin/Wein.

Global Crop Protection Federation's Non-target Plant Working Group (21 May 2001). Terrestrial Non-target Plant Testing: The Conservative Nature of the Test.

Klingaman, T E; King C A; Oliver L R (1992). Effect of application rate, weed species, and weed stage of growth on imazethapyr activity. *Weed Science.* **40**:227-232.

McKelvey R A; Wright J P; Honegger J L (2001). A Comparison of Crop and Non-crop Plant Sensitivity to Eleven Herbicides in Laboratory Testing (to be published).

Organization of Economic Cooperation and Development (OECD) (2000). OECD guideline for the testing of chemicals, proposal for updating Guideline 208, Terrestrial (Non-target) Plant Test: 208A: Seedling Emergent and Seedling Growth Study and 208B: Vegetative Vigour Test.

Rodales-Robles E; Chandler J M; Senseman S A; Prostko E P (1999). Influence of growth stage and herbidide rate on postemergence johnsongrass (Sorghum halepense) control. *Weed Tech.* **23**:525-529.

Wicks G A; Martin A R; Hanson G E (1997). Controlling Kochia (Kochia scoparium) in soybean (Glycine max) with postemergence herbicides. *Weed Tech.* **11**:567-572.

Recent developments in non-target terrestrial plant test protocols and risk assessment.

P Ashby

Pesticides Safety Directorate, Mallard House, Kings Pool, 3 Peasholme Green, York YO1 7PX, UK
Email: paul.ashby@psd.defra.gsi.gov.uk

ABSTRACT

The main points of the draft revised OECD 208 Terrestrial (Non–target) Plant Test and the draft EPPO Decision-Making Scheme for Non-target Plants are discussed. The current approach to non-target plant risk assessments is outlined. Some outstanding areas of concern are identified. The potential need to consider indirect effects arising from the removal of plants from the agro-ecosystem and of the 'in-crop' effects is highlighted. Ongoing research to better establish the level of concern is discussed.

INTRODUCTION

Within the EU the risk to the main areas of wildlife from the commercial use of plant protection products (hereafter referred to as pesticides) is assessed under Directive 91/414/EEC. For non-target plants, Section 8.6, Annex II of the Directive lays down the following requirement for applicants:

"A summary of the available data from preliminary tests used to assess the biological activity and dose range finding, whether positive or negative, which may provide information with respect to possible impacts on other non-target species, both flora and fauna, must be provided, together with a critical assessment as to its relevance to potential impact on non-target species."

Due to the variation in the methods used in preliminary plant toxicity testing and the lack of a clear reason as to why they should be done, risk assessments for flora have lacked the detailed consideration given to other areas. Within the EU the term 'flora' is generally interpreted as meaning terrestrial non-crop species (either mono- or di-cotyledons). For pesticides the risks to crop plants and aquatic plants are considered separately in the EU and are excluded from further consideration in this paper.

Within the UK there is increasing concern over the possibility of indirect effects arising from the removal of non-crop plant species from arable areas (i.e. Campbell *et al.* 1997), and over the wider issue of biodiversity and sustainability of modern agriculture. A joint proposal between the US Environmental Protection Agency and the Canadian Pest Management Regulatory Agency to harmonise non-target plant toxicity testing under NAFTA was considered by the Scientific Advisory Panel (SAP) in June 2001. The SAP agreed that the non-target plant testing scheme needed to be improved, but could not reach consensus on a number of key issues (The Weekly Report of the US EPA Office of Pesticides Programs (for week ending 13 July)).

Thus the need to develop standardised test protocols and risk assessment schemes to allow a more refined assessment of the risk to non-target plants posed by the use of pesticides is now greater than ever. This paper sets out some recent developments in these areas.

REVISION OF OECD GUIDELINE 208 (Terrestrial (Non-target plant test)

The need to globally harmonise plant toxicity testing and for revision of the Guideline 208 (1984) has been acknowledged by OECD. Following meetings in 1997 and 1999, a draft version of the revised guideline was produced in July 2000. The Guideline serves for general chemicals as well as pesticides. Hence the use to which the results will be put needs to be fully understood before testing is undertaken. The main points of the revised Guideline are highlighted below.

Guideline 208 now consists of two protocols:

- Part A, a seedling emergence and growth test in which the test compound is incorporated into the growing medium, and

- Part B, a vegetative growth test in which young plants are oversprayed with the test compound.

The vegetative growth test was developed primarily for pesticides as spray drift is considered to be a major route of exposure for foliar applied compounds.

The issues of number and type of species tested were major and prolonged areas of discussion. Testing of up to 10 species is proposed. Annex 2 of OECD 208 provides a list of recommended test species; these are all crop species. Traditionally screening studies for herbicidal activity have used representatives of the main crop types.

Concern has been expressed as to the representativeness of these species for non-crop species. Boutin & Rogers (2000) in their analysis of two Canadian and US EPA data sets conclude that there is no consistent pattern in the available data. In separate studies using 5 common herbicides and 15 test species (8 dicots + 7 monocots), 'selectivity factors' >44,000 have been estimated based on ED50 values (Pestemer 1999). Thus, given the current knowledge base, the likelihood of selecting representative species suitable for all pesticides seems low. OECD 208 does make the important statement "The list may be extended to include non-crop species if a suitable seed source is provided...". [As part of the OECD discussion Boutin (Environment Canada) produced a list of 35 non-crop species which have been tested and for which suitable seed sources are known.]

The two new OECD 208 guidelines will not address all potential concerns. For example, they do not address the issue of potential effects on reproduction or of repeat applications. Without modification they are not suitable for testing compounds whose main activity is via the vapour phase.

DRAFT EPPO DECISION-MAKING SCHEME FOR THE ENVIRONMENTAL RISK ASSESSMENT OF PLANT PROTECTION PRODUCTS (Chapter 13. Non-target plants)

Following several years of discussion and changes in panel membership, a draft scheme has recently been produced (October 2000). The key points of the draft scheme are highlighted below:

Definition of "non-target" area

The scheme is concerned with the assessment of the risk in the "off-crop" area. Field margins of 1 m and 3 m are assumed for arable and orchard crops respectively. Initial risk categorisation is based on predicted environmental concentrations (PEC) at these distances.

Selection of toxicity endpoint

A number of potential endpoints exist for plants; seedling germination, biomass (fresh or dry weight shoot weight or shoot height) and visual stress (chlorosis, mortality, developmental abnormalities). For risk assessment it is proposed that the toxicity endpoint used should be the most sensitive one measured for each species. It is also proposed that the 50% effect value (EC50) should be used in the initial risk assessment.

The main reason for this is that it will be based on the most sensitive of the sub-lethal effects obtained from glasshouse studies (*i.e.* OECD 208), which are assumed to overestimate toxicity compared to naturally exposed field grown plants of the same species. Furthermore, the natural variability in responses of plants, particularly if non-crop species are tested, is considered too large to justify using lower effect values such as NOECs or EC5s.

Selection of species

Estimations of the number of species for which testing is required to establish a reliable estimation of the range of sensitivity vary, but figures in excess of 30 species have been quoted (Breeze *et al.* 1999). Given the number of species potentially exposed this is not surprising, but if data for such numbers of plants species were required then it would be disproportionately higher than for other areas (i.e. aquatics, birds). For herbicides, which it is reasonable to assume pose the highest risk to non-target plants, there is often other valuable information, which can be taken into account. For such products specific label claims of activity are made; in some countries (*i.e.* UK) these claims must be supported by efficacy field data. Thus there exists a body of evidence, which identifies some of the more sensitive non-crop species. This information can be used to focus a more detailed laboratory dose response testing regime on these or closely related species. This principle underpins the draft EPPO scheme. Results from tests on such species can then form the basis of a risk assessment. For herbicidally active compounds dose response testing for at least 6 species is proposed.

Calculation of toxicity endpoint for use in decision making

Where acceptable EC50 values for 6 species are available a statistical approach based on the distribution of the EC50 values derived from the OECD tests is proposed in order to determine a calculated toxicity value (*i.e.* HD5). Thus the scheme differs from classical deterministic risk assessments, where an uncertainty factor (typically 10 or 100) is applied to the lowest observed endpoint. However, for plants there is currently no substantive body of data to support this approach. Validation of this step is likely to be required before the scheme can be accepted.

Routes of exposure

The calculated toxicity value is then compared with the appropriate exposure estimate to derive an Exposure:Toxicity Ratio. The routes of exposure considered are spray drift, run-off and gaseous transport. Aerial drift of herbicides is known to cause impacts on plants in areas close to the point of application. This route of exposure is considered to represent the main route of exposure for plants outside of the treated area. The predicted exposure level for each route of exposure is to be obtained from the relevant EPPO Chapter. For spray drift, the exposure value will come from the EPPO Air Scheme (this is likely to be taken from the published BBA spray drift data set (www.bba.de)). For gaseous transport, it is unlikely that the EPPO Air Scheme will be able to produce a value in the short term, hence for compounds which are expected to pose a risk via volatilisation non standard tests/scenarios will be required. The EPPO soil scheme should provide a run-off PEC. All exposure scenarios in the scheme may be defined as "off-crop".

Refinement of risk

The susceptibility of plants to pesticides may be affected by many variables (Marshall 2001 this publication). The scheme acknowledges this and suggests some possible refinement options including; more detailed consideration of the dose response data, more realistic exposure scenarios, testing of less sensitive growth stages (if appropriate to the intended use), consideration of importance of seedbank for sensitive species and use of higher tier studies (**i.e.** semi-field studies). Experience in the conduct and evaluation of semi-field studies is however very limited and such studies should only be conducted once the overall object has been clearly identified.

FUTURE DEVELOPMENTS

The proposed EPPO Decision-making scheme provides a basis for categorising the risk to non-target plants ('Negligible', 'Low', 'Medium' or 'High'). As such it does not attempt to define the 'acceptability' of the risk identified; the final decision on which will, in the foreseeable future, rest with individual countries. In defining 'acceptability' regulators must address the challenge of clearly defining the overall protection goal; this has yet to be done.

Currently risk assessments for non-target plants are limited to the 'off crop' area and tend to be rather qualitative. This situation has arisen because of the general belief that all non-crop plants within the cropped area have the potential to significantly reduce yield and/or cause contamination of seed lots. A reflection of this can be seen in the current UK approach, which for highly active compounds (*i.e.* some sulfonylurea herbicides), consists of the use of advisory label warnings such as

"Take extreme care to avoid drift onto nearby plants"

In contrast to the restrictions which can be applied to the use of certain pesticides near surface waters, there are no specific non-target terrestrial plant buffer zones in the UK. Where data are available to indicate phytotoxicity to non-target plants at distance from the point of application, authorisation has been refused in the UK.

The well publicised reductions in populations of some arable bird species, the demise of certain arable plants and the potential introduction of crops tolerant to broad spectrum herbicides has meant that the view that the cropped area should be free of all non-crop plants is being increasingly challenged (Marshall 2001 this publication). In response to such concerns over the sustainability of modern agriculture, the UK has begun to ask the questions which species of non-target plants are present, and what role do they play, in the agro-ecosystem?

A MAFF commissioned desk study by Breeze *et al.* 1999, identified a number of the more common non-crop plant species associated with agricultural systems. This study also identified some possible associations between these species and some invertebrates and birds. This work has recently been updated by Marshall *et al.* 2001. Existing evidence indicates that certain species *i.e.* blackgrass (*Alopecurus myosuroides*), winter wild oat (*Avena fatua*) and common cleavers (*Galium aparine*) are of such high competitive ability that there is limited opportunity to reduce the high levels of control currently used. However, for other species of far lower competitive ability, the need for consistently high levels of control is more questionable.

The limited available evidence suggests that some plant species which may be important for invertebrates and birds are those which pose less of a threat to agricultural production. Further research is underway to establish whether for some species a balance between weed control and biodiversity can be found (P Lutman BBSRC Rothamsted *pers comm*).

Evidence of the extent to which the use of herbicides *per se* may have impacted on the long-term diversity of non-crop plant species in arable areas is contradictory. Surveys in West Sussex (England) appear to show limited effects of herbicide usage on arable weed populations in cereal fields over the period 1970 to 1995 (Ewald 1999). For the following reasons these results are questionable; surveys conducted at approximately the same time of year, assessed presence/absence only, started after herbicide usage was already well established.

In contrast, claims of increases in plant diversity in organic compared to conventional production fields have been made in Germany, Denmark and Sweden, although again the impact of herbicides cannot be accurately judged. There are a number of other factors, which are considered to play an important role in the diversity of arable weeds. Several authors conclude that the current floristic composition of arable areas is dominated by a relatively small number of species better suited to high nutrient levels. Removal or restrictions on herbicide usage may thus result in the increased dominance of a small number of the more competitive species and not achieve any significant increase in biodiversity. Cropping regime is also considered to be another important factor. The potential scale of changing cropping practice is highlighted by the major reduction in the area of spring barley from 44.7% to 10% of total arable area which occurred in the UK between 1974 and 1998 (based on published MAFF Pesticide Usage Survey Data).

Whilst the evidence that the use of herbicides *per se* is adversely affecting the long term diversity of plants in arable areas is not conclusive, the use of such compounds is likely to have a major impact on their short term abundance (Breeze *et al.* 1999). For associated species *i.e.* phytophagous insects and insectivorous/seed eating birds this potential short-term loss of habitat/food supply may have important implications.

Thus the potential for indirect effects of herbicides is an area which requires further detailed consideration. The Department for Environment, Food and Rural Affairs (DEFRA) has taken over from MAFF the responsibility for a major 5 year research project 'Assessing the indirect effects of pesticides on birds.' (Commission No PN0925). This project will produce a framework for the assessment of the indirect effects of pesticides on birds reflecting the causal chain of pesticide effects on resources, the effects of resources of bird performance and the effects of performance on bird populations. The framework will be tested by expanding ongoing studies on 11 farmland bird species and large-scale replicated field experiments. The study will provide a basis for the decision as to whether indirect effects are substantial enough to warrant regulatory action and an assessment of the extent to which current risk assessment methods provide protection against potential indirect effects.

If future research does identify certain plants with important ecological roles then a potential refinement of the EPPO approach to species selection could be to require specific testing on such species, or their close relatives. It is acknowledged that if several countries were to adopt such an approach it could result in the need to supply and evaluate data on numerous different species. This situation would place a heavy burden on both agrochemical companies and regulators alike and, if possible it should be avoided.

However, this serves to highlight one of the main problems with non-target plant risk assessments i.e. the lack of a robust toxicity database on which to make a judgement as to the representativeness of different species. Indeed, Boutin & Rogers (2000) considered this aspect so important as to conclude, "an improved database on phytotoxicity is a pre-requisite to refine the risk assessment of pesticide effects on non-target plants." Taken in isolation this is a valid statement. However, it is unlikely in the short term that such a comprehensive data set of sufficient quality will be available. The proposed EPPO scheme therefore represents a pragmatic compromise between the increasing pressure to address the issue and the current lack of detailed knowledge.

The recognition of ecologically important plant species currently considered as being 'weeds' would require some consideration of the 'in-crop' risk. Such a development would require a new approach to risk assessment and risk management techniques. If this scenario does arise, then the challenge of protecting/encouraging such species, whilst not unduly compromising the ability to control pernicious weeds, is one which will require the combined efforts of researchers, agrochemical companies, pesticide regulators, environmental policy makers and field based advisory services.

CONCLUSION

The proposed revision of OECD Guideline 208 provides protocols suitable for testing the phytotoxicity of the majority of pesticides. Such harmonisation of testing lays the foundation for the proposed EPPO decision-making scheme. Current risk assessments for non-target plants are focused on the potential for effects in the 'off-crop' area. Concern over the sustainability of some modern intensive agricultural practices is currently challenging the basis of this. If it is deemed necessary to assess the risk to non-crop plants in the 'in-crop' area, a whole new approach to risk assessment and risk mitigation will be required and a clear overall protection goal for non-target plants will need to be defined. The pesticide regulatory process provides a potential route via which appropriate phytotoxicity data can be demanded. However, potential risk management options for non-target plants will need careful consideration and a multi-disciplined approach if the desired objectives are to be achieved.

REFERENCES

Boutin C, Rogers C A (2000). Pattern of sensitivity of plant species to various herbicides – an analysis with two databases. *Ecotoxicology*, **9**: 155-271

Breeze V G, Marshall E J P, Hart A, Vickery J A, Crocker J, Walters K, Packer J, Kendall D, Fowbert J, and Hodkinson D (1999). *Assessing pesticide risks to non-target terrestrial plants: A desk study. Commissioned by MAFF Pesticide Safety Directorate* (Project No PN0923)

Campbell L H, Avery M I, Donald P, Evans A D, Green R E, & Wilson J D (1997). A review of the indirect effects of pesticides on birds. *JNCC Report* No **227**. Joint Nature Conservation Committee. Peterborough.

Council Directive, (1991). Council Directive 91/414/EEC of July 1991 concerning the placement of plant protection products on the market. *Off. J. Eur. Commun.*, No. **L230,** July, 1-32 (as amended and adapted)

European and Mediterranean Plant protection Organisation and Council of Europe: Decision-making scheme for the environmental risk assessment of plant protection products. *Proposal for Chapter 13 Non-Target Plants* (draft October 2000)

Ewald J A, Aebischer N J (1999). Pesticide use, avian food resources and bird densities in Sussex. JNCC Report No **296**. Joint Nature Conservation Committee. Peterborough.

Marshall E J P, Brown V, Boatman N, Lutman P, Squire G (2001). *The impact of herbicides on weed abundance and biodiversity. Commissioned by DEFRA Pesticide Safety Directorate* (Project No PN0940)

Organisation for Economic Co-operation and Development (draft July 2000). Proposal for revision of Guideline 208 Terrestrial (Non Target) Plant Testing: (Part A) Seedling Emergence and Seedling Growth Test and (Part B) Vegetative Vigour Test.

Pestemer W, Zwerger P (1999). Application of a standardised bioassay to estimate the phytotoxic effects of frequently used herbicides on non-target plants. *Proceedings of the XI Symposium Pesticides Chemistry*, Cremona Italy pp 762-770.

Assessing the potential risks of herbicides to non-target aquatic plants

S J Maund, R Grade, J F H Cole, J Davies
Syngenta, Jealott's Hill International Research Centre, Bracknell, Berkshire RG42 6EY, UK
Email: steve.maund@syngenta.com

ABSTRACT

The current preliminary risk assessment scheme for non-target aquatic plants in the EU is described. Reviews of laboratory and field data have demonstrated that under most circumstances, the current study requirements and risk assessment procedures for herbicides should afford reasonable protection for non-target aquatic plants (and other non-target aquatic organisms) in the field. However, where concerns are identified (either through triggering or because of regulatory concerns about inadequacies of standard studies for certain modes of action), higher-tier studies and risk assessment procedures are needed. The approaches described by the HARAP workshop provide a suitable framework for developing higher-tier studies, and some examples of potential approaches for aquatic plants are reviewed. Effective implementation of higher-tier aquatic non-target plant risk assessment will require the development of clear protection goals. Ideally, these goals should be based on ecological information about the aquatic plant assemblages that are associated with agro-ecosystems. A number of initiatives are underway that may enable such risk assessment procedures to be developed in the future.

INTRODUCTION

Assessing the impacts of herbicides on aquatic plants can be a complex matter. On the one hand, they may be a target organism. On the other hand, protection of certain aquatic plants may be a key goal, for example rare, threatened or endangered species. Among lists of threatened and endangered plant species, aquatic and wetland plants are often well-represented, possibly due to habitat declines and land/water management practices. Furthermore, it is important to attend to the functional role of aquatic plants in aquatic ecosystems. Plants are of key importance for their role in primary production and community metabolism. Less obviously, but perhaps of equal importance, they also provide substrates and habitat or micronutrients for other organisms. What is more (but less commonly considered), the presence of aquatic plants may have a profound influence on the fate and distribution of pesticides in the aquatic ecosystem. For these reasons, aquatic plants are beginning to receive more attention in pesticide regulation.

The preliminary risk assessment process for aquatic plants is well-established and generally appears to be effective at identifying low risk compounds. However, for compounds which fail the preliminary assessment, whilst there are a range of options available for higher-tier studies, methodologies are far from standardised and implementation of such data into risk assessment is still under discussion. In this paper, current risk assessment procedures in the EU are discussed, and potential higher-tier approaches are described.

PRELIMINARY RISK ASSESSMENT FOR AQUATIC PLANTS

In the EU risk assessment scheme under 91/414/EEC, all active ingredients must be tested for effects on the growth of a green alga (usually *Pseudokirchneriella subcapitata* previously known as *Selenastrum capricornutum*). For herbicides, an additional algal species is required (the blue-green *Anabaena flos-aquae* is suggested), as well as studies on the floating pond weed *Lemna* sp. (usually the species used are *L. gibba* or *L. minor*). In some cases, where regulatory authorities are concerned that the specific mode of action of the compound is not covered (e.g. if the mode of action is specific to dicotyledonous plants, considering that *Lemna* is a monocot) other studies may be needed. In such cases, the draft EU Guidance Document on Aquatic Ecotoxicology recommends that data from terrestrial plant studies may also be useful for evaluating selectivity. Such data are also relevant for assessing potential risks to emergent (also called semi-aquatic) plants. In some cases, tests with other species (e.g., *Myriophyllum* or *Glyceria* sp.) have been requested by certain authorities, although as yet there are no harmonised guidelines for such studies (see below). This is usually only required if it is anticipated that the standard test species will not be sensitive to the mode of action of the compound. The effect concentrations from these studies (usually 72 or 96 h EC50s for algae, and 7-14 d EC50 for *Lemna*) are then compared to the relevant exposure concentrations, and if the resulting toxicity exposure ratio is less than 10, higher-tier assessments are required.

VALIDITY OF THE PRELIMINARY RISK ASSESSMENT SCHEME

A number of authors (e.g. Fairchild *et al.*, 1998; Peterson *et al.*, 1994) have suggested that testing schemes for aquatic plants may need to be extended because comparison of toxicity endpoints for various herbicides with different algal and macrophyte species do not show consistent results (*i.e.*, no one species is consistently the most sensitive). Selecting 'sensitive' species for toxicity testing is a long-recognised problem (Cairns, 1986). A counter-balancing consideration, though, is that for routine regulatory testing purposes it is essential that test methods involve organisms which can be readily cultured in the laboratory, are reproducible, and are cost-effective. At present, such methodologies for a much broader range of species are limited.

Whilst the conclusion that no one species can ever be the most sensitive is incontrovertible, it also perhaps misses the key point of species selection for risk assessment. This is that species are selected for risk assessment purposes as indicator organisms, not as surrogates. The principle aim of preliminary risk assessment scheme is to identify compounds which present low risks to aquatic plants. So the fundamental question should not be whether the species tested are always the most sensitive, but whether the risk assessment process using the standard species affords adequate protection. What we really need to know is whether the toxicity data that are generated, in combination with an uncertainty factor, are protective of effects seen under field conditions (additionally of course there is the consideration of the likelihood of the exposure concentration that is used in the risk assessment actually occurring from normal uses).

It has generally been assumed in the EU that the lower tiers are conservative, because of the combination of the worst-case nature of the exposure estimates and the sensitivity of the toxicity test endpoints used, combined with the use of a safety factor. For the EU risk assessment scheme, a recent comprehensive review of the latter two assumptions has been made by Brock *et al.* (2000) using laboratory and field studies published in the literature. For herbicides, studies were reviewed on compounds with a wide range of modes of action (photosynthesis inhibition, auxin simulating, and 'other' growth inhibition mechanisms). Generally, they found that the EU risk assessment criteria (based on laboratory toxicity data) were protective of the effects observed in the field. The one exception to this was auxin simulating herbicides, which were not particularly toxic to algae or *Lemna*, but did have some effects on other macrophyte species in the field. The conclusions of the study are encouraging and suggest that in most cases, the proposed scheme will be effective at identifying safe compounds.

OPTIONS FOR HIGHER-TIER STUDIES

If a compound fails the preliminary risk assessment, there are two options for further refinement. Firstly, it may be appropriate to refine the exposure concentrations. Previously in Europe, there have not been many options to do this, but under the new FOCUS surface water scheme, a series of steps will be available with which to refine exposure estimates. Alternatively, it may be appropriate to refine effect concentrations by performing further ecotoxicological studies. Guidance on the conduct of higher-tier aquatic studies was developed at the HARAP workshop (Campbell *et al.*, 1999). In this guidance, there are a number of options for assessing higher-tier risks, and these fall in to several categories:

- Interrogation of core data,
- Additional species testing,
- Modified exposure studies,
- Indoor and/or outdoor micro- and mesocosm studies.

Each of these study areas has potential application for higher-tier assessments of aquatic plants, and are discussed further below.

Interrogation of core data

If higher-tier assessments are triggered, the first point to establish is what is known about mode of action and therefore likely species affected. Valuable information on this can be gathered from reviewing data from terrestrial plant studies (where a range of monocots and dicots are studied) or from data from herbicide efficacy screens. These data may then also be used to refine the risk assessment, particularly if the major route of entry for the herbicide is determined to be spray drift.

A second consideration is what the critical endpoint of the studies are that have triggered the concern. It is important to consider what the likely environmental consequences of the measured effects will be. For example, in algal studies, compound may be algistatic (*i.e.* they limit growth but do not kill algal cells) or algitoxic (resulting in cell death) at concentrations relevant to the predicted environmental concentration. The former has potential consequences for recovery, and aids the design of any necessary higher-tier studies.

Additional species testing

There is a wide range of algal species which can be used to evaluate relative sensitivity (see Lewis (1995) for a review of methods and relative sensitivity data). Reviews of published methods for testing aquatic macrophytes have been produced by Freemark & Boutin (1994) and Lewis (1995). Until recently, the use of submerged plant species in toxicity tests has been limited by the difficulty of generating algae-free cultures. Work by Roshon has led to production of a draft American Society of Testing and Materials guidance for *Myriophyllum sibiricum*. Additionally, there are few cited laboratory methods for emergent species (Davies *et al.*, 1999). However, none of these proposed tests have been validated under a regulatory testing framework. Whilst development of standard, harmonised methods for macrophytes is a clear need for the future, validation of any new test is critical before it can be implemented as a regulatory requirement. Furthermore, there will need to be a clear understanding of how data so developed will be used in the risk assessment process (e.g., the ecological relevance of the various endpoints measured).

At present, comparatively little is known about the relative sensitivity of macrophyte species. Although much data have been published on effects of herbicides on aquatic plants, studies have often been conducted with a view to controlling nuisance species, where aquatic plants are the target species. Consequently, data are difficult to compare due to the use of different methods. A few authors have attempted to make comparisons in species sensitivity, (Davies *et al.*, 1999; Fairchild *et al.*, 1998), but clearly relative sensitivity will depend on the mode-of-action of the compound and the route of exposure of the pesticide.

Many endpoints have been proposed including root and shoot dry weight, root and shoot height, side shoot production, chlorophyll content, photosynthetic rates and enzyme activities such as peroxidase. Measurements of dry weight and biomass are more easily interpreted while measurements of chlorophyll content, photosynthetic rates and enzyme activities are more prone to sampling variation and low-dose enhancement. Thus data can be very difficult to interpret in terms of detrimental effects on a population. In particular, photosynthetic inhibitors like isoproturon have been reported to stimulate chlorophyll content while having no visible effect on biomass (J Davies, unpublished data). Further studies are needed to establish the link between effects at the sub-organism level to effects at the individual level, with linkages of these to effects at the population and community level being a necessary longer-term goal.

Modified exposure and recovery studies

One option for refining effects concentrations is to modify the exposure conditions in the toxicity test. Two approaches to this have been developed. The first is where the exposure concentration in the test vessel can be modified using a variable dosing system e.g., for algae (Grade *et al.*, 2000). Flow-through methods are mentioned for *Lemna* in OECD draft guideline and have also been published for other rooted macrophytes (Steinberg & Coonrod, 1994). Alternatively, it is possible to modify the exposure by adding sediment to the test system, where it is anticipated that the test compound will be dissipated more rapidly in the presence of sediment e.g. for algae (Shillabeer *et al.*, 2000). Similar approaches would be also possible for macrophytes.

Micro- and mesocosm studies

Algae and aquatic macrophyte have been studied extensively in micro- and mesocosm studies. There have been a number of review of such studies, and the reader is again referred to the reviews of Lewis (1995) and Brock *et al.* (2000). The considerations that apply to micro- and mesocosm studies on aquatic fauna also translate in most part to studies on flora, and recommendations for conduct and interpretation can be found in the HARAP (Campbell *et al.*, 1999) and CLASSIC (Heger *et al.*, in press) workshop proceedings. Indeed, even in small microcosms, it is possible to study assemblages of macrophytes that are reasonably representative of natural systems. Williams *et al.* (in press) have found for example that in 1 m³ outdoor microcosms, the assemblage composition of submerged macrophytes was similar to that found in natural ponds.

FURTHER CONSIDERATIONS FOR HIGHER-TIER RISK ASSESSMENT

The paper so far has focused mostly on the methods that are available for higher-tier aquatic plant assessment. In relation to developing a higher-tier risk assessment scheme, this comes at the problem from the wrong direction. The key need for further development of aquatic plant risk assessment is a fundamental review of risk assessment goals for aquatic plants. As in other areas of ecological risk assessment, a frequently unanswered question is "what are we trying to protect?" This is a particularly difficult question to answer for most pesticides, because they are designed to kill organisms (or at least their close relatives) that under other circumstances we may want to protect. However, in order to produce a rational and cost-effective risk assessment procedure, it is a question that must be tackled. This also leads on to the perennial question of "what is an unacceptable impact?"

Perhaps one of the first steps in trying to answer this difficult question is to know which species of aquatic plants are associated with the water bodies in agroecosystems, and to understand their life-history (e.g., when and how quickly they grow, their reproductive rate, etc.). This information would help in formulating appropriate experiments to assess for potential impacts, and also enable the development of suitable risk assessment paradigms. A number of projects are underway at the moment which may offer potential in this direction in the future. For example, the UK Pesticide Safety Directorate is currently funding a project which will develop scenarios for aquatic ecosystems in the UK agricultural landscape. Information on the floral assemblages associated with these ecosystems will be gathered. In addition, the Freshwater Biological Association in collaboration with the Ponds Conservation Trust have initiated a project called Freshwater Life (www.freshwaterlife.org) which will gather together information on the life-history and taxonomy of aquatic flora and fauna. Furthermore, the National Biodiversity Network in the UK will be collating distribution maps for British macrophyte species (www.nbn.org.uk). Similar intiatives are also underway in other EU countries, so the potential for better informed risk assessment procedures in the future is increasing.

REFERENCES

Brock T C M; Lahr J; van den Brink P J (2000). *Ecological risks of pesticides in freshwater ecosystems. Part 1: Herbicides.* Alterra-Rapport 088. 124 pp., Alterra Green World Research, Wageningen, Netherlands.

Cairns J (1986). The myth of the most sensitive species. *Bioscience* **36**: 670-672

Campbell P J; Arnold D J; Brock T C M; Grandy N J; Heger W; Heimbach F; Maund S J; Streloke M (1999). *Guidance Document on Higher-tier Aquatic Risk Assessment for Pesticides.* SETAC-Europe Press.

Davies J; Pitchford H F; Newman J R; Greaves M P (1999). Toxicity tests for assessment of pesticide effects on aquatic plants. *Proceedings of the Brighton Crop Protection Conference – Weeds 1999*, 717-722.

Fairchild J F; Ruessler D S; Carlson A R (1998). Comparative sensitivity of five species of macrophytes and six species of algae to atrazine, metribuzin, alachlor and metolachlor. *Environmental Toxicology and Chemistry*, **17**: 1830-1834.

Freemark K; Boutin C (1994). Nontarget-plant risk assessment for pesticide registration. *Environmental Management* **18**: 841-854.

Grade R; Gonzalez-Valero J; Höcht P; Pfeifle V (2000). A higher tier flow through toxicity test with the green alga *Selenastrum capricornutum*. *The Science of Total Environment* **247**: 355-361.

Heger W; Brock T C M; Giddings J M; Heimbach F; Maund S J; Norman S; Ratte H-T; Schäfers C; Streloke M (in press). *Guidance document on Community Level Aquatic System Studies - Interpretation Criteria*. SETAC Press.

Lewis M A (1995). Algae and Vascular Plant Tests. In: *Fundamentals of Aquatic Toxicology*, ed/ G M Rand. pp. 135-170. Taylor & Francis, Washington DC.

Peterson H G; Boutin C; Martin P A; Freemark K E; Ruecker N J; Moody M J (1994). Aquatic phytotoxicity of 23 pesticides applied at expected environmental concentrations. *Aquatic Toxicology* **28**: 275-292.

Shillabeer N; Smyth DV; Tattersfield L (2000). Higher tier risk assessment of agrochemicals, incorporating sediment into algal test systems. *Proceedings of the BCPC Conference – Pests and Diseases 2000*, 359-364.

Steinberg S L; Coonrod H S (1994). Oxidation of the root zone by aquatic plants growing in gravel-nutrient solution culture. *Journal of Environmental Quality*, **23**: 907-913.

Williams P; Whitfield M; Biggs J; Corfield A; Walker D; Fox G; Henegan P; Jepson P; Maund S J; Sherratt T N and Shillabeer N (in press). How realistic are mesocosms? - a comparison of the biota of mesocosms and natural ponds. *Environmental Toxicology and Chemistry*.